Forensic Biomechanics

Second Edition

Patrick Hannon, Ed.D.
Mark Cornwall, Ph.D.
Kerry Knapp, Ph.D.

Contributors

Scott Anderson, M.S. in Engineering
David Bosch, Ph.D.
Michael Iliescu, M.D.
Robert Perry, D.C.

 **Lawyers & Judges Publishing Company, Inc.**

This publication is designed to provide accurate and authoritative information in regard to the subject matter covered. It is sold with the understanding that the publisher is not engaged in rendering legal, accounting, or other professional service. If legal advice or other expert assistance is required, the services of a competent professional person should be sought.

—From a Declaration of Principles jointly adopted by
a Committee of the American Bar Association
and a Committee of Publishers and Associations.

The publisher, editors and authors must disclaim any liability, in whole or in part, arising from the information in this volume. The reader is urged to verify the reference material prior to any detrimental reliance thereupon. Since this material deals with legal, medical and engineering information, the reader is urged to consult with an appropriate licensed professional prior to taking any action that might involve any interpretation or application of information within the realm of a licensed professional practice.

 **Lawyers & Judges
Publishing Company, Inc.**

P.O. Box 30040 • Tucson, AZ 85751-0040
(520) 323-1500 • FAX (520) 323-0055
e-mail: sales@lawyersandjudges.com
www.lawyersandjudges.com

Library of Congress Cataloging-in-Publication Data

Hannon, Patrick, 1947- author. | Cornwall, Mark W. (Mark Westover),
  1952- author. | Knapp, Kerry, 1947- author.
 Forensic biomechanics / Patrick Hannon, Ed.D., Mark Cornwall, Ph.D.,
 Kerry Knapp, Ph.D.
 ISBN: 978-1-936360-75-8 (hardcover)
 ISBN: 1-936360-75-6 (hardcover)
 1. Medical jurisprudence. 2. Human mechanics. 3. Biomechanics.
 RA1051.H26 2020
 614'.1—dc23
                    2005033934

ISBN 13: 978-1-936360-75-8
ISBN 10: 1-936360-75-6
Printed in the United States of America
10 9 8 7 6 5 4 3 2

Contents

My contribution to this text is dedicated to my daughter Ember Davidson and my wife Cleofe Hannon.

Patrick Hannon

Foreword

Kenneth J. Saczalski, Ph.D.

In performing a forensic analysis the scientists and engineers have an obligation to follow the ethical investigative practices that are advocated by recognized professional organizations such as the American Society of Biomechanics or the American Academy of Forensic Sciences, and others. These investigative practices require identification of all potential injury-causing factors and the application of proper methods for investigation, testing and forensic analysis. This treatis provides a spectrum of information needed for scientific assessment of injury biomechanics, with consideration given to professional society guidelines.

As in the previous edition of Forensic Biomechanics, this new treatise on the subject, written by Patrick Hannon, Mark Cornwall and Kerry Knapp, once again provides a well organized and valuable reference tool that will assist those interested in the subject area, whether experienced or new to the world of forensic biomechanics, to better understand and analyze the many factors that must be considered when scientifically sorting out, from the forensic viewpoint, the biomechanical factors likely to cause injury to the human body. In essence, a fundamental of good forensic biomechanical analysis requires that all potential injury-producing factors must be considered, especially in evaluating whether or not a product defect caused the injury. Obviously, the subject of "human body injury biomechanics" is a broad and complex field dealing with many disciplines such as human anatomy, engineering sciences, knowledge of hard and soft tissue properties, injury tolerance levels, physics, chemistry, and mathematics, to name a few.

Fortunately, like the first edition, this volume also provides detailed anatomical background information, in conjunction with associated physical principles and fundamentals, that will assist in the understanding of both hard and soft tissue injury mechanisms. The text materials cover the range from "gross" human body kinematics (i.e., motion study) and kinetics (i.e., forces necessary to cause body motions) to "detailed" injury mechanics of body regions (i.e., head, neck, thorax, spine), and body components, such as hard tissue (i.e., skeletal-bone), soft tissue (i.e., brain, lung), and connective tissue (i.e., muscles, ligaments). Several examples are provided throughout the text to assist the reader in understanding associated physical principles. In addition, the authors continue to use their "real-world" experiences to provide numerous helpful case studies to illustrate the process of synthesizing, analyzing, and identifying the most probable causes of a given type of injury.

Finally, as noted in the foreword of the first edition, this treatis should be of particular interest to attorneys and legal scholars who are often faced with the task of sorting out "fact" from "fiction" in conflicting biomechanical expert opinions. The text provides the tools necessary to analyze, discuss, and question the facts and basis of various expert opinions related to causes of human body injury. I also believe, as I stated before, that this treatise will be a valuable reference tool for the more experienced members of the scientific community involved in the field of "injury biomechanics." And, as before, I strongly recommend that this new edition also be added to any biomechanics reference library.

Preface

Kerry Knapp

Biomechanical analysis provides a critical link in understanding the relationship between personal injury and injury-producing events. Whether the events and injuries are minor, as in the case of the low speed automobile impact, or they are sudden, violent, and fatal, the biomechanical analysis can be critical in demystifying the relationship between the event and the damage to human tissue. This is especially true when there are no witnesses or the witness testimony is conflicting.

The basis for all biomechanical analysis is a solid grasp of human structural and functional anatomy. The application of Newtonian physics and the mechanics of materials to the human body and its various tissue types provides the context for matching force and acceleration loading to the potential for damage to human tissues. Through the use of standard analytical techniques, it is possible to structure the physical evidence in a manner that will produce a clear understanding of an injury-producing event based on the evidence available, even in the face of missing evidence or conflicting witness testimony.

Forensic Biomechanics begins with an overview of the field of injury biomechanics by addressing such questions as: "What is a biomechanist?," "Who is qualified?," "What will a biomechanist provide?," "When can a biomechanist help?," and "How does one work effectively with a biomechanist?" The introductory chapters are followed by a discussion of the systematic approach to analysis (Chapter 3), designed not as a guide to doing a complete analysis but as a reference for judging the completeness and quality of an analysis.

Forensic Biomechanics then provides an overview of the important principles and concepts used in injury analysis along with human kinematics (human motion) and kinetics (causal factors of human motion). The structure, characteristics, and mechanical properties of human tissues, how they fail, and the characteristic patterns in which they fail is found in the following chapters.

The focus of the body of the text is injury biomechanics. The text provides a concise and brief discussion of regional anatomy, supplemented by detailed dissection CDs. With the anatomy in mind, *Forensic Biomechanics* examines the common injuries to specific regions of the human body, their causation and characteristics. The injury profiles are logically organized and presented in terms that are easily understood without complex medical terminology. Case examples are provided throughout to illustrate important concepts.

We have approached this project from our experience-base and an academic-research perspective. Consequently we have relied heavily on other publications for much of the background material. Together we have over fifty years of experience with the subject matter presented in *Forensic Biomechanics*. The text represents our effort to communicate what we have learned from our experience regarding the application of science to the understanding of human injury and how the principles can be applied in the court environment. This book is for anyone interested in the use of human functional anatomy and biomechanics as a tool to the complete understanding of how, why, and when injuries occur to people. We hope we have produced a concise, clear, and comprehensive reference on the essential elements of biomechanical analysis of injury.

Chapter 1

Introduction

Kerry Knapp

The material presented in *Forensic Biomechanics* is intended to guide the user toward a more complete understanding of the injury process that occurs as external forces interact with people. The authors believe strongly in the premise that our judicial system is based on the concept of truth-seeking. Both the criminal and civil sides of the system seek to know the truth of the allegations being litigated and then to reach an equitable result via compensation (civil) or incarceration (criminal).

1.1 What is Biomechanics and Injury Biomechanics?

The discipline of biomechanics integrates the laws of physics, human structural anatomy, and working concepts from engineering to describe the motion of the body and body segments. Injury biomechanics couples the knowledge of force and motion with a thorough understanding of functional human anatomy and human tissue mechanics to explore the possible relationships between external events and mechanically induced human tissue injury. Newtonian mechanics, structural and functional human anatomy, human physiology, and injury biomechanics, including a knowledge of human soft and hard tissue tolerances, form the basis for the discipline.

Because biomechanics is an integrated science, the body of literature applicable to the biomechanics profession is diverse, encompassing both medical and engineering literature. Research on occupant response and occupant loading in motor vehicle accidents and aircraft accidents appears predominantly in automotive engineering publications and armed services publications. The tissue damage and tissue tolerance data are presented in biomechanics and select medical publications. Issues related to radiology, bone fracture, and structural changes in human tissue with time are presented in the medical literature.

Texts and papers on these various subjects form the scientific basis for engineering design of human transports, work environments, safety regulations, surgical techniques, organ transplants, medical treatment plans, and teaching curriculum. These materials also define the underlying scientific data necessary to understand and explain human injury. These data and appropriate conclusions form a basis for injury biomechanics.

1.2 Who are Biomechanists? What is their Role?

Biomechanics, as an integrated science, encompasses parallel routes of study. The American Society of Biomechanics (ASB) membership illustrates this fact. The ASB limits its membership to individuals whose research work, teaching, and experience qualify (by application) them for approval. The membership in ASB includes individuals trained in engineering, exercise science, physics, biology, physical therapy, and medicine. A biomechanist may be an engineer or medical doctor; however, biomechanics is not the sole domain of either of these professions. A review of an individual's education, training, and work experience is necessary to determine the qualification of a biomechanist to offer expert opinions regarding injury.

The minimum training or education for the biomechanist must include Newtonian mechanics, structural and functional human anatomy, human physiology, and injury biomechanics, including a knowledge of human soft and hard tissue tolerances. Medical practitioners are generally skilled in identifying and healing tissue damage, but they are not extensively schooled in the mechanisms of tissue damage, the related areas of occupant kinematics, or the response of human tissues to various levels and types of loading. Engineers, on the other hand, understand the physics of movement and the principles necessary to analyze the mechanics of materials but traditionally lack the detailed study of human anatomy and physiology necessary to apply that knowledge to human tissue. The biomechanist integrates aspects of these disciplines and fills the gap between the engineer's explanation of external loading and the medical practitioner's diagnosis and treatment of damage to human tissues.

The biomechanist has a valuable role in both criminal and civil litigation when human tissue injury is an issue or human mechanics plays a role in interpreting the evidence. Where external forces have caused tissue damage, the result may vary from mild muscle strain to death. The result of the event is generally documented by a medical practitioner (injury) or medical examiner (death). The external event that produced the forces may be known or unknown. Many times the event has been described by an engineering analysis or accident reconstruction. The role of the biomechanist is to function as the interdisciplinary integrator, determining and describing how the interaction of the human body with the external environment occurred and the injury-producing probability. Finally, the biomechanist must communicate the analysis and its results effectively so that the court clearly understands the relationship between the event or events and the probable relationship to the actual documented tissue damage (injury or death). The testifying expert in biomechanics must "assist the trier of fact" as the court seeks to understand the events about which it is to pass judgment.

The biomechanist is the best professional, based on education, training, and experience, to function as the integrator of interdisciplinary and multi-disciplinary information for the court. To redeem the integrator function objectively, each case must be systematically organized, rigorously analyzed, and impartially evaluated. The evidence available must be organized in a manner that illuminates important relationships. The lack of important evidence must be documented along with its significance. The strengths and the weaknesses of the case must be clearly understood, and both must be presented. Toward this end, it is not only useful, but it is absolutely necessary that each case be approached individually and analytically. Although the specific focus of the case may vary with the issues, injuries, and events, a consistent analytical approach must be maintained.

The use of the biomechanical expert in personal injury, wrongful death, and criminal cases involving tissue damage has increased dramatically over the past decade. The increase has been due to the biomechanical expert's ability to "assist the trier of fact to understand the evidence or to determine a fact at issue," as described by Federal Rule of Evidence 702. Well-qualified and well-prepared experts in the field of injury biomechanics have become increasingly influential and persuasive witnesses regarding injury causation and other aspects of injury-producing events. The proliferation of "experts" in the field of injury biomechanics is likely to continue, and if the biomechanics discipline is not well defined, opportunists are a certainty.

The increase in the use of biomechanists and the resulting increase in "experts" offering biomechanical opinions have led to frequent motions to exclude the biomechanical testimony. Legitimate attempts have been made to exclude the biomechanical expert on the basis of *Frye* and *Daubert* rulings by challenging several specific points from the opinions. First is the argument that biomechanics is not a legitimate area of scientific endeavor or that injury biomechanics is not science. Second, that the biomechanical expert is not qualified to offer opinions on the issue of injury causation when those opinions refer to a specific individual, injury, or event. Attorneys often argue that injury causation is a medical opinion, and therefore only a medical practitioner is qualified to offer such an opinion. The third argument is based on the use of human subject and animal studies and the applicability of the literature to specific individuals. Especially in low speed motor vehicle cases, the validity and utility of the low speed impact human subject literature have been attacked on a publication-by-publication basis. The attacks attempt to discredit the methods, subject numbers, and findings expressed in the publications. The attack on the literature hopes to exclude the expert testimony of the biomechanist based on misuse of the literature or use of literature which is too limited to be applied to the specific case under consideration. The fourth challenge, which is used less frequently but represents the most appropriate attack, is a thorough questioning of the biomechanist's education, training, and experience—what qualifies him as an expert in the field?

A. Biomechanics: A scientific discipline

Biomechanics is a scientific discipline concerned with understanding and improving human biological function and response as well as the biological function and response of other species. Human biomechanics limits the focus to the mechanics of human systems while incorporating some aspects of the physiological or biochemical function influencing human performance. The physiological functioning as well as the biochemical and structural properties of tissues are often important considerations within the discipline of injury biomechanics especially when effects of aging and tissue remodeling after injury are essential elements for analysis.

Human biomechanics research has addressed a broad range of topics related to human function and performance. Studies include examining the mechanical function and performance changes of muscles, connective tissue, cartilage, skin, nerves, bones, joints, and internal organs. Biomechanics research also includes studies focused on human movement and performance where the interaction of internal and external forces, moments, and torques that produce movement are examined; for example, movement during competitive swimming or high performance jet pilot ejection. Biomechanics also addresses internal and external loading and overloading which may lead to the remodeling or injury of biological tissue and organs. Lastly, biomechanics research includes projects such as the mechanical heart, joint resurfacing and replacement, as well as new work on tissue engineering and the development of biomaterials for the replacement or healing of human tissue.

During the last part of the twentieth century, biomechanics has developed from a relatively obscure area of study to a widely recognized professional discipline. Today the study of human biomechanics is a widely recognized area of scientific study and professional practice. Biomechanics is offered as an area of study in university graduate programs in over 85 universities in the United States and Canada. Many more universities offer biomechanics courses at the undergraduate and graduate levels as a part of other degree focus areas (exercise science and engineering, for example). Professionally, there are thousands of biomechanics scientists working in universities, institutes, and a variety of worldwide industries. The discipline's national professional organization, the American Society of Biomechanics, has a large membership of biomechanics researchers from such diverse areas as general biological science, exercise science, engineering, medicine, applied physics, health sciences, and human factors or ergonomics. The Society's journal and meetings are characterized by the presentation of high quality research applicable to a broad range of subjects important to the function and performance of humans and injury biomechanics.

B. Biomechanical causation versus medical causation
Definitions

> Biomechanics: The science concerned with the action of forces, internal and external, on the living body. (From Stedman's *Medical Dictionary for*

> *the Health Professions*, Third edition. 1997.)

> Biomechanics: The application of the principles and techniques of mechanics to the structure, functions, and capabilities of living organisms. (From *Webster's New World Dictionary*.)

> Medicine: The art of preventing, diagnosing, and treating disease. (From *Stedman's Medical Dictionary for the Health Professions,* Third edition. 1997.)

> Medicine: The science and art of diagnosing, treating, curing and preventing disease, relieving pain, and improving and preserving health. (From *Webster's New World Dictionary*.)

These two sets of definitions illustrate the recognized basis for making a clear distinction between a biomechanical injury causation opinion and a medical diagnosis of injury. Medicine is focused on diagnosing the cause of the symptoms expressed by a patient. Especially when the diagnosis is related to tissue injury, the causal event, and its relationship to injury are absent from the medical diagnosis except as it relates to history. Consider the example of an individual who presents to a physician with complaints of upper extremity loss of strength and "tingling" in the hands. The physician will immediately recognize that the cause of the expressed symptoms may be psychological, organic neurological (brain or spinal cord), or neuromuscular (motor neuron and/or skeletal muscle patho-physiological). By history, the patient may attribute the change and symptoms to a horseback-riding fall. Based on the patient history provided, the physician may quickly determine that the problem is organic neurological. He will test to determine if the problem is brain centered or cord centered. If he ascertains that the problem is cord centered, he knows that the problem could be due to a cord lesion or cord compression. Finally, if the symptoms are secondary to cord compression, the physician must determine if the compression is due to a vertebral fracture, intervertebral disc failure, spinal instability (for example, retrolisthesis or spondylolisthesis), or cord swelling. The end product of the medical thought process is the diagnosis of the physiological cause of the cord compression which constitutes a medical causation opinion (diagnosis) and leads the medical provider toward a specific treatment regime.

By contrast the biomechanist does not dispute the medical diagnosis. In this example, the biomechanist will not argue that the symptoms expressed by the patient are due to brain trauma rather than a spinal cord compression. Nor would the biomechanist argue that the spinal cord compression is the result of vertebral body fracture or failure rather than retrolisthesis. The biomechanist, unless he is a medical doctor, is not qualified to express such opinions. The biomechanist accepts the medical diagnosis but focuses on the process that produced the diagnosed injury: in this case vertebral fracture or the retrolisthesis—the result of internal or external forces on the structures of the human vertebral column and the spinal cord. How did the physician-diagnosed pathology (medical causation opinion) occur? That is the question that focuses the biomechanical inquiry. Systematic analysis will lead the biomechanist to an understanding and expression of an injury causation opinion (a biomechanical opinion).

The medical diagnosis (opinion) answers the question: *What injury produced the observed symptoms?* The biomechanical opinion answers the question: *How did (or how could) the observed injury (medical causation) occur given the specific circumstances of the injury-producing event?* In most instances it is the biomechanical expert rather than the medical practitioner who is most qualified, on the basis of education, training, and experience to express opinions on issues of injury causation.

1.3 How to Work with a Biomechanist: A Low Impact Example

The low impact automobile accident case can be especially difficult to resolve. With low speeds and minimal damage, it may be difficult for an insurance company to justify the payment of thousands dollars for treatments that seem excessive and unnecessary in light of the documented information on human tolerance to impact. Here the biomechanist is able to offer an important analysis. Generally, treating physicians are not made aware of the vehicle dynamics or the occupant kinematics when treating a patient (except by patient self report). A biomechanical analysis is not within the field of expertise of most physicians. Similarly, it is not within the biomechanist's field of expertise to evaluate a physician's diagnosis or treatment of patient injuries, and therefore the biomechanist should not address those issues.

In order for the biomechanist to render an opinion on injuries sustained in a low impact motor vehicle accident, it is necessary to first obtain the vehicle dynamics of the event from a qualified expert. Usually, the biomechanist will limit his or her field of expertise to the biomechanical aspects of the accident. Performing both the vehicle dynamics analysis and the injury biomechanics analysis often leads to prejudiced assumptions that can bias or invalidate an otherwise completely objective analysis. Therefore, an accident reconstructionist will need to provide prerequisite information to the biomechanist. The vehicle dynamics should include the change in linear velocity, the principal direction of force, and if possible, the acceleration impulse applied to the vehicle (or at least the assumed time to maximum engagement). Any angular motion (rotation) applied to the vehicle must also be documented since it may be important to the occupant loading and occupant motion in some motor vehicle accidents.

The biomechanist is then able to take the information on the loading history applied to the plaintiff's vehicle during the motor vehicle accident and formulate an analysis of the occupant kinematics (occupant movements). (A complete example is shown in Chapter 3.) Determining an accurate estimate of the forces, moments, and torques acting upon the occupant's body will result in an accurate description of the occupant displacements, velocities, and accelerations (kinematics).

The biomechanical analysis also involves an examination of the available medical reports and radiographs by the biomechanist. The documents should be summarized in some logical format.

Finally, the biomechanist is able to perform an analysis of fit between the medical records (injury claim) and the occupant kinematic/kinetic response. Generally, it is at this phase of the analytical process that the published human tissue literature is incorporated into the analysis. If there is a good match, then the plaintiff's medical claims are probably justified. However, if there is a mismatch, then the plaintiff's injuries may have been exaggerated, a result of some other event, or may be nonexistent. In biomechanics, as with medicine and engineering, human individuality and variability due to age, disease, and injury mean that all humans do not have the same tissue tolerances. However, within a probability framework, it can be stated with some descriptive degree of certainty that the loading applied to the occupant either can or cannot be reasonably linked to the medical pathology of the plaintiff.

The biomechanist also should address competing etiology when appropriate. The medical pathology may be due to preexisting conditions that may or may not have been previously documented. In some cases, there may be real injury to soft tissues. However, recreation or work history may be the true etiology. In such cases a brief analysis of the plaintiff's physical activity (work or recreation) often reveals loading which has a much higher probability of being the injury mechanism. Frequently it is possible to make comparisons that clearly illustrate how work or recreation events produced loads that far exceeded the loads that would have been imposed upon the plaintiff during the injury event under consideration.

1.4 When Can a Biomechanist Help?

In general, a biomechanist is a useful expert when liability questions involve human motion, human tissue damage, mechanisms of injury, or any combination of the three. A well-qualified biomechanist is helpful in all types of impact accidents where the match between forces and tissue damage may be in question. Such cases include slip, trip, and fall claims where the mechanics of motion as well as tissue damage may be at issue; sports injury situations; product liability cases where the relationship between the product design or characteristics and the injury biomechanics are at issue; in criminal cases where the relationship between human motion or human actions and tissue damage and/or the trauma-producing event require analysis; and in situations where the failure to wear protective clothing or equipment (for example, seatbelts, motorcycle helmets, knee pads, hardhats, gloves, or shoes) causes or increases the event-related trauma.

Biomechanists have been helpful in identifying, understanding, and answering biomechanical questions in the following types of cases:

- Motor vehicle accidents
- Bicycle accidents
- Motorcycle accidents
- Industrial injuries
- Dance injuries
- Playground accidents
- Boating accidents
- Drowning
- Athletic injuries
- Construction accidents
- Beatings/shootings
- Child abuse
- Slips/trips/falls
- Gait analysis
- Horse and other farm accidents

1.5 Some Non-Automotive Examples

There are a wide variety of cases where the biomechanist may be able to play a central role in understanding the event and its relationship to a plaintiff's injury claim. Here are a few brief examples to stimulate thought.

Trip and fall—An elderly diabetic amputee fell while walking through a casino lobby. Was the resultant injury to the plaintiff due to a carpet irregularity or was the ongoing/preexisting diabetic condition responsible for the fall? By carefully examining the video surveillance tape of the incident it was possible to analyze the gait (walking mechanics) and to determine the cause of the fall as well as the point of the trip.

Amputation of fingers—An individual suffered a traumatic amputation of all or part of two fingers. Could a person strike his own hand five times or more without eliciting a flexor withdrawal response to the pain stimulus? Biomechanics analysis demonstrated how the amputations could and could not have occurred. Neuromuscular research answered the question regarding the flexor withdrawal response.

Ladder fall/degloving—A construction worker caught his hand in a large mixing tank, producing a traumatic "degloving" beginning just below the right elbow. A comprehensive biomechanics analysis demonstrated the possible mechanics associated with a slip and fall, displacement of the tank cover, and the ultimate mechanism that produced the arm exposure resulting in forearm degloving.

The mystery fall—An elderly woman fell, suffering a comminuted supracondylar fracture of the femur, while being returned home in a small transport van. Would the presence of an attendant at the side exit from the transport van have been of value in preventing the plaintiff's fall and injury? A biomechanics analysis of the fracture and the configuration of the transport van demonstrated where and how the fall occurred. The preventive value of a trained attendant at the van exit was also addressed.

Fireman/epileptic seizure—Fire department emergency medical personnel responded to a home where an adult male had experienced an epileptic seizure. The patient was confused and became aggressive. It was necessary to restrain the individual during the seizure. Were the thoracic vertebral fractures suffered by the plaintiff caused by the actions of the trained paramedics? The biomechanics analysis contrasted the direction and magnitude of force applied by the emergency medical personnel with the forces necessary to produce the specific vertebral fractures which were present. A comprehensive review of the appropriate literature regarding injury from internal muscle forces of the muscle contractions during grand mal epileptic seizures was also conducted.

Attorneys may well consider the broader use of the analytical skills of well-qualified biomechanical experts. Many times the injury is unquestionable. The time and place of the injury event are known and not in dispute. However, the complete understanding of the mechanism of injury is generally lacking. Finally, the relationship between the plaintiff's position or action and the injury-producing event is important to appropriate, timely, and equitable resolution of the case.

Chapter 2

The Analytical Approach

Kerry Knapp

2.1 Introduction

An injury biomechanics injury causation analysis is directed toward understanding the relationships, discoverable from the evidence, between a specific event and a specific injury. It is not a discussion of how injuries occur generally nor is it a discussion of the epidemiology of injuries or events although it may include both. To be technically valid and admissible in court, the analysis should rigorously adhere to a structured analysis format. The material presented in this chapter is intended; (1) to establish a methodology that will assist forensic biomechanists (and other experts) in meeting the court requirements for demonstrating the validity of reasoned opinions as a prerequisite for admissibility; and (2) to demonstrate the effective application of the methodology.

2.2 Statement of Problem

The forensic biomechanist has a key role in judicial cases in which tissue damage (including death) has occurred and has been documented by a medical practitioner or medical examiner. The external loading causing the tissue damage can be unknown or quantified by an engineering analysis. The role of the forensic biomechanist is to function as an interdisciplinary expert with the primary role to discover and illuminate the entire injury/fatality-causing event. Further, the forensic biomechanist must communicate effectively via performance/presentation so that the court clearly sees the relationship between the event(s) and the actual documented tissue damage (injury). The testifying expert in biomechanics must "assist the trier of fact" as the court seeks to understand the events from which the litigation has arisen (*Werth v. Makita Electric Works*).

Injury causation analysis is a specific application of the failure analysis principles developed over decades and commonly used in engineering. Failure analysis is an orderly, logical process that is performed in order to determine the causes or factors that have led to an undesired loss of functionality. It is an iterative process that involves examination and analysis of the physical evidence related to an event or an element failure. In the context of injury causation analysis, it is the systematic examination of all available evidence that pertains to a specific event/injury question. Two of the critical goals in a failure investigation are to identify both the damage mode(s) and damage mechanism(s) that are present. Damage mechanisms are a key component in categorizing damage and failures.

During an injury causation analysis the forensic biomechanist often integrates interdisciplinary and multi-disciplinary information for the court. To make the information understandable, the forensic biomechanist must systematically organize, rigorously analyze, and impartially evaluate each case. The evidence available must be illuminated, and the lack of evidence documented. The strengths and the weaknesses of the evidence in the case must be understood, and both must be presented. To this end, it is not only useful but also absolutely essential that each case be approached as a unique event. Although the specific focus of the case may vary with the issues, injuries, and events, the same unbiased approach in the presentation of evidence must be maintained.

The use of the biomechanical expertise in personal injury, wrongful death, and criminal cases in which tissue damage has occurred has increased dramatically over the past decade, due in part to the increasing complexity of cases as well as the availability of the expertise and technology. Federal Rule of Evidence 702 provides that if "scientific technical or other specialized knowledge will assist the trier of fact to understand the evidence or to de-

7

termine a fact in issue, a witness qualified as an expert by knowledge, skill, experience, training, or education may testify in the form of an opinion or otherwise." The two guiding principles in this federal rule are that the testimony must be helpful as well as reliable. Well-qualified and well-prepared experts in injury biomechanics have generally been influential and persuasive witnesses regarding injury causation.

Expert evidence has long been a part of judicial proceedings. People qualified by skill, knowledge, education, or experience have been permitted to testify to help the trier of fact understand the evidence or determine a fact at issue. Increasingly, however, the resolution of both civil and criminal cases has depended more on the help of experts. It is impractical or impossible for judges and jurors to rely solely on their common sense and personal experience in evaluating the testimony of experts. The justice system must adapt its process to ensure that expert evidence and testimony leads efficiently to well-informed decisions.

The American judicial system is an adversary process. Attorneys must present evidence on behalf of their clients; judges must manage the process by making the necessary and appropriate rulings concerning admissibility of evidence; and juries must resolve issues of fact. In today's courts, the process often yields conflicting expert testimony on complicated, confusing, and unfamiliar issues. If the participants in the process cannot fully understand the nature of the dispute, they might not render a reasonable and principled decision. During the early 1990s the Carnegie Commission on Science, Technology, and Government studied the role of science and technology in judicial decision-making. The Commission concluded:

The courts' ability to handle complex science-rich cases has recently been called into question, with widespread allegations that the judicial system is increasingly unable to manage and adjudicate science and technology issues. Critics have objected that judges cannot make appropriate decisions because they lack technical training, that jurors do not comprehend the complexity of the evidence they are supposed to analyze, and that the expert witnesses on whom the system relies are mercenaries whose biased testimony frequently produces erroneous and inconsistent determinations. If these claims go unanswered, or are not dealt with, confidence in the judiciary will be undermined as the public becomes convinced that the courts as now constituted are in-

capable of correctly resolving some of the most pressing legal issues of our day. (Carnegie Commission on Science, Technology, and Government, 1993, pg.11)

This concern was hardly new in 1993; in fact, the federal courts had been struggling with the issue for at least two decades. In 1990, the Federal Courts Study Committee recognized the increasing importance of economic, statistical, technical, and scientific data in the courts. The Committee recommended that the judiciary enhance its ability to manage and adjudicate cases involving scientific and technical complexity. To further the recommendation, the Federal Judicial Center prepared and issued its first reference manual on scientific evidence in 1994.

Although expert, science-based testimony has been effective when presented to juries, it can also bring with it the risk of improper persuasion. The courts have been diligent in establishing and exercising their role as "gatekeepers" to ensure that anyone offering expert opinion in biomechanics demonstrates the reliability of the opinion. In recent years the United States Supreme Court has significantly expanded the requirement for experts previously established under the 1923 *Frye* decision. The *Frye* decision states that if the scientific theory at issue is generally accepted in the relevant scientific community it should be admissible under Federal Rule of Evidence 702 (*Frye v. United States*). Justice Blackmun, writing for the court in *Daubert*, declared that trial judges were to be the "gatekeepers" against improper expert testimony (*Daubert v. Merrell Pharmaceuticals, Inc.*). As "gatekeepers," federal trial judges are required to do more than just determine general acceptance. *Daubert* requires courts to assess whether proposed testimony is scientifically reliable: that is, whether the scientific methodology is valid and can be tested, and if a reliable basis in the knowledge and experience of the biomechanics discipline exists. Reliance by an expert on prior legal cases does not establish the expert's validity. The expert must demonstrate that:

1. The theory applied has been or can be tested,
2. The test, technique, or theory has been peer reviewed,
3. The error rate, if known, and standard parameters established for the test, technique, or theory can be demonstrated,
4. The test, technique, or theory is generally accepted in the scientific field.

In *Daubert v. Merrell Dow Pharmaceuticals, Inc.* (1993), the United States Supreme Court focused on the admissibility of testimony from expert scientific witnesses. The Court found that such testimony is admissible only if the trial judge, acting in the capacity of "gatekeeper," decides that scientific expert testimony is "relevant to the task at hand" and rests on a "reliable foundation." The trial judge must determine relevance: if an untrained person cannot understand the facts of the case and make a determination, then testimony from someone with specialized scientific knowledge becomes relevant.

In regard to reliability, the *Daubert* case presents a "non-exclusive" checklist for the judge assessing scientific expert testimony. Following the *Daubert* ruling, the Federal Rules of Evidence (FRE) were modified to address and codify the decisions of *Daubert*. Article VII, Rule 702—Testimony of Experts states:

> If scientific, technical, or other specialized knowledge will assist the trier of fact to understand the evidence or to determine a fact in issue, a witness qualified as an expert by knowledge, skill, experience, training, or education, may testify thereto in the form of an opinion or otherwise, if (1) the testimony is based upon sufficient facts or data, (2) the testimony is the product of reliable principles and methods, and (3) the witness has applied the principles and methods reliably to the facts of the case. (FRE 2001, p. 13)

The second case that adds to the understanding of Federal Rule 702 is *Kuhmo Tire Company v. Carmichael et al.* The most important element of the *Kuhmo v. Carmichael* case is the expanded notion of the "gatekeeping" function. Federal courts require the screening of all expert opinion testimony proposed under Rule 702. The courts reviewed *Kuhmo* and expanded the *Daubert* standards to help establish criteria for determining the reliability of expert witnesses, though trial judges have great latitude and discretion in determining how to test a particular expert's proposed testimony against the reliability benchmark of Rule 702 (*Kumho Tire Co., Ltd., v. Carmichael et al.*).

As the law evolves in application, it is clear that the most important element in judging the reliability of testimony is not the opinion itself but the way in which the opinion or conclusions are reached. The issue of reliability generally comes down to an expert's ability not only to state conclusions but, more important, to demonstrate the logic leading to those conclusions. An expert's opinions are recognized as being the product of a reasoning process.

The soundness and clarity of the reasoning process, therefore, must be demonstrated to the court as a logical and systematic progression from evidence to conclusion. The process includes determining the soundness and degree of certainty of every inference and assumption made during the analysis. Unless the soundness of the foundation can be demonstrated to the court, an expert may never be allowed to offer an opinion.

The court does not seek to judge the correctness of an expert's testimony. Rather, the court attempts to determine whether the testimony is more likely than not to be reliable. The ultimate question for the court is how to assure that all experts testify from a basis of valid and reliable knowledge. Toward this end the court demands that experts demonstrate the same standards of intellectual and methodological rigor that their professions require.

The extensive and expanding population of biomechanical (and other) experts has not led to an increase in quality decision-making. The courts have had some difficulty in fulfilling their "gatekeeper" function with respect to biomechanists. The biomechanical expert has also struggled with his or her ability to present not only an opinion but also the logic and rationale leading to the development of the opinion to the court. Consequently, courts have taken varying positions, ranging from viewing all biomechanical testimony as "junk science" to allowing all testimony into the court with the jury permitted to place "weight" on the testimony or disregard it. As previously noted, the presentation of scientific testimony can be very persuasive, but if the testimony is incorrect or misleading, it detracts from, rather than enhances, the function of the court. Likewise, experts who are polished presenters can sway a jury based on the strength of their personality rather than the strength of their knowledge.

Over the last couple of decades, experts have paid closer attention to the courts' requirement that the formulation of their opinions meet the test of being generally accepted in the scientific field. For experts in the field of biomechanics the transition has not always been easy. However, the correct approach lies in realizing that a valid biomechanics analysis is simply the adoption of the failure analysis techniques from engineering.

Injury causation analysis is simply a specific application of the failure analysis principles developed over decades and commonly used in engineering. Failure analysis is a process that is performed in order to determine the causes or factors that have led to an undesired loss of functionality. It is an iterative process that involves examination and analysis of the physical evidence related to an event or an element failure. In the context of injury causation analysis, it is the systematic examination of all available evidence that pertains to a specific event/injury question.

Failure analysis is a process that is performed in order to determine the causes or factors that have led to an undesired loss of functionality. The process embraces the concepts inherent in learning how to define objectives, define and/or limit the scope of an investigation, look at the physical evidence, structure both the investigation and the data that it reveals, and clearly state the conclusions based on the general problem solving performed. Failure analysis is an iterative and creative process founded in critical thinking.

The science of critical thinking has a principle called the confirmation bias, which refers to the tendency to look only for what one expects to find: that is, "Ye shall find only what ye shall seek". Humans have a natural tendency to see only what they expect to see or to perceive things according to preconceived expectations. As Mark Twain wrote, "To the man who wants to use a hammer badly, a lot of things look like nails that need hammering." This proclivity presents a special problem for the expert witness who often wants to support the side of the case that is paying his invoice.

It may be that there is no true injury present. In fact, one important question that should always be asked is: "Did an injury (failure) really occur?" It is possible to have medically observed pathology that involves fracture, wear and deformation but that is not the result of a traumatic event. For example, discovering lumbar disc pathology in a 40-year-old overweight human, is less of a surprise than finding one that is free from such pathology.

Two of the critical goals in a failure investigation are to identify both the damage mechanism(s) and damage mode(s) that are present. Damage mechanisms are a key component in categorizing damage and failures. The definitions are:

Damage mode

Damage mode is a description of the physical characteristics of damage observed. For example, disc space narrowing and endplate spurring represent damage modes for the disc. Damage mode describes what specific damage is present and is an important element in identifying the damage mechanism. For example, disc space narrowing and endplate spurring are age-related disc pathologies rather than "injuries" that can be attributed to a specific event.

Damage mechanism

Damage mechanism is the specific series of events that describe both how the damage was incurred and the resulting consequences. Examples of damage mechanisms from inline motor vehicle accidents that relate to cervical disc injury include potential flexion/extension loading to cervical spine discs, disease pathology and common aging effects. The damage mechanism describes how the observed damage came to be present. Identifying the potential damage mechanisms present (or absent) in an event illuminates the event/injury relationship.

Finally, the process of drawing inferences from evidence is inductive, although a certain amount of deduction may also be involved. A deductive argument is valid if and only if it is **logically impossible** that its conclusion is false while its premises are true. In contrast, an inductive argument is strong if and only if it is **improbable** that its conclusion is false given that its premises are true. The measure of the strength of an inductive argument is known as an inductive probability. That is, an inductive probability measures how probable the conclusion is given that the premises are true. In litigation the inductive probability is generally expressed as "scientific certainty."

Currently, there is no single accepted systematic approach that the forensic biomechanics expert—or, for that matter, technical experts in most other disciplines—must use as a standard methodology either for judgment by the court or for presentation. What follows is a successful systematic approach, or decision model, to assist the court in determining the relevance and reliability of expert testimony. The model from the broad field of decision theory provides a tool to help the court exercise its "gatekeeper" function as well as providing a tool for the expert to demonstrate for the court the process by which the "expert" opinion was developed.

The methodology demonstrated here will serve to address both of these important functions. With a prescriptive method for organizing, evaluating, interpreting, documenting, displaying, and communicating the evidence available in a specific case, the expert can illustrate to the court the entire intellectual process undertaken. The methodology illuminates the logic of the expert; it demonstrates where the expert must make assumptions and inferences, and reveals the strength or weakness of those assumptions. The methodology also makes apparent the role of each piece of evidence, the absence of evidence, and the expert's assumptions in reaching the opinions. In short, the methodology becomes a useful tool for the expert in identifying the strength of his or her opinion, the attorneys in understanding the strengths and weaknesses of both sides of the case, and the court in determining the reliability of the final biomechanical opinion. The methodology, in addition, offers the jury an opportunity to judge the importance of certain evidence and assumptions made within the process.

2.3 Mental Models and Situation Awareness

Mental models are "internal belief structures" that interpret external reality (Burns, 2000). The decision-maker constructs and manipulates mental models to describe or explain specific situations (i.e., situation awareness). Klein and Crandall (1995) define four primary functions served by mental simulation:

- Generate a course of action. The decision-maker plans a course of action: creating a plan, generating information, and developing expectations. A plan is especially important when time constraints are severe or the risks are high.
- Inspect/evaluate. The decision-maker creates a mental simulation assessing the impact of a planned course of action. Will the plan work? What can go wrong? The decision-maker uses experiences to detect flaws and warning signs as a simulation unfolds.
- Explain. A decision-maker focuses on the sequence of events to understand how and why an event occurred; in other words, he or she searches for a plausible explanation.
- Model/discovery. A decision-maker envisions a hypothetical system in action.

Two important non-cognitive factors affect mental simulation. First, when time constraints are severe, even experienced decision-makers truncate the evaluation phase of mental simulation and do not always have time to check for flaws. In a real-world setting in which solutions often involve complex, dynamic trade-offs for which there is no single "right" answer, "decisional errors in this and other cases can be characterized as 'normal' (i.e., rational) consequences of the decision-makers' mental models" (Burns, 2000, p. 1). Second, the quality of mental simulation is affected by the decision-maker's experience. Without experience a decision maker does not have the "building blocks" to construct adequate mental simulations; in fact, novices may not be able to construct adequate mental models to create an initial mental simulation (Klein and Crandall 1995).

The decision-maker's level of expertise and experience can influence his or her strategies as well as the speed and accuracy of a decision. Klein and Hoffman (1993) state that "Novices see only what is there; experts can see what is not there" (p. 203). Novice decision makers can generally see what is happening in front of them; however, they are limited to objective and measurable tasks at hand.

Expert decision-makers, on the other hand, can envision what is not there. Drawing from a larger store of knowledge than novices, they can size up problems more quickly, develop analogies/stories and more complex mental models, make fine/discriminating distinctions, analyze the consequences of actions, and visualize how a situation will evolve. Experts can use their knowledge base to size up a situation as "typical" and can quickly simulate plausible goals, relevant cues, expectant events, and feasible courses of action. An expert decision-maker's ability to know what is typical for a given situation allows him or her to handle difficult scenarios under time-compressed conditions more effectively than novices (Klein and Hoffman, 1993). De Groot (1965) describes how chess grand masters quickly size up threats as deviations from the norm and recognize the best move as the first one they consider. Calderwood et al. (1988) observe a high degree of degradation in class B chess players' moves under high-speed, "blitz" conditions, suggesting that experts can rapidly size up a situation, but that novices and journeymen cannot.

Experienced biomechanical experts interpret ambiguous cues and underlying causes in real-world situations. They draw from their experiences to determine if a problem exists and whether and how to act on it. Expert decision-makers quickly focus on "highly likely" options and do not waste time on "low-payoff" leads (Orasanu and Connolly, 1993). Experts are distinguished by their "situation assessment ability," not their reasoning ability alone. Decision-making is driven by the expert's knowledge of a situation, his or her ability to search out and assess information, and the ability to build a "good enough" model rather than an optimal choice.

Biomechanical expertise requires a great deal of experience, but accumulation of a large knowledge base alone is not enough. Expert decision-makers are able to use their knowledge to make judgments that are difficult for most people; they apply their experience to a wide range of daily tasks and set standards of ideal performance. An expert no longer relies on analytic skills, such as rules and guidelines, to make a decision; instead, performance is highly proficient because the expert can intuitively zero-in on key issues of a problem without "wasteful consideration" (Klein and Hoffman, 1993, p. 206). An expert decision-maker can simply handle a wider range of tasks compared to the inexperienced decision-maker.

How can a trial judge determine the validity of a biomechanical expert's decision? Klein and Hoffman (1993) suggest the following:

- Performance. Expert decision-makers are "smoother" than novices and can be assessed by their consistency, accuracy, completeness, and speed of decision. Novices can at times be compulsively fast, but the expert will generally perform more accurately.
- Content knowledge. Experts can also be assessed based on their knowledge rather than performance.
- Development milestones. Experts can finally be assessed based on their progress along skill-development milestones.

Summary

Can one adapt a model to help a trial judge in his or her "gatekeeper" function determine the reliability and relevance of expert testimony? Traditional, normative theories with their emphasis on mathematical-based, linear, inductive processes seem to offer the trial judge little help. These models focus on the outcome rather than the process of decision–making. Their emphasis on an ideal decision-maker optimizing decisions in a controlled setting is unrealistic in real-world litigation.

Naturalistic decision theory (NDM), however, focuses on how people actually make decisions given the pressures of the real world. The expert decision-maker is aware of the problem at hand and does not waste time comparing options or searching for optimal outcomes. Naturalistic decision models, especially the recognition-primed (RPD) model, target experience as the basis of the decision. In real life, experts use their expertise and judgment to make decisions: experienced decision-makers construct arguments for a preferred choice, construct stories based on memories of previous encounters, and take incremental actions. Significantly, the complementary relationship between NDM and the powerful communication tool of decision trees (a more general form of process-tracing) extends the utility of both.

Naturalistic decision theory, with its reliance on how experts make decisions, is most relevant to addressing the "gatekeeper" function of the court. The theory provides a basis for assessing the relevance and reliability of expert opinion, especially when the opinion is expressed using decision trees.

Process tracing models delineate the decision-maker's thought process in a specific circumstance. The approach (Beach and Mitchell, 1978) captures the natural evolutionary development of the expert opinion. As stated by Brehmer (1990):

The study of decision-making in a dynamic real time context relocates the study of decision-making and makes it part of the study of choice. The problem of decision-making, as seen in this framework, is a matter of directing and maintaining the continuous flow of behavior towards some set goals rather than as a set of discrete episodes involving choice dilemmas (p. 26).

The process-tracing strategies are directly applicable to expert opinion formulation. This framework leads to the natural integration of two factors: the features of the task and the knowledge and experience of the decision-maker (Klein et al., 1993). Logic–based and linear, process tracing models represent the opinion production system (Spangler et al., 1999). Process tracing models are based on the assumptions that (1) decisions occur within a specific context; (2) few cases are sufficiently well defined to allow the application of engineering or statistical models (output models); and (3) expert opinion is an evolutionary process which must necessarily be responsive to the ongoing evidentiary discovery process (Rouse and Valusek, 1993).

Lave and March esoterically describe the search for the best decision-making model: one which integrates the real world with aesthetics and ethics to produce truth, beauty, and justice (Lave and March, 1975). Klein et al. (1993) suggest concrete attributes:

A model must:
1. Be capable of handling poorly structured or ill-defined problems;
2. Work in uncertain environments;
3. Be applicable in dynamic situations;
4. Have action/feedback loops; and
5. Illustrate the influence of time on the decision process.

Finally, a good process tracing model is most valuable when it can visually display the relationships that the expert has established and communicated through oral presentation as well as in text (Branch and Moore, 1990). At this juncture the power of decision trees becomes apparent to the application of naturalistic decision models.

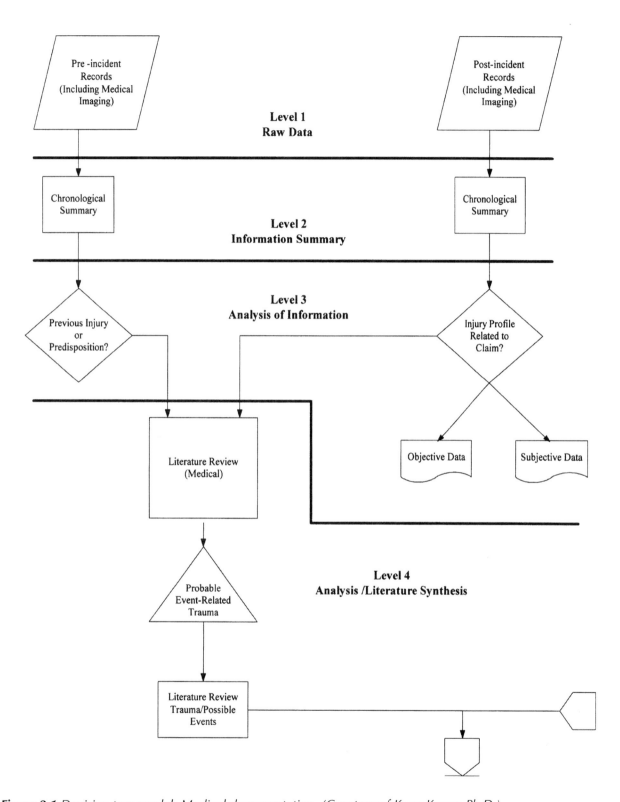

Figure 2.1 Decision tree model: Medical documentation. (Courtesy of Kerry Knapp Ph.D.)

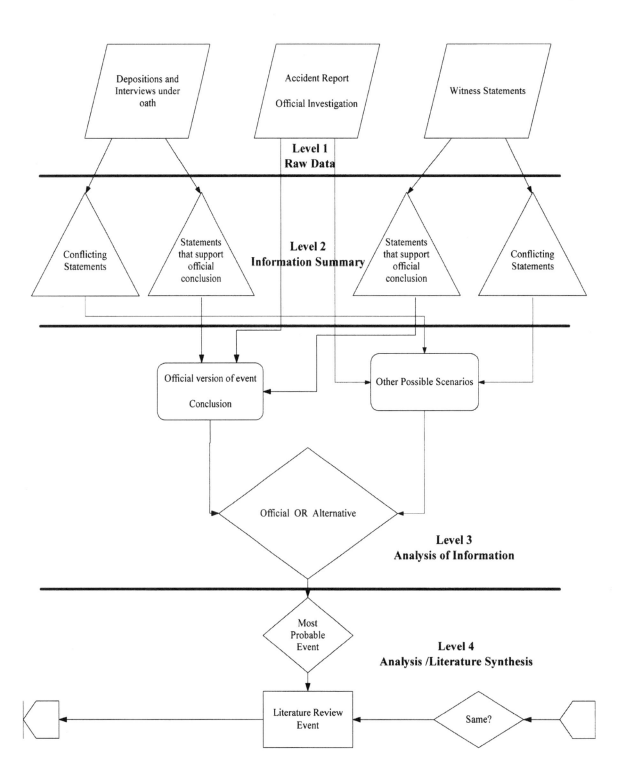

Figure 2.2 Decision tree model: Event history. (Courtesy of Kerry Knapp Ph.D.)

Decision trees, flow charts, and flow diagrams are synonymous forms of process tracing with wide ranging applicability to naturalistic decision models (NDM). Decision trees have been used to illustrate the decision strategy in image theory (Beach, 1990), simple and complex cropping decisions (Gladwin, 1983), general decision tasking (Rouse and Valusek, 1993), finance decisions (Lehman, 2000), and almost any other decision arena one can imagine. These simple-to-construct models satisfy the multiple desirable elements described previously. Thus far, this process tracing tool has not been applied to the problem faced by the courts with respect to the "gatekeeper" function.

One of the principal values of decision trees is that they themselves are hybrids, a blend of quite different research approaches (Gladwin, 1989). They lend themselves to cyclical discovery (Spangler et al., 1999), a typical process during case development in biomechanics and other areas of forensic science. Like all models, decision trees are somewhat simplified pictures of the actual decision process (Lave and March, 1975). They enable the expert decision-maker to check his or her own thinking and to detail for the court the development of that opinion.

The decision tree also has the advantage of being a testable form (Gladwin, 1989). An opposing expert can examine the process as described by the decision tree and analyze the strengths and weaknesses of the logic underlying an opinion. While this scrutiny may not seem desirable from the standpoint of the expert, it certainly is a desirable property from the standpoint of the ultimate judicial goal of truthseeking.

Decision trees are a useful vehicle for displaying the assessment of uncertainty. It should be understood that uncertainty exists at each step in the decision process, partially due to the availability and quality of evidence (Fishcoff, 1984; Hammitt, 1995). Uncertainty is inherent in the ability to match the specific event in question to available literature at each point in the analysis (Walker et al., 2001). Uncertainty exists in the ability of any specific expert to analyze and extrapolate literature and models to particular case situations (Morgan and Keith, 1995; Slob, 1994; Wilson and Crouch, 2001).

The concepts of risk analysis can be applied throughout the decision process and displayed within the decision tree. By incorporating an analysis of risk and uncertainty into the display of the decision tree, the expert, the lawyers on both sides of the issue, and the court can determine the strengths and weaknesses of the testimony (Hammitt, 1995; Morgan and Keith, 1995; Tversky and Koehler, 1994). Most important, the expert must be able to display for the court not only the logic path by which he or she

reached opinions and conclusions but also the testability, reproducibility, and the inherent uncertainty (confidence) of those opinions and conclusions.

2.4 The General Decision Tree Model

The decision tree for forensic biomechanics is a model with three main branches (Figures 2.1 through 2.4). The branches can be developed concurrently or sequentially, depending on skill, time, and other constraints. The expert should avoid circumventing the analysis by "reasoning from a conclusion" on the basis of a single line of evidence that develops early in the process. It is appropriate to incorporate portions of the literature review at any point in the process. Each main branch of the decision tree is structured with respect to five levels of analysis from the raw data (Level 1) to the summary/conclusions (Level 5).

Medical documentation (Figure 2.1)

Forensic biomechanics analysis is injury or tissue damage based; consequently, the first major branch of the decision tree illustrates the analysis of the medical documentation. Because forensic biomechanics analysis nearly always takes place months or years after the event, the quality of the medical documentation of tissue damage affects the ability of the analyst to reach a conclusion. When considering a specific injury or an injury-producing event, the analyst examines two medical lines of evidence or two minor branches within the medical documentation branch.

First, the forensic biomechanist considers the pre-incident medical records of the individual (Level 1). The summary is developed in chronological order (Level 2) and carefully analyzed for previous injury or pre-existing medical conditions that can lead to a predisposition for injury (Level 3).

Second, the medical documentation is the post-incident medical record (Level 1). Again, the records are summarized chronologically (Level 2) to allow interpretation of the injury within the context of tissue physiology and healing. From analysis of the post-incident medical records comes an injury profile related to the claim event. The chronological post-incident injury profile is further subdivided into objective evidence of injury (elements of injury that can be accurately measured by a medical professional) and subjective evidence (generally consisting of symptoms based on the patient's self-report, neither verified nor rejected by a medical professional) (Level 3).

These two branches of the medical documentation tree are merged with a summary of literature applicable

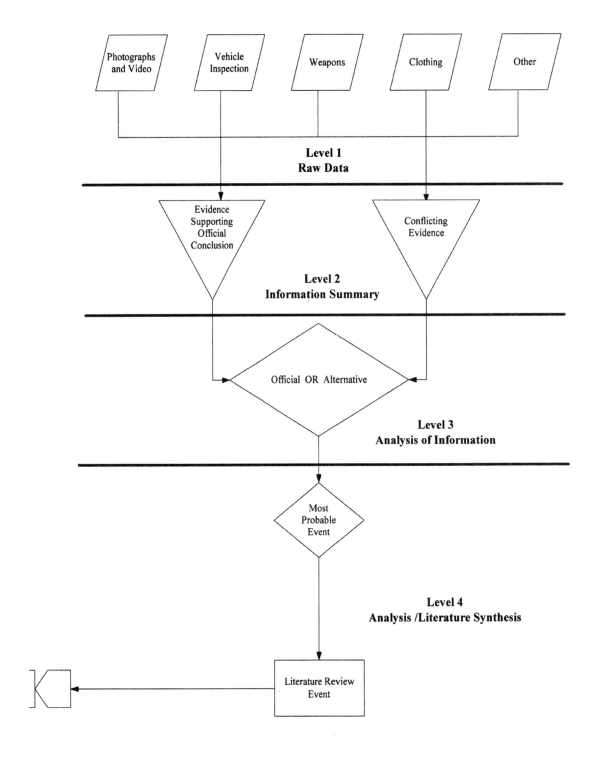

Figure 2.3 *Decision tree model: Physical evidence. (Courtesy of Kerry Knapp Ph.D.)*

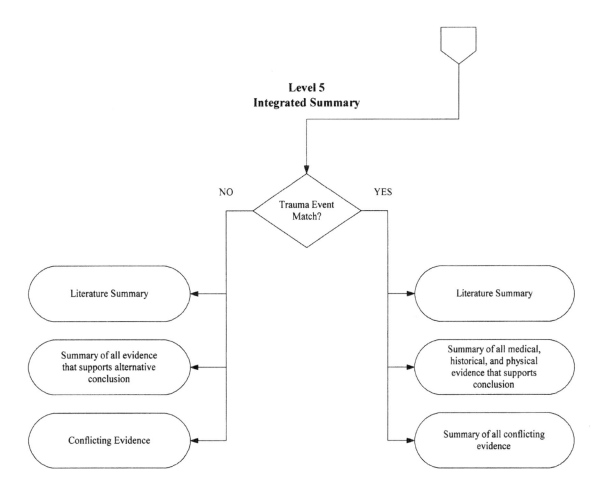

Figure 2.4 *Decision tree model: Summary. (Courtesy of Kerry Knapp Ph.D.)*

to the particular tissue tolerance limits under consideration and other related data associated with the claimed and identified injury profile (Level 4). From the merged data comes a written probability statement explaining and identifying how the two branches of the medical documentation branch are integrated, how the integrated result affects the probability of injury in the event under examination, and the relationship of the medical evidence to the appropriate literature. The disparity between the objective and the subjective injury evidence data with reference to the claimed injury should be made apparent.

Event history (Figure 2.2)

The second major branch of the forensic biomechanics decision tree is the event history. Three subbranches can be identified under event history. The first of these is the accident report or official investigation (Level 1), consist-

ing primarily of specific physical evidence and personal observations of the investigating authorities (usually police officers). Also included are the preliminary witness statements and other material developed by the investigating authorities during the initial on-site investigation. It is important to separate the initial investigation materials, because of their potential for having greater value, from those items and statements collected later. Witness memories change over time, evidence is lost, and in some cases evidence is altered. The closer in time the evidence and statements are to the actual event, the more reliable they are likely to be.

The second subbranch is the post-incident information associated with the official investigation (Level 1). Witness statements are separated into statements of two types: the ones supporting the official conclusion (as identified by the official investigation) and the others conflicting with other witness statements and/or with the official investigation conclusion (Level 2). Although these statements and evidence lack the temporal significance of the material collected earlier, they can be rich in content. They must be examined cautiously because opinion often begins to mingle with observation over time.

The third subbranch consists of depositions and interviews taken under oath (Level 1). This subbranch is distinctly different from the others because of the very long temporal separation (often years) from the event. As noted, memory of specific observations and facts often becomes inextricably mingled with supposition and opinion as the event retreats in time, requiring caution in the integration of the material into the analysis.

Another difference in this subbranch is that the statements being provided by the deponents are made under penalties of perjury, an element that gives them strength. Again, the deposition and interview statements are separated into those statement elements that conflict with the official investigation and those statements that support the official conclusion (Level 2).

With the three subbranches clearly identified, the analyst (forensic biomechanist) can proceed down the event history branch, substantiating the observational data by investigators and others (Level 3). This process supports the official accident report or investigation and identifies possible scenarios (other than the official report) that logically result from the analysis. The result of the analysis path is the identification of the most probable event. The identification of the most probable event should be followed by a literature review of similar and associated events always looking for opportunities from the literature to support the official version or other possible scenarios which have been identified (Level 4).

Physical evidence (Figure 2.3)
The third major branch of the forensic biomechanics decision tree is the physical evidence branch. All of the subbranches of the physical evidence branch are post-investigation evidence developed by the analyst or other investigators outside the official investigation. The subbranches include analysis of photographs, videotapes, vehicle, site, weapons, clothing, and any other tangible evidence related to the incident or the scene, or both (Level 1). All the physical evidence is sorted and categorized as either evidence supporting the official report or evidence conflicting with the official report (Level 2). At this juncture all evidence must be used and accounted for in the case analysis. Selectively ignoring physical evidence, witness statements, or medical information is not acceptable.

From the physical evidence branch an analyst formulates an explanation of events that seems most probable as well as identifies other reasonable scenarios (Level 3). This branch also includes a literature review directed toward analysis of specific items from the evidence branch (Level 4). For instance, if the analyst is considering a gunshot incident, he or she must look at the research and ballistics characteristics specific to the weapon involved. In a motor vehicle incident, the physical characteristics of vehicles or its crash data can be important.

Case summary (Figure 2.4)
The three branches are then integrated into a summary branch or trunk (Level 5). The conclusion of the trunk identifies the valid and reliable evidence (including the physical evidence, the event history evidence, the medical documentation evidence, and the applicable literature) that supports the official, reported version of the incident. Any evidence or literature, including witness statements and medical evidence, that does not support the conclusion is adequately explained and not ignored. The summary material and conclusions are then prepared in narrative form and presented as an expression of the expert's final integrated and documented opinion.

A. Application 1: The low speed motor vehicle accident
The low-speed motor vehicle accident represents the largest body of personal injury cases litigated in the civil courts. Presenting the methodology as it applies to a low speed impact example, therefore, has wide applicability and is familiar to most practicing biomechanical experts, attorneys, and judges. This case study demonstrates the use of the general model and incorporates the relevant low speed rear impact literature. In the particular case study presented, the absence of evidence increases the importance of the literature review in the analysis.

> Case Study 2.1
> Introduction to *Reba v. Nabor.* On July 15, 1996, the vehicle driven by Amy Reba was impacted from the rear by a vehicle driven by Jazlee Nabor. The incident occurred in a Walgreen's parking lot. There were no witnesses, and the police were not called. There was no apparent damage to either vehicle, and both parties denied injury at the time. No insurance information or other identification was exchanged between the parties. Ms. Reba, however, did record the license plate number of the striking vehicle.

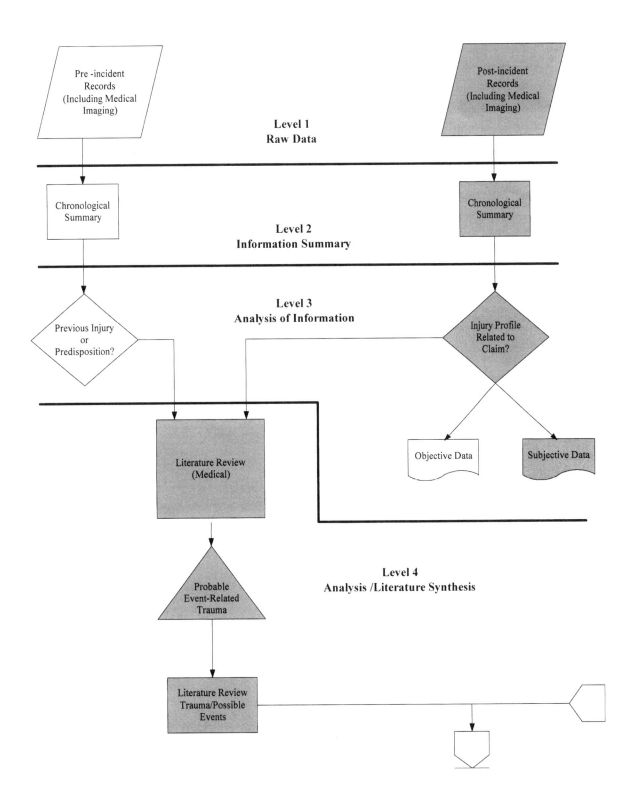

Figure 2.5 *Medical documentation. (Courtesy of Kerry Knapp Ph.D.)*

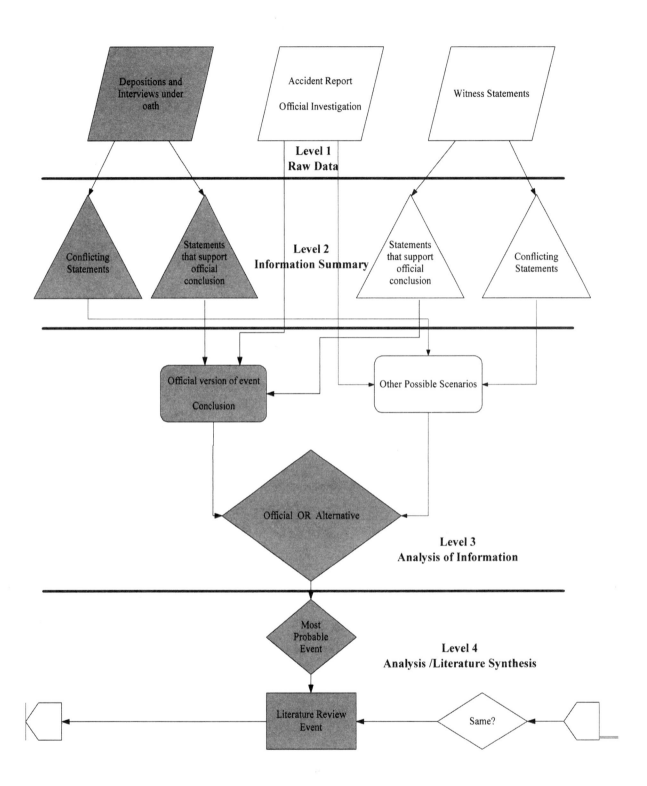

Figure 2.6 *Event history. (Courtesy of Kerry Knapp Ph.D.)*

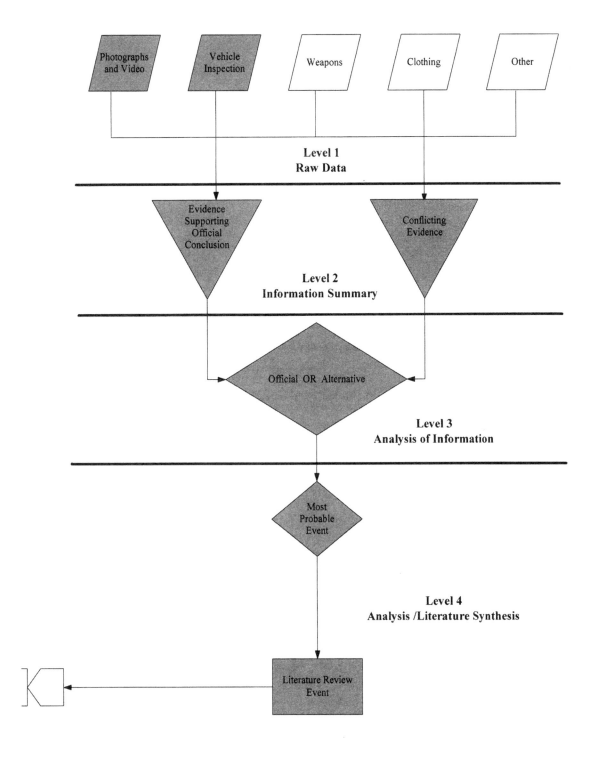

Figure 2.7 Physical evidence. (Courtesy of Kerry Knapp Ph.D.)

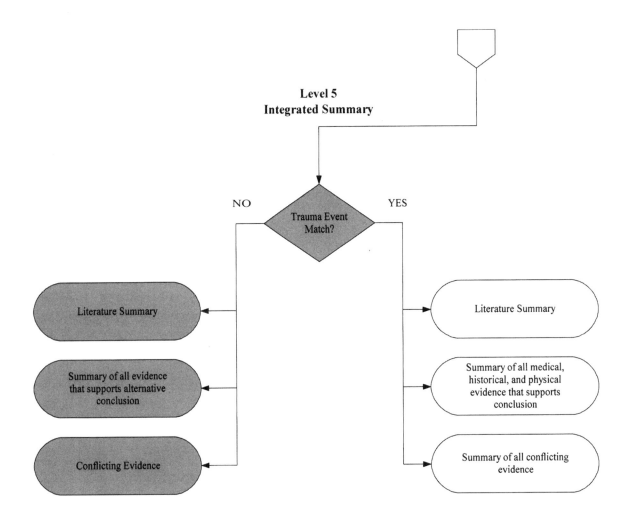

Figure 2.8 *Integrated summary. (Courtesy of Kerry Knapp Ph.D.)*

The day after the incident Ms. Reba sought chiropractic care and reported the incident to her insurance company. Ms. Reba also sought legal council on the advice of her chiropractor. Civil litigation followed with Ms. Reba claiming permanent injury and seeking financial remuneration. The role of the biomechanist in this case was to determine the causal relationship between the July 15 motor vehicle impact and injuries claimed by Ms. Reba.

The decision tree branch 1: Medical documentation (Figure 2.5)

Level 1 data is represented by the raw medical documents associated with Ms. Reba's medical history. The documents are the treatment notes and the other materials obtained from the primary care providers. In this specific case, there were no pre-incident records.

Level 2 Information Summary: The chronological summary of Ms. Reba's medical records. No interpretation of medical records is performed; rather the raw records are condensed into diagnosis/treatment capsules which, when taken in total, describe the chronology of Ms. Reba's injuries.

Level 3 Analysis of Information and Injury Profile
1. Cervical, thoracic, and lumbar spine strain-sprain.
2. Temporomandibular joint dysfunction.
3. Right wrist injury (non-specific).

Other notes of interest from the medical documentation:
1. Ms. Reba consulted 14 medical providers over 11 months (might indicate opinion shopping);
2. The results of examinations by the multiple pro-

viders indicate inconsistent test results and diagnosis; and

3. On 11/26/96 Ms. Reba reported an inaccurate history to Provider #7: "Rear ended at 40 mph resulting in nine (9) vertebrae dislocated, whiplash and internal bleeding."

The decision tree branch 2: Event history (Figure 2.6)

The subject case study occurred in a private parking lot and was not investigated by any official authority (police department). Consequently, there are no items of analysis for the event history branch except the single deposition of Amy Reba taken on September 23, 1999 (Level 1, raw data).

Level 2 information summary includes the following statements extracted from Ms. Reba's deposition:

1. The subject event was a rear impact collision for Ms. Reba (p. 10);
2. Ms. Reba saw the striking vehicle approaching and braced for the impact with her hands (steering wheel) and feet (brake pedal and firewall) (p. 20); and
3. The impact speed was at least 40 mph (p. 22).

The decision tree branch 3: Physical evidence (Figure 2.7)

In this particular case, Level 1 data consist entirely of the two vehicles involved in the accident. Both were available to Mr. Smith, the accident reconstructionist, for inspection and documentation. Level 2 information consists of Mr. Smith's vehicle dynamics analysis. Based on the measurements and inspections of Mr. Smith, a qualified accident reconstructionist (ACTAR certified), the following vehicle dynamics were identified:

1. The July 15, 1996, motor vehicle accident was a rear impact collision for Ms. Reba;
2. The principal direction of force (PDOF) was 180 degrees;
3. The change of velocity for the Reba vehicle was a maximum of 2.5 mph; and
4. The maximum average acceleration of the Reba vehicle was 1.14 g (36.71 ft./sec./sec).

In the case of *Reba v. Nabor*, Levels 3, 4, and 5 of the decision tree are most appropriately merged into an integrated narrative presentation rather than pursued in further detail as separate branches.

The case summary narrative (example report) (Figure 2.8)

Vehicles involved:
Vehicle 1: 1987 Ford Tempo (Reba–struck vehicle).
Vehicle 2: 1990 Plymouth Acclaim (Nabor–striking vehicle).
Reviewed:
1. Medical Reports;
2. Vehicle Dynamics from Mr. Smith–Report of July 14, 1998; and
3. Deposition transcript of Amy Reba–December 19, 1998.

July 15, 1996 motor vehicle incident:
1. On July 15, 1996, the vehicle in which Ms. Reba was the restrained driver (three-point restraint) sustained a single rear end impact *without* a subsequent front-end collision.
2. The loading was centric through the X-axis of Ms. Reba's vehicle.
3. The delta velocity of Ms. Reba's vehicle was 2.5 mph or less.
4. The average acceleration applied to the Ms. Reba vehicle was 1.14 g's maximum, based on a 100 ms time frame for this collision.

Cervical spine kinematics and kinetics

Ms. Reba's 1987 Ford Tempo could move forward from the rear impact. This vehicle motion has the effect of moving the seatback/headrest into the posterior torso and posterior head of Ms. Reba. **Please note that the motion described by Ms. Reba during her deposition of December 19, 1997 pgs. 48 to 50 is incorrect.** (Occupants commonly express the misperception of their kinematic motion.) Subsequent forward acceleration of the head and torso *may* occur as the head and torso rebound off of the seatback and headrest. While the forward acceleration of the head and torso will be similar to the forward vehicle acceleration, it is generally less. For example, in a 15 g horizontal acceleration applied to a sled vehicle (rear loading), a measured 6–9 g's of forward acceleration was applied to the occupant as the head bounced off of the headrest (Strother and James, 1987), a loading reduction of 40 to 60 percent. Peak g's applied to the head link occur in a rear impact when the head moves backward (in relation to the vehicle) and produces maximum deformation of the headrest. As noted above, the head in a rear impact with the headrest may then rebound. However, West et al. (1993) indicate that human volunteers who are not braced for a rear impact will not strike their heads against the headrest until the delta velocity reaches a minimum of 3 mph for the struck vehicle. In other words, the loading in a rear impact with a delta velocity below 3.0 mph is insufficient to produce head contact with the headrest; consequently, there will not be any head rebound. This is the most probable scenario for Ms. Reba in the July 15, 1996 MVA. Furthermore, there is no significant head rebound until the delta velocity of the struck vehicle reaches at least 5.4 mph (West et al., 1993).

McConnell et al. (1993) also used human volunteers (males age 45 to 56 years) to examine rear impact at delta velocity levels between 2.5 and 5.0 mph. In all of the tests, the cervical spine extension and flexion displacements are always found to fall within the subjects' physiological limits (normal range of motion) (McConnell et al., 1993). Digitized high speed cinematography data indicate minimal head link motion throughout the 400 ms of torso and head movements (McConnell et al., 1993).

Szabo et al. (1994) confirmed the McConnell data, finding that cervical flexion and extension of the five human test subjects never exceeded their normal physiological limits for rear-end collisions occurring at speeds of 10 mph or less (delta velocity approximately 5 mph). McConnell et al. (1995) extended the human subject data to a delta velocity of 6.8 mph, confirming the previous observations and including one subject who underwent multiple impacts with head rotation of 30 degrees. Nielsen et al. (1996) performed an additional 25 rear impacts on vehicles with stiff bumpers; human volunteers were without injuries.

Human cervical spine tolerance (moments)

Ewing and Thomas (1967) tested human volunteers in addition to anthropometric dummies. Three of the human volunteers developed dynamic bending moments in a forward direction of 22.5 ft.-lbs., 33.2 ft.-lbs. and 36.9 ft.-lbs. without any neck injury. These data are consistent with Mertz and Patrick (1967), who tested one human volunteer in a dynamic flexion test producing 65 ft.-lbs. of torque without injury (some neck pain). Other much less conservative injury results come from the Mertz and Patrick cadaver data, which indicate that, for flexion, a resulting bending moment of 140 ft.-lbs. may be a lower boundary for the ligament injury tolerance level. No discernible ligamentous damage was produced to the cadaver subject. While caution must be exercised when applying these findings to the injury of a specific individual, these data suggest tolerance limits (accelerations and moments) that are many times higher than the maximum values experienced by Ms. Reba in this July 15, 1996, MVA.

Human cervical spine tolerance (linear and angular acceleration)

Ms. Reba's July 15, 1996, MVA represents a very low impact collision (rear loading). The linear acceleration applied to the head link of this driver is minimal. The maximum average acceleration level of the head link and the torso link in a backward direction relative to the vehicle does not exceed the average acceleration of the vehicle (1.14 g's max.) as it moves forward from the rear impact. Further, the forward (possible bounce back) average acceleration levels applied to the head and torso of Ms. Reba are likely to be reduced by 40 to 60 percent to a level of 0.46 to 0.68 g's. Muzzy (1976) reports the data on five male volunteers who were subjected to head forward peak accelerations ranging from 29.38 g's to 40.95 g's without injury. Angular velocities on the order of 1500/rad/sec/sec were not uncommon yet did not produce injury. Szabo et al. (1994), whose work included two women, found that angular head accelerations in rear-end collisions with impact speeds of 10 mph or less (delta velocity less than 5 mph) are insignificant for occupants who cannot anticipate the moment of impact and are relaxed (not braced). McConnell et al. (1995) found that unbraced human subjects in rear impacts with a delta velocity up to 6.8 mph are not injured (including the subject with a pre-impact head rotation). Meyer et al. (1997) report the results of 37 human subject rear impacts in cars and 70 human subject rear impacts in bumper cars with delta velocities up to 9 mph without injury. In all of these low impact rear collisions, the volunteer subject obviously knows that at some point he or she is going to experience a rear impact collision; however, the investigators took care to ensure that the subject is relaxed and unbraced prior to the loading event. Szabo (1996) and Brault et al. (1998) found that electromyographical readings of neck musculature in instrumented rear impact subjects does not begin prior to impact, indicating muscle inactivity and an absence of subject "pretensing" prior to impact. In the first experiment on human subjects, performed by Brault et al. and published in 1998, 42 human subjects solicited from the general population (21 men and 21 women) were subjected to rear impacts. The subjects responded to the impacts in a manner consistent with the previous human testing in low speed rear impact collisions.

There have now been over 650 volunteer exposures to low-speed rear impacts reported in the literature. The volunteer data include 59 tests involving women, an age range from 22 to 63 years, delta velocities from 1 to 10.3 mph. The human subjects reported no injury symptoms from the majority of these studies. The most severe symptom reported was minor neck pain lasting one week, **which resolved without treatment**. It should be noted that the subject reporting the most severe symptom was a 73-inch tall male who was subjected to four frontal impacts (delta velocity 4.8 to 8.7 mph) plus four rear impacts (delta velocity 3.2 to 8.0 mph) in the same day. In addition, the subject volunteer was without adequate head restraint (Nielsen et al. 1996).

Torso kinematics and kinetics

As described previously, the large energy absorbing pad represented by the seatback initially moved forward into the torso of Ms. Reba, absorbing energy and damping the impact to the torso. The torso link can subsequently rebound and move forward after initial deformation of the seatback. The three-point restraint that Ms. Reba was wearing then acts to arrest the forward bounce-back torso movement as this body link separates from the seatback (McConnell et al. 1993) if any such rebound occurs. In the McConnell test series with human volunteers, the shoulder strap consistently autotightened during backward motion of the occupant's torso into the seatback, and therefore in these cases, the torso forward excursion is at an absolute minimum (McConnell et al. 1993). When the torso moving forward impacts the shoulder belt (if the impact has been large enough to produce this result), then the torso of Ms. Reba can experience greater negative accelerations. However, these negative accelerations load the anterior chest. The belt impact upon the chest does not significantly load the lumbar or thoracic spine in compression or bending. Additionally, the lap belt, which secures the pelvis, does not produce a bending moment upon the thoracic or lumbar spine because the shoulder belt prevents forward torso excursion. West et al. in their 1993 study make a very strong statement regarding loading to the lumbar and thoracic spine:

> rebound, forward of a neutral position does not occur until collision magnitudes approach 8 km/hr [5 mph delta velocity] and even at the highest level of testing we performed, significant relative movement between the thoracic and lumbar spine did not occur. If the current medical description (i.e., that strain is the mechanism of low back injury) is valid, then our testing indicates that minor rear-end collisions have no potential to cause such injury (p. 25).

This statement is supported by McConnell et al. (1995):

The relative lack of human test subject low back differential motion, as it becomes quickly braced by the advancing seat back, makes any injury to this area quite unlikely as a result of a low velocity rear impact [delta velocity to 6.8 mph] (p. 229).

None of the human subjects involved in the 650 volunteer exposures to low speed rear impacts reported lumbar spine symptoms, including even mild muscle soreness in the lumbar spine region.

Transient symptoms versus injury

The rear impact studies using human volunteers sometimes produce transient or temporary symptoms when the delta velocity is above 5 mph. These symptoms range from a headache lasting a few seconds to neck stiffness/soreness lasting several days. As mentioned previously, one subject who was subjected to repeated impacts at delta velocities above 5 mph reported neck pain (soreness) for a period of one week (Nielsen et al. 1996). In all these human volunteer studies, the symptoms are limited to short duration headache and/or neck pain that is *completely* resolved without treatment within minutes or days. Temporary muscle soreness in the neck, shoulders, or low back resulting from a low velocity rear impact MVA cannot be confused with injury.

Conclusions: cervical, thoracic, and lumbar spine

1. Human voluntary movement of the head or torso links is capable of producing linear and angular accelerations that exceed those encountered by Ms. Reba during this July 15, 1996, motor vehicle impact.
2. The maximum possible forward head acceleration level (less than 0.68 g's) due to the MVA is less severe than the accelerations that one would experience in some amusement park rides at facilities such as Disney World's Space Mountain.
3. Triano and Schultz (1990) indicate that upper cervical moments of 16–18 ft.-lbs. and resultant forces of 27–29 lbs. are commonly achieved during chiropractic manipulations. It should be noted that Ms. Reba received osseous manipulative chiropractic treatments following this MVA. In view of the Triano and Schultz (1990) data, the loading administered to the cervical and lumbar spine during these chiropractic manipula-

tions far exceeded the loading that was applied during this July 15, 1996, MVA.

4. We live in a world in which the head link is subjected to g levels of 1 to 2 g's and moments of 5–7 ft.-lbs. on a daily basis. Allen et al. (1993), indicate that peak g's applied to the head (sagittal plane neck movement) can be as high as 5.96 g's when subjects are asked to "plop" backwards into a chair. A maximal loading moment of 2.3 ft.-lbs. due to the *Reba v. Nabor* impact is not consistent with *any* injury, including mild cervical muscle strain (and note that this loading represents an absolute maximum).

5. The level of loading from a biomechanics point of view is extremely low in this MVA. Therefore, even a mild (soft tissue) cervical spine injury due to the Nabor impact is highly improbable.

6. The human volunteer experimental evidence and the cadaver testing indicate that even mild soft tissue injury in thoracic or lumbar spine is extremely improbable in a rear impact of this magnitude. Based on several lines of evidence, thoracic or lumbar spine pathology in Ms. Reba could not be caused or aggravated by this July 15, 1996, MVA.

Temporomandibular Joint (TMJ) Syndrome

Several anecdotal studies suggest that temporomandibular joint dysfunction can be caused by low speed rear impact collisions in the absence of a head strike. The hypothesized mechanism for injury involves the opening of the jaw during the initial phase of the impact (backward motion of the head and torso) as the head rotates rearward, thereby producing mechanical stress at the temporomandibular joint.

Howard et al. (1991), in a study of flexion-extension in C-spine and the possible link to TMJ syndrome, found that "the normal physiologic activity of mastication possesses a greater potential to produce traumatic injury to the temporomandibular joints...than does mild to moderate extension-flexion motion of the cervical spine" (p. 1213). The human subject studies by Szabo et al. (1994), and West et al. (1993) demonstrate conclusively that no jaw motion relative to the cranium occurs during rear end collisions at impact speeds less than 10 mph. This experimental evidence supports the logical arguments advanced by Howard et al. (1991) and Orner (1992). Furthermore, it should be noted that in the absence of anatomical abnormality, TMJ syndrome is most commonly associated with psychological stress rather than acute mechanical trauma.

Conclusions: Temporomandibular Joint Dysfunction

1. The literature and the lack of a blunt trauma injury (or head strike) make any and all competing etiologies more probable causes of Ms. Reba's TMJ syndrome than this July 15, 1996, MVA.

2. There is no causal link between the loading history applied to the temporomandibular joints and associated soft tissues during this July 15, 1996, MVA and Ms. Reba's TMJ pathology.

Right wrist pathology

There is no rationale that would link the accelerations experienced in this MVA to Ms. Reba's right wrist pathology. It is important to reiterate that the rear impact has the effect of moving Ms. Reba rearward relative to her vehicle and the steering wheel.

This motion unloads the right hand and wrist. Furthermore, *any* rebound in an MVA of this magnitude and direction is improbable; even if any rebound occurs, the magnitude is limited by the three-point restraint. Finally, please note that Ms. Reba first reported wrist pain in October of 1996, approximately three months after this subject MVA. Any ligament disruption would have resulted in inflammation and swelling of the affected area within forty-eight hours or less.

Conclusions: right wrist

The late onset of Ms. Reba's right wrist symptoms is inconsistent with acute trauma due to the Nabor impact.

Summary discussion

In the low-speed motor vehicle impact case presented, objective evidence of injury is lacking. The development of the medical documentation branch (Figure 2.1) is nebulous, relying almost exclusively on patient self-report. In addition, it is clear from the exaggerated and inconsistent history provided by the plaintiff as well as the *opinion shopping* by the plaintiff that any self-report must be viewed with some degree of skepticism. Organizing the medical documentation in a format consistent with Figure 2.1 of the methodology makes the inconsistencies and weaknesses of the plaintiff's injury claim apparent to even a casual, untrained observer.

The event history branch of the decision tree (Figure 2.2) is also weak, consisting solely of the plaintiff's deposition and the information that can be extracted from it. The minimal information (impact configuration, bracing by the plaintiff, and speed) is both useful and important

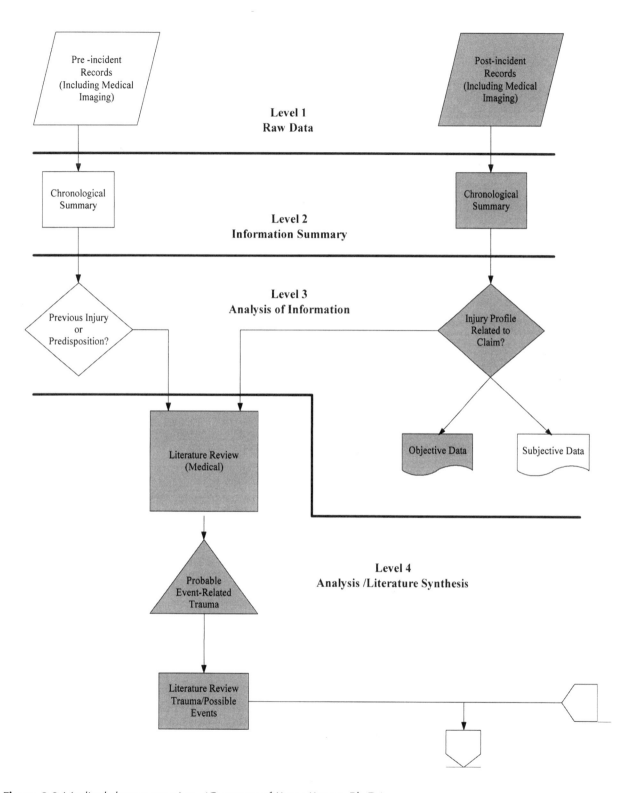

Figure 2.9 *Medical documentation. (Courtesy of Kerry Knapp Ph.D.)*

to the analysis. Placing the information within the context of the decision tree allows the analyst to illuminate the information and demonstrate its relevance.

The physical evidence branch (Figure 2.3) represents the only reliable objective evidence in the case. The information developed from the vehicles is quantifiable, verifiable, and reproducible. The physical evidence, although minimal, clearly dominates the analysis of injury in the case.

The methodology illuminates where data is present or absent; it demonstrates the strength of the data and the information that can be generated from it; and it makes apparent the relationship (or lack of relationship) between the lines of evidence as expressed by the branches of the decision tree (Figures 2.1 to 2.3). Finally, the integrated narrative summary (Figure 2.4) illustrates the strength and applicability of the experimental and clinical literature as it applies to the case.

B. Application 2: Gunshot death

Criminal cases involving the death of one or more individuals represent the most complex end of the judicial scale: the consequences, potentially the life or death of an accused, make the opinion of an expert extremely important. Applying the methodology to a specific incident involving a mortal gunshot wound demonstrates the efficacy of the decision tree analysis for attorneys, experts, and judges practicing in the criminal arena. This case study illustrates the use of the general model and incorporates the appropriate literature regarding gunshot wounds, blood spatter evidence, and biomechanics literature. The case study underscores the importance of detailed analysis as well as literature review.

Case Study: Introduction to homicide or suicide case

On August 21, police officers responded to a 911 shooting call at 1 a.m. On arrival the officers approached the residence and met a hysterical female subject who directed the officers to a bedroom in the residence where they observed a male subject kneeling over a nude female subject lying on the floor. The officers proceeded to secure the area and to document the available scene.

There were no witnesses to the event other than the deceased female and the aforementioned male. The male claimed he was not in the room when the female took her own life. As the case developed, the police investigators were unable to reach a conclusion as to whether the case could reasonably be classified as a suicide, the initial inclination of the medical examiner and the claim of the male witness. There was insufficient evidence to charge the male present at the scene with homicide. The role of the biomechanist was to review all the evidence and answer the single question: "Was the shooting death a suicide?"

The decision tree branch 1: medical documentation (Figure 2.9)

Level 1 data are represented by the body of the deceased female subject. In this particular instance, because the body was not available for direct examination, ten months post-incidence, the body data consist of the uninterpreted aspects of the autopsy and the photographs of the body, both at the scene and in the autopsy room.

Level 2: Information Summary
Name: Janice A. Smith
DOB: September 7, 1964
Height: 62"
Weight: 121 lbs.
There were no injuries to Ms. Smith other than the single gunshot wound to the head. The complete autopsy detail, external and internal examination, is irrelevant in this case except for the summary description of the head wound. The head demonstrated two wounds.

1. The first wound was a 20 x 4 centimeter gaping wound over the right side of the scalp, extending from the right cheek to the right occipital region.
2. The second wound occurred over the left temporal scalp, 6 centimeters posterior to the medial eyebrow ridges and 4.5 centimeters from the top of the head. The wound was 7 x 3.5 centimeters and irregular in shape.
3. The bullet passed into the cranial cavity through both cerebral hemispheres and exited the head.
4. Much of the brain was avulsed with only 460 grams of brain, primarily the left, temporal, occipital brain, and cerebellum, and brain stem remaining within the cranial cavity.
5. There were numerous skull fractures coursing over the skull convexity.
6. There were numerous fractures involving the base of the skull.
7. Slight para-orbital contusions were present.

Level 3: Analysis of Information and Injury Profile
It is important to recognize and record the medical examiner's analysis and conclusions based solely on his exami-

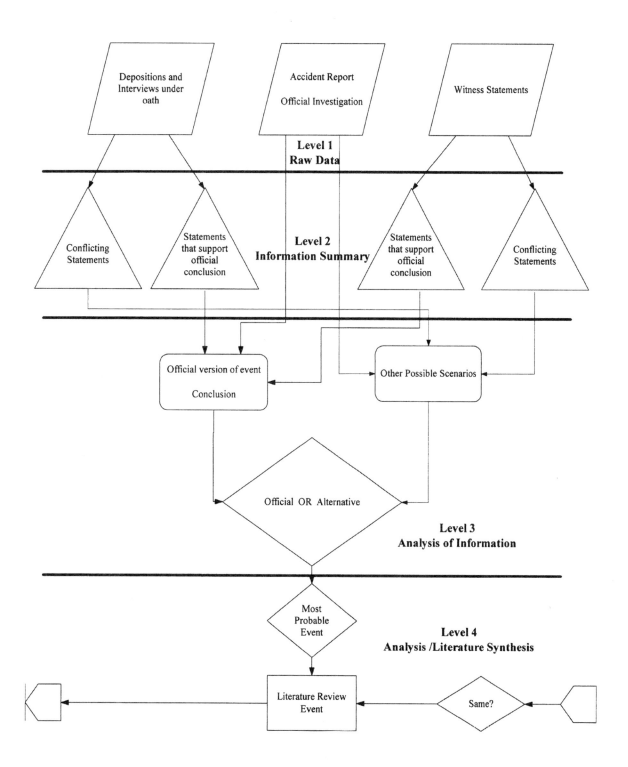

Figure 2.10 Event history. (Courtesy of Kerry Knapp Ph.D.)

nation of the wound. At this point the medical examiner's observations and conclusions are presented without interpretation or challenge.

1. Entrance wound. The 21 x 4 centimeter gaping entrance wound over the right side of the scalp extends over the right cheek and right occipital region. The edges approximate a ragged, stellate opening seen above the right ear, 8.5 centimeters from the top of the head and 8.0 centimeters posterior to the medial eyebrow ridges.
2. The exit wound is over the left temporal scalp, 6 centimeters posterior to the medial eyebrow ridges and 5.5 centimeters from the top of the head. This wound is 8.0 x 3.5 centimeters and is an irregular exit wound.
3. The path of the bullet is to the left, upward, and forward.

Other notes of interest from the autopsy:

1. While the medical examiner attempted to approximate the edges of the right side scapular wound and photograph same, he made no attempt to approximate the edges of the irregular, left side wound, nor did he take more than a single photograph of the wound as it appeared prior to autopsy.
2. The autopsy report also mentioned the observation of a small amount of soot within the subcutaneous tissues of the right temporal region. There was, however, neither photograph nor other documentation of such soot, nor was there any attempt to quantify it.
3. The left side wound was not inspected for soot, nor was it photographed.

The decision tree branch 2: Event history (Figure 2.10)

Branch 2 of the decision tree, the event history, is absent in this particular case. The official investigation was ongoing. There are no depositions or interviews that bear on the issue of suicide specifically, and there are no witnesses to the event other than the single male individual. While the statements, interviews, and witness statements regarding events leading up to the actual shooting death of Ms. Smith are relevant with respect to building a homicide case, they are not relevant to establishing from the physical evidence whether or not the shooting of Ms. Smith can reasonably be classified as a suicide. Branch 2 of the decision tree is, therefore, absent in this case study.

The decision tree branch 3: Physical evidence (Figure 2.11)

In this case study, Level 1 data are extensive:

1. Sixty-three photographs of the scene;
2. A twenty-minute video of the scene, which included areas of the house leading to the scene;
3. The weapon used to inflict the wound, a .40-caliber, Berretta automatic pistol;
4. The discarded clothing of the deceased female;
5. A scale drawing of the room in which Ms. Smith was found, including mapped evidence within that room;
6. The body of the deceased, included under physical evidence; and
7. The body of the male present at the scene on the arrival of the officers.

The body of the deceased and the body of the attending male are important because of evidence which can be generated at the next level, regarding such things as powder burns and the presence of blood and/or brain matter on various parts of both bodies.

Level 2: Information

1. The weapon was examined for the presence of fingerprints.
2. The weapon was examined for the presence of blood and/or brain matter.
3. The .40-caliber Berretta automatic was test fired, and the bullet was matched with the actual bullet that produced the wound in the deceased.
4. The weapon was test fired to establish the direction and distance of ejected casings.
5. The hands of the deceased were examined for the presence of blood and/or brain.
6. The hands of the victim, Ms. Smith, were also examined for the presence of gunpowder residue.
7. The hands of the male subject were examined for the presence of blood and brain matter and photographed.
8. The hands of the male subject were also examined for the presence of gunpowder residue.
9. Fingerprints of both individuals were on file and also entered as a part of the information summary data.
10. The position of significant amounts of blood and brain matter on the interior surfaces of the room were mapped and photographed.

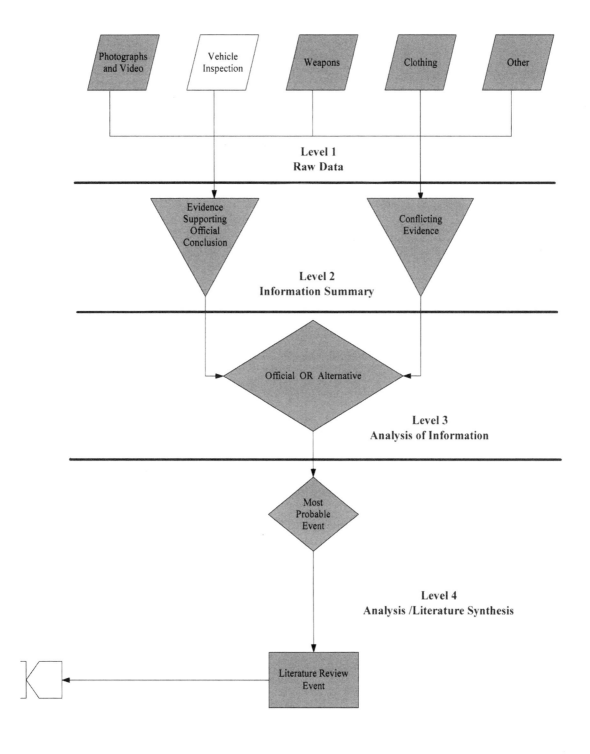

Figure 2.11 *Physical evidence. (Courtesy of Kerry Knapp Ph.D.)*

11. The resting location of the gun, the spent bullet, and the ejected cartridge casing from the Berretta automatic were located and noted.
12. The resting position of the decedent, Ms. Smith, was recorded. It is important to note that Ms. Smith's resting position was face up with her legs under the bed to a level above the knees and her head resting nearly against the wall to the west.

Level 3: Analysis of Information
1. A detailed inspection of the .40-caliber Beretta by the crime lab indicated only minute amounts of blood confined to the slide action of the weapon.
2. There were no fingerprints on the weapon.
3. There was no blood or brain matter on the exterior of the weapon.
4. There was no blood or brain matter in the barrel of the weapon.
5. There was no blood or brain matter on either hand of the deceased.
6. There were no traces of gunpowder residue on either hand of the deceased.
7. The hands of the male subject were negative for blood, brain matter, and gunpowder residue (it was noted that the male had been known to have washed his hands at least three times prior to being examined for trace materials).
8. The gun was found on the bed, a minimum distance of three feet from the body of the deceased.

At this point in the case study analysis it is useful to merge the two decision tree branches, one and three, and discuss the analysis of both branches and the literature in common. (Figure 2.12)

Garavaglia and Talkington (1999) conducted a study of 498 suicides by gunshot. In 93 percent of the cases examined, the weapon was found in the hand of the victim, on the body of the victim, or within one foot of the body of the victim.

In the case of Ms. Smith, the .40-caliber Beretta Brigadier was found over three feet from the probable location of her hand at the time the wound was inflicted. The three-foot distance implies that Ms. Smith was the shooter and used her left hand (off hand) and that the entrance wound was on the left (contrary to the opinion of the medical examiner). If the entrance wound is assumed to be on the right side of the skull (as per autopsy), the weapon is even

more unlikely to come to rest on the end of the bed where it was found.

Betz et al. (1995) studied 103 suicidal contact wounds, 70 involving handguns. All the handgun wounds were to the head or neck. In the Betz study:

1. In 33 to 35 percent of the cases, back spatter was present on the hand of the shooter; and
2. As the bullet caliber increased, the frequency of back spatter was also found to increase, with back spatter being observed in 50 percent of cases involving 9mm or larger weapons.

In the case of Ms. Smith, there is an absence of blood/brain material on either hand that could reasonably be attributed to back spatter. Most important, if one assumes that the medical examiner is correct with regard to the entrance wound (right side), then it is impossible for the right hand of Ms. Smith not to be completely covered with both blood and brain matter given the massive right side wound.

Stone (1992) also investigated back spatter (blowback) on weapons used in shootings producing contact wounds. The Stone study included 895 handguns, 242 of which were pistols. Stone found:

1. In 76 percent of the cases involving pistols, blood was found on the barrel;
2. In 57 percent of the cases involving pistols, blood was found inside the barrel; and
3. The absence of blood (either in or on the barrel) occurred only 24 percent of the time when a pistol was the weapon.

In the case of Ms. Smith, traces of blood were found only on the slide of the Beretta Brigadier. No blood was found within the barrel or on other exterior elements of the weapon. Again, if the medical examiner correctly identified the entrance wound on the right of Ms. Smith's head, then it is impossible for the weapon not to be completely covered with blood and brain matter given the massive right side wound.

Spitz and Fisher (1993) report that death is instantaneous in injury events such as shootings if the midbrain and/or lower brain structures are significantly affected by the gunshot wound. In the case of Ms. Smith not only are these structures disrupted, but much of the brain is avulsed. In such cases, body movement is limited to the effects of gravity: the victim is found in the position she was in when the wound occurred (with the exception of

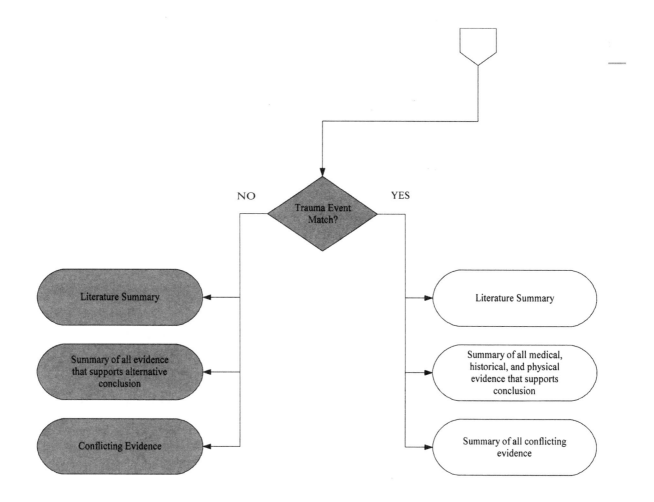

Figure 2.12 *Integrated summary. (Courtesy of Kerry Knapp Ph.D.)*

falling if standing and slumping if sitting). Specifically with respect to Ms. Smith, it can be stated that she was sitting in the position in which she was found; her legs, feet, and buttocks are in the same position as they were when the mortal shot occurred. This is an important fact only because it requires that Ms. Smith prepare for her suicide by disrobing, getting the weapon, and then seating herself in an awkward position—in this case, half under the bed. The evidence is not consistent with a suicide event.

The lack of post-wound movement is also extremely important when considering the post-incident position of the Beretta Brigadier. As mentioned previously, the suicide weapon is found on or within a foot of the body 93 percent of the time. In the case of Ms. Smith, she most certainly falls within this statistic if her wound was self-inflicted. As with her torso, the weapon could fall only under the effect of gravity—either with her hand or directly to the floor.

Clearly the physical evidence from the scene does not support a self-inflicted wound to the right side of the skull

slightly above the right ear of Janice A. Smith.

One must consider the possibility that the entrance wound in the Smith case is the left side wound. When examining this possibility, the most likely based on all of the scene evidence and the wound profile, the previous discussion regarding the position of the weapon, the position of the body and the probability of blowback spatter are equally valid. The potential volume of blowback spatter is somewhat decreased due to the smaller wound size on the left side of Ms. Smith's skull.

In addition, it is physically impossible for Ms. Smith to have fired the shot using a normal weapon grip (pulling the trigger with a finger) into her own skull at the observed angle from the left side. When the left hand is placed in flexion to the extent necessary to achieve the height and angle required for the observed shot, the flexor tendons of the fingers of the left hand can no longer generate the force necessary to fire the Beretta Brigadier (approximate 12 pound pull). It would be possible to fire the observed shot from the left if the trigger of the Beretta were pulled using the thumb. In that case the weapon would be hooked over the thumb and would have been either in the left hand (most probable) or adjacent to the body of Ms. Smith.

Clearly the physical evidence from the scene does not support a self-inflicted wound to the left side of the skull above and slightly forward of the left ear of Janice A. Smith.

Conclusion

The death of Janice A. Smith was not a suicide. There was a considerable amount of physical evidence in the case, which could be used to argue for the probability of a left side entrance wound, a contradiction of the medical examiner's conclusion. However, because the question asked was limited to the probability of Ms. Smith's demise being a suicide, there is no need for further analysis.

Summary discussion

The medical documentation branch (Figure 2.1) of the decision tree in the mortal gunshot injury case, unlike the low-speed motor vehicle impact case, is rich with highly specific data from which much relevant information is generated. One of the greatest values of the methodology in this second case is its utility in focusing both the analyst and the court on relevant data while properly subjugating irrelevant information.

The event history branch (Figure 2.2) is "absent" in the case study. While it could reasonably be argued that much of the material included in the physical evidence branch (Figure 2.3) rightly belongs in event history, it is grouped otherwise by definition. The event history branch is focused on a sub-analysis of an official investigation, the elements of which are incomplete in the case study.

The physical evidence branch (Figure 2.3) is also data rich in the case study. In fact, the wealth of data is detrimental to the official investigators, making it difficult for them to orient properly the data and develop useful, interpretable information. The decision tree methodology provides a framework for the analyst, around which the data are sorted and organized. It provides a vehicle for displaying and appropriately linking the case elements.

The methodology illuminates where data are present and where data are absent; it demonstrates the strength of the data and the information that can be generated from it; and it makes apparent the relationships between the lines of evidence as expressed by the decision tree (Figures 2.1 to 2.3). Additionally, in the gunshot death case the methodology serves to focus the analysis by providing a framework within which to organize and display the large quantity of highly specific evidence and the detailed information generated from it. The integrated narrative summary (Figure 2.4) illustrates the applicability of the literature, the significance of the evidence, and the reliability of the conclusion.

2.5 Conclusion

The civil court system seeks to know the truth of the allegations being litigated before it and then to reach an equitable result through compensation. If the participants in the process cannot fully understand the nature of the dispute, however, a reasonable and principled decision may not result. Today's science-rich cases often require expert testimony; when the issue is human tissue damage resulting in injury or death, the biomechanist is the most qualified expert. If judges cannot make appropriate decisions regarding expert testimony because they lack technical training and if jurors do not comprehend the complexity of the evidence they are supposed to analyze, erroneous and inconsistent determinations are likely to be the result.

As the law has evolved in application, it has become clear that the most important element in judging the reliability of expert testimony is not the opinion itself but the way in which the opinion or conclusions are reached. The issue of reliability generally comes down to an expert's ability not only to state conclusions but, more important, to demonstrate the logic leading to those conclusions. An expert's opinions are recognized as the product of a reasoning process; therefore, the soundness and clarity of the reasoning process must be demonstrated to the court. The material presented herein has (1) established a methodology for forensic biomechanists (and other experts) that will assist the expert witness in meeting the court requirements for demonstrating the validity of reasoned opinions as a prerequisite for admissibility, and (2) demonstrated the effective application of the methodology. The process tracing model (decision tree), with its focus on how experts make decisions, provides a relevant method for addressing the needs of the court as it exercises its "gatekeeper" function by displaying the relevance and reliability of expert opinion. Ultimately, society will benefit from courts that find the truth through a more complete understanding of the relationships discoverable from the evidence.

References

Adair, TW, Gallardo, AC. "Considering the Target Surface in Bloodstain Pattern Analysis: an Unusual Case of Blood Pooling," *Journal of Forensic Identification* 49 (5), pp. 485–492. (1999)

Allen M, Motiuk D, Flewin K, Goring R, Kobetitch R, Broadhurst A "Acceleration Forces at the Head/Neck during Commonly Experienced Controlled Sudden Movements" SFU- submitted to Spine. (1993- in submission)

Beach, L.R. *Image Theory: Decision Making in Personal and Organizational Contexts.* Chichester: Wiley. (1990)

Beach, L.R. and Mitchell, T.R., "A Contingency Model for the Selection of Decision Strategies." *Academy of Management Review*, 3, 439–449. (1978)

Berryman, HE, Smith, OC and Symes, SA. "Diameter of Cranial Gunshot Wounds As a Function of Bullet Caliber," *Journal of Forensic Sciences*, JFSCA, Vol. 40, No. 5, Sept., pp. 751–754. (1995)

Betz, P., Peschel, O., Stiefel, D., Eisenmenger, W. "Frequency of Blood Spatters on the Shooting Hand and of Conjunctival Petechiae Following Suicidal Gunshots Wounds to the Head," *Forensic Science International.* 76: 47–53. (1995)

Branch, R. C., Moore, D.M., "Effects of Using Instructive Questions with Flow Diagrams and Text Presentations," *International Journal of Instructional Media* 17(1) p.51, 12p, 1 diagram, 1 graph. (1990)

Brault JR, Wheeler JB, Siegmund GP, Brault EJ "Clinical Response of Human Subjects to Rear-end Automobile Collisions. *Archives of Physicians Medical Rehabilitations*, 79. (1998)

Braun, H. and Chandler, J. "Predicting Stock Market Behavior through Rule Induction: an Application of the Learning-from-Example Approach", *Decision Sciences*, 18, 3: 415–429. (1987)

Brehmer, B. "Strategies in Real-time Dynamic Decision Making." In R. Hogarth (Ed.), *Insights in decision making.* 262–279. Chicago: University of Chicago Press. (1990)

Burnett, BR. "Detection of Bone and Bone-Plus-Bullet Particles in Backspatter from Close-Range Shots to Heads," *Journal of Forensic Sciences*, JFSCA Vol. 36, No. 6, Nov., 1745–1752. (1991)

Carnegie Commission on Science, Technology, and Government, *Science and Technology in Judicial Decision Making: Creating Opportunities and Meeting Challenges* p.11. (1993)

Chung, H.M., and Tam, K.Y. "A Comparative Analysis of Inductive Learning Algorithms." *Intelligent Systems in Accounting, Finance and Management*, 2(1), 3–18. (1993)

Clemen, R.T. "Making Hard Decisions: An Introduction to Decision Analysis." Belmont, CA: Wadsworth Publishing Company. (1996)

Cohen MS, Freeman JT, Thompson BB. "Training the Naturalistic Decision Maker." Unpublished report of research funded by the Army Research Institute. Contract number MDA903-92-C-0053. (1995)

Daubert v. Merrell Pharmaceuticals, Inc., 509 U.S. 579, 589.

DiMaio, VJM. "Gunshot Wounds: Practical Aspects of Firearms, Ballistics, and Forensic techniques." Boca Raton, FL: CRC Press. (1999)

Dixon, DS. "Foreshoring": Characteristics of Shored Entry Wounds and Corresponding Wounds with Shoring Material as an Intermediate Target," (1980)

Eisele, JW, Reay, DT, and Cook A. "Sites of Suicidal Gunshot Wounds," *Journal of Forensic Sciences*, JFSCA, Vol. 26, No. 3, July, pp. 480–485. (1981)

Ellsberg D. *Risk, Ambiguity and Decision.* New York: Garland Publishing, Inc. (2001)

Ewing, Channing and Thomas, Daniel "Torque versus Angular Displacement Response of Human Head to –Gx Impact Acceleration." SAE 730976, *Proceeding of the 17th Stapp Car Crash Conference*, Oct. (1967)

Fackler, ML. "Gunshot Wound Review," *Annals of Emergency Medicine*, Vol. 28, No. 2, August, 194–213. (1996)

Fackler, ML. Civilian Gunshot Wounds and Ballistics: Dispelling the Myths, *Emergency Medicine Clinics of North America,* Vol. 16, No. 1, February 17–29. (1998)

Fischoff, B. "Defining Risk." *Policy Sciences* 17: 123–139. (1984)

Frye v. United States, 293 F.2d (D.C.Cir 1923)

Garavaglia, Jan C M.D., Talkington, Billy B.S. "Weapon Location Following Suicidal Gunshot Wounds." *The American Journal of Forensic Medicine and Pathology*, Vol. 20, No. 1, March, 1–5. (1999)

Gigerenzer G, Todd PM, eds. "Simple Heuristics that Make Us Smart." New York: Oxford University Press. (1999)

Gladwin, C. "Contributions of Decision-tree Methodology to a Farming Systems Program." *Human Organization* 42(2), 146–157. (1983)

Hammitt, J.K. "Can More Information Increase Uncertainty?" *Chance,* Summer, 8:3. (1995)

Henery, R.J., Classification. In Michie, D., Spiegelhalter, D.J. and Taylor, C.C. (Eds), *Machine Learning, Neural and Statistical Classification.* New York, Ellis Horwood, 1994, pp. 6–16.

Herbert RD, Sherrington C, Maher C, Moseley AM. *Evidence-based practice — imperfect but necessary.* Physiotherapy Theory and Practice 17:201–211. (2001)

Hildebrand, P. *Combining Disciplines in Rapid Appraisal: the Sondeo Approach.* Agricultural Administration 8, 423–432. (1981)

Hogarth RM, ed. *Insights in Decision Making: A Tribute to Hillel J. Einhorn.* Chicago: The University of Chicago Press. (1990)

Howard, R., Benedict, J., Raddin, J. Jr., and Smith,H. *Assessing neck extension-flexion as a basis for temporomandibular joint dysfunction* American Association of Oral and Maxillofacial Surgeons. 1210–13. (1991)

Huber O, Kₜhberger A. "Decision Processes and Decision Trees in Gambles and More Natural Decision Tasks." *The Journal of Psychology* 130:329–339. (1996)

Hung-Min MC, Kar YT. "A Comparative Analysis of Inductive-Learning Algorithms." *Intelligent Systems in Accounting, Finance and Management* 2:3–18. (1992)

Jo, H., Han, I. And Lee, H. "Bankruptcy Prediction using Case-based Reasoning, Neural Networks and Discriminant Analysis." *Expert Systems with Applications,* 13, 2, 97–108. (1995)

Johnson, R.W. and Wichern, D.W. *Applied Multivariate Statistical Analysis.* Upper Saddle River, NJ. Prentice Hall, pp. 629–725.(1998)

Journal of Forensic Sciences, JFSCA, Vol. 25, No. 4, Oct. pp. 740–759.

Journal of Trauma: Injury, Infection and Critical Care, Vol. 40, No. 3, pp. S16-S21.Kahenman DK, Slovic P, Tversky A. *Judgment under Uncertainty: Heuristics and Biases.* Cambridge University Press.(1982)

Karlsson, T. *Multivariate Analysis ('Forensiometrics") – a New Tool in Forensic Medicine. Differentiation Between Firearm-related Homicides and Suicides.* Forensic Science International 101 pp. 131–140.(1999)

Keeney RL. *Value-Focused Thinking.* Cambridge, MA: Harvard University Press. (1992)

Kim, C. N., Chung, H.M., and Paradice, D.B. *Inductive Modeling of Expert Decision Making in Loan Evaluation: a Decision Strategy Perspective.* Decision Support Systems, 21(2), 83–98.(1997)

Klee CH, Friedman HJ. "Neurolitigation: A Perspective on the Elements of Expert Testimony for Extending the Daubert Challenge." *NeuroRehabilitation* 16:79–85. (2001)

Kleiber, M., Stiller, D., Wiegand, P. "Assessment of Shooting Distance on the Basis of Bloodstain Analysis and Histological Examinations." *Forensic Science International,* 119 pp. 260–262. (2001)

Klein, G.A., Orasanu, J., Calderwood, R., and Zsaambok, C. E. (eds.). *Decision Making in Action: Models and Methods.* Norwood, NJ: Ablex. (1993)

Kumho Tire Company, Ltd., et al. v Patrick Carmichael, et al. Supreme Court of the United States No. 97-1709 argued December 7, 1998-decided March 23, 1999.

Lave, C., and March, J. *An Introduction to Models in the Social Sciences.* New York: Harper and Row. (1975)

Lehman, M. "Flowcharting Made Simple.*" Journal of Accountancy.* October 77–88. (2000)

McConnell W., Howard R., Guzman H., Bomar J., Raddin J., Benedict J. Smith H., and Hatsell C . "Analysis of Human Test Subject Kinematic Responses to Low Velocity Rear End Impacts." (SAE Paper 930889) *Society of Automotive Engineers, Inc.* (1993)

McConnell WE, Howard RP, Van Poppel J, Krause R, Guzman HM, Bomar JB, Raddin JH, Benedict JV, and Hatsell CP. "Human Head and Neck Kinematics after Low Velocity Rear-End Impacts-Understanding 'Whiplash'." (SAE Paper 952724) *Society of Automotive Engineers, Inc.* (1995)

Mertz and Patrick. "Investigation of the Kinematics and Kinetics of Whiplash." (SAE Paper 670919) *Society of Automotive Engineers, Inc.* (1967)

Meyer S, Weber M, Castro W, Schilgen M, Peuker C. "The Minimal Collision Velocity for Whiplash." *Proceedings of the IROCBI*, Fall. (1997)

Morgan, M.G. and Keith D.W. "Subjective Judgments by Climate Experts." *Environmental Science and Technology* 29:468–476. (1995)

Muzzy, William and Lustick, Leonard. "Comparison of Kinematic Parameters between Hybrid II Head and Neck System with Human Volunteers for -Gx Acceleration Profiles." *Society of Automotive Engineers, Inc.* (1976)

Nielsen GP, Gough DM, Little DM, West DH, and Baker VT. "Repeated Low Speed Impacts with Utility Vehicles and Humans." *Accident Reconstruction Journal* 8, 5 (1996)

Nielsen GP, Gough DM, Little DM, West DH, and Baker VT. "Low Speed Rear Impact Test Summary - Human Test Subjects." *Accident Reconstruction Journal* 8, 5 (1996)

Norton ML. "The Physician Expert Witness and the U.S. Supreme Court-an Epidemiologic Approach." *Med-Law* 21:435–449. (2002)

Orner, PA . "A Physician- Engineer's View of Low Velocity Rear-end Collisions" (SAE Paper 921574) *Automobile Safety: Present and Future Technology.* (1992)

Peters, CE, Sebourn, CL. "Wound Ballistics of Unstable Projectiles. Part II: Temporary Cavity Formation and Tissue Damage." (1996)

Peterson, BL. "External Beveling of Cranial Gunshot Entrance Wounds," *Journal of Forensic Sciences, JF-SCA,* Vol. 36, No. 5, Sept. pp. 1592–1595. (1991)

Quatrehomme, G, Iscan, MY. "Characteristics of Gunshot Wounds in the Skull." *Journal of Forensic Sciences.* 44(3):568–576. (1999)

Quatrehomme, G, Iscan, MY. "Gunshot Wounds to the Skull: Comparison of Entries and Exits," *Forensic Science International,* 94 pp. 141–146. (1998)Raiffa, H. "Decision Analysis: Introductory Lectures on Choices under Uncertainty." Reading, MA: Addison-Weasly.(1968)

Rouse, W.B. and Valusek, J. "Evolutionary Design of Systems to Support Decision Making," In Klein, G.A., Orasanu, J., Calderwood, R., and Zsaambok, C. E. (eds.). (1993). *Decision Making in Action: Models and Methods.* Norwood, NJ: Ablex. (1993)

Sackett, D.L. "The Sins of Expertness and a Proposed Remedy for Redemption", *British Medical Journal,* 326: 1283. May 6, 2000.

Shick F. *Making Choices: A Recasting of Decision Theory.* Cambridge: Cambridge University Press. (1997)

Spangler, W.E., May, J.H. and Vargas, L.G. "Choosing Data-Mining Methods for Multiple Classification: Representational and Performance Measurement Implications for Decision Support." *Journal of Management Information Systems* 16(1), 37–62. (1999)

Spitz, WU editor . *Medicolegal Investigation of Death.* Springfield, IL: Charles C. Thomas. (1993)

Stone, IC. "Observations and Statistics Relating to Suicide Weapons," *Journal of Forensic Sciences, JFSCA,* Vol. 32, No. 3, May, pp. 711–716. (1987)

Stone, IC, DiMaio, VJM and Petty, CS. "Gunshot Wounds: Visual and Analytical Procedures," *Journal of Forensic Sciences,* Aug, pp. 361–367. (1977)

Strother and James . "Evaluation of Seat Back Strength and Seat Belt Effectiveness in Rear End Impacts" (STAPP 872214). *Society of Automotive Engineers, Inc.* (1987)

Szabo T, Welcher J, Anderson R, Rice R, Ward J, Paulo L, Carpenter N . "Human Occupant Kinematic Response to Low Speed Rear-end Impacts" (SAE Paper 940532) *Society of Automotive Engineers, Inc.* (1994)

Szabo T, and Welcher J. "Human Subject Kinematics and Electromyographic Activity During Low Speed Rear Impacts" (SAE Paper 962432) *Society of Automotive Engineers, Inc.* (1996)

Thornton, JI. "Close Proximity Gunshot Residues," *Journal of Forensic Sciences, JFSCA,* Vol. 31, No. 2, April, pp. 756–757. (1986)

Triano, JJ and AB Schultz. "Cervical Spine Manipulations: Applied Loads, Motions and Myoelectric Responses." *Advances in Bioengineering.* 249–50. (1990)

Tversky, A. and Koehler, D.J. "Support Theory: A Nonextensional Representation of Subjective Probability." *Psychological Review* 101:547–567. (1994)

Wakeford, R., Hutell, B.A. and Leigh, W.J. "A Review of Probability of Causation and its Use in a Compensation Scheme for Nuclear Industry Workers in the United Kingdom." *Health Physics* 74:1–9. (1998)

Walker, K.D., Evans, J.S. and MacIntosh, D. "Use of Expert Judgment in Exposure Assessment: Part I—Characterization of Personal Exposure to Benzene." *Journal of the International Society for Exposure Assessment.* (2001a)

Werth v. Makita Electric Works, 950 F.2d 643, 648 (10th Cir. 1991)

West D, Gough J, Harper G. "Low Speed Rear-end Collision Testing Using Human Subjects." *Accident Reconstruction Journal* 5, 3. (1993)

Williamson JW, Ranyard R. "A Conversation-Based Process Tracing Method for Use with Naturalistic Decision: An Evaluation Study." *British Journal of Psychology* 91:203–22. (2000)

Wilson, J. "Wound Ballistics (Trauma Rounds)." *West Journal of Medicine* 127:49–54, Jul. (1977)

Wilson, R., and Crouch, E.A.C. (2001). *Risk-Benefit Analysis,* Second Edition, Harvard University Press.

Chapter 3

Basic Principles of Biomechanics

Patrick Hannon

3.1 Introduction

Biomechanics is a diverse field involving the synthesis of biological and mechanical principles to explain animal movement and the effect of forces acting on living creatures. From the earliest recorded history, artists, scientists, and philosophers have been fascinated with how the human body works and have attempted to draw, describe, and explain how we move. Aristotle (fourth century B.C.) was among the first to describe human motion, analyzing how muscles and bones work together in a geometric fashion to facilitate human movement. Today, biomechanists, biologists, engineers, mathematicians, zoologists, and others continue to explain the movement of animals and humans through the use of basic mechanical principles.

    Understanding the mechanisms of injury is important to the attorney both in terms of understanding the concepts presented by his or her own expert and in crossexamining the opposing expert. Therefore, it is important to understand the basic principles of mechanics and the basic structure and function of human tissues. This chapter defines the key principles of biomechanics and Chapter 4 introduces application of these principles to impacts and collisions. Later chapters address specific biological tissues or body regions and the mechanisms of injury to these tissues. Together these chapters are designed to provide a working knowledge of biomechanics to help an attorney analyze, discuss, and question the facts of a case involving loading (forces, moments, and torques) to the human body that may result in tissue damage injury.

    Injury to tissue is the result of applied forces and physical stresses. The tissue response to these forces and stresses involves basic principles of anatomy, engineering, and physiology. Fung (1993) states that "a trauma to a person is equivalent to the failure of a machine or a structure." Machines, however, can be designed to withstand stress levels considerably above what they can reasonably be expected to encounter. Human tissues, on the other hand, model and remodel to variable (biological individuality) but finite loading tolerance levels based on probable extremes. Above these loading levels, tissues fail (i.e., bones break and soft tissues rupture) and injury occurs. A working knowledge of applied mechanics will lead to a better understanding of how human tissues react to the loads and stresses applied in personal injury, wrongful death, and physical assault criminal cases.

3.2 Linear and Angular Movement

It is through movement that individuals interact with the world; activities of daily living, fleeing from danger, sports and recreation, and the essential functions of organs and tissues all require movement. Movement can be described in a variety of ways.

    There are two basic forms of motion: linear and angular. *Linear motion*, sometimes referred to as translation, is movement in either a straight line (rectilinear motion) or a curved line (curvilinear motion), such as the parabolic motion of a projectile (e.g., bullet or rocket). Pure human translation involves the body moving as a unit; that is, all particles of the body moving in one parallel direction at one time (Figure 3.1). It can also describe the movement of body segments or joints in a straight line rather than around a relatively fixed point of rotation.

Angular or rotational motion is movement around a relatively fixed axis. The spinning of an airplane propeller is a classic example of rotational movement; the propeller blades rotate around a fixed shaft or axis of rotation. Bending of body segments at a joint is another example of angular motion, for instance, flexing and extending the forearm at the elbow. (Figure 3.2) Most human movements involve the combination of both linear and angular motion, referred to as *general motion*. The motion of a pitcher's arm in baseball, for example, involves both linear motion, as the body and arm move forward to release the ball, and angular motion around the axes of rotation at the shoulder, elbow, and wrist during the throwing sequence of motions.

A. The anatomical position: planes, axes, and movements

Describing human movement requires specific orientation and defined points of reference. By placing the body in a standard reference position called the *anatomical reference position*, with the body erect, arms hanging relaxed and feet and palm of the hands facing forward, movement can be defined in terms of standardized reference planes bisecting the body and rotational axes perpendicular to these planes. The cardinal planes are three reference planes that divide the mass of the body in half. All three cardinal planes intersect at one point called the *center of mass* or *center of gravity*, the balancing point around which the mass of the body is evenly distributed. The *sagittal plane*, sometimes referred to as the *anterior-posterior (AP)* plane, is a vertical reference plane that divides the body into left and right halves. Movement of the thighs and lower legs in running can be described as sagittal plane motion.

The *coronal plane*, also referred to as the *frontal plane*, divides the body into front and back halves. Move-

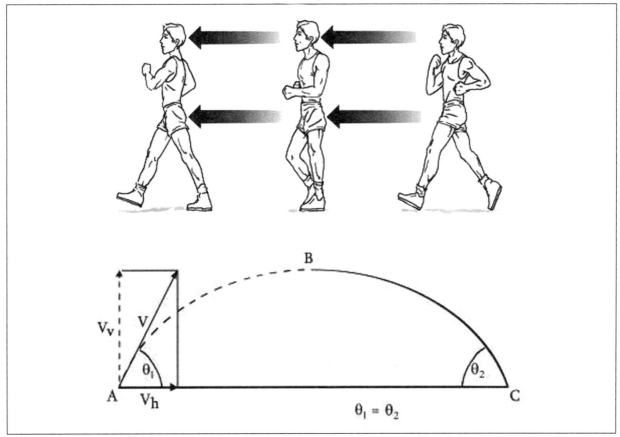

Figure 3.1 *Rectilinear and curvilinear motion are illustrated above. Note that the vertical and horizontal velocity components stem from the total or resultant velocity vector. If we ignore air resistance, a projectile will exhibit an angle of takeoff and an angle of entry that are identical when the takeoff and landing elevation is the same. (Courtesy of Robert Perry, D.C., M.U.A.C.)*

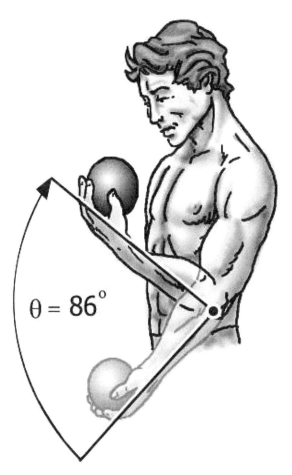

Figure 3.2 *The motion of the arm is around a relatively fixed axis of the elbow. (Courtesy of Robert Perry, D.C., M.U.A.C.)*

ment of the arms away from the midline of the body to the side is one example of motion in the coronal plane. A child lying on her back in the snow and moving her arms and legs up and down to create a snow angel is a simple example of coronal plane motion of the extremities.

The *transverse plane* (or *horizontal plane*) bisects the body into top and bottom halves. A vertical spin of the body such as a scratch spin or one-foot spin in figure skating can be defined as transverse plane motion.

Rotational or angular movements of body segments are described by axes of rotation through the joints perpendicular to these three cardinal planes. The *mediolateral axis* is perpendicular to the sagittal plane; therefore, rotational movement of a body segment in the sagittal plane occurs around the mediolateral axis. Likewise, rotation in the coronal plane occurs around the *anteroposterior axis*, and rotation in the transverse plane occurs around the *longitudinal* or *vertical axis*. (Figure 3.3)

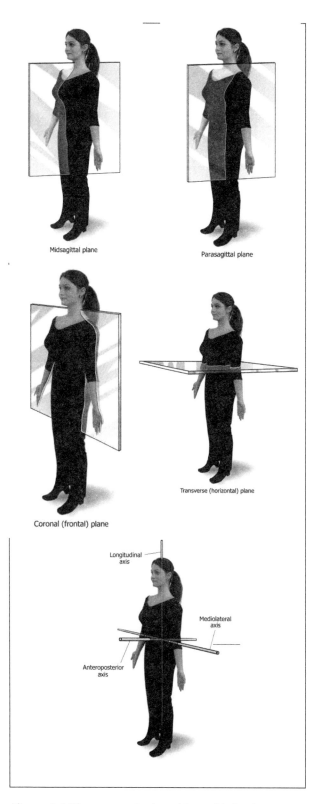

Figure 3.3 *The anatomical position with its three cardinal planes and axes are illustrated above. The body's center of gravity is a point in this position where the three cardinal planes of motion intersect. (Courtesy of Robert Perry, D.C., M.U.A.C.)*

B. Vectors and scalars

Biomechanical parameters involved in human movement can also be described as scalar or vector quantities. *Scalar quantities*, such as mass, distance, time, temperature, and speed, are described by magnitude only and represented by standard units of measure. Mass, for instance, represents the particles of matter that make up a human body, expressed completely by the number of kilograms (kg) or slugs (English system) of matter. Time, also a scalar quantity, is described fully by magnitude expressed in seconds, minutes, or hours. On the other hand, vectors are represented by arrows and require not only a description of magnitude expressed by the length of the vector but also by direction and sense. The direction is expressed by the line of action, and the sense is expressed by the arrowhead of the vector. Commonly, physicists and biomechanists use the term "direction" to include the line of action and the sense. (Figure 3.4)

Displacement, velocity, and acceleration are examples of *vector quantities*. When an object is displaced, both how far an object has moved (distance) and the direction of movement are used to describe the change in location. Velocity is described by displacement and time; its scalar counterpart, speed, requires only a description of distance and time without reference to direction. If more than one vector is needed to describe an event, the length of the vector arrows must be proportional to the vector magnitudes that they represent; equal vector quantities can be represented by arrows of the same length that are pointed in the same direction.

Finally, movement can be described relative to time

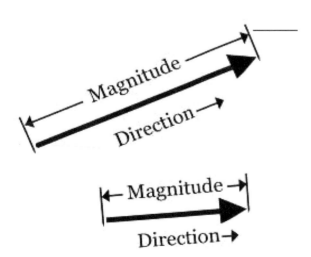

Figure 3.4 *Two vectors, each with a different magnitude and direction, are illustrated above. (Courtesy of Robert Perry)*

and space without discussion of the forces causing the motion (*kinematics*) or assessed relative to the forces causing movement (*kinetics*).

3.3 Kinematics

Kinematics is a description of human motion without regard to causal forces. Describing a human fall or two motor vehicles post collision in terms of displacement, delta velocity, and acceleration is a description of kinematics. Kinematic analyses involve a variety of temporal and spacial (a.k.a., spatial) variables, including time, position, displacement, velocity, and acceleration. Linear motion or translation is described in linear units of meters, feet, or miles.

A classic example of angular or rotational motion is a spinning wheel; the wheel rotates around an axis of rotation perpendicular to the reference plane in which the wheel is spinning. The spokes on the wheel intersect at the axle (i.e., axis of rotation) forming angle B (two lines or planes intersecting at a point, or vertex). In biomechanical analyses, angles are formed from body segments intersecting at a joint (i.e., vertex). The forearm and upper arm, for example, form two sides of an angle that intersects at the elbow. It is more difficult to describe the magnitude and direction of angular motion than of linear motion. As we know, vectors describing linear motion are represented by arrows, with the body length of the arrow representing the magnitude of the vector and the arrowhead representing direction. Because it is confusing and impractical to represent angular motion with curved lines and arrows, the direction of rotation is described in accordance with what is known as the right-hand rule or right-hand thumb rule. This is accomplished by circling the fingers of the right hand in the direction of the motion of the body or body segment. The angular motion vector is described by the direction that the outstretched thumb is pointing and is sometimes referred to as the polarity of the vector. (Figure 3.5)

A. Time

Time is a measure of the duration of motion. Temporal patterns of movement are important in kinematic analyses because changes in position take place over time; the duration of stride and cadence when walking, for instance, are important factors used to describe the basic human gait that is so important in understanding a trip and fall. Most acute injuries occur from the application of a large applied force to the body or body segment over a very short period of time.

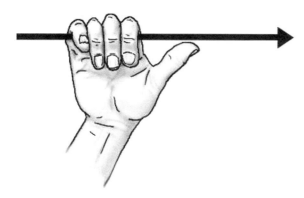

Figure 3.5 *The right-hand thumb rule is used to describe angular motion. The direction that the thumb points indicates the clockwise or counter-clockwise direction of the rotation. (Courtesy of Robert Perry)*

B. Position

Position is the location of an object from a point of reference. Body or body segment position may play an important role in the extent of injury caused by a given load. The posterior cruciate ligament, for instance, is more vulnerable to injury when the knee joint is fully extended (zero degrees). Position may be described quantitatively as a joint angle in degrees or expressed as a unit of length (e.g., meters) from a reference point. In a biomechanics laboratory, standard spatial reference systems can be used to analyze position based on data from videos or other motion recording systems. In this setting, two- or three-dimensional rectangular coordinate systems are used to describe position in reference to two or three axes: a horizontal axis, a vertical axis, and a "z" axis perpendicular to x and y in the case of a three-dimensional analysis. (Figure 3.6)

Position may also be described in terms of a joint angle as per the example of the cervical spine at 70° flexion when an impact was imposed on the posterior head link. In most real-world injury cases, however, position is derived from evidence obtained after the fact or from reconstructions of an injury-producing event. In the absence of surveillance recordings or event films, position must be determined from such things as the end position of a vehicle involved in an accident, body position after a fall, or a bone fracture pattern that results from a specific joint position.

C. Displacement

Displacement is a change in position of an object caused by movement.

1. Magnitude of displacement

When describing linear motion, the *magnitude of displacement* (*d*) is the straight-line difference between starting and ending points measured in units of length (e.g., meters). When a soccer player, for instance, dribbles a ball down the field, displacement magnitude is measured in a straight line from one position to the next. Retracing the player's path might result in a total distance traveled of 100 meters; his displacement, however, measured as a straight line from start to finish, may only be 50 meters. Similarly, if a runner completes one lap around the 400 meter track and finishes back at the starting point, displacement for the round trip is zero. Displacement is a vector quantity, so it is defined by not only the magnitude but also the direction of movement; the direction of displacement relates the final position to the starting position of the person or object. The scalar counterpart of displacement is distance and can be defined as the magnitude (i.e., total length) of the path covered without regard to direction. In the track example presented above, a runner completing one lap exhibited no displacement, but the distance covered was 400 meters.

2. Angular displacement

Angular displacement (ω) is a change in angle of a vehicle or body rotation. The magnitude may be expressed in degrees, radians, or revolutions. In the example

Figure 3.6 *A calibration frame allows for a three-dimensional kinematics system. After the calibration procedure and within a limited area, point markers placed on a human subject may now be ascribed to x, y, and z coordinates for a precise description of position. (Courtesy of Patrick Hannon)*

of a human joint motion, the elbow may pass through 90°
of rotation during an elbow flexion, or a figure skater may
rotate at an ice skate–ice interface around her longitudinal
axis. In ballet, the performer may rotate on one foot (en
pointe). (Figure 3.7) Angular displacement is also a vector
quantity, and direction (clockwise or counterclockwise)
should also be indicated.

D. Linear and angular velocity

Linear velocity (V) is a vector and a measure of how
quickly something is displaced; that is, the rate of movement (i.e., displacement divided by time) or the amount of
time needed to move an object from the starting to ending
position. Direction must be specified. The scalar counterpart of velocity is speed. Speed is expressed as distance
over time; when an automobile speedometer registers 50
mph, it is an expression of speed, or the magnitude component of velocity without regard to direction. Angular
velocity (ω) is a vector with a magnitude that is calculated by angular displacement (θ) divided by time (t).

E. Linear and angular acceleration

1. Linear acceleration

Linear acceleration (a) is a vector quantity and represents a change in linear velocity over time, or simply
the rate of change in velocity. Acceleration refers to both
an increase or decrease in rate, but in everyday usage, a
decreased velocity is commonly referred to as deceleration. Most human movements do not occur at a constant
velocity. An elite middle-distance swimmer swimming a
100 meter race, for instance, may average 50 meters in
30 seconds (1.67 meters/second), but in reality the velocity magnitude changed (i.e., the swimmer accelerated or
decelerated) throughout the course of the 50 meter race
segment, as becomes clear when we examine smaller time
intervals. If a power boat is traveling north at 60 miles per
hour (mph), velocity can be increased or decreased, that
is, the boat is accelerated or decelerated by pressing or
pulling back on the throttle. Velocity alone will not produce injury, but if the velocity changes abruptly (a change
in direction or magnitude), acceleration creates an opportunity for differential motion of the body and the vehicle
or differential motion of human body segments that may
produce injury. A sudden deceleration of a forward traveling automobile can cause injury to an unrestrained occupant because the body continues moving forward at a
relatively constant velocity until striking the dashboard or
steering wheel.

Figure 3.7 An ice skater and ballerina rotate around
their cardinal longitudinal axes during spins, with an
angular velocity depending on their relative angular
inertias. (Courtesy of Patrick Hannon)

2. Angular acceleration

Angular acceleration (α) represents a change in
angular velocity over time. Human joint movements in
the upper extremity undergo a positive acceleration during the initial phases of throwing motions. In the latter
stages, proximal joints (shoulder and elbow) are decelerated due to actions by opposing musculature so as to
reduce the chance for injury and, interestingly, to increase
the transfer of angular momentum to the hand and the
thrown projectile's linear velocity (i.e., improved throwing velocity).

The formula for these kinematic linear and angular

measures is summarized below.

The following represent average values over time:

$$V = d / t$$
$$\omega = \theta / t$$
$$a = \Delta v / t$$
$$\alpha = \Delta \omega / t$$

F. Kinematic case examples

Two cases are presented below illustrating the use of kinematic principles. The first case involves the reconstruction of an injury in the laboratory; the kinematic variables of time and displacement are used to determine whether a criminal suspect was injured during a chase or beaten by a police officer. The second case uses position and displacement to help determine how a shooting took place; the analysis is based on physical and medical evidence obtained after the fact.

Case example 3.1

The first case involves a head injury (left-side skull fracture with minor brain damage) sustained by a suspect apprehended by two police officers in the parking lot of an apartment complex. Two different scenarios emerged. The officers alleged that they chased the suspect between a wall and a commercial van in an apartment parking lot. The suspect allegedly ran at full speed in a crouched position, dove under the back of a parked commercial van, and struck his head on the truck bumper, causing the depressed skull fracture. The officers further stated that one officer struck the suspect on the back four to five times with a PR24 police baton during the eight-to twelve-foot chase but was careful to avoid the suspect's spine or head.

The suspect presented a second scenario and alleged that the officers pulled him from underneath the commercial van and repeatedly kicked him while he was lying on the ground. One officer beat him repeatedly with a baton.

The approach taken was to reconstruct the officer's scenario in our university biomechanics laboratory. Two subjects were selected from a student population to match the physical characteristics of the suspect and police officer. A PR24 baton identical to the one used in the incident was furnished to our laboratory, and an experiment was conducted that involved swinging the

PR24 as described by one of the officers through a full range vertical motion (as per his previous interview testimony). The number of full baton swings was counted during the recorded video sequence, and the linear and angular displacements and velocities of the elbow and shoulder joints were recorded during repeated swings. Full cycle swings (up and down) were accomplished by our exemplar subject at a rate of 1.5 to 2 cycles each second. A running sequence was then filmed to match the pursuit described by the officers in the reconstructed scene (eight- to twelve-foot run). In our laboratory, it took approximately 0.7 to 0.9 second to traverse eight to twelve feet, respectively, with our exemplar suspect in a crouched position. Based on this simulation, the officer could not have stuck the suspect four or five times while chasing him over this linear displacement. Therefore, the event was inconsistent with the officer's testimony. Furthermore, the radiography images of the suspect's head upon examination indicated a depressed skull fracture which matched the diameter of the subject PR24 baton.

Case example 3.2

The second case study involved the shooting of a suspect by a border patrol agent. Again, two scenarios emerged. The suspect alleged that the agent shot him three times (stomach, right elbow, and left hip) while he was walking toward the agent with his hands empty and raised. The suspect stated that these were the only shots fired by the officer.

The agent's scenario was consistent with the suspect's version of the initial contact in which the suspect admitted to crouching and attempting to hide in the brush. However, the agent's scenario differed significantly from that point forward. The border patrol agent allegedly identified himself, and at that point the suspect stood up and started throwing rocks at the border patrol agent and started to pursue the agent. The agent contended that he retreated, drew his weapon, and fired near the suspect as he continued to retreat in a zigzag pattern over about 60 feet. Finally, blocked by heavy brush and unable to continue running, the agent stated that he stopped, aimed at the suspect, and fired as the suspect continued to charge; the suspect dropped to one knee and then fell completely to the ground.

Examination of the physical evidence indicated that there were eight ejected cartridge casings from the weapon scattered over a distance of approximately 55 linear feet (distance). In addition, a ballistics analysis determined that the weapon used in this case ejected expended cartridges an average distance of 20.6 feet to the right and rearward when held parallel to the ground at a height of 50 inches. The eight shots fired over a considerable distance were consistent with the agent's description of a suspect charge and an officer retreat. Furthermore, findings from the ballistics and medical analyses indicated that two bullets struck the suspect. One bullet entered his right elbow on the lateral side of the upper arm, exited medially, and reentered the lateral side of the right abdomen. The second bullet entered the suspect on the left side at the level of the femoral head and neck, with resulting fracture failure of the femoral neck of the femur (i.e., thigh bone). Since one bullet entered the right elbow and then continued into the suspect's abdomen, clearly the suspect's arms were not raised at the time of the shooting as alleged by the suspect. In addition, the lateral entry of both bullets (abdomen and hip) was not consistent with the weapon being fired while the suspect was directly facing the officer. Therefore, the border patrol agent's testimony was consistent with the physical kinematic evidence and trauma biomechanics evidence.

3.4 Kinetics

While kinematic analyses describe the spatial and temporal characteristics of motion, kinetic analyses focus on the causes of motion, that is the forces or loading effects of forces upon human movement. Forces are interactions (i.e., pushing or pulling) between objects that produce or stop motion, accelerate an object in motion, or change the direction of motion. Kinetic analyses are important to the study of injury or trauma biomechanics because the resultant change in motion from an applied force or load can cause acute injury. Because we see only the effects of forces following an injury and not the actual forces themselves, kinetic injury analyses are often more difficult to complete and evaluate than descriptive, kinematic analyses of motion. To make use of kinetic analyses requires a basic understanding of the characteristics of force, the principles governing the relationship of force and movement, and a working knowledge of some of the common forces causing human movement and injuries.

A. Characteristics of forces, moments, and torques

Forces are always vectors and therefore have magnitude and direction. In addition, forces have two other important characteristics: the point of application, and the line of action. The point of application of force is the point where force is applied to an object or body; it determines the direction of motion resulting from an applied force and whether the resulting motion is linear or angular.

The line of action of force is a straight line of infinite length in the direction of the applied force. (Figure 3.8) Linear motion occurs when the point of application of force causes the object to move in the direction of the applied force. Sometimes other forces such as gravity contribute to the object's motion.

Angular or rotational movements are produced when a force is applied at a displacement from the axis or pivot point. The magnitude of the applied force times the shortest straight-line, perpendicular distance to the line of action of force (e.g., moment or lever arm) is referred to as either a torque (i.e., the result of a force causing a torque rotation) or a moment of force (i.e., the result of a force

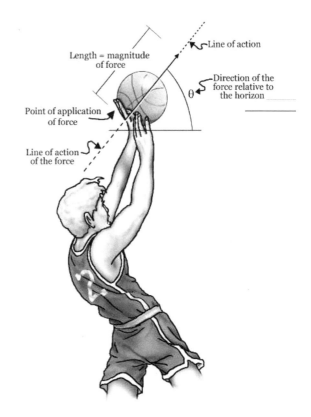

Figure 3.8 *The point of application and line of application of a force vector are indicated, in addition to the magnitude and direction of the force vector. (Courtesy of Robert Perry)*

causing a bending action). For most discussions, the terms torque and moment of force are used synonymously, but by convention when referring to rotational movement of the body, moments refer to bending of body segments around a mediolateral axis (e.g., flexion or extension) or an anteroposterior axis. The term torque is reserved for rotational forces that produce twisting or spinning (longitudinal axis). Torques and moments are vectors and are expressed using arrows, with direction being specified by the right-hand thumb rule as previously discussed.

As an example, if a mechanic attempts to loosen a bolt with a wrench 16 inches long applying 50 lbs. of force, the torque is 800 inch-lbs. If instead he uses a wrench 24 inches long and applies the same amount of force at the end of the wrench, the resultant torque will be 1,200 inch-lbs. Lengthening the moment arm with a longer wrench increases the torque and gives the mechanic a better chance to loosen the bolt. The same result can be achieved if he applies more force (75 lbs.) to the original 16-inch wrench. This equation may be expressed as:

Torque $(T) = F_X$ force moment arm (fma).

B. Classical mechanics

A basic working knowledge of the principles of classical mechanics is necessary to understanding how applied forces cause movement of the body. Sir Isaac Newton formalized centuries of seemingly contradictory knowledge about the movement of objects in *Principia Mathematica* (1687). Newton's laws of motion and gravity remain the foundation for understanding how forces interact with objects and provide a framework to explain human motion.

1. Newton's first law of motion

The law of inertia states that, unless acted on by an external force, an object at rest will remain at rest and an object in motion will continue in uniform motion at a constant velocity in the same linear or angular direction. Inertia is an object's resistance to a change in motion. Linear inertia is directly proportional to the object's mass. The larger the mass, the greater the external force needed to overcome inertia and get the body moving. Linear inertia is measured in slugs (English system) or in kilograms (Standard International system). When a body is at rest, it is obvious that a push or pull is needed to move it. But when a body is moving with a constant velocity, the law of inertia applied to linear motion is not quite as obvious. Humans rarely move at a constant velocity, and external forces (e.g., air resistance) slowing or changing the direction of movement are not always visible.

The rotational counterpart to linear inertia is the moment of inertia (i.e., mass moment of inertia). The mass moment of inertia (a.k.a. angular inertia) depends on the distribution of mass around an axis of rotation, or radius of gyration (k), as well as the total mass of the object. There is less resistance to a change in rotation if the mass is distributed closer to the axis of rotation. For example, starting or stopping a merry-go-round on a playground is more difficult if the children are grouped to the outside of the apparatus (i.e., the mass is further from the vertical axis of rotation) rather than grouped near the center. The equation $I = mk^2$ illustrates that k, the distribution of mass, is a squared factor and is predominant in determining angular inertia. Small changes in the radius of gyration (k) may result in large effects upon the angular inertia expressed in slug-ft^2 or kg-m^2.

2. Newton's second law of motion

The law of acceleration describes the relationship among elements of force, mass, and acceleration. Newton's second law is expressed by the equation, Force = mass x acceleration $(F = ma)$ and is one of the most recognizable equations in mechanics. The law states that for an object of a given mass, the acceleration of the object is directly proportional to the applied force, with a larger force resulting in a greater acceleration of a moveable object. Conversely, if a given force is applied, the object's acceleration is inversely proportional to its mass, that is, the larger the mass, the lower the acceleration for the given force. Stated in yet a different way, this law defines another important concept in injury biomechanics: momentum (M). Linear Momentum is a vector quantity expressed as mass times velocity expressed in slug-ft/s or kg-m/s. A stationary object has no momentum. A force, therefore, must be applied to an object for momentum to change. This may be expressed as force x time (Ft) = a change in momentum (M), or the average reaction force acting in the *opposite direction* of the linear momentum vector equals the change in momentum divided by the change in time (average F = -M/t).

When objects collide, momentum changes. In motor vehicle collisions, for example, if a large force is applied to a vehicle over a short period of time, momentum changes quickly, often dropping to zero. Such collisions generally result in large reaction forces and may produce injury to the occupants. Decreasing the body's momentum magnitude is generally not an option in an accident; however, measures can be taken to increase the time over which the body's linear or angular momentum is brought to zero. If a person falls from a height of 10 feet and lands on his back on a concrete floor, the reaction force at impact is very high, and momentum drops to zero over a very short period of time. The probability of injury, in this case, is very high. If the landing surface is changed to a 12-inch-thick foam pad and all other parameters remain the same, momentum is brought to zero over an extended period of time because the foam cushions the fall, lowering the reaction force and the probability of injury.

These same principles apply to the application of Newton's second law of motion to a discussion of angular motion. A moment or torque = angular inertia (I) χ angular acceleration (α). Furthermore, angular momentum (L) = angular inertia χ angular velocity expressed as $L = I\omega$. Angular momentum may be expressed in slug-ft^2/s or kg-m^2/s. Angular momentum is not affected by the force of gravity when a body is free of external moments or torques (in mid-air) because gravity acts through the body's center of mass. Therefore, a vehicle rotating in mid-air will maintain its original angular momentum (negating air resistance) until it strikes the ground, which imposes an additional moment to add or subtract from the original angular momentum vector. Once again the right-hand thumb rule should be applied to designate the angular momentum vector.

3. Newton's third law of motion

This law is sometimes termed the law of action-reaction and states that for every applied force, there is a reaction force of equal magnitude acting in the opposite direction. This equal and opposite force applies at all instants during the force application event. To illustrate, if we push with our hand on the flat surface of a desk with a given amount of force, the desk surface pushes back with equal force in the opposite direction. Forces never act in isolation; when two objects interact, action and reaction forces of equal magnitude are always paired and act on the objects in opposite directions. Although action and reaction forces are equal in magnitude, the result of the forces on each object is different because the objects have different masses and other material properties that may differ (e.g., a pedestrian and a motor vehicle). This is important in kinetic analyses of injury. If an automobile hits a pedestrian, an action force is generated from the motor vehicle to the pedestrian, and the pedestrian exerts an equal reaction force on the automobile in the opposite direction. The effects of the interaction, however, are much different for the pedestrian than for the automobile, in large part because the mass of the vehicle is much larger than the pedestrian and because the motor vehicle materials have different material properties than the biological tissues of the human pedestrian.

Newton's third law applied to angular motion necessitates an equal and opposite torque or moment for every torque and moment applied. Simply swinging one's arm around to the side produces a torque and counter-torque. However, with the feet on the ground, the counter-torque is absorbed by the massive Earth. However, if one were to jump up in mid-air and turn the upper torso and swing the upper extremities to the right, the pelvis and the lower extremities will rotate correspondingly to the left (i.e., in the opposite direction).

Several common forces important to human movement involve a direct application of Newton's third law of motion. Two good examples are ground reaction force and joint reaction force. Ground reaction force is one of the most common forces in normal human movement. When a pedestrian applies a force to a ground surface while walking, running, etc., the reaction force (i.e., ground reaction force) from the floor or sidewalk pushes back against the pedestrian.

Secondly, a joint reaction force is the net force acting across a joint. When standing still, for example, the lower leg exerts a reaction force upward across the knee in response to the force of gravity acting on the body's mass downward. These joint reaction forces become considerably more complex when muscle tension forces are added in a free body analysis and may exceed several times the individual's body weight.

4. Newton's law of gravity

Most forces involve the interaction or contact between two objects: the pushing or pulling of an object in contact with the other. Not so obvious, however, are noncontact forces: attractive forces exerted by objects separated by distance. Newton described the most important noncontact force for human movement (i.e., gravity), and introduced his law of gravitational force in *Principia Mathematica* (1687). Any object released from a height will be pulled to the surface of the Earth by the force of gravity. The gravitational pull of the Earth on an object or individual is referred to as weight and can be defined as the mass of the object times the acceleration due to gravity ($W = mg$). Note that this is just a simple application of Newton's second law of motion ($F = ma$). Since the Earth's mass is large, the attractive force on a smaller object is significant, causing objects to accelerate toward the Earth at a rate of 32.2 feet per second squared (ft/s^2) at approximate sea level (negating air resistance).

As an aside, we now know that gravity within the universe acts as a gravitational wave traveling at the speed of light. However, Newton's concept of gravity is still fully functional in biomechanics.

C. Special application of forces

Since a detailed analysis of all applied forces is beyond the scope of this text, the remainder of the chapter focuses on a few common forces involved in human movement that have application in injury analyses: friction and the relationships among force, work, energy, and pressure.

1. Friction

When two objects contact one another, for instance a stationary coffee mug sitting on the surface of a desk, the weight of the mug acts as a force in a vertical direction on the table and a reaction force of equal magnitude acts in the opposite direction on the mug (i.e., Newton's third law of motion). If a horizontal force is applied to the mug to slide it across the tabletop, friction acts at the interface of the contacting surfaces as a resistive force in opposition to the sliding motion. Movement occurs only if the applied force is greater than the frictional force; the frictional force increases in proportion to the applied force until a maximum static friction is reached, beyond which the coffee mug begins to slide. Once moving, the magnitude of the frictional force, referred to as kinetic friction, generally remains constant regardless of the amount of sliding force applied or the speed of motion unless the surfaces or material properties of the two objects change.

Friction affects all forms of movement; walking across a surface without slipping and falling, skiing down a snowy slope, or driving a car on a wet road all require the appropriate amount of frictional force. It is obvious that it takes more force to slide a heavy lead paperweight across the surface of a table than a coffee mug, and it takes more force to slide the mug across a rubber surface than a glass surface. Two factors determine the amount of force needed to overcome a maximum static friction (F_s): 1) reaction force (R) and 2) the coefficient of sliding friction (μ_s). Therefore $F_s = R \times \mu_s$.

The reaction force, also termed the normal force (N), generally depends on the weight of the object. For example, the heavy paperweight creates a greater reaction force than the coffee mug and more friction is generated. In the second example, the rubber surface has a greater coefficient of friction than the glass surface; so the mug will move with less friction across the glass surface.

The coefficient of friction for sliding (μ_s) is a unitless number indicating the ease or difficulty of sliding: the higher the number, the greater the frictional force and the greater the resistance to sliding. The coefficient of friction is related to the hardness and the composition (i.e., molecular and mechanical characteristics) of the opposing two surfaces. (Figure 3.9)

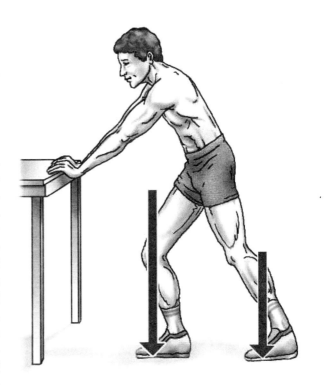

Figure 3.9 *Static friction is determined by the perpendicular force (normal or reaction force) holding the two surfaces together and by the coefficient of friction. The normal force is imposed upon the athletic shoes of the individual pushing the table. The coefficient of friction (μ) depends on the nature of the shoe sole surfaces and the flooring material. (Courtesy of Robert Perry)*

One common misconception is that increased apparent surface area increases traction or friction. Some people may erroneously believe that wider tires or an elaborate tread design provides better traction, whereas only an increase in the reaction force or the coefficient of friction will increase traction (i.e., friction). However, this statement applies only to dry, compact, clean surfaces and surfaces that are not being modified during slippage. The treads of the tire or the tread pattern on a shoe sole may affect slipping on surfaces that are wet, soft, or dirty.

In summary, the coefficient of friction is important in injury biomechanics. When the coefficient of friction is too low, a person may slip and fall, and when the coefficient is too high, there is greater likelihood that a person will trip and fall with an inadequate foot clearance during walking gait swing phase. The coefficient of friction depends on both surfaces and may be lower than normal in slip and fall accidents. Walking across ice or walking on a smooth surface covered with water or oil are examples which would present a low coefficient of friction. On the other hand, ankle and knee injuries may be caused by a high coefficient of friction. Examples include some artificial playing surfaces or transitions from one surface to another surface (e.g., packed snow to patchy snow or dirt surface while snow skiing) which may cause a significant increase in frictional force and a resultant increase in the reaction force transferred to the feet, shoes or skis. The coefficient of friction can be adjusted by changing flooring materials, by using appropriate footwear, and by keeping surfaces clean and dry (e.g., shoveling snowy/icy sidewalks).

Rolling friction (i.e., F_r or rolling resistance) is different than sliding friction and is usually much lower than sliding friction. It is determined by: $\mu_r = F_r/N$ where F_r is the resistive force of rolling friction and N is the normal force of the wheel (or body) perpendicular to surface (e.g., ground surface). The actual calculation of μ_r and F_r is more complicated than determining sliding friction and the sliding coefficient of friction. Rolling friction usually should be determined experimentally for a specific vehicle such as a wheelchair. The rolling coefficient of friction (μ_r) is proportional to the width of the wheel and inversely proportional to the wheel's radius. Furthermore, increased friction within the axle (axis of rotation) and in the case of soft wheels or tires, an increase in the surface area against a ground surface will increase F_r and μ_r. In forensic biomechanics, rolling resistance (a.k.a. rolling friction) is usually not as important a topic as is sliding friction. However, it is sometimes considered in forensic vehicle dynamics analyses.

3.5 Work and Energy

In science and engineering, work and energy have specific meanings. Both terms are important from a mechanical point of view because they involve special applications of forces that can cause injury. Mechanical work equals the magnitude of force applied to an object times the distance the object is moved: Work = F x d (i.e., the distance traveled by the object in the direction of force). No work is done if a force is applied and the resisting force (i.e., wind resistance or friction) is great enough to preclude movement. If one holds a 50-pound weight overhead as a stationary object, no mechanical work is done unless the weight is lifted to a higher level. Likewise, an isometric muscle contraction (no joint movement or muscle shortening) does not involve mechanical work because the active muscle elements are not generating movement and yet muscular force is being produced.

Energy and work are intricately linked and are often confused. Simply stated, energy is the capacity to do work. Although there are many forms of energy, mechanical energy and thermal energy are primary causative factors in most human injury cases. Our focus in this text is on mechanical energy which may be classified as kinetic or potential energy. Kinetic energy (*KE*) results from an object in motion (the object has a speed or velocity), and potential energy (*PE*) is stored energy that can be converted to do work. Linear kinetic energy is defined as one half the mass times the velocity squared ($KE = 1/2\ mv^2$). Since kinetic energy is exponentially linked to velocity (i.e., v^2), small changes in velocity dramatically increase the energy in the object in motion.

Potential energy, on the other hand, refers to the capacity or potential to convert stored energy into kinetic energy. Potential energy can take two forms: potential energy of position (i.e., stored energy due to height) and strain energy (i.e., stored energy due to elastic deformation of an object such as a metal spring). Potential energy of position (PE_p or PE_h) is directly related to the height of an object above the Earth's surface; that is, the potential energy of position equals the object's weight (i.e., mass x gravitational acceleration) times the height of an object from a surface ($PE_h = mgh$). Because the object's weight is typically fixed, changes in potential energy are generally due to changes in height or position. Potential energy due to strain is sometimes referred to as elastic energy (PE_k). Elastic energy varies depending on the elasticity of a material and the ability of a material to store energy when it is deformed (i.e., bent, twisted, stretched, or compressed). The force that deforms an object or material may be stored as elastic energy and can be released during reformation of the material. The rate at which an object is able to reform is measured by its coefficient of restitution. Athletic equipment such as pole vaulting poles and diving springboards rely on the principle of stored elastic energy; specific materials are used to store the maximum potential (elastic) energy when deformed and then these materials release the energy in the form of kinetic energy when they reform. Biological materials respond differently in terms of elastic energy depending on the rate of deformation and, to a lesser degree, the temperature as they are loaded.

When the only external force acting on an object is the force of gravity, the object's mechanical energy remains constant (PE + KE = constant or total energy); that is, mechanical energy cannot be created or destroyed. This connection between kinetic and potential energy is called the law of conservation of mechanical energy (von Helmholtz, 1847). As an example, in a hypothetical injury case, a wall rock climber positioned five meters above a landing mat possesses a potential energy equal to his mass times the acceleration due to gravity (9.8 m/s²) times the height from the landing mat (i.e., 5 meters). If the rock climber falls without the benefit of a safety belay rope, his falling body acquires linear kinetic energy (i.e., mv^2) and loses potential energy at a constant rate. At impact, potential energy completely disappears, and all the energy has been converted to kinetic energy, which is absorbed by his body and the landing mat. The amount of energy after an impact has occurred will only be the same as the pre-impact energy (KE at first impact) when the collision is perfectly elastic. However, when the body strikes the landing mat, the mat deforms and pushes back on the body, stopping its motion in this real world nonelastic impact example. Ideally, the mat deforms and re-forms very slowly, which dramatically reduces the amount of deformation to the human body. This is desirable because significant deformation to the human body can produce injury. (Figure 3.10)

3.6 General Material Mechanics

A. Rigid body mechanics versus deformable solids

In rigid body mechanics we examine bodies as if they were rigid structures that do not deform or change shape when forces, moments, and torques are applied. The rigid body mechanics approach is useful in examining movement characteristics, and further assumptions may be

Figure 3.10 When the body falls on the surface of the deforming mat, kinetic energy is absorbed. Furthermore, the mat does not re-form quickly and therefore does not return a significant amount of stored elastic potential energy to the human body. (Courtesy of Robert Perry)

made about the body or body segment, including non-deformability, a fixed center of mass and homogeneity of the material (Zernicke and Whiting, 1998). Reasonable approximations in the field of biomechanics may make use of rigid body mechanics when addressing body and body segment motion. However, biological tissues are deformable and, therefore, in examining the biomechanics of injury, we also need to explore the mechanics of deformable solids, which more accurately portray real human tissues. Furthermore, the way in which biological materials do deform under different stress magnitudes, directions, and rates of deformation will affect the consequent strains and injury trauma. Stresses and consequent strains are dependent upon the magnitude of the loading and upon the area over which the load is imposed as well as the properties of the biological and non-biological materials involved.

B. Material properties of biological materials

1. Effect of loads, stresses, and strains

As per an example of bone, a tension load that tends to elongate the cylinder would tend to make the cylinder longer. A compression load would tend to make the cylinder shorter. A torsion load will twist the cylinder. Finally, a shear load applied to a bone cylinder due to offset parallel forces will tend to change angles within the structure. (Figure 3.11) Shear loads will produce a horizontal or vertical sliding of one layer over another as they act across a plane of an area (Zernicke and Whiting, 1998). (Figure 3.12) These consequent changes in form for the various loads are termed deformations and can be measured in English or Standard International linear unit measures (e.g., inches or centimeters) for tension and compression loads or in degrees (change in angle) for shear deformations.

When a load is imposed upon a tissue, it will result in a stress. An axial load (compression or tension) will produce tension or compressive stresses. These stresses are termed normal stresses. Compression and tension stresses may result from a uniaxial load that is applied perpendicularly over a cross-section surface area. It is defined as σ = load/area, with stress being directly related to the magnitude of the load and inversely related to the cross-section surface area. Please note that in physics, a compression stress is termed positive, while in engineering, a compressive stress is negative with a tension stress being termed positive.

Pressure is another term related to a compressive stress. However, pressure describes the way in which

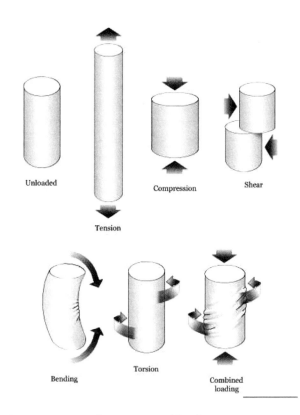

Figure 3.11 *Five basic types of loading exist: compression, tension, bending, shear, and torsion. (Courtesy of Robert Perry)*

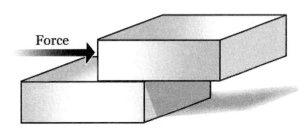

Figure 3.12 *One layer slides over an area plane. This shear load results in a shear stress (t) which is the parallel plane load over the cross section surface area. (Courtesy of Robert Perry)*

stresses are applied in the x, y, and z directions (i.e., the average of the sum of x , y , and z) resulting in a change in volume (i.e., bulk compressive stress), and pressures are always expressed as positives in physics and engineering nomenclature. Furthermore, pressure has the potential to perform work (related to energy density) and pressure is also a measure of potential energy per unit volume. Therefore, it differentiates from "compressive stress" in that it

may be expressed in units such as joules per cubic meter (J/m^3).

Compressive stress is defined as the force per unit area and may be expressed as pounds/inch^2 (psi). In Standard International, compressive stress may also be expressed in Pascals (Pa); one Pascal is of measure 1.0 Newton per square meter. Forces are tolerable when spread over a large area, but focal concentrations of force cause compressive stress to rise dramatically and are more likely to cause injury. Compressive stress is increased when the area of impact is decreased (e.g., the point of a knife contacts the skin) or the applied force is increased. It now becomes clear that by decreasing the load or increasing the area, we can reduce stress with a consequent reduction of a tension or compression strain and a decreased probability of injury trauma in terms of deformation or penetration of biological tissues. Manufacturers and biomechanists have analyzed force platform measurements of walkers and runners and have developed shoes to reduce overall compressive stresses on the feet while increasing compressive stress in select areas of plantar foot surface (e.g., under the foot longitudinal arch). Furthermore, snowshoes and cross country skis help distribute loads over a greater area, reducing compressive stress and allowing individuals to walk or ski on the snow surface with limited ground surface penetration. Hard hats used on construction sites are designed to spread a force of impact over a broader area, reducing compressive stress, preventing penetration, and reducing the potential for injury when small objects are dropped from above (albeit to a limited degree).

A shear stress (tau: τ) is equal to the shear load $_{Tangential}$/cross-section surface area. Here shear stress will also be decreased by decreasing the shear load or by increasing the cross-section surface area over which the shear load acts. Shear stresses may also result from tension, compression, and torsion loads. Structures within a material may be subjected to shear stresses during axial loading depending on the orientation of structural material elements. When a shear stress occurs, it results in a shear strain which involves a change in angle or geometry within material structures and is represented by the symbol gamma (γ). The equations for normal stresses and shear stresses are presented in Figure 3.13.

Strains are deformations that occur as the result of stresses. Normal strains are the result of compression or tension stresses and may be measured in absolute terms (identical to deformations) or are more commonly presented as a percent deformation based on the original length or shape of the material and the new length or shape of the material (i.e., percent strain). The equations for normal strains and shear strains are presented in Figure 3.14.

The relationship of stresses and strains can best be appreciated by a stress/strain graph. It should be noted that the relationship that relates shear, tension, and compression stresses and strains is an example of a material function. In the example presented below, a tension stress is applied to cortical bone. (Figure 3.15)

Compression and Tension Stresses (i.e., normal stresses):

Compressive or Tension Stress = Load or Force/Area

$\sigma = F/A$

These normal stresses are expressed as newtons per square meter (pascals) in Standard International or in pounds per square inch (psi) in the English System

Shear Stress:

Shear Stress = Force $_{tangential}$ /cross sectional area

$\tau = F_t /A$

Figure 3.13 The equations for tension/compression and shear stresses are presented.

Positive Strain (ε) = Δ l/l
(a lengthening strain is equal to a change in length divided by the original length)

A compression stress producing a shortening. In the field of engineering, this is termed negative.

Negative Strain (ε) = Δ l/l
(a shortening strain is equal to a change in length divided by the original length)

A shear strain γ = d /h
(a shear strain results when the horizontal displacement is divided by the height as per the rectangle deforming into a parallelogram.)

Figure 3.14 The equations for tension/compression and shear strains are presented.

There are six specific points that are labeled as O, P, E, Y, U, and R. Point O is at the origin of the stress/strain diagram with both tension stress and tension strain at zero. No stress or deformation exists at this point. Point P represents the proportionality limit where tension stress and strain exhibit a linearly elastic relationship (point O to point P) (Ozkaya and Leger, 2001). A given amount of stress produces a proportional and equal amount of strain as evidenced by the straight line within this segment of the stress/strain curve and this is known as Hookian behavior (Hookes Law). Point E represents the elastic limit of a material, and point Y is the yield point. Point E indicates that point where the material moving past point E begins to enter into the plastic zone where permanent deformation takes place. Please note that reformation may still take place when the load is removed past point E, but the material will not return to its original shape (e.g., length). At point Y, the material deforms rapidly to small increases in stress, and therefore the curve flattens out with increasing amounts of strain or deformation along the horizontal axis. The yield stress (on the vertical axis) and the yield strain (horizontal axis) of the graph are represented by this point. The yield point is also a representation of the yield strength of the material. Point U is the highest stress point on this stress-strain diagram and is known as the ultimate failure point, also termed the ultimate strength of the material. Ultimate stress is represented on the vertical axis and the ultimate strain is represented on the horizontal axis in our graph. The last point on the stress-strain graph is R, which represents the rupture or complete failure point. This is also termed the rupture strength of the material. For some materials such as bone, points U and R typically occur at the same point and at the same time. Other materials, such as peripheral nerve, represent a point U much before point R is reached on the strain axis. Points P, E, Y, U, and R are usually read off of the vertical (ordinate) scale.

2. Flexible versus stiff materials

Another value derived from stress/strain curves is an assessment of flexibility versus stiffness. In terms of normal stresses and strains, this is known as the elastic or Young's modulus and may be specified as either the tension modulus or the compression modulus. The modulus is really a ratio and typically E is used for the elastic modulus. $E = \sigma / \varepsilon$, or stress divided by strain. This ratio really describes the curve on a stress/strain curve within the elastic region. When the elastic modulus is measured up to point P on our stress/strain curve in our example, it exhibits Hookian or linearly elastic behavior. Here, equal amounts of stress produce equal

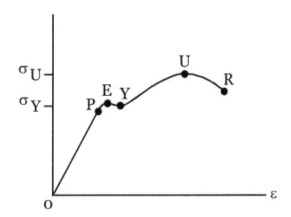

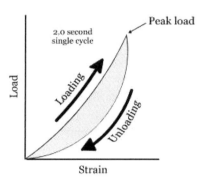

Figure 3.16 The area of hysteresis is illustrated during loading and unloading of a material in tension over 2.0 seconds. (Courtesy of Robert Perry)

Figure 3.15 The stress/strain graph for a cortical bone subjected to tension is represented above. In all cases the slope of the curve and the various points described are markers of tissue behavior and are important in terms of predicting tissue injury. (Courtesy of Robert Perry)

amounts of strain (albeit in different units). If the curve is steep, we have a stiff biological material (e.g., compact bone). If the curve is shallow, we have a flexible biological material (e.g., peripheral nerve). Therefore, biological materials fall along a continuum between stiff and flexible. Past point P, we enter into a stress/strain behavior and curve that is nonlinear in nature. When we reach point E, we establish the end of the elastic region, and if we were to stop applying the stress and release the load, the material would return to its original shape or length. However, as previously discussed, when the stress takes the biological material past point E, it will not return to its original length or shape. Furthermore as previously discussed, a biological material at the yield point will experience a comparatively large deformation with a relatively small increase in stress.

The shear modulus or (G) is shear stress divided by shear strain ($G = \tau / \gamma$) It is also known as the modulus of rigidity. If a small shear stress produces a large shear strain within the elastic zone, we would categorize the material as very flexible (a low shear modulus; G). On the other hand, if a large shear stress is required to produce a relatively small shear strain, we have a stiff material. Once again, biological materials fall along a continuum in terms of G.

3. Viscoelastic material properties

Viscoelasticity is due to the fact that biological materials have both fluid and solid material properties. Elastic solids will deform in response to a stress and then will re-form after the stress is removed if they remain within their

elastic zones. Potential energy is stored during deformation and is released as kinetic energy during reformation. The rate at which the stress is applied will not affect the response of the solid elastic material. Spring steel or the metal alloys that make up some crush-resistant eyeglass frames exhibit this property.

A fluid will also deform and has the additional property of being able to flow. Viscosity is a fluid property which really examines the resistance to this flow. Viscoelastic materials have both fluid (viscous) and solid (elastic) mechanical properties. Animal biological materials as well as polymer plastics and metals at high temperatures exhibit viscoelastic (rate-dependent) behavior (Ozkaya and Leger, 2001). Within the elastic zone, when biological materials re-form, there is some variable loss in energy and the reformation curve does not match the original deformation curve. The area between the deformation and the reformation curves on the stress/strain graph is known as the area of hysteresis and represents the loss of energy of the viscoelastic material during the loading cycle. (Figure 3.16) Sometimes the material is taken past its elastic zone when loaded rapidly and may be taken to the point of rupture, at which point the potential energy is released as kinetic energy. Because biological materials will become stronger (variable in biological materials) and will store more potential energy when they are loaded quickly, the rupture point will release a larger amount of kinetic energy. (Figure 3.17) For example, in bones the fracture pattern may become very explosive, with fragments moving into soft tissues that surround bones. Gunshot projectile wounds to bones may produce extremely explosive, comminuted fractures due to a very high loading rate.

4. Creep and stress relaxation

Viscoelastic biological materials also exhibit creep and stress relaxation. These two properties may affect

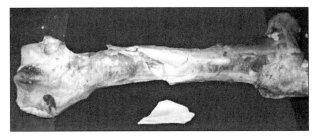

Figure 3.17 *The loading that occurs over a very short time will produce an explosive fracture as indicated in this highly comminuted Elk femur subjected to very rapid loading. The femur is able to store more energy when loaded rapidly, and when brought to failure, the energy release is enormous. (Courtesy of Patrick Hannon and Kerry Knapp)*

biological tissue behavior. Creep occurs, for example, when an orthodontist applies braces to a patient. Teeth will move due to creep deformation within bone and connective tissues within the maxilla and mandible that hold the teeth. This is followed by tissue remodeling of bone and connective tissue. Another very familiar example is that of stretching and may be illustrated by bending down from a standing position to touch one's toes. After an approximate 20 to 30 second wait, one is able to bend down even further with greater hip and lower spine flexion. The stretching (deformation) of muscle and tendon tissues depends on the time of loading, with additional deformation (creep) occurring with additional time. Biological materials subjected to a constant stress will usually exhibit the most amount of deformation and strain early on, with lesser deformation/strain occurring as time progresses. If

the stress level is increased, however, more creep (within rupture limits) will take place. (Figure 3.18)

Stress relaxation takes place when a viscoelastic biological material is able to deform internally (component deformation) or permit fluid flow within the biological tissue. In our orthodontic example, cross-links of primarily type I collagen are initially broken within gum tissue as teeth begin to move. Gum soreness during the first three to four days typically results. Stress relaxation then occurs during these collagen cross-link failures and the internal stress within gum tissue is markedly reduced with a consequent decrease in soreness (until the braces are tightened during the next patient visit). Other tissues such as articular cartilage (see Chapter 6) experience stress relaxation due to a redistribution of fluid (i.e., fluid flow) during compression loading as will occur during hip, knee and ankle joint weight bearing for example. This stress relaxation may occur in as little as two to three seconds and has a protective effect on articular cartilage. High-rate and high-magnitude loading of articular cartilage within joints does not permit substantive fluid flow stress relaxation within the time frame because the high load is applied too quickly and therefore damage to the articular cartilage may occur to diathrodial joints.

5. Ductile versus brittle material properties

This material property is related to the relative area of the plastic zone of the stress/strain graph. Materials that

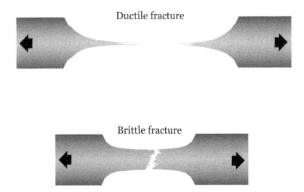

Figure 3.19 *A ductile metal rod experiences "necking" when subjected to a tension stress. This deformation point may lead to a steep drop in the engineering tension stress. Note that the physicist will point out that the "true stress" is actually still increasing as greater tension strain takes place. The necking is simply reducing the cross-sectional area of the metal rod, which results in a structural defect (Watts, 2003). (Courtesy of Robert Perry)*

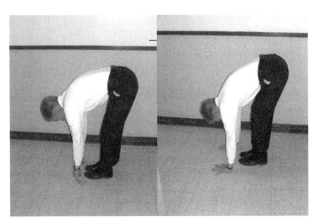

Figure 3.18 *Creep deformation occurs within the thigh hamstring and spine musculature as the time of the stretching is increased over a thirty second period. This results in a greater joint range of motion at the iliofemoral (hip) joints and the thoraco-lumbar spine in this man. (Courtesy of Patrick Hannon)*

are relatively ductile have a large plastic zone (e.g., many metals) and therefore may undergo a large amount of permanent deformation before they reach rupture. Other materials, such as window glass at normal temperatures, have a relatively small plastic zone and will break soon after reaching their yield point and are therefore termed brittle. Points yield (Y) and rupture point (R) are very close together in brittle materials. Please note that these properties are separate from material strength properties. Both ductile and brittle materials may be strong or weak under tension, compression, or shear stresses. Biological materials such as compact bone are relatively brittle and are only able to endure approximately 2.5% strain before rupture occurs. Other materials such as peripheral nerve are relatively ductile and in the laboratory setting can be exposed to long tension deformations before complete rupture of the nerve. Ductile materials such as peripheral nerve may exhibit some necking, albeit not to the extent of ductile metals. (Figure 3.19)

6. Toughness and resilience

Toughness is a measure of the total area within the elastic and plastic zones on a stress/strain test. If a material (e.g., metal) is able to undergo a large amount of deformation and absorb a large amount of energy (equal to the total area under the stress/strain curve), it has high toughness. This is obviously important in terms of materials used in motor vehicles that, when struck, will absorb large amounts of kinetic energy and therefore not transfer this energy to the occupants of the vehicle. Some degree of toughness is exhibited in biological tissues; however, the high loads and consequent permanent deformations of human tissues is not considered to be desirable. These elastic and plastic deformations in humans may result in significant tissue injury damage.

Material resilience is measured by the modulus of resilience and is related to the area under the elastic zone of the stress/strain graph. For example, a ligament structure that is exposed to a rapidly applied tension load and still manages to stay within its elastic zone exhibits the property of resilience. This is a desirable result. Biological materials fall along a continuum in this regard. However, many non-biological materials exhibit considerably more resilience than do biological tissues.

7. Isotropic versus anisotropic

This material property, unlike the other properties discussed previously, is not related to the stress/strain graph. However, it is an important consideration in biomechanical analysis of injury. Materials may respond differently depending on the direction of loading (termed anisotropic). Isotropic materials are not affected by the direction of the load vector. Internal elements/structures of many biological materials make them anisotropic, and therefore they may enter into the plastic zone or may reach failure at different load magnitude levels depending on the direction of loading. Compact bone is strongest, for example, when the loading is parallel to microscopic structures termed osteons within the compact bone walls. Furthermore, biological anisotropic structures sometimes will exhibit fracture failure patterns that coincide with the orientation of the internal elements that make up the tissue. Therefore, the anisotropic material property may be an important consideration in the biomechanical analysis of injury in tissues such as bone. (Figure 3.20)

3.7 Functional Anatomy—Machines of the Body and Implication for Mechanisms of Injury

An area related to biomechanics is functional anatomy, which demands a full initial understanding of structural anatomy. Introductory course work for the biomechanics expert is undergraduate courses (usually eight semester hours) in "anatomy and physiology" followed by coursework in functional anatomy. Functional anatomy in orthopedics, biomechanics and physical therapy focuse upon machine systems consisting of bones, joints and muscles. These machine systems with muscle actuators are driven by the central and peripheral nervous systems (see Chapters 9 and 19). Basic functional anatomy is

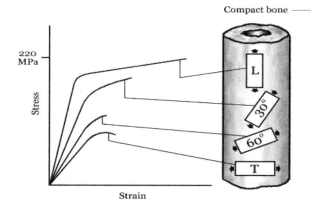

Figure 3.20 The direction of loading may affect the stiffness and strength of biological materials such as bone. The stiffness is illustrated by the slope of the stress/strain curve in the elastic zone with bone becoming stiffer (steeper curve) and stronger when it is loaded in line with microscopic structures within compact bone. (Courtesy of Robert Perry)

briefly addressed in Appendix B in regard to simple bone/joint machine force and motion mechanics.

The importance of this information and the consequent approach to analysis cannot be overemphasized and biomechanics experts, regardless of their masters or doctoral course of study (physics, engineering, biology or exercise science), must fully understand how human machine systems operate and the mechanism of injury that results in failure of these machine systems. Understanding the structural and functional human anatomy of bone-joint-muscle machines has important implications for forensics analysis.

The mechanism of injury may be clarified by the biomechanics expert in terms of: 1) Did the injury occur during a specific incident? or 2) How did the injury occur? Impacts are by no means the only example of body loading which may produce injury. In fact, some impacts do not have the potential to produce some injuries. For example, a blow to the side of the shoulder (upper arm at one's side) in a near side vehicle impact is very unlikely to produce a tear of subscapularis (one of the 4 rotator cuff muscles). At an appropriately high magnitude, one may see a fracture of the clavicle or ligament trauma to the acromioclavicular (i.e., AC) joint but this shoulder impact would not be consistent with a rotator cuff tear. Another example is that of the knee hitting a dashboard and the claim of a knee anterior cruciate rupture (i.e., AC ligament tear). At the appropriate magnitude, a posterior cruciate ligament (PCL) tear or rupture may occur with the tibia being pushed backwards in relation to the femur as it strikes the dashboard in a bent knee position. However, absent a complete knee (tibiofemoral joint) dislocation, damage to the knee ACL is not a match for this described incident regardless of temporal correctness. A biomechanics/functional anatomy analysis would indicate that ACL trauma, if present, is a pre-existing pathology.

Finally, a functional anatomy-biomechanics analysis may explain how an injury occurred in complex injuries such as a bimalleolar or trimalleolar fracture of the foot-ankle complex in sliding into second base or descending a staircase. The results of such analyses may clarify the issues for the plaintiff or the defense attorney.

3.8 Summary
In this chapter, I have introduced many of the guiding mechanical principles used in injury biomechanics. Although it was not the goal of this text to provide an exhaustive study of mechanics, it is important to understand the basic kinematic parameters used to describe motion, the causative forces and kinetic principles of motion, the

basics of classical mechanics, and the general material properties of biological tissues when preparing a personal injury case or criminal physical assault/shooting. An understanding of human body machines is many times also very important.

In the next few chapters, material properties are discussed in more detail and related to specific biological tissues and anatomical areas.

References

Fung, Y.C. "The Application of Biomechanics to the Understanding of Injury and Healing," in J.W. Na-hum and A.M Melvin, eds. *Accidental Injury Biomechanics and Prevention*, Second edition (NY: Springer-Verlag, 1993).

Levangie, P. and Norkin, C. (2011) *Joint Structure and Function: A Comprehensive Analysis 5th ed.* F.A. Davis Company, Philadelpha.

Mow, V. and Hayes, W. (editors) (1997) *Basic Orthopadic Biomechanics*. Lippincott Williams & Wilkins, Philadelphia.

Oatis, C. (2004) *Kinesiology: The Mechanics & Pathomechanics of Human Movement*. Lippincott Williams & Wilkins, Philadelphia.

Ozkaya, N. and D. Leger. "Introduction to Biomechanics: Basic Terminology and Concepts," in Nordin and Frankel Editors, *Basic Biomechanics of the Musculoskeletal System*, Third edition. Lippincott Williams, Wilkins - Philadelphia 2001.

Watts, Alan. *Low-Speed Automobile Accidents: Accident Reconstruction and Occupant Kinematics, Dynamics, and Biomechanics*, Third edition. (Tucson, AZ: Lawyers & Judges, 2003).

Zernicke, R. and W. Whiting. *Biomechanics of Musculoskeletal Injury* (Champaign, IL: Human Kinetics, 1998).

Recommended Reading

LeVeau, B.F. *Biomechanics of Human Motion*, Third edition. (Philadelphia: W.B. Saunders, 1992).

Nigg, B. and W. Herzog. *Biomechanics of the Musculoskeletal System*, Second edition (NY: John Wiley)

Zatsiorsky, V. *Kinematics of Human Motion* (Champaign,
    IL: Human Kinetics, 1998).

Chapter 4

The Application of Biomechanical Principles to Impacts

Patrick Hannon

4.1 Introduction

Chapter 3 introduced the basic principles of biomechanics and material mechanics. Chapter 4 takes the next step and applies many of these same concepts to impacts and other loading events. The goal is to illustrate how the concepts presented in the previous chapter are applied to real-world situations. Application of key biomechanical principles is intended to further the overall goal of this text in providing the attorney or graduate biomechanics student with the ability to analyze, discuss, and question the facts of a case involving loading to the human body which may have produced injury. Injuries are routinely caused by the impacts or collisions and forces (loads) applied to the body, and tissues deform at impact. Sometimes the collisions occur between two people of equal size, as in some sports injuries. However, in many injury-producing situations, collisions occur between the body and an object of greater mass. In the case of a slip and fall, for example, the body strikes a hard surface of considerably greater mass. When impact occurs, linear and angular momentums are brought to zero by a reaction force from the ground.

In most injury cases, force is applied to the body or body segment over a short period of time; the short duration loading must be of sufficiently high magnitude to produce injury. Situations that produce this level of loading include falls, vehicle collisions, sports accidents, and industrial or construction workplace incidents. In these situations, injury is produced when loads are applied to the human body that accelerate or decelerate, penetrate, or deform the body. Tissues are deformed, resulting in hard- and soft-tissue injury at both the cellular and gross anatomical levels. The extent of the injury depends on the magnitude of the applied force, the direction of the loading, and the point of application of the force vector on the human body.

4.2 Falls

When an individual falls, the body produces an action force against the ground at impact; the ground then produces a reaction force of equal magnitude acting in the opposite direction against the body (i.e., Newton's third law of motion). Velocity of a free-falling body is governed by the equation: $V_v = \sqrt{2\,(g)(h)}$—the vertical velocity at impact (V_v) is equal to the square root of two times the acceleration due to gravity (g) times the height (h) dropped. The acceleration due to gravity is approximately 32.2 ft/s^2 or 9.81 meters/s^2 (Figure 4.1). Furthermore, time for a free fall ignoring air resistance is: $t = \sqrt{2\,(height/g)}$.

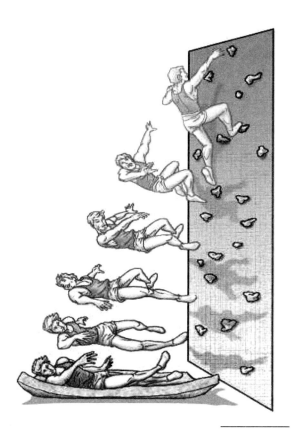

Figure 4.1 *A man falls from 15.0 feet to his side onto a foam pad cushion. As he falls, his vertical velocity due to the force of gravity is steadily increased up to the impact point. (Courtesy of Robert Perry)*

Problem 1

If an individual falls 15.0 feet to the ground, what is the vertical velocity at impact?

$$V_v = \sqrt{2(g)(h)}$$
$$V_v = \sqrt{2(32.2 \text{ ft/s}^2)(15.0 \text{ ft})}$$
$$V_v = \sqrt{(64.4 \text{ ft/s}^2)(15.0 \text{ ft})}$$
$$V_v = \sqrt{966 \text{ ft}^2/\text{s}^2} = 31.1 \text{ ft/s}$$

A fall in this manner will result in a vertical velocity of 31.1 ft/s at impact. Falls from a standing position present more complex calculations involving a tip mechanism, an estimate of the body's center of gravity at mid-height, and body joint movements during the fall event. One such approximation calculation is an inverted pendulum equation approach of: $V_v = \sqrt{3(g)(h)}$ which involves a relatively straight body tip over to the ground. The reader is referred to Hyde et al. (2002) for a more in-depth discussion of falls and fall prevention.

It should be appreciated that in the absence of recorded surveillance imaging acquired during the actual fall event,

some variables must be estimated by the biomechanist and therefore a range of values may be bracketed. Estimate errors can lead to erroneous conclusions, and therefore precise calculations of final vertical velocity during some fall events and/or subsequent loading at ground impact are impossible to make without recorded kinematic data unless there is a free fall from a known height. Sometimes in the absence of surveillance recording, more elaborate calculations of slips, trips, and falls are misleading to attorneys and the trier of fact. These calculations may not be supportable by the scientific evidence. Calculated results based on erroneous input do not gain validity as the result of mathematical approaches. In this example of human falls, it is often best to bracket results in terms of low loading up to the highest reasonable loading level when the fall distance must be grossly estimated or when human joint bending reduces the vertical velocity of a same level inverted pendulum fall.

A. The impulse equation approach

A falling body acquires linear momentum due to an increase in vertical velocity (V_v). When the body strikes the ground, as in the case of the human fall discussed above, the acquired linear momentum drops to zero very quickly and the change in momentum is governed by the time of force application as well as the magnitude of the applied force. Derived from Newton's second law of motion, impulse or the change in momentum (M) is the product of force and time (i.e., impulse or $M = F \times t$). As discussed in Chapter 3, time is inversely proportional to the reaction force; increasing the length of time for momentum to drop to zero decreases the reaction force (load) on the body. When an individual falls and lands on a rigid surface, the individual's momentum drops to zero quickly and the ground reaction force is large; the probability of injury is quite high. However, if the individual bends at the hips, knees, and ankles at impact, the time for momentum to drop to zero (i.e., the time to absorb the ground reaction force) is increased, reducing the chance or extent of injury resulting from decreased force and deceleration magnitudes. Allowing human joint articulations to move during this process lowers the deceleration rate and the resultant reaction force with consequent less deformation of soft and hard human tissues.

An extreme example of this is illustrated in the domestic cat species. Urban veterinarians are familiar with high-rise syndrome in felines. Cats in high-rise buildings will sit on open window sills and subsequent multi-story falls sometimes take place. Perhaps falls are a mis-characterization. Cat owners' descriptions indicate that their pets have jumped out for a nearby bird. This instinctual predatory act at sixty or seventy stories above the street is a big mistake for the cat. What is surprising is that many times the cats do survive these falls, albeit with fore and hind limb fractures. Recovery may occur. This is accomplished largely at landing when the cat lands on all four feet with its back raised and its four limbs in full extension. Joint bending in the extremities and spine extension allow for the survival of the domestic cat by increasing the time over which the cat's linear momentum is brought to zero.

Problem 2

An individual weighing 150 lbs falls 15.0 feet (body's center of gravity) onto foam padding and comes to a complete stop in 150 ms. What is the average reaction force on the individual at impact?

> First: $m = w/g$; mass (m) = weight (w) / acceleration due to gravity (g); since the individual weighs 150.0 lbs, then: m = 150.0 lbs / g (acceleration due to gravity = 32.2 ft/s^2)
> m = 4.66 slugs (a slug is a unit of mass: 1 slug = 32.2 lbs / 32.2 ft/s^2 = 1 lbs-ft/s^2)
> V_v = 31.1 ft/s (determined in Problem 1)
> Momentum (M) = m x V_v = 4.66 slugs x 31.1 ft/s = 144.9 slug-ft/s
> The Impulse Equation: Average $F = -M / t$

Note that the average reaction force and momentum (i.e., –M) are acting in opposite directions.

(Derived from Newton's second law of motion: $F = ma$)

> Average F = 144.9 slug-ft/s ÷ 150 milliseconds (i.e., ms or 0.15 seconds)
> Average F = 966.0 lbs

If the above variables remain the same, except the time to complete stop is increased to 250 milliseconds (i.e., 1/4 second), then:

> Average F = 144.9 slug-ft/s / 250 ms or 0.25 second.
> Average F = 579.6 lbs—the reaction force is reduced because the time to bring the falling body's linear momentum to zero is increased.

B. The energy equation approach

Impact from collisions may also be described using an energy equation approach. Here linear kinetic energy is considered ($KE = 1/2\ mv^2$). Angular kinetic energy may be important in some collisions ($KE = 1/2\ I\ \omega^2$) but is omit-

ted in this simplified motor vehicle collision example. As described in Chapter 3, kinetic energy is acquired as an object is put in motion. For example, when an automobile is brought to a stop by impact with another vehicle, KE is transferred from the striking automobile to the struck vehicle and this KE is absorbed (absorbed energy; AE) by both vehicles as they deform (i.e., bullet and target vehicles). At impact, some kinetic energy may be stored as elastic potential energy (PE_k), and the remainder of the mechanical kinetic energy (both vehicles) performs work (KE = work = force x distance) as vehicles move or plastically deform. This kinetic energy, which plastically deforms the vehicles (performing work), is desirable for the vehicle occupants. Modern large vehicles with long front end crumple zones are able to undergo more deformation with consequential greater extraction of kinetic energy (Watts, 2003) with less energy transferred to the vehicle occupants. Kinetic energy that is not absorbed (extracted) by vehicle deformation results in loading to the enclosed occupants as abrupt changes in vehicle velocities occur (i.e., accelerations or decelerations). Some amount of energy resulting from this collision example is also lost to sound and heat. A more detailed discussion of energy related to automobile collisions may be found in Watts (2003, pp. 85–98).

These same energy concepts apply equally in non-motor-vehicle events.

The following example again involves our human fall from height. The individual's center of gravity begins at 15.0 feet above a landing pad as in Problems 1 and 2.

Problem 3

A sport climber weighing 150 lbs falls 15.0 feet onto foam padding and comes to a complete stop in 150 ms. Mechanical energy is equal to the sum of the potential energy (PE) and the KE and remains constant up to the impact event. Potential energy of position (PE_h) equals mass x gravity x height.

What is the initial potential energy?

> $PE_h = m$ x g x h
> PE_h = 4.66 slugs x 32.2 ft/s^2 x 15.0 ft
> PE_h = 2,250.8 ft-lbs

As the fall is occurring PE is lost and linear KE is gained so that the sum total energy remains constant.

Using the energy equation, what is the reaction force on the individual at impact?

Please note that this approach considers only linear KE acquired and absorbed through linear motion, which is appropriate in this human fall example.

$m = 4.66$ slugs

$V_v = 31.1$ ft/s determined previously in Problem 1

Kinetic Energy $(KE) = 1/2\ m \times v^2$

$KE = 1/2 \times 4.66$ slugs $\times 31.1$ ft/s^2

$\qquad = 2.33$ slugs $\times 967.2$ ft^2/s^2

$\qquad = 2,253.6$ ft-lbs of energy at impact (2,253.6 f t -

lbs) equal to the PE_h before the fall event.

The kinetic energy equals the work done on the pad which equal the force $\times$ distance

$KE = W = Fd$

(Deformation of the human body is ignored in this simplified example)

Therefore the average $F = KE/d$ *(where d = displacement deformation of the pad)*

$F - 2,253.6$ ft lbs $\div 2.33$ feet of foam compression (i.e., deformation of a very thick pad)

Average $F = 967.2$ lbs

The very small difference between A the previous impulse equation (momentum approach) and this present energy equation approach B is due simply to rounding error.

A body with acquired kinetic energy at the time of impact may deform with a displacement deformation. This geometric deformation of the body or any material is the primary factor in the absorption of energy (AE) as per the example above. Heat and sound energy release accounts for a very small amount of the total kinetic energy and has been ignored in Problem 3. Note that 967.2 lbs is the approximate same reaction force that we calculated for a time duration impact of 150 ms using the impulse equation (albeit by design to illustrate that both approaches are roughly equivalent). Please note that this force of 967.2 lbs is applied for a short time, and when applied to the mass of the entire body in this example (4.66 slugs), the resulting acceleration (a = force / mass) is only 207.6 ft/s^2, or approximately 6.4 g (a tolerable level for humans).

Finally, please note that I have simplified this energy equation approach by ignoring the fact that gravity continues to act to increase KE during the large foam crush (2.33 feet), and therefore the average force of 967.2 lbs is really underestimated to a small degree. When drop distance is relatively high and crush distance is relatively low as is typically the case, this becomes an insignificant factor.

The impulse and the energy equations can be used in the absence of quantitative data to estimate the average force produced to bring the body's momentum or kinetic energy to zero. The impulse equation estimates the time of impact while the energy equation estimates the deforma-

tion of both objects (body and landing surface). The time estimate utilized in the impulse equation may be based on measurement when film or video surveillance data records the time duration of impact, but in the absence of these data, it must be estimated (sometimes via the literature). Alternatively, the average reaction force applied to the human body may be estimated from the distance over which the KE was extracted by the landing mat due to mat deformation (AE) as work is performed. Note that experience with impacts and the characteristics of biological as well as non-biological materials serves as the basis for these time and distance estimates made by biomechanists.

4.3 Vehicle Impacts

Vehicle impacts follow Newton's laws of motion and the principles discussed in Chapter 3. Automobile, motorcycle, boat, and airplane vehicle dynamics determine the loads applied to the occupants of these vehicles. Often an accident reconstructionist provides the biomechanist with data after the vehicle impact, including the principal direction of force (PDOF), the linear and angular changes in vehicle velocity, and the linear and angular acceleration levels of the vehicle involved in the accident. Pedestrian, bicycle, and some motorcycle impacts with automobiles present an enormous mass ratio favoring the larger vehicle; in these cases, a change in the vehicle kinematics and deformation of the larger vehicle may be small, but the effects of impact upon the pedestrian or cyclist may be quite severe.

A. Automobile impacts

In impacts involving automobiles, one or both vehicles are moving. The linear and angular motion of the vehicles determines occupant movement; the occupant's acceleration is dependent on the force applied to the vehicle during impact. Linear movement of the vehicle usually plays the most important role in front, side, and rear collisions; occupant movement in these cases is in line with the PDOF applied to the occupant vehicle. The accident reconstructionist will use the impulse equation, the energy equation, or a combination of these two approaches (i.e., MER; the momentum-energy-restitution approach). The reader is referred to Watts (2003) for a discussion of vehicle dynamics related to impact over a broad range of vehicle dynamics (low and high). Vehicle dynamics related to vehicle performance, braking and automobile component performance are discussed in detail in Gillespie (1992) Watts, (2011) and Russell, (2014).

The automobile occupants will move directly toward the PDOF (negating the vehicle's angular motion). The magnitude of the occupant acceleration vector is dependent on the force vector applied to the occupant's vehicle during impact.

The occupant's motion may lead to a second collision when he or she contacts a structure within the vehicle such as the dashboard or steering wheel; this second collision is largely responsible for occupant injury. Restraint systems, such as airbags, seat belts, or seat backs will reduce the average and peak acceleration levels applied to the occupant and in many cases may reduce or eliminate injury resulting from this second impact. This relates to the previous discussion in that deforming restraints or airbags absorb (extract) kinetic energy during human body impact (energy equation), and the time over which the human body's momentum is brought to zero (impulse equation) is increased by three-point restraints or airbags with a resulting decrease in the average and peak reaction forces compared to body contact with stiff vehicle interior compartment structures. (Figure 4.2)

The National Highway Traffic Safety Administration conducts many types of "crash tests." One test, the New Car Assessment Program test (NCAP test), will serve to illustrate the basic principles of vehicle crashes. The NCAP test produces an "equivalent barrier velocity" (EBV) of approximately 35 mph. The delta-velocity (i.e., change in velocity) may be slightly higher due to bounce back of the vehicle from the stationary barrier. The motor vehicle will come to an abrupt stop over approximately 100–120 ms (Hyde, 1992). Forward movement of the occupants takes place toward the PDOF and is simply the result of Newton's first law of motion. A good deal of vehicle crush (AE) will occur before any significant movement of the occupants takes place (relative to the vehicle). Newer vehicles make use of engineering advances to maximize the total crush but still avoid crush intrusion into the occupant compartment. This engineering approach has the effect of slowing the vehicle in a less abrupt manner so as to reduce the vehicle deceleration profile. The front bumper may collapse quite easily initially. As the vehicle frame and upper vehicle body structures are loaded, structural stiffness may increase. However, built-in crush zones act as force limiting structures and therefore become deceleration limiting. Kinetic energy is extracted during this crush deformation process. Furthermore, components, such as the engine, are placed in such a position so as to drop down out of the way during a frontal crash. Initially during the last part of vehicle crush at approximately 60 ms post-impact, the vehicle and the occupants are still both moving forward relative to the ground. The knees of the driver occupant may and usually do strike the dash in front as occupant-vehicle differential motion occurs. However, note that in the past four years many vehicles have introduced knee airbags in many vehicle models in order to provide increased protection from knee, thigh and hip trauma. An unrestrained driver occupant without an airbag will continue forward and strike the steering wheel at approximately 75 ms (Hyde, 1992). The head of an unrestrained occupant will continue forward, striking the front vehicle windshield or the windshield header. This head strike will occur after the vehicle has come to a stop, and the head of the unrestrained occupant may experience a very high acceleration level in a header contact (Hyde, 1992). Please note that these times are approximations and will vary from one vehicle to another. Other factors such as restraint system slack, seat position, the occupant layout volume (flail space), occupant posture, occupant height or weight, and occupant muscle bracing may all affect the occupant kinematics and subsequent loading for restrained or unrestrained occupants (Hyde, 1992). (Figure 4.3) Furthermore, new advances in safety and technology serve to significantly reduce occupant loading in vehicle collisions.

Angular motion of the vehicle around one or as many

Figure 4.3 The unrestrained driver occupant continues forward in accord with Newton's first law of motion and, in a high-speed impact, will strike interior compartment structures within the vehicle. (Courtesy of Patrick Hannon)

Figure 4.2 The occupant moves toward the PDOF applied to his vehicle in accord with Newton's first law of motion. (Courtesy of Robert Perry)

as three principal axes (e.g., rollover sequence) of the vehicle may also play a part in dictating occupant movement within the vehicle. The principal problem in angular motion vehicle dynamics is that these angular vectors may produce unrestrained occupant contacts within the vehicle (second collisions) that result in high linear decelerations (deceleration vectors), producing body injury. Unrestrained occupants may also be ejected or partially ejected from the vehicle during vehicle rollovers, which increases the probability of injury or death. Finally, a high angular acceleration of the human body's head link, in a high-speed frontal collision for example, may produce neck, brain stem, and brain injury with or without head-neck to vehicle interior structure contact. The mechanism of injury in these cases is due to the angular inertia of the head link. Specific head and brain injuries in this regard are addressed in Chapter 9.

B. Watercraft impacts

These vehicles are subject to the same three laws of motion as automobile accidents. However, very little data exist for boating accidents, and many fatalities are from drowning after an impact or from the boat's capsizing. When a boat strikes a stiff barrier at a high speed, the occupants, in accordance with Newton's First Law of Motion, will move toward the PDOF. Because boat occupants are usually unrestrained, ejection in moderate and high-delta velocity impacts are common. In many boats, a clear exit is available to the water's surface for the occupants and injury may be avoided or relatively minor during watercraft exit without interior compartment contact. If the occupants land in the water, the human body's momentum is brought to zero over a relatively long time period and reaction loads applied to the body are necessarily reduced. Striking another boat (bullet vehicle) or a horizontal barrier, on the other hand, will result in high deceleration loads in the same fashion as being ejected from an automobile and striking a solid upright structure.

Furthermore, watercraft are not designed to absorb large amounts of kinetic energy at impact in large part because high-speed impacts between two watercraft or of watercraft into fixed barriers are relatively infrequent; occupants are usually unrestrained and therefore not able to make good use of absorbed energy and the force limiting crush of the watercraft. The reader is referred to Hickman and Sampsel (2002) as a good source of information in watercraft accidents.

C. Aircraft impacts

These accidents usually occur at higher speeds and are the result of (1) takeoff and landing activity and (2) impact with the ground or more vertical terrain such as a mountain. Direct impact with mountains at aircraft speeds is generally not survivable regardless of standard passenger aircraft lap belts or even five point restraint use. The delta velocity and the resulting decelerations are simply too high to permit survival. However, landing and takeoff accidents may be survivable depending on a number of factors. For example a near horizontal skid down the runway presents a long duration deceleration of the aircraft but a deceleration of relatively low magnitude.

Aircraft accidents present deceleration impulses that may be quite variable in terms of direction and magnitude, and therefore occupant loading varies considerably. Aircraft design attempts to integrate factors of energy absorption in impact events while maintaining a minimal total aircraft weight. The solution is a compromise of these two factors. Furthermore, a crash may result in a fire initially beginning with aircraft fuel and this presents a significant danger to crew and passengers.

The United States Air Force has been a leader in investigating aircraft occupant biomechanics. Much of this work is the result of research efforts at the former Biodynamics Laboratory at Wright-Patterson Air Force Base in Dayton, Ohio. The reader is referred to McCormick and Papadakis (2003) for a comprehensive discussion of aircraft accident reconstruction.

D. Bicycle and motorcycle impacts

These accidents fall into two major categories: single vehicle and two vehicle accidents. A single vehicle accident, where a bicycle or motorcycle is "put down" resulting from a loss of control, may present minimal loading to the occupant rider. The reason is that horizontal momentum and vertical momentum are orthogonal vectors and as such are independent of one another. On a relatively flat surface, the horizontal momentum is not the major concern unless a vertical wall is struck which would rapidly reduce one's momentum to zero. Rather, on a flat pavement surface, frictional forces are of some concern to a human body with a high horizontal momentum and these forces may result in severe road rash. However, in terms of impact loading, dropping to the pavement represents a relatively short fall, and therefore in accord with the vertical velocity equation ($V_v = \sqrt{2gh}$), a large vertical momentum is not acquired before ground contact. A tip over fall on a bicycle or motorcycle to one side increases the vertical velocity and therefore linear momentum. Vertical velocity during a tip over may be estimated by the equation ($V_v = \sqrt{3gh}$). In both a free fall, or more likely tip over falls, the unhelmeted bicycle or motorcycle occupant may still experience life threatening brain injury in a 1.0 to 2.0 meter fall to a stiff ground surface. This author has been involved in many cases involving skull/brain and hip injuries from such falls.

The human body's horizontal velocity momentum may be substantial if the initial speed is high when the vehicle is put down (e.g., low side fall). However, it is important to appreciate that the bicyclist or motorcyclist may not be exposed to any large deceleration impulses along the pavement during sliding or tumbling. Aside from very severe road rash (without protective clothing), injury may be minimal in this type of single vehicle crash. (Figure 4.4)

Wearing "leathers" provides considerable protection in regard to this body friction-induced road rash. On the other hand, if any fixed barrier (or an automobile) is struck by the cyclist who is moving horizontally at a higher speed, then the horizontal momentum will be dramatically reduced quickly, with a consequent increase in the deceleration impulse and an increase in the injury profile. Furthermore, in what are termed "high side" falls in motorcycling, a motorcycle rider may be ejected to a point of considerable height with consequent increased linear and angular momentums at ground impact.

In a bicycle or motorcycle collision involving two vehicles, the mass ratio favors the larger automobile or truck vehicle. Therefore, the transfer of momentum to the rider occupant and his bike is substantial. Furthermore, bicycles and motorcycles are not designed to absorb large amounts of energy. On a bicycle or motorcycle, it is simply best for the rider occupant to avoid the collision. During such a collision at moderate to high speeds, the loading to the occupant may be enormous with little protection for the rider occupant. However, the use of helmets by cyclists is an obviously important protective mechanism, and head injury remains the principal life threatening loading mechanism to the motorcyclist or bicyclist. Helmet protection is discussed in Chapter 9.

The reader is referred to Obenski and Hill (2003) and Broker and Hottman, (2016) for information addressing motorcycle accident reconstruction.

4.4 Pedestrian Impacts

In a collision involving a motor vehicle-pedestrian interaction, again the mass ratio dramatically favors the large vehicle. In almost all cases, the pedestrian does not reduce (significant reduction) the momentum of the motor vehicle. In the worst case scenario for the pedestrian, his or her mass is taken up to the level and direction of the motor vehicle's

Figure 4.4 The motorcyclist drops approximately 3.5 feet after being ejected from his motorcycle. His center of gravity vertical velocity will be 15.0 ft/sec. He is moving horizontally along the road surface at approximately 50 mph or 73 ft/s. Note the gross disparity between his vertical and horizontal velocities which are orthogonal (right angles) to one another. (Courtesy of Robert Perry)

velocity vector immediately. Under these conditions, high acceleration levels will be imposed upon the pedestrian. These high acceleration levels, combined with some focal point contacts with the vehicle, will result in significant human body deformation and may involve catastrophic trauma or a certain fatality. Sharp forward hood edges of motor vehicles have been known to actually sever the human body in half at high speed impacts. At the other end of the continuum, the vehicle in braking may almost be at a stop and the pedestrian may experience only a slight bump or the impact may involve the pedestrian simply pushing against the hood with outstretched arms-hands.

Pedestrian impacts may involve several "trajectories." As one might suppose, the height of the pedestrian and the configuration of the leading edge of the motor vehicle, in addition to the vehicle's speed and mass, will affect these pedestrian trajectories and the resulting injury to pedestrians.

The kinematics have been categorized into five trajectory descriptions: fender vault, roof vault, wrap, forward projection, and the somersault (Ravani, Brougham and Mason, 1981).

A. Fender vault trajectory

The fender vault trajectory is described in Figure 4.5 and occurs when an adult pedestrian is struck by the fender of a conventional passenger vehicle. Because of the angle of impact, the pedestrian usually ends up behind and to the side of the striking vehicle. If the striking vehicle is braking before impact, the pedestrian will usually move over the fender and then fall to the ground. If the vehicle does not brake pre-impact, the pedestrian is more likely to wrap and slide over the hood, incurring injury to upper body structures during contact with the vehicle hood and windshield, in addition to the lower extremity injuries resulting from the initial impact (Ravani et al., 1981). Ravani et al. (1981) reported in their epidemiology study that the average speed at impact was approximately 40 km/hr in cases of fender vault.

B. Roof vault trajectory

The roof vault (Figure 4.6) involves the pedestrian passing over the hood, windshield, and roof of the striking vehicle and subsequently landing behind the vehicle. Two prerequisites are necessary for this trajectory. The first is that the height of the center of gravity of the pedestrian must be above the leading hood edge of the striking vehicle. Therefore, vehicles with front box-like configurations, such as many sport utility vehicles, will not result in this roof vault trajectory. The second prerequisite factor is that no significant braking takes place previous to or during the impact contact. A high speed vehicle intentional homicide is just one example of what may result in a pedestrian roof vault. Ravani et al. (1981) reports that the average speed at impact in roof vault trajectories is approximately 60 km/hr and that this pedestrian trajectory was not observed in impacts involving a vehicle moving

at less than 32 km/hr at initial pedestrian impact. (Figures 4.5 and 4.6)

C. Wrap trajectory

The wrap trajectory generally occurs at lower impact speeds (average approximate 30 km/hr) (Ravani et al., 1981). In the wrap trajectory, the human body, in a sequential manner, will wrap around the leading configuration of the vehicle. This trajectory is illustrated in Figures 4.7a and 4.7b and may occur in situations where the pedestrian's center of gravity is above the hood height, in the example of an adult pedestrian, or below the hood height, as in the example of vehicle strike to a child. In this latter case, a wrap may occur when the forward bumper of some vehicle models strike a child below the waist and a tip mechanism provides enough elevation to bring part of the head and torso above the vehicle hood. The child pedestrian is very quickly brought up to the vehicle's speed which may, depending on vehicle impact speed, result in significant pedestrian injury.

In the wrap trajectory, the striking vehicle is braking during and after impact. Therefore, the pedestrian in accord with Newton's first law of motion will separate from the braking vehicle after the impact as the vehicle slows at a 0.5 to 0.8 g deceleration rate. Ravani et al. (1981) report that in most cases, the pedestrian will separate from the vehicle and will contact the roadway and suffer some abrasive ground injury on the same side of the body that

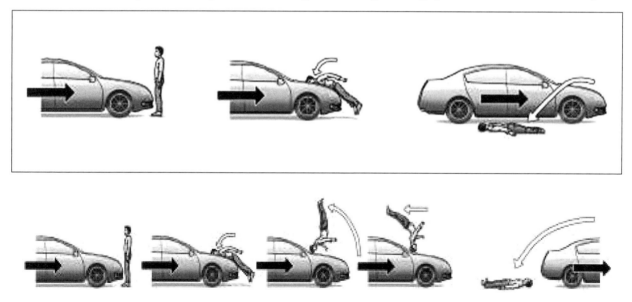

Figure 4.5 (top) The pedestrian fender vault trajectory. (Courtesy of Robert Perry)
Figure 4.6 (bottom) The pedestrian roof vault trajectory. (Courtesy of Robert Perry)

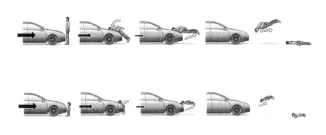

Figure 4.7a (top) The pedestrian wrap trajectory–adult. (Courtesy of Robert Perry)
Figure 4.7b (bottom) The pedestrian wrap trajectory–child. (Courtesy of Robert Perry)

experienced vehicle impact damage. Interestingly, Ravani et al. (1981) reports that in his sample of 109 cases of pedestrian wrap (the most common trajectory), contact with the windshield or cowl of the vehicle was not observed at impact speeds below 40 km/hr.

D. Forward projection trajectory

The forward projection trajectory according to Ravani et al. (1981) is the second most common pedestrian trajectory and occurs when the pedestrian's center of gravity is below the principal impact force vector (Figure 4.8). This impact trajectory is probably more common today with an increased number of sport utility vehicles in urban areas. This trajectory may also occur with small children who are struck by passenger vehicles. The torso, and the lower extremities, are accelerated in the direction of the vehicle impact and the body is then forward projected to the ground with ground induced impact and abrasion damage usually occurring on the body side opposite the body's impacted side. Ravani et al. (1981) indicate that the forward projection is also observed in taller pedestrians with their centers of gravity above the principal force vector when the vehicle impact speed is below 15 km/hr. In these cases, a wrap of the body does not occur because momentum transfer is insufficient to produce this result. Instead the body simply jackknifes over the hood and subsequently moves forward during vehicle deceleration braking striking the contralateral side of the body against the pavement.

Examination of body injuries may provide good evidence of the forward projection trajectory and credible evidence of vehicle impact side versus ground impact body side. As one might suppose, head and torso injuries are as frequent as lower extremity injuries in these forward projection trajectories.

In both fender vault and forward projection trajecto-

ries, newer vehicle designs with a front bumper and vehicle face that is curved outward may lead to a "wedge effect." When a pedestrian is struck off-center by the front of the vehicle with a convex forward bumper, a significant pedestrian body movement to the driver's side will also occur in addition to the forward projection movement. For example, in a frontal projection trajectory, a high speed strike primarily on the driver's side of a vehicle may project the pedestrian forward a hundred feet and also project the pedestrian's body to the driver's side 35 feet. The projection will be resolved into both forward and driver's side motion components as the result of this wedge effect resulting from the rounded front bumper and other front rounded components.

E. Somersault trajectory

Ravani et al. (1981) observed only four of 241 cases involving the somersault trajectory, which is similar to the wrap trajectory except with greater angular momentum. A partial or complete somersault may result, and a three-quarter somersault is illustrated in Figure 4.9. The increased angular momentum in this case is the result of a higher vehicle impact speed, again combined with a principal vehicle force vector below and eccentric to the pedestrian's center of gravity. Ravani et al. (1981) observed an approximate average of 60 km/hr in these four cases.

A research effort is being made to reduce pedestrian injuries by altering vehicle design in passenger cars. Vehicle hoods which are deformable, leading edges which are rounded, and deformable A-pillars may all contribute to a reduction in the severity of torso and head injuries. Injuries to the lower extremities, however, seem to occur with high frequency, regardless of energy absorbing bumpers, at speeds at and above 30 km/hr (Kallieris and Schmidt, 1988) and remain the most prevalent set of injuries in vehicle-pedestrian accidents.

Reduction or elimination of pedestrian impacts may also result from vehicles that are able to detect pedestrians in front of the vehicle. This detection and the computer controlled algorithms are then able to apply maximum vehicle braking with this artificial intelligence (AI) innovation. Presently, this new innovation is increasingly being implemented into new model vehicles to prevent collisions with pedestrians and vehicles. (Figures 4.8 and 4.9)

4.5 Seat Belt Restraint Use in Vehicles

The three-point restraint is in common use in passenger vehicles, sport utility vehicles, and light trucks. It consists of a lap belt and a shoulder strap with three anchor points usually secured to the floor and B pillar (the pillar at the back of the side window). The history and evolution of the three-point restraint is interesting, with the two-point lap belt developing first in the United States in the mid 1950s only to be followed by front seat outboard three-point restraints in 1968. In 1956, Volvo Corp. initially developed a two-point diagonal shoulder strap restraint (without a lap belt) for the European market, followed by a three-point restraint (lap and shoulder) in 1959. Volvo also developed a four-point restraint that was used in some selected European markets (Bohlin, 1990).

Seat belts are designed to prevent forceful contact with interior forward compartment structures during frontal impact, to limit excursion during opposite side impact, and finally to limit forceful contact with the roof structure during vehicle rollovers. Three-point restraints have a less beneficial effect on human kinematics during near-side and rear impacts. (Figure 4.10)

A complete discussion of how seat belts work to accomplish these objectives is important from a biomechanics perspective. Restraint effects may be discussed in a similar manner to our previous discussion of vehicle impacts. An energy approach illustrates these principles. In Figure 4.10a, a vehicle traveling at 35 mph has acquired kinetic energy (KE). During vehicle braking, the kinetic energy is extracted as work is performed on the impacting vehicle and the vehicle comes to a complete stop (measured at 3.17 seconds). Alternatively, the same vehicle without airbags is now involved in a fixed barrier collision and comes to an abrupt stop (Figure 4.10b). Because the vast majority of kinetic energy is not transferred away from the vehicle to a non-deforming barrier, work is only performed on the impacting vehicle. Consistent with the conservation of energy law, the previously acquired kinetic energy stays within the impacting vehicle and is transformed into mechanical energy of deformation (ignoring sound and heat energy lost) and work is measured by the barrier reaction force acting on the front of the vehicle over the distance that the reaction force acts (i.e., crush distance). In this latter case, the motor vehicle is deformed, extracting the mechanical energy and bringing the vehicle to a stop (Eppinger, 2002).

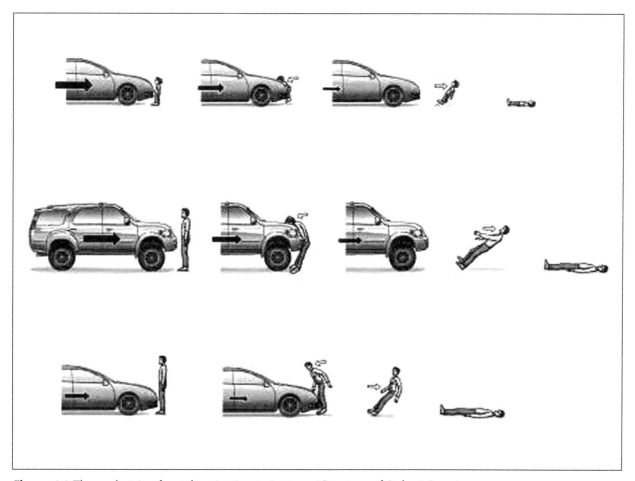

Figure 4.8 *The pedestrian frontal projection trajectory. (Courtesy of Robert Perry)*

The restraint system is designed to eliminate the second impact (body impact with an interior compartment structure) and modify the loading during the deceleration event. In Figure 4.11, the braking and the collision response are again contrasted in terms of the occupant response. In both cases, the end result is that the KE of the unrestrained occupant's body is completely absorbed. However, in the barrier example, the vehicle crush at barrier impact has already extracted the kinetic energy in this collision and the vehicle is no longer moving over ground (Eppinger, 2002). The still moving unrestrained occupant with his acquired KE now strikes interior compartment structures which are not moving and relatively stiff (exception being the energy-absorbing flexible steering wheel column). The reaction forces from these stiff structures that are imposed upon the occupant to bring his forward velocity to zero are very large, with consequent large accelerations, significant body deformation (work = F x d), and injury. Eppinger (2002) contrasts the vehicle and occupant acceleration

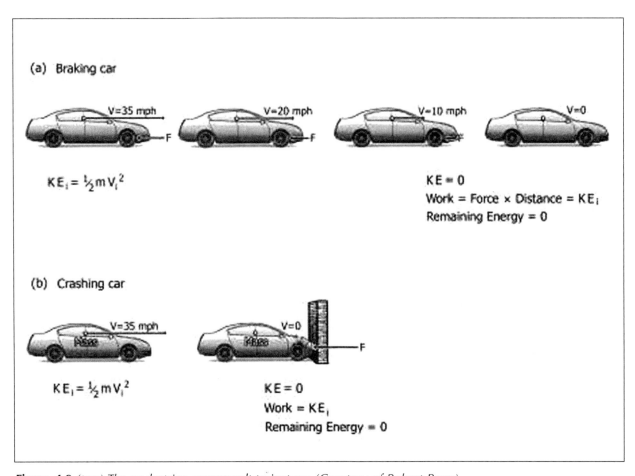

Figure 4.9 (top) *The pedestrian somersault trajectory. (Courtesy of Robert Perry)*
Figure 4.10 (bottom) *(a) During vehicle braking a small force over a long distance performs work on the moving vehicle to bring it to a stop. (b) is an impact example, the vehicle's kinetic energy is transformed into absorbed energy during the crush deformation of the vehicle. Work is performed on the vehicle (force × distance) as kinetic energy is extracted by the crush of the vehicle. (Courtesy of Robert Perry)*

profile (time-velocity curves) of: (1) the simple standard braking response, (2) a collision with an unrestrained occupant, and (3) the collision with a restrained occupant. The typical hard braking response on the velocity-time axes may yield a 0.5 to 0.75 g level applied to the vehicle with approximately the same g level applied to the occupant, as illustrated in Figure 4.12. Obviously no injury occurs during this braking event example.

The example of an unrestrained occupant in an older model vehicle without air bags at the same delta velocity level of 35 mph yields an average 19.8 g deceleration of the vehicle during a crash and subsequent stop of the vehicle. This example illustrates that the vehicle has moved forward 25 inches over the ground (crush) as it comes to a stop as work is performed on the vehicle. The occupant without restraining belt forces continues in a forward direction at 35 mph (Newton I) and impacts the dash. If one assumes that the dash was initially 20 inches in front of the occupant, a total of 45 inches of occupant over ground forward translation motion occurs at occupant dash impact (25 inches vehicle over ground motion plus 20 inches for the occupant to translate into the dashboard) without any reduction in the occupant's KE, (ignoring muscle bracing forces). If the deformation of his body and the dash only allows for an additional 3.0 inches of deformation as the occupant is brought to zero forward velocity and his body's KE now equals zero, an impulse is applied to the occupant over 10 ms at an average g level of 158.7 g. (Figure 4.13; adapted from Eppinger, 2002). This loading level to the occupant has the highest probability of producing upper torso and head injury which are at a life-threatening level. (Figures 4.11, 4.12, 4.13)

However, if a standard three-point restraint is applied to the occupant as soon as the occupant has moved forward only eleven inches (belt strap slack) and therefore begins to decelerate the occupant, the acceleration profile from the time-velocity graph brings the occupant's average g level down to a more manageable level (22.7 g) over 70 ms (40 ms to 110 ms) and although injury will still occur, the severity of the injury is reduced (Figure 4.14) from the previous example. (Figure 4.13) In this case, the occupant ends his deceleration and comes to a stop 30 ms later than the vehicle and is decelerated over approximately 22 inches. Note that in this restrained occupant case, the occupant still begins his deceleration 40 ms later than the vehicle and moves an additional 11 inches further over ground before his deceleration begins. This factor serves to increase the deceleration level of the occupant above the vehicle deceleration in this

hypothetical example (occupant = 22.7 average g versus vehicle = 19.8 average g). Note that this average acceleration of 22.7 g applied to the restrained occupant may only represent about one half of the peak deceleration applied. However, the peak acceleration is applied over a short time period, and therefore the integrated acceleration x time impulse presents manageable loading to the restrained occupant.

The absolute ideal restraint system would begin and end the occupant deceleration profile coincident with (or briefly beyond) the vehicle deceleration profile. Belt restraints that deploy within a very few milliseconds of the initial crash create an optimum restraint for the occupant(s) (Zellmer et al. 2005). This is not possible at present given current restraint systems and may never be possible. One should note, however, that an approximation of this ideal restraint system would be of significant

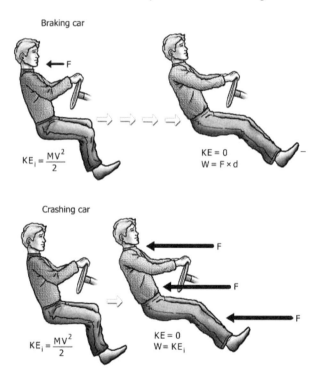

Figure 4.11 *Small forces are imposed upon the unrestrained occupant during braking to extract the KE of the vehicle and the occupant. Work is performed upon the occupant during the braking event (small force over a long distance). In the collision event, a large reaction force applied to the unrestrained occupant's body over a short distance results in a deforming structure (e.g., dash). The occupant's KE is extracted (i.e., work) with consequent damage to the steering wheel and dash and injury to the occupant. (Courtesy of Robert Perry)*

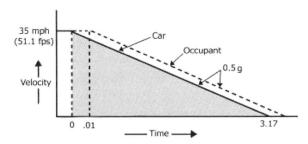

Figure 4.12 *An approximate 0.5 g deceleration is applied to the vehicle and its occupant during a hard breaking response. (Courtesy of Robert Perry)*

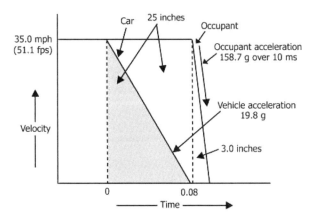

Figure 4.13 *The vehicle deformation results in an average g level of 19.8 g. In contrast, the velocity-time graph illustrates that the unrestrained occupant decelerates over 10 ms in time and 3.0 inches distance as the average acceleration level applied to his body equals approximately 158.7 g, producing a fatal injury. (Courtesy of Robert Perry)*

value to vehicle occupants, and such a system would lengthen further the deceleration time over which belt reaction forces act and therefore reduce the magnitude of these reaction forces with a consequent elimination or reduction of occupant injury in many cases. This is the rationale behind using pretensioning seat belts which by various mechanisms reel in the restraint system slack when a collision vector of the appropriate magnitude and direction is imposed upon a vehicle. These pretensioning belts do not jerk the torso backward, but rather provide a rapidly applied tension force that takes out the slack of the torso strap before forward occupant movement takes place in a frontal collision. (Figure 4.14)

Watts (2003) makes the point that the "fixed" three-point restraints of the late '60s and '70s performed better

than the "standard three-point restraints" in the 1990s. Belt restraints that are loose and lock up in response to inertial or spool out locking mechanisms apply restraint forces later during the collision event and were not developed to provide more occupant protection but rather with the rationale of increasing occupant use compliance. The old fixed three-point restraints that buckled and were always locked, if worn appropriately with little slack, began to restrain the occupants much earlier within the collision time frame and therefore provided better ride down as the belt straps stretched during vehicle deceleration in a significant frontal collision. Finally, more sophisticated seatbelt restraints in addition to the pretensioning feature also act in a force limiting function. These restraint mechanisms incorporate a device that allows for additional spool out of the shoulder belt strap when peak force levels reach a specific critical force magnitude and thereby eliminate or reduce additional increases in belt strap reaction loads. These restraint systems have become the standard for front seat occupants and are now being applied to rear seat occupants as well. However, it remains a biomechanics challenge to construct a load limiting restraint device that permits greater occupant forward excursion and yet prohibits occupant contact with vehicle interior compartment structures.

In addition to reducing reaction forces, occupant deceleration rate, and occupant tissue deformation produced by contact with stiff interior compartment structures, the three-point restraint has other significant values. A three-point, four-point, or five-point restraint system distributes the reaction force load over a larger area and results in lower compression stresses imposed

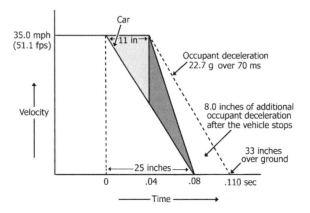

Figure 4.14 *The velocity-time graph illustrates that the restrained occupant decelerates over 70 ms in time as the average g level applied to his body equals approximately 22.7 g over a distance of 22 inches with reduced injury. (Courtesy of Robert Perry)*

upon the body (compressive stress = compressive load ÷ compression area). An ideal belt performance would distribute a load over a large belt contact surface area. Increased area results in decreased average and peak compressive stresses. This is the approach involved in five-point restraints that are used in auto racing and the belt straps are quite wide. It should be emphasized that these five-point restraints also minimize torso movement to a greater degree because the belt slack is at an absolute minimum during the racing event. In similar fashion, inflatable belt restraint prototypes in development through the United States Air Force Office of Scientific Research (AFOSR) have been shown to be of some value primarily because they increase the belt strap surface area in contact with the body and they provide substantive restraint sooner in the collision event by significantly extending the torso impact delta time and therefore reducing load magnitudes.

Eppinger (2002) further points out that a belt system should be able to change direction during forward movement of the body. This is illustrated in Figure 4.15. Load distribution (increased belt strap-body area) increases as a change in belt direction allows for an increase in belt strap restraining tension (magnitude).

The three-point restraint system will also distribute forces over relatively hard bony structures, such as the anterior-superior pelvis (lap belt) or multiple ribs (shoulder strap), and therefore avoid placing significant stresses over areas that are not well protected. Finally, the ability of a belt system to change direction will affect the excursion displacement of various anatomical body regions. Figure 4.16 illustrates how the largest belt reaction load is shifted from the abdominal area to the shoulder area during later torso forward displacement. Therefore, deep organ systems within the abdominal area are better protected, albeit with increased loading to the clavicle bone and the shoulder girdle joints (acromioclavicular and sternoclavicular joints).

Furthermore, the shoulder strap component of the three-point restraint will significantly limit the forward bending excursion of the torso and therefore protect the lumbar and sacral spine by limiting lower spine flexion. Significant lower spine injury would not be expected to occur, excepting muscle strains. The lap belt of the three-point restraint should be placed across the anterior-superior iliac spines (ASIS) of the occupant. The net result is that the lap belt position will restrain the pelvis and limit the lower torso movement forward and upward. Vaulting upward and forward is reduced in a seat belt restrained condition regardless of occupant upper or lower extremity bracing. (Figure 4.17)

Body size and composition may also affect the effectiveness of a restraint system. Increased body mass will increase the loading to the three-point restraint, and this factor alone may result in a greater forward excursion of the torso in the old standard three-point belt system (Eppinger, 1976). However, the current pretensioning three-point restraint belt systems will rarely be brought to a failure point under these circumstances. Increased superficial adipose (fat) tissue or muscle tissue will act to absorb energy during tissue deformation (AE) and will serve to decrease the average reaction force loads

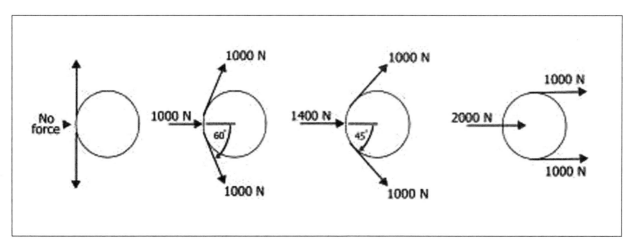

Figure 4.15 Forward movement of the body changes the wrap angle and increases the length of belt applied to the body in this schematic representation of a belt-body restraint. This has the effect of increasing the total belt area and decreasing the average and peak compression stresses applied to the body. However, in this case there may be some small increase in the compressive loads applied to the spine with a greater resolved force component applied coincident with the spinal column of the occupant. *(Courtesy of Robert Perry)*

applied to a body with increased soft tissues between the body and the torso belt. The strain and consequent injury to superficial adipose tissue will actually serve to decrease the loading to deeper critical organ structures. For example, an obese individual with excess fat tissue coming into early contact with a safety belt serves to decrease the compressive load and consequent compressive deformation of deep organ structures. Rather than increasing the risk of injury, this obesity variable serves to decrease the risk of injury to organ structures such as the liver or the ascending and descending portions of the colon.

Our discussion has focused on three-point restraints without air bags. This discussion is still applicable to the vast majority of rear seat occupant restraint systems. However, clearly advanced airbag systems along with advanced pretensioning-load limiting belt restraints are now in current use in 2019. (Figures 4.16 , 4.17)

4.6 Air Bags and Air Curtains

Air bags offer inflatable padding to absorb occupant energy during impact to bring occupant momentums to zero over a longer time frame and to distribute compressive loads over a larger area and therefore reduce compressive stresses. Watts (2003) argues that frontal air bags would not have been necessary if it were not for the fact that current standard three-point restraint systems are not fixed systems. However, the epidemiological evidence over the past 25 years and new smart air bags clearly argue in favor of this technology.

Air bags are most effective when combined with the three-point belt restraint system as evidenced by the epidemiological data in frontal collisions. The frontal airbag is not as effective in reducing torso and head injury in unrestrained occupants. Furthermore, air bags are of only moderate value over and above current three-point restraint systems in severe frontal collisions. Please note however that the standard three-point restraint alone allows considerable head excursion, which in a severe frontal collision may result in head and cervical spine injury. Nevertheless, especially in vehicles that are not equipped with pretensioning three-point restraints for the driver and front passenger occupants, air bags will prevent head and torso impact with forward compartment structures, such as the steering wheel or dashboard, during moderate to severe frontal impact. Please note that the frontal airbag by means of its positive gas pressure is able to mitigate the motion of the head link around cervical spine axes and therefore protect the cervical spine in addition to providing protection to the face and head, albeit sometimes with facial injury, eye injury, minor burns, etc.

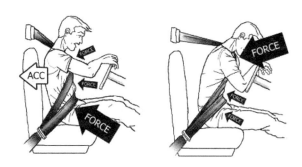

Figure 4.16 *The load (force) vector applied to the shoulder region of the occupant is increased and the load vector applied to the abdominal region is decreased during forward motion of the occupant. (Courtesy of Robert Perry)*

Figure 4.17 *Vaulting of the occupant is arrested by the lap belt portion of the three-point restraint. (Courtesy of Robert Perry)*

A. Front air bags

It is important to note that front air bags fully deploy within 25–50 ms and before significant (if any) occupant forward motion takes place. Therefore, they are not a significant loading threat to the head or torso unless these human body structures are already within the deployment zone at the time of the forward impact. If the airbag begins deployment with the occupant in the deployment zone, then the airbag may produce an inflation force that can produce death or serious injury (inflation induced injury; Melvin and Mertz, 2002). Individuals of small stature and infants in child seats are at greater risk for airbag-induced injury to head and torso structures. Depowering the inflators (a voluntary modification of FMVSS 208) has been one approach taken by manufacturers to reduce these inflation forces to occupants during less severe frontal impacts and when the driver occupant is of small stature. This approach results in the air bags being filled slower and using bags which inflate to a reduced depth (Melvin and Mertz, 2002). Other approaches include the automatic depowering or deactivation of an airbag if the weight load sensor within the seat pan indicates a small child or when infrared or radar sensors detect a passenger occupant body that is in close proximity to the dashboard.

Finally, it should be noted that there have been reports of more serious facial and eye (cornea) abrasions as well as fracture of the radius and ulna in the forearm due to airbag deployment in average or large adults who were in three-point restraints. New systems are in development to address a number of these safety concerns.

B. Side air bags

Side air bags and side air curtains provide some protection in near side impacts by the same mechanisms listed above. These supplemental restraint systems have in some vehicles been programmed to trigger during rollover as well as during side impact. These air bags must deploy faster, and in the case of side air curtains, they have been designed to remain inflated for a longer period of time because some rollovers involve multiple ground strikes and an increased number of consequent impulses applied to the vehicle.

Finally, in cases of an impact producing severe intrusion deformation of the door panel into the near side occupant compartment, side air bags (as well as belt restraint systems) have very limited value, as might be expected. Side impact reinforcement structures limit interior compartment intrusion providing occupant protection and

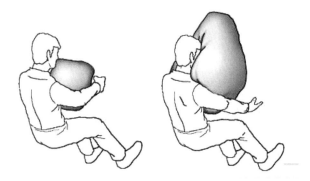

Figure 4.18 *The human figure moves into the frontal air bag which increases the time over which the occupant's head and upper torso are brought to zero momentum and increases the distance over which work is performed to absorb the occupant's KE with a consequent reduction in reaction force applied to the head and upper torso (work = force ×distance = KE). (Courtesy of Robert Perry)*

complement side impact air bag deployment in the side impact crash environment.

4.7 Gunshot Wounds—Ballistics-Impact-Penetration Trauma

Ballistics is a study of the mechanics of projectiles and may be divided into three areas:

1) Interior ballistics which address the performance of missiles in the gun barrel. This only applies to missiles that are fired by barreled weapons including pistols, rifles or artillery weapons.

2) Exterior ballistics is the study of missiles through a medium (usually air) and includes bullets, bullet fragments, and fragments of bombs grenades, etc.

3) Terminal ballistics is the study of missiles or fragments and their penetration properties. Wound ballistics is a subdivision of terminal ballistics and is most important in terms of our forensic biomechanics discussion (Belkin, 1978).

Our discussion of ballistics in this text is limited to small arms such as pistols and rifles, shotguns, etc., which project non-exploding missiles. In section 4.8 following, I address explosions due to bombs, exploding projectiles, etc.

A. Internal ballistics

Briefly, interior ballistics is determined by the weapon and its ammunition. Excepting shot guns, we refer to the projectile itself as a bullet. The bullet is a component of the modern centerfire cartridge which also includes the metallic case, the propellant, the rim and the primer which ignites the propellant. The caliber of a bullet is the diameter of the bullet or bore (interior diameter) of a firearm. To convert caliber to millimeters when describing a firearm simply divide the caliber by four (e.g., 45 caliber = 11.25 mm bullet).

Modern rifles for example impart a spin on the bullet projectile as it moves down the barrel which serves to increase the stability of the projectile and therefore improve accuracy through an air medium. Ballistics authorities do not refer to this spin around the long axis of the bullet as yaw as we might in biomechanics or engineering. Rather, bullet yaw is around a vertical axis perpendicular to the ground and passes through a bullet from side to side. Bullet yaw in flight is undesirable due to an increase in air drag and consequent wobble. Bullet spin produces a desirable result of bullet gyroscopic stability which eliminates or limits the tumbling or yaw of the projectile bullet and makes it more resistant to air drag and lift effects during the exterior ballistics (Belkin, 1978). In effect, twist of the bullet projectile is imparted by means of a machined helical groove pattern within the rifle barrel. This helical grooved barrel interior usually does not begin at the beginning (i.e., throat) of the barrel, in order to make the most effective use of the chemical combustion propellant and maximize the initial gain in linear momentum as the missile bullet is being accelerated. This is known as the "freebore" area of the barrel. The bullet then transitions into the helical rifled portion of the barrel which serves to impart the spin and increase the angular momentum which continues as the bullet leaves the barrel. Interestingly, this is another example of how a large angular (spin) momentum is preserved and the external ballistics become more accurate. Another example is that of a football forward pass by the quarterback. A football with a high rate of spin at release from the quarterback's hand is much more likely to be an accurate pass compared to a wobbling football throw. Some small arms pistols also make use of similar machining by means of polygonal rifling within the much shorter barrel. Shotguns do not make use of this effect and therefore this is one reason that the spherical shot during external ballistics are disbursed over a relatively greater area when fired from a distance which is desirable in bird hunting but not for precise targeted use of munitions force.

B. Missile mass and speed (external ballistics)

Small firearms may release bullets at barrel exit at speeds under 200 meters per second to over 1,000 meters/second for weapon grade small arms. As stated earlier in this text, "linear momentum" = mass x velocity. Both factors, mass and velocity, therefore may increase linear momentum when both the mass and the velocity are increased. However, linear momentum is not the key variable for human trauma in small arm munitions. Linear momentum of the bullet has a minimal impact effect upon the human body and the depiction of a human body being blown back against a wall or the human head, arms or torso moving in a flailing manner due to rapid fire 9mm or even a .45 caliber round (bullet mass of 14.9 grams) is pure fiction and is Hollywood's version of "fake news." This is perhaps forgivable and may be attributed to Hollywood's poetic license but importantly small arm bullets do not produce this result. Unlike artillery missiles, the momentum is too low for bullets with masses of 3.5 to 15 grams to impart large impact momentums regardless of the magnitude of present bullet speeds. Instead bullets impart a great deal of energy and power and these are the key factors in both hard and soft tissue human gunshot trauma. The energy

factor is most important and is comprised of both linear and rotational energy (both vector quantities). When a bullet penetrates the human body, the energy is determined by 1) linear kinetic energy = 1/2 mass x velocity^2 and 2) rotational kinetic energy $KE= 1/2 \ I \ x \ \omega^2$ imparted by the spin of the bullet. Another factor of some importance is that a penetrating bullet that does not exit the body releases all of its energy into the body. However, if the bullet exits, it may be termed a perforating injury and the bullet retains some of its kinetic energy until it strikes another object such as a wall. Therefore: kinetic energy applied to the body is $KE= mass \ x \ (Vi^2 - Vr^2) \ /2$. Note that Vi = impact energy and Vr = residual energy.

C. Wound (terminal) ballistics

Our focus in ballistics is wounding of the human body which in some cases results in a fatality. Bullets do damage by a combination of mechanisms depending upon the type of bullet and most importantly, its speed or velocity. The first mechanism is by means of crushing and laceration of tissues as the bullet passes through the human body. In most civilian gunshot wounds, this mechanism of injury is predominant in most body areas (Adams, 1982). Furthermore, a bullet that strikes a body bone may produce an explosive comminuted fracture due to the high kinetic energy imparted to a skeletal bone.

The second mechanism of injury is the shock wave described in more detail in Section 4.8. This shock wave is a very important factor in head/brain injuries where the bullet penetrates and may perforate the skull. The skull is a relatively closed container and the bullet will create a shock wave that will compress the brain matter in front and at all sides of the bullet travel path, with additional enhanced shock wave effects due to the reflection off of interior skull walls.

The third mechanism of injury is that of the cavitation effect and is similar to the blast wind discussed in Section 4.8. Cavitation is the result of the positive pressure wave which accelerates tissue (e.g., brain neuron and glia cells) away from the bullet. Larger cavities are created within tissue such as brain tissue when the bullet speed/velocity is very high. When brain tissue moves away from the bullet and the bullet moves forward of the created cavity, a negative subatmospheric pressure develops and the cavity rapidly fills in with brain tissue. However, the damage and disruption are already complete. Created cavities are therefore temporary and the entire cavitation process may be over in 10 to 25 microseconds with volume pressure increases close to the bullet's path of over 1000 psi (Adams, 1982). The bullet track will remain but the cavity itself is now absent. One important point is that both the shock wave and the cavitation effect produce tissue injury a significant distance from the bullet's path or tract. This is important in forensic biomechanics and forensic pathology. Adams (1982) states that "Thus, the inspection of the missile [bullet] tract after injury gives little indication of the violent distortion produced by the high velocity missile [bullet]", p. 833. Another example of cavitation is that of a high speed bullet striking a fluid and/or air filled set of organs within the abdomen. Early experiments have made use of an animal model and exposure of the abdomen to a high velocity bullet projectile. High speed cineradiography revealed that the abdomen enlarges within one to two milliseconds which is followed by a second abdominal expansion which is less intense but of longer duration. Again, during cavity formation, cineradiography images measured in microseconds show that gas and/or liquid filled organs temporarily enlarge with the net result, for example. of multiple intestinal perforations a significant distance away from the bullet tract (Adams, 1982). Adams (1982) further states that the explosive cavity within air filled abdominal organs result in "displaced viscera, tears [in] mesenteries, and ruptures [of] blood

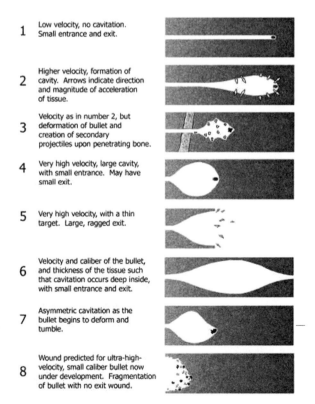

1 Low velocity, no cavitation. Small entrance and exit.

2 Higher velocity, formation of cavity. Arrows indicate direction and magnitude of acceleration of tissue.

3 Velocity as in number 2, but deformation of bullet and creation of secondary projectiles upon penetrating bone.

4 Very high velocity, large cavity, with small entrance. May have small exit.

5 Very high velocity, with a thin target. Large, ragged exit.

6 Velocity and caliber of the bullet, and thickness of the tissue such that cavitation occurs deep inside, with small entrance and exit.

7 Asymmetric cavitation as the bullet begins to deform and tumble.

8 Wound predicted for ultra-high-velocity, small caliber bullet now under development. Fragmentation of bullet with no exit wound.

Figure 4.19 *Ballistic effects on animal tissue. (Adapted from Swan and Swan, 1989 in Zernicke and Whiting, 1998.)*

vessels away from the bullet tract" (p. 833). It should be emphasized that the entire scope of abdominal or thoracic gunshot wounds is the result of all three mechanisms of injury discussed previously.

More detailed information regarding ballistic physics, bullet path trajectories within a room or through a human body and recent developments may be found in Decker et al., (2017), Wang, (2018), DiMaio and DiMaio (2001) and Spitz and Fisher (2006).

4.8 Explosions/Blasts

Explosions result from a rapid release of energy. The release of energy frequently results from a chemical reaction but it may also result from pressurized steam in a boiler, a volcano (steam or magma) or a thermonuclear device. Certainly, mechanical failure of a steam boiler or pressure cooker leading to personal injury will lead to many of the same effects as a chemical explosion; albeit on a much smaller scale. The discussion of chemical explosions which follows still has some application to smaller explosion personal injury product failure "non-chemical" explosions that may happen in a factory or at home. Explosions may be the result of accidents (majority of litigation) or may be deliberate as in acts of terror or warfare.

Harris (2014) estimated that 151 of 162 countries were involved in some form of conflict with the remaining 11 countries at peace. Armed conflicts include civil wars, nation state armed conflicts with other nations and terrorist acts. Black powder was discovered over 1,000 years ago and blast injuries came into use. Currently, explosive blast injuries inflict a unique pattern of mass killing when detonated in close proximity to a human population. Terrorist explosive devices such as improvised explosive devices (IEDs) are used to destroy or incapacitate a massive number of people (Shuker (2016).

A. Physics of explosions

Harrisson et al. (2008) discusses physics of explosions which I refer to as blast loading. Initially, the damage of a conventional (non-nuclear) chemical explosion is a reaction and depends upon a number of factors, such as the type of chemical explosive material, the amount of explosive material, the use or non-use of projectile elements within the explosive device, and the detonation environment (e.g., air versus water).

A bomb or similar device in an air environment can change a solid or liquid into a rapidly expanding gas with an increase in volume of up to 100,000 fold. The key to the damage is the rate by which this gas expansion occurs. Faster expansion rates are dependent on the type of explosive. A chemical explosive device triggered by a detonator which explodes a C4 explosive mixture with the explosive component being RDX (i.e., cyclotrimethylene-trintramine) can cause a gas expansion speed of 26,400 ft/second (Harris, (2019). This expansion is the "blast wave" which is composed of 1) the shock wave and 2) the blast wind (Cullis, 2001). The two mechanisms are different but are many times lumped together in discussing the blast wave. Harrisson et al. (2008) explains that the shock wave travels through air; it is not the mass movement of air or products that may have been picked up by moving air (i.e., the blast wind).

Cullis (2001) states that "a shock wave is an integral part of the blast wave and heralds it's approach" (p. 17). In an air medium, the shock wave is supersonic relative to the undisturbed air medium from an explosion and this event dramatically increases the positive pressure and heat surrounding the epicenter of the explosion, which results in a faster transmission of the shock wave. The blast front is sometimes a term used to describe the leading edge of the blast wave and is responsible for raising the density of the air, raising its temperature and accelerating the air molecules at a rate much faster than ambient-pressure air (Stuhmiller et al., 1991). Furthermore, this positive pressure wave and increased temperature in a chemical explosion propagates out from the blast epicenter into areas now filled with the expanding chemical gas explosive and serves to increase the rate at which a continued chemical reaction occurs, which coincidently drives the positive pressure wave ever faster away from the epicenter (Cullis, 2001). The shock wave component of the blast wave is the result of an increase in a pulse of increased air pressure (positive pressure wave) measured in milliseconds which peaks as an overpressure and also initiates a positive "blast wind" behind it; a flow of gas *away* from the epicenter of the explosion (Stuhmiller et al., 1991 and Cullis, 2001). Secondly, and immediately following the positive pressure wave, is a negative pressure wave which results in the former high pressure area dropping to sub-atmospheric pressure levels for a very short time (i.e., suction). Stuhmiller et al., (1991) further explains that this negative pressure wave is produced as the gas of an explosion is expanding away from the epicenter and now the area behind the positive pressure area (nearer to the epicenter) becomes decompressed. The term for this latter mechanism is the negative pressure blast wind where air and products picked up by air are moving rapidly towards the explosion epicenter. The positive blast wind has a higher magnitude (speed) and can move bomb material such as shrapnel or metal ball bearings into bodies quite some distance from the blast epicenter. Furthermore, the positive blast wind in high performance chemical explosions can move objects and people in the blast environment into buildings, trees, etc. Finally, Harrisson et al. (2008) note that underwater (liquid medium), the shock wave pressure is propagated for a much longer distance and therefore the distance from the detonation point at which human trauma and death may occur is increased.

The magnitude of the blast positive pressure wave may far exceed 60-80 pounds per square inch (psi) which is considered potentially life threatening. Other factors that influence the damage to the surrounding area in an air environment include the distance from the incident shock wave and the degree of shock wave focusing due to walls within an explosion confined area. This focusing of the shock wave within hard solid wall, floor and ceiling surfaces within a room may amplify the shock loading effect 2-9 times due to reflection of shock waves which can interact with the original shock wave so as to result in complex waves and dramatically increase human injury or mortality (Harrison et al. 2008 and Pathology of Blast Injury and Overview of Experimental Data-Gulf War and Health, Vol. 9 - NCBI Bookshelf 2014).

B. The blast wave

The shock wave component of the blast wave in an air environment is one factor responsible for the "primary blast injury." It is the result of direct exposure to the positive pressure wave resulting in injury to gas containing organs such as the lungs, intestines, facial sinuses, etc. Shock waves have very deleterious effects upon the lungs and it is believed that it is primary blast injury (PBI) that results in air emboli entry into the bloodstream through the lungs resulting in a rapid death. It is thought that at lower blast energy levels, it is simply the loss of pulmonary function which leads to an immediate incapacitation (Stuhmiller et al., 1991). This may occur as the result of a collapsed lung. Furthermore, increasing evidence indicates that brain and brain stem injury may occur (blast traumatic brain injury; bTBI) (Courtney and Courtney, 2015). The consequences of kinetic energy transfer suggest that these effects also depend upon the frequency of the shock wave with high frequency, low amplitude stress waves damaging organs within the human body of different densities (e.g., air and blood in the lungs) (Pathology of Blast Injury and Overview of Experimental Data-Gulf War and Health, Vol. 9 - NCBI Bookshelf 2014). Alternatively, low frequency, high amplitude shock shear waves may disrupt tissue by generating regional motions that exceed the tissue's elasticity. For example, the boundary of grey and white matter within the human upper central nervous system (i.e., brain and brain stem) may be disrupted as per animal model blast experiments (Gorbunov et al., 2004, and Cullis, 2001). Diffusion tensor imaging tractography is a new medical technology which is sensitive to moderate and severe TBI. The brain exposed to blast trauma will show numerous broken connections within white matter.

Therefore, the shock wave will have a direct effect upon human tissues; albeit with some complexity in terms of human trauma. The blast wind injuries which occur milliseconds after the shock wave are less complex in terms of concept and result from hurricane force winds and especially from objects that are propelled by these winds into the human body producing impact and penetration trauma. These injuries may be termed "secondary blast injuries." Tertiary blast injuries are the result of the body being blown by the blast wind into a building, etc. but may also be the result of building structure collapse (Harrisson et al., 2008).

Recently in development is a patch that is worn by combatants on their uniform over the thorax and on helmets. The sensitive measure on the patch is a phototonic crystalline material that will change color and therefore provide an objective measure of blast exposure to the solder.

C. High temperature effects and quaternary blast injuries

Chemical explosions with high performance explosives such as C4 may produce very high temperatures and again gases expanding out from the epicenter as the blast wind continues to chemically react and may be inhaled by personnel resulting in a thermal insult and death. These blast injuries are termed "quaternary" injuries resulting from burns to the body and/or damage again to the lungs resulting from the inhalation of hot and toxic gases (Harrisson et al, 2008). Flash burns are another example and may present upon the skin quite some distance from the chemical explosion epicenter.

In conclusion, this chapter provides some common examples of force loading and other common mechanisms of human trauma. Many of the biomechanical principles applied to the examples within this chapter may be applied to other applications in personal injury, wrongful death and criminal forensics.

References

Adams, D. Wound Ballistics: A Review. *Military Medicine*, V. 147, October, pp. 831-835.

Alexander, C (2015) The invisible war on the brain. www.Nationalgeographic.com/healing-solders/blast-force.html

Belkin, M. (1978) Wound Ballistics. Prog. Surgery. v. 16, pp. 7-24.

Bohlin, N.H. Deposition transcript in *McKinley v. American Safety Equipment Corporation and Chrysler Corporation*, United States District Court for the District of Nevada, Vol. 1, March 9, 1990.

Broker, J., and Hottman, M. (2016) *Bicycle Accidents, Crashes and Collisions*, 2nd Ed.., Lawyers and Judges Pub., Tucson, Az.

Courtney, A. and Courtney, M. (2015) The complexity of biomechanics causing primary blast-induced traumatic brain injury: a review of the potential mechanisms. Frontiers in Neurology, October, v. 6:221

Cullis, I. (2001) Blast waves and how they interact with structures. Fr Army Medical Corps, v. 147, pp. 16-26.

DiMaio and DiMaio (2001) *Forensic Pathology*, 2nd ed. CRC Press, Boca Raton Fl.

Decker, R., Duca, S., Spickert-Fulton, S. (2017) Measurement of bullet impact conditions using automated inflight photography system. Defence [a.k.a. Defense] Technology v. 13, pp. 288-294.

Eppinger R. "Prediction of Thoracic Injury Using Measurable Experimental Parameters. Report on the Sixth International Technical Conference on Experimental Safety Vehicles," USDOT HS-802-50by manufacturers to reduce these inflation forces to occu1 (1976)

Eppinger R. "Occupant Restraint Systems," in J.W. Nahum and A.M Melvin, eds. *Accidental Injury Biomechanics and Prevention*, Second edition. (NY: Springer-Verlag, 2002)

Gillespie, Thomas. *Fundamentals of Vehicle Dynamics* (Warrendale, PA: SAE, 1992)

Gorbunov, N. McFaul, J., Van Albert, S., Morrissette, C., Zaucha, G., Nath, J. (2004) Assessment of inflammatory response and sequestration of blood iron transferrin completxes in a rat model of lung injury resulting from exposure to low-frequency shock waves. Critical Care Medicine, v. 32(4). pp1028-1034.

Harris, T. (2019) How C-4 works. in Howstuffworks.com/C-42.htm

Harrisson, S., Kirkman, E., and Mahoney, P. (2008) Lessons learnt from explosive attacks. Journal of the Royal Army Medical Corps. January 2008.

Hickman, R. and M. Sampsel. *Boat Accident Reconstruction and Litigation*, Second edition. (Tucson, AZ: Lawyers & Judges, 2002)

Hyde, Alvin. *Crash Injuries: How and Why They Happen* (Key Biscayne, FL: Hyde Associates, 1992)

Hyde, A. et al. *Falls and Related Injuries: Slips, Trips, Missteps and Their Consequences* (Tucson, AZ: Lawyers & Judges, 2002)

Kallieris, D. and G. Schmidt. *New Aspects of Pedestrian Protection Loading and Injury Pattern in Simulated Pedestrian Accidents*, paper 881725 (Warrendale, PA: SAE, 1988)

McCormick, B. and M. Papadakis. *Aircraft Accident Reconstruction and Litigation*, Third edition. (Tucson, AZ: Lawyers & Judges, 2003)

Melvin, J.W. and A.M. Nahum. "Airbag Inflation-induced Injury Mechanics," in J.W. Nahum and A.M Melvin, eds. *Accidental Injury Biomechanics and Prevention*, Second edition. (NY: Springer-Verlag, 2002)

NCBI Bookshelf: Blast Injury and Overview of Experimental Data-Gulf War and Health, Vol. 9 - NCBI Bookshelf 2014).

NHTSA. *Third Report to Congress: Effectiveness of Occupant Protection Systems and Their Use*. (Washington DC: U.S. Dept. of Transportation, 1996)

Obenski, K. and P. Hill. (2002) *Motorcycle Accident Reconstruction and Litigation*, Second edition. Lawyers & Judges Pub., Tucson, AZ.

Ravani, B., Brougham and R.T. Mason. *Pedestrian Post-Impact Kinematics and Kinetics and Injury Patterns*, Paper 811024 (Warrendale PA: SAE, 1981)

Russell, C. (2014) Equations & Formulas for the Traffic Investigator and Reconstructionsist, 3rd ed. Lawyers and Judges Pub., Tucson, Az.
Scott, W., Bain, C. Manoogian, S., Cormier, J., and Funk, J.(2010) Simulation model for low-speed bumper to-to-bumper crashes SAE International. Paper # 2010-01-0051.

Shuker, S. (2016) Explosion blast injuries: Physics, biomechanics and pathophysiologic effects: A unique pattern and masked killing effects. TOFIQ Journal of Medical Sciences TJMS., v. 3(1), pp. 1-16.

Spitz, W. (2006) Injury by Gunfire, ch. XII in Spitz and Fisher's Medicolegal Investigation of Death, 4th ed. Charles C. Thomas Pub., Springfield, Illinois.

Wang, J. (2018) Determining entrance-exit gunshot holes in skulls: A real time and in situ measurement method. Journal of Forensic Pathology, v. 3: 113.

Watts, A., (2003) *Low-Speed Automobile Accidents: Accident Reconstruction and Occupant Kinematics, Dynamics, and Biomechanics*, Third edition. Lawyers and Judges Pub., Tucson, AZ.

Watts, A., (2011) *Accident Reconstruction Science*, 4th ed. Lawyers and Judges Pub., Tucson, AZ.

Zellmer, H., Kahler, C. Eickhoff, B. (2005) Optimised pretensioning of belt system: A rating criterion and the benefit in consumer tests. June, 2005 ESV Conference, Washington DC.

Chapter 5

Biomechanics of Bone Tissue

Patrick Hannon

5.1 Bone Growth and Development

Bones can develop from a membrane model or a cartilage model prenatally. The ossification process (becoming bone) begins within four to six weeks post-conception in the human fetus. When ossified bone initially develops prenatally, it is termed woven bone and exhibits much less organization than mature cancellous bone or compact bone. Bone growth and ossification continues until full skeletal maturity is reached between twelve and twenty-five years of age. Females reach maturity earlier.

Most long bones, which are weight supporting, develop from a cartilage model and exhibit three ossification centers: a central area (diaphysis) that develops first (prenatally) and one or two ossification centers at each end (epiphyses) of the bone that generally develop after birth. A hyaline cartilage growth (epiphyseal) plate is present at each end of long bones. Long bones continue to grow at both ends as hyperplasia (increased number of cells) and hypertrophy (increased size of cells) take place

within the cartilage growth plates at each respective end of a long bone. As skeletal maturity approaches, growth in the cartilage plates ceases, while the formation of new bone through ossification continues, resulting in fusion of the epiphyses to the central shaft (diaphysis). A faint epiphyseal line remains on the long bone ends at the completion of this process. (See Figure 5.1.)

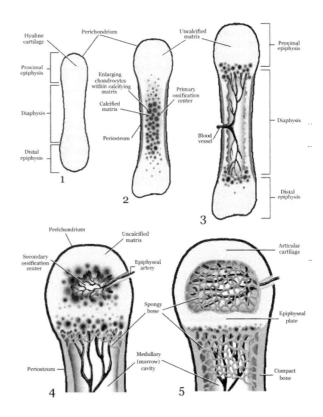

Figure 5.1 *Long bones form and grow from three ossification centers within the cartilage model with closure occurring at the two ends when the bone is fully mature. (Courtesy of Robert Perry)*

5.2 Function of Bones

From a biomechanics standpoint, bone has three very important functions. First, bone provides protection to soft organs encased or surrounded by bone by preventing direct contact (penetration) and by increasing the load distribution of any contact force that may be applied to the body. Examples of this protection are the skull protecting the brain and brain stem, and the rib cage protecting the lungs, liver, and spleen within the upper torso.

Second, bones provide the rigid framework to resist the force of gravity and therefore provide support under this loading condition.

Third, bones provide the skeletal framework for the simple machine systems that permit movement of the body. Bones are the simple levers, wheels and axles, and pulley wheels for our human body mechanics. Consequently, bones arc rigid enough to maintain their shape and structure and to permit the efficient transfer of muscle-pulling forces. Other functions of bones include the production and storage of red and white blood cells and the storage of mineral salts and lipids.

5.3 Biological Properties of Bones

Bone is made up of mineral salts and primarily type-I collagen. The mineral salts include calcium phosphate, which reacts with calcium hydroxide to form hydroxyapatite crystals, some of which actually form covalent bonds around the long strands of type-I collagen. Other minerals such as calcium carbonate, magnesium, sodium, and fluoride may be incorporated into these crystals and can affect material properties of bone (Martini, 1995; Mow and Hayes, 1997). The collagen fibers make up the majority of the organic component (90%) accounting for 25 to 30% of the dry weight (Nordin and Frankel, 2001). The mineral component comprises the remaining approximate 75% of the dry weight. Compact bone and cancellous bone are identical in terms of chemical composition.

The microstructure of bone distinguishes woven, cancellous (trabecular), and compact bone. Immature woven bone is present prenatally and during the early postnatal development stage and is also found within the growth areas of bone before maturity. It is not highly ordered, and the strength properties are not well defined. Compact bone, on the other hand, is highly ordered into units called osteons (Haverson systems) which form columns that may be close to an inch long but microscopic in cross section area diameter (approximately 200 micrometers). Osteons initially form concentric lamella (layers) around the outside of the bone, and as osteons mature over weeks and months, concentric layers are added within to "fill in" the osteon, resulting in a gradual increase in density (0.7 to

0.95 gram per cubic centimeter) and concomitant strength properties (Mow and Hayes, 1997). (Figure 5.2)

Cancellous bone is not composed of osteons but

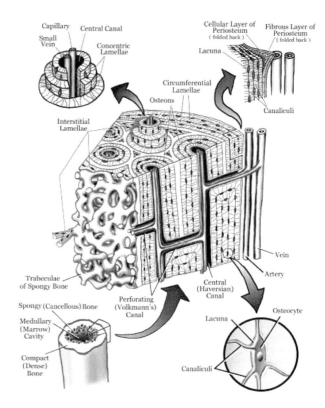

Figure 5.2 *In a cross-section microscopic view of a long bone shaft, osteons may be viewed as packed layered (rings) tree trunks laid on end. The spaces between the roughly circular osteons are filled in with interstitial layers and a glue substance composed primarily of glycosaminoglycans (GAGs) and glycoproteins. (Courtesy of Robert Perry)*

rather thin rods and plates (trabecula). Lamella make up these plates and rods which are manufactured from osteoblasts. In similar fashion to compact bone, the osteoblasts become trapped between lamella and transform into osteocytes within the cancellous bone rods and plates. Cancellous bone does not require an extensive network of blood vessels because red marrow fills the voids between the rods and plates. Oxygen-CO_2 exchange is achieved by a diffusion gradient. Individual trabecula of cancellous bone have the same approximate density of compact bone (over 1,800 kg/m3) (Gibson and Ashby, 1988). However the cell-like structure of trabecular bone produces densities that vary considerably. Cancellous bone density may range from .005 to 0.7 grams per cubic centimeter, and therefore functional strength will vary, with more dense cancellous bone being much stronger (Mow and Hayes,

1997), approaching that of compact bone. Cancellous bone is surrounded by compact bone or in this instance commonly called cortical bone. In the case of vertebral bodies, cancellous bone is largely responsible for resistance to compression loads, and therefore the significance of cancellous bone structure to fracture resistance should not be underestimated. (Figure 5.3)

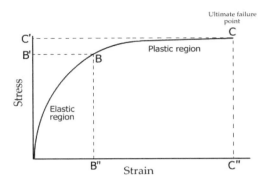

Figure 5.4 *A simplified typical stress-strain curve for compact bone tested in tension. The yield point B indicates the point at which the bone starts to experience permanent plastic deformation, and the ultimate failure point C is that point past which results in failure of the bone sample. Yield stress, yield strain, ultimate stress, and ultimate strain are also indicated. The elastic and plastic (inelastic) regions are indicated for this bone sample, and the area of these respective regions under the curve indicates the energy stored during the bone loading process. (Courtesy of Robert Perry)*

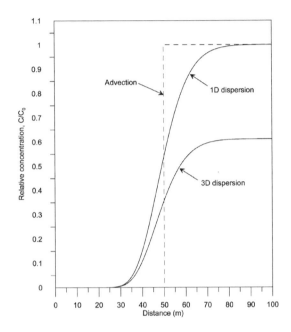

Figure 5.3 *Cancellous bone illustrates Wolff's law in that structure in part is influenced by the loading and stresses applied to the biological material. When loading is high, thicker plates tend to form parallel to the direction of the loading vector (i.e., gravity vector). When loading is low, rods form a more open cell network similar to very porous open cell foams. (Courtesy of Robert Perry)*

5.4 Material Properties of Compact and Cancellous Bone

Bone exhibits the properties of a composite material. The type-I collagen in bone provides strength in tension in the same way that a leather strap is able to resist a tension stress. Many analogies have been offered, including fiberglass (Nordin and Frankel, 2001) and steel reinforced concrete (Martini, 1995). In reinforced concrete, the concrete acts to resist compression loads and the steel re-bar acts to resist tension loads. Similarly in compact and cancellous bone, mineral salts are embedded in a matrix of type-I collagen fibers, GAGs, and glycoproteins to provide strength in resisting compression stresses. The type-I collagen fibers act to resist tension

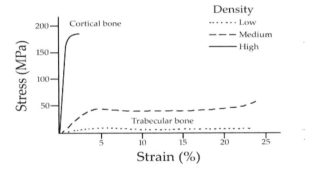

Figure 5.5 *Compact bone and cancellous bone of different densities tested under a compression stress. Adapted from Keaveny and Hayes, 1993. (Courtesy of Robert Perry)*

stresses applied to bone. Because compact is denser than cancellous bone, it therefore exhibits increased strength and stiffness properties. (Figures 5.4 and 5.5) Adult compact bone is strongest in compression stress, slightly weaker in tension stress, and weakest when exposed to a shear stress.

The type of loading dictates the biomechanical mode of failure at the microscopic level in compact bone. Under compression loading, oblique cracks develop directly through the osteons, while under tension loading the osteons remain relatively intact and are pulled apart, indicating a failure of the glue substance binding the osteons and the interstitial lamella. This microscopic failure will in part dictate the gross failure fracture pattern of compact bone. (Figures 5.6, 5.7, and 5.8)

Case Study 5.1

A male construction worker was climbing a fixed ladder on the side of a commercial building when he slipped and fell. He landed some thirty feet below, on his feet, on hard pavement. One lumbar vertebral body was crushed, but with-

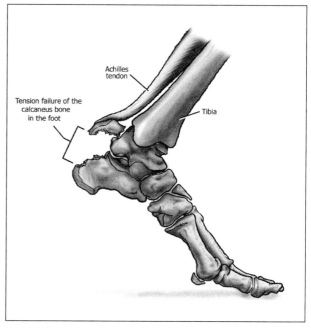

Figure 5.7 Calcaneal fracture produced by the shank plantar flexors during forceful muscle contraction resulting in high tension stresses. (Courtesy of Robert Perry)

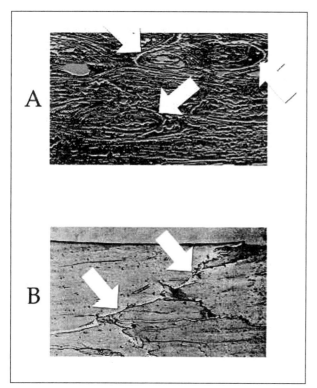

Figure 5.6 (A) an optical photomicrograph of human compact bone specimen tested in tension. Arrows illustrate debonding at the cement line interface and a pulling apart of the osteons (magnification at 30x). (B) A scanning electron photomicrograph of a human compact bone specimen tested in compression. Arrows indicate oblique cracking through the osteons (magnification at 30x). (Courtesy of Dennis R. Carter)

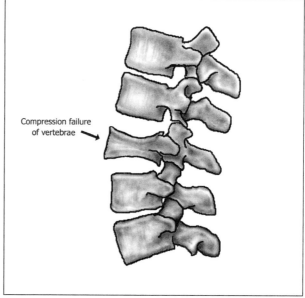

Figure 5.8 Arrow indicates a compression stress fracture of a lumbar vertebral body. (Courtesy of Robert Perry)

out neurological sequella, and both heels of the feet (calcanea) suffered explosive highly comminuted fractures. Finally, complex fractures of both tibia (complex loading) occurred in the superior region of the tibia.

5.5 Bone Anisotropy

Rods and plates (trabeculae) in cancellous bone and osteons in compact bone will orient themselves in the best possible direction to resist everyday loading. This is an example of bone anisotropy (i.e., bone is not equally strong in all directions). (Figure 5.9) The bone and specific areas within a bone have adapted structure to the external environment (Wolff's law). The loads that are placed upon bones can affect the internal and external structures (shape, size, architecture, and material properties). Muscle pulling on bone to produce movement at bone-muscle attachment sites will result in larger bumps (tubercles and tuberosities) on bone. This optimal orientation allows osteons and trabeculae to act as columns in resisting compression and tension stresses. Individuals who receive much lower levels of loading or abnormal direction loading (i.e., sedentary humans) will experience less than optimal structure orientation and a concomitant loss of strength properties, especially in cancellous bone.

Case Study 5.2

High impact loading to the knee joints may result in fracture failure of the femoral neck. A frontal automobile collision drove a man's knees (patellae strikes) into the unpadded metal dash at a delta velocity of approximately twenty-five miles per hour. One femoral neck (unilateral subcapital fracture) failed in this instance due to loading that was applied through the longitudinal axis of the femoral shaft. The patellae in both knees did not fracture although there was certainly bone bruising on both the left and right knee patellae. A possible reason that the kneecaps did not fracture was that the metal dash significantly deformed and cupped the knees so as to produce beneficial load distribution during this occupant driver unrestrained vehicle impact.

5.6 Ductile and Brittle Properties of Bone

Brittle and ductile material properties may be viewed on a continuum. Fracture patterns will also differ dependent properties. (Figure 5.10) A material that falls on the brittle

end of the continuum will have smaller elastic and plastic zones on the stress-strain graph. A material that falls at the ductile end of the continuum will deform to a greater degree within the plastic zone of the stress-strain graph. Cancellous bone in vivo, because of its cell structure, is much more ductile than is compact bone, although both types of bone should be considered at the brittle end of the brittle-ductile continuum.

5.7 Bone Stiffness

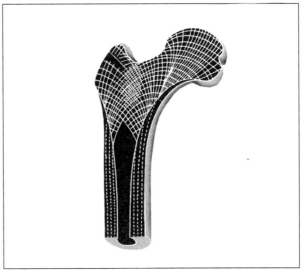

Figure 5.9 *The orientation of rods and plates within cancellous bone may be very complex. In the femoral neck (femur bone), the rods and plates form a complex orientation to compensate for what is termed a cantilever effect. The shaft of the femur is offset from where the head (ball) of the femur fits into the pelvis acetabulum and this results in offset forces cantilever bending. This complex trabecular internal structure makes it possible for the neck of the femur to resist the bending load and the resulting tension and compression stresses that are imposed during normal lower extremity weight bearing. Failure in the elderly may still occur when the loading exceeds the strength of the femoral neck structure. In some cases, offset loading may be of such magnitude so as to produce a break in the femoral neck in osteoporotic bone simply by one stepping down to a lower level. In these instances, it is the break that produces the fall rather than the fall producing the break (i.e., commonly referred to as a broken hip). (Courtesy of Robert Perry)*

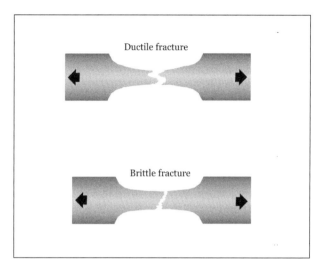

Figure 5.10 *Fracture patterns of a ductile material sample (above) and whole bone (below). The ductile material will enter into its long plastic zone and initially experience "necking" (a thinning of the material at the area of deformation) until it eventually reaches failure. The brittle material deforms very little prior to failure, and the fracture surfaces may be re-approximated after failure (e.g., whole bone). (Courtesy of Robert Perry)*

Materials may be viewed as flexible or stiff. This stiffness continuum may be expressed by Young's modulus (a.k.a. modulus of elasticity), a shear modulus (modulus of rigidity) or Poisson's Effect (a.k.a. Poisson's ratio) depending upon the stress imposed upon a material. The modulus of elasticity is constant for each homogenous material and really is a measure of the material's ability to maintain a length when external loads (a normal stress in this example) are applied (Burstein and Wright 1994). The modulus of elasticity (E) is defined and calculated by: "E = Normal stress/Normal strain" with normal strain measured in Standard International units (e.g., mm). This may also be expressed as: $E = \sigma / \varepsilon$. The concept is the result of the ratio of stress over strain and may best be illustrated by the steepness of the slope along the ordinate axis within the elastic zone of a material (e.g., bone). A steep stress strain curve (in tension or compression) indicates that a large stress is required for relatively little strain. Figure 5.5 indicates that compact bone is much stiffer than cancellous bone, and that cancellous bone is much more flexible than compact bone. Adult compact bone will fail at approximately 2 or 3% normal strain.

The modulus of rigidity (G) measures the material's ability not to change shape under a shear stress (τ) acting at a right angle to normal compression and tension

stresses (σ). A shear stress resulting from an off-set force couple or from a torsion load will result in a change in angle of two line segments that were originally perpendicular to each other. For example, when a bone such as the humerus is exposed to a torsion load and then reforms to its original shape, it has stayed within its elastic zone. The modulus of rigidity is defined and calculated by: "G = Shear stress/shear strain" or $G = \tau / \gamma$ with shear strain being measured in radians of rotation in this example. See example below:

> Shear Modulus of Modulus of Rigidity:
> $G = \tau / \gamma$
> G bone = 4 megapascals / 0.000845 radians = 4.7 gigapascals

Poissons' effect or ratio is another form of elasticity of a material (e.g., compact bone) named after the French mathematician Simeon Poisson. Burstein and Wright (1994) state that "The effect is quantified by observing the strain magnitude in the direction perpendicular to loading and comparing this to the strain magnitude in the direction of loading" (p. 111). It is therefore the ratio of transverse strain (i.e., perpendicular strain) over longitudinal strain (i.e., parallel strain). It may be expressed as:

Poisson's ratio (V) = $\varepsilon_{Transverse} / \varepsilon_{Longitudinal}$.

An example would be to impose a quantified compressive stress to the tibia bone or any bone biopsy sample. As the tibia bone or the bone biopsy sample becomes shorter due to the parallel compressive stress, it also becomes wider (i.e., perpendicular transverse strain expressed as a minus measurement). Generally, Poisson's effect is under 0.5 and the negative sign is usually omitted (Burstein and Wright, 1994).

5.8 Bone Viscoelasticity

Bone becomes stronger and stiffer when the rate of loading is rapid. One end of the loading rate continuum is that of a high velocity bullet that penetrates a bone, producing a high energy fracture. This is due to the fact that most biological tissues become stronger when they are loaded rapidly. This is especially true of compact bone tissue which is able to store a good deal of energy prior to failure. In many cases involving rapid loading lower energy impacts, this viscoelastic property prevents bone failure. (Figure 5.11)

5.9 Bone Fracture–Failure Behavior in Response to Loading

The susceptibility of bone to fracture is a function of the

basic biological properties of bone, including structure and material properties. Furthermore, aging and structural defects will affect bone fracture failure. The probability of bone fracture as well as the characteristics of bone fracture is also related to the following: the magnitude and direction of the force applied to the bone, the orientation of the bone with respect to the applied force, and the position and function of surrounding soft tissues.

Several considerations important to forensic biomechanics in assessing bone fracture were described by Salter in 1983.

The first of these considerations is the injury site itself. This should include the specific area of the body, the bone, and specific bone site.

The second consideration is the extent of the injury. This includes the specific area of injury and the soft tissues involved on all sides of the injury. It is important to note whether or not the soft tissue injuries related to the fracture are secondary to the fracture itself or preceded the fracture. The details of the fracture must also be described; for example, whether the fracture is complete or incomplete, whether the fracture line completely traverses the bone segment under consideration (complete) or whether it only partially traverses the bone (incomplete).

The third consideration is configuration. Configuration refers to whether there is a single fracture line or whether there are multiple fracture lines. In the case of

Figure 5.11 *Viscoelasticity in bone is a mixed blessing. Bone becomes stronger during rapid loading, and bone failures may be avoided. However, when bone is loaded rapidly, it may accumulate a large amount of energy to the failure point and the stored energy released results in an explosive fracture with fragments moving into surrounding soft tissues rather than a smaller amount of stored energy being released through a single crack in a low energy fracture failure. (Courtesy of Robert Perry)*

multiple fracture lines, the fracture is termed comminuted. In addition, the direction of the fracture line with respect to bone orientation is important. Specifically, one should document whether the fracture line traverses the bone in a perpendicular manner, is oblique to the axis of the bone, or is spiral around the long axis of the bone in the case of a long bone fracture.

The fourth consideration is fragment relationships. Are the bone fragments displaced or non-displaced with respect to one another? In the case of non-displaced fractures and fracture fragments, the analysis is relatively easy. In the case of displaced fragments, both the direction and cause of displacement are of interest. The fragments may be displaced linearly or angularly with respect to one another. The cause of displacement may be rotation (secondary to muscle activity), distraction, overriding secondary to muscle activity or the result of very high energy loading. The displacement may be front-back or sideways and caused by the force which produced the fracture itself. These four considerations require the biomechanist to examine the actual images (e.g., radiographs, CT scans, etc.) from a biomechanics perspective. Radiology reports do not usually offer the necessary detail. This demands training. Alternatively, the biomechanist may consult with a physician expert.

The fifth consideration is environmental. The environmental factor relates not to the fracture event but to the interaction of the bone fracture with the external environment. In cases where the bone fragments pierce the skin and expose the internal elements of the body to the external environment, the fractures are termed open. Open fractures are important because they expose the internal body to opportunities for infection. Open fractures also have the potential to create rather serious secondary soft tissue injuries.

The sixth area of consideration refers to complications, which may relate to surrounding soft tissues of the bone fracture site, but may significantly affect the analysis of fracture cause as well as fracture effects. Complications may include damage to blood vessels, a lipid embolism, as well as damage to nerves and muscles. Associated damage, particularly to blood vessels, may affect the healing and future function of the bone. Such complications may also be related to some of the bone characteristics, particularly age-related changes in bones.

The final area of consideration, and of particular interest to the biomechanist, is etiological factors. Particularly important in this regard are the biological properties of bone previously discussed as they relate to bone strength, stiffness, and susceptibility to fracture failure. Such factors are age and disease related which may make a particular individual's skeleton more susceptible to fracture due to lower bone failure tolerance.

Bone fractures can also be examined on the basis of bone type. Compact bone, as previously described, has very different biomechanical characteristics compared to cancellous bone and, consequently, experiences fracture failure in a very different manner, even in response to similar forces.

Prior to discussing bone fracture patterns and dynamics, a short review of the forces that produce bone fracture is useful.

First is the concept of force. A force is a physical quantity represented by a vector that has magnitude, direction, a line of action, and a point of application and which may accelerate or deform a bone. (Figure 5.12)

Most important to the analysis of bone fracture and the application of force is the term force couple. A force couple is the term applied to the two parallel forces of equal magnitude and opposite direction applied to a bone structure and resulting from a force. These parallel forces may be co-linear or offset. Bone fractures are the result of the application of Newton's third law, which states that for every action force there is an equal and opposite reaction

force.

Force couples result in loading, which produces stresses that are expressed as the compression, tension, or shear load per unit area applicable to a plane surface within the bone structure. Therefore, loading in the form of a force couple may result in compression, tension, or shear stresses.

When the loading to a bone creates a force couple, which results in a theoretic shortening and/or widening of the bone structure, the force couple is said to produce compression loading and may result in compression, tension, and shear stresses. (Figure 5.13)

When the force loading produces a force couple that results in a theoretic lengthening and narrowing of the bone structure, the force is said to produce tension loading and may also result in compression, tension, and shear stresses. (Figure 5.14)

When the force produces a force couple that results in internal angular deformation of the bone, the force is said to produce shear loading with a resulting shear stress. (Figure 5.15a and 5.15b)

If the force produces a force couple that results in rotation about the long axis of a long bone, the force is said to produce torsion loading. This torsion load results in a combination of shear, tension, and compression stresses within the bone structure. (Figure 5.16)

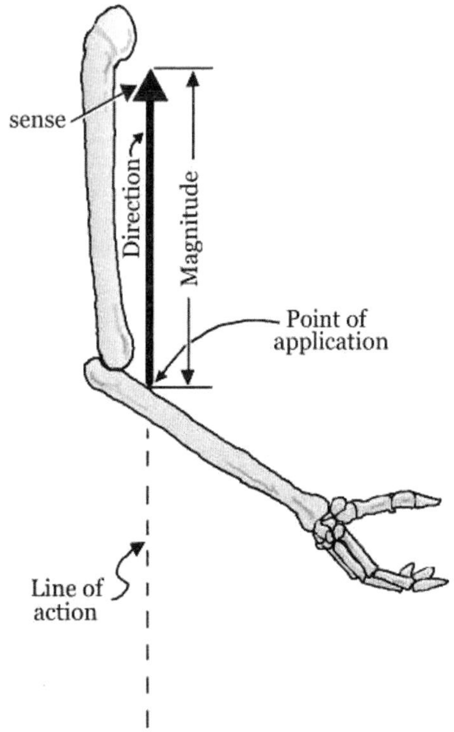

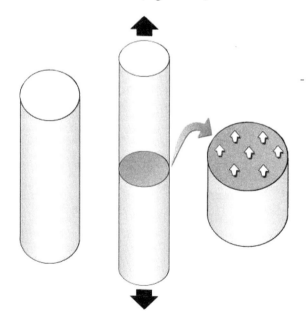

Figure 5.12 The five properties of a force or load. (Courtesy of Robert Perry)

Figure 5.13 Tension stress, secondary to axial loading, produces two types of fractures: (a) a transverse fracture or (b) an avulsion fracture. Under tension, the bone structure tends to lengthen and narrow. This process leads to failure of the bone as whole osteons are pulled apart. (Courtesy of Robert Perry)

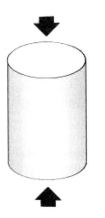

Figure 5.14 *Compression stress secondary to axial loading produces a shortening and widening of the bone structure, resulting in compression of the bone tissue and leading to oblique fracture lines through the osteons. Compression fractures are most commonly found in cancellous bone, vertebral bodies, as well as through the femoral neck in the hip joints of the elderly due to direct axial loading to the greater trochanter during ground impact from a fall. (Courtesy of Robert Perry)*

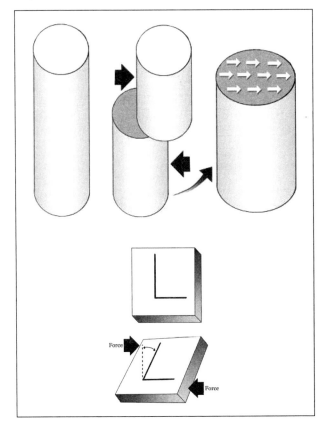

Figure 5.15 *Angular deformation takes place as the result of a shear stress. (Courtesy of Robert Perry)*

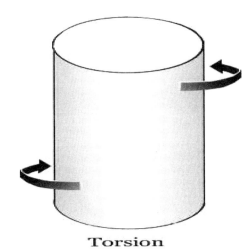

Torsion

Figure 5.16 *A torque is applied to the bone cylinder, resulting in shear, tension, and compression stresses. (Courtesy of Robert Perry)*

If a force produces a force couple that results in the bending of a long bone (beam), the force is said to produce bending. This bending load may result from three or four point bending and results in a combination of compression and tension stresses on each respective side of the bone relative to the application of the forces in addition to shear stresses within the bone. (Figures 5.17 and 5.18)

When compression, tension, shear, bending, or torsion loads are applied to a long bone, displacements occur to microscopic structures within the bone. Figures 5.19 and 5.20 illustrate how tension, compression, and torsion loads may result in compressive, tensile, and shear stresses. These microscopic failures within bone produced by various loading modes and resulting stresses can lead to gross fracture of a bone.

Please note the crinkling on the compression stress side of the long bone side with an imposed bending load. In children's bones this is not uncommon due to a bending load. (Figure 5.17) A torus fracture of the lateral side of the distal radius bone in the forearm due to fall to the hand of a child (no crack develops) is one example of this type of fracture failure where failure occurs first on the compression side of the long bone.

It should also be noted that bending load fractures can take place in long bones when apparent axial forces are applied but do not result in true axial loading. If a force is applied to the end of a long bone but the line of force does not pass through the centroid of the bone, the result may be a bending load, which produces the typical bending fracture patterns. A common example is impact loading to the ribs of the thorax where a compression load may be applied to the front and back of the upper torso. The resulting fractures may occur due to bending loading on the lateral side of the ribs.

Case Study 5.3

A teenage girl was involved in jumping on a trampoline at an outdoor recreation center. During this activity, the young woman bounced upward off the trampoline bed in a tilted, off-balance position. When she returned to the bed of the trampoline, she landed predominantly on one foot and a compressive load was transmitted up the tibial shank of her lower extremity, resulting in an offset bending load. This loading resulted in the lateral side of the tibial plateau being sheared off and disruption of what is known as the lateral compartment of the lower leg. During hospitalization, there was marked swelling in the lateral compartment which was not released and the blood supply to the lower leg was compromised. Necrosis set in, and subsequently the lower leg required amputation. (Figure 5.21)

Fracture patterns are not always easy to characterize based upon the standard radiographs. Sometimes a close

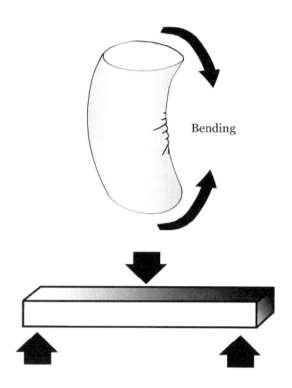

Figure 5.17 *Three-point bending is produced when the application of the force produces force vectors at each end of the long bone. The result is tension on the convex side of the long bone and compression on the concave side of the bone. The tension stress in the bone is greatest directly opposite the point of application of the force, while the largest compression stress in the long bone takes place at the force application point in three-point bending. Since adult long bones are weaker in tension than in compression, fracture failure is usually initiated on the tension side of the bone with the crack propagating across to the compression stress side. Once the crack develops, stress is concentrated at the tip of the crack and because bone is not a ductile material, the crack, continues to propagate in accordance with the loading pattern without being blunted. Fractures in long bones which result from mid shaft application of forces typically result in a transverse fracture line and/or a butterfly fragment fracture on the compression stress side. (Courtesy of Robert Perry)*

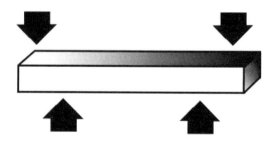

Figure 5.18 *Four point bending is produced by a more complex force application, involving two forces and their associated force couples. While the mechanisms of loading are somewhat different, the resultant fracture pattern due to the bending load tends to be similar; a transverse fracture due to failure first on the tension side. The fracture will begin at the weakest point between the two middle forces. (Courtesy of Robert Perry)*

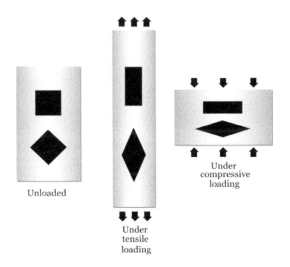

Figure 5.19 *Structures with sides that are aligned coincident to the line of push or pull are lengthened or shortened and are therefore subjected to tension-compression stresses and resulting tension-compression strains. Microscopic structures with sides that do not align with tension or compression load vectors are subjected to shear stress and strain as indicated by a change in angle between any two or more sides of the structure. (Courtesy of Robert Perry)*

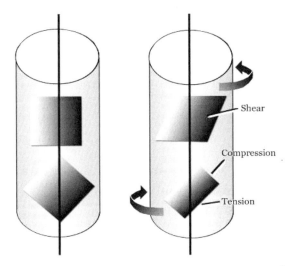

Figure 5.20 *When torsion is applied to a long bone, these same microscopic structures deform. In torsion loading, the schematic diamond structure experiences normal stress and strain, whereas the cube structure with sides parallel to the long axis of the bone cylinder experience shear stress and strain. (Courtesy of Robert Perry)*

examination of the bone fragments that are present during surgery will provide better detail in terms of the method of biomechanical loading. (See Figure 5.22.)

5.10 Direct and Indirect Loading

Direct application of forces includes loading from a gunshot wound to a bone or a large heavy object being applied to an immovable bone (being run over by a vehicle or dropping a rock on your foot). In situations of direct application, the fracture pattern of the bone, the nature of the crush, and the associated soft tissue trauma are of interest with respect to direction, magnitude, and breadth of application of the force (load distribution), but there is seldom any question regarding the relationship between the bone fracture and its cause.

Indirect application of a force is the more typical problem addressed by the biomechanist where injury causation and injury mechanisms are of interest. The force couple may produce axial loads resulting in compression or tension; bending loads resulting from three or four point bending with compression, tension, and shear stresses in each case; torsion loading resulting in tension, compression, and shear stresses; or combined loading. Each of these loading modes is now considered in terms of the resulting fracture patterns in the following concept figures. (Figure 5.23)

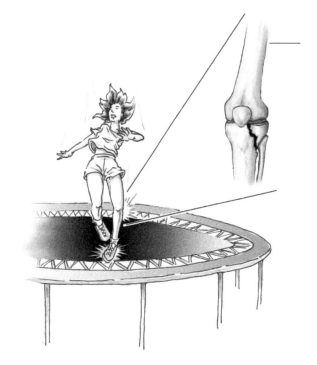

Figure Case Study 5.3 *(Courtesy of Robert Perry)*

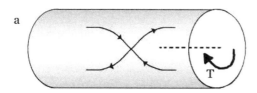

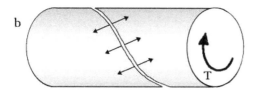

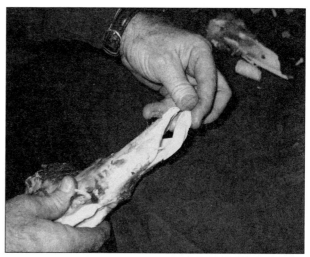

Figure 5.21 *A torsion load results from the application of a force, which produces force couples that twist the bone around the long axis. Lower extremity long bones are frequently exposed to these torsion loads with the tibia being especially vulnerable if bone failure occurs. Torsion produces a shear stress which is the result of a torsion load distributed throughout the bone. Torsion loads also result in tension and compression stresses within the bone. Generally the bone fracture begins first in shear with the formation of cracks parallel to the long axis of the bone. Secondarily, the bone will fail in a helical tension stress trajectory that occurs to form the characteristic spiral fracture pattern. The end result of torsion and its associated shear and tension stresses is a characteristic spiral fracture. In compact bone, compression stress, although present, probably does not play a substantive role in the fracture pattern because the energy is released through the fracture lines before compression stress is brought into play. (Courtesy of Robert Perry)*

Figure 5.22 *Note the fracture patterns of two elk femurs that have been subjected to twisting (torsion loading) (above) and three-point bending (right). The similarity of these fracture patterns could be obscured on a standard radiograph. (Courtesy of Knapp, Paradise and Hannon)*

5.11 Combined Loading

Bones may fracture secondary to combined loading. Combined loading, as the term implies, is a combination of forces that produce axial, shear, torsion, and/or bending loads. Bones in active people are typically subject to complex loading mechanisms and this is almost always true when the injuries result from an activity such as a sports activity or a fall. When examining fractures secondary to the combined loading, the complex nature of the fracture is important, but the analysis of the application of force

and the force couples becomes the essence of the biomechanical analysis. Case Study 5.4 illustrates compression and torsion applied in a sequential manner. Other combinations of loading are possible as well, and combination loading is common in real-world trauma.

Case Study 5.4

A man in his early fifties was skiing on a beginner's slope. In making a slow snow plow turn, this individual twisted, tipped and fell on his left side. He subsequently landed on a surface that had turned to a slushy surface with hard ice underneath. The skier suffered a comminuted fracture of the left femoral neck. His ski binding did not release as he struck the ground, with the point of contact being coincident with the greater trochanter in line with the femoral neck. In this case, the highest probability was that the femur was loaded in significant torsion due to the twisting of the pelvis and upper body over a left ski boot and ski that were embedded in the icy slush. Normally, the femur is much more resistant to torsion loads compared to the soft tissues of the knee or the tibia bone (a lower leg bone). However, torsion loading occurred first without failure resulting in stored potential energy. At greater trochanter impact with the ground, failure occurred with an explosive release of energy and a concomitant comminuted fracture pattern. This combination loading produced the serious comminuted fracture, with high compression and torsion loading applied concurrently through the femoral neck long axis.

5.12 Bone Geometry Affects Fracture Failure

Bone geometry in conjunction with how the loading is applied to the bone will affect a long bone's resistance to fracture failure. A longer bone may be subjected to a greater moment (force moment arm) when three or four point bending is applied as illustrated in Figure 5.24. The longer force moment arm makes long bones more vulner-

able to bending loads. In addition to the moment arm, the area moment of inertia (I) and the elastic section modulus (S) determine the resistance to a bending load. The area moment of inertia (I) depends on the cross sectional area of a long bone shaft. An example of this structural engineering principle is that of joists that are applied over a crawl space in a house. These wooden beams are turned on end so as to maximize the area moment of inertia rather than being laid flat. Please note that rectangular beams with the greatest height (note $I = b\,h^3/12$) will maximize

Figure Case Study 5.4 (Courtesy of Robert Perry)

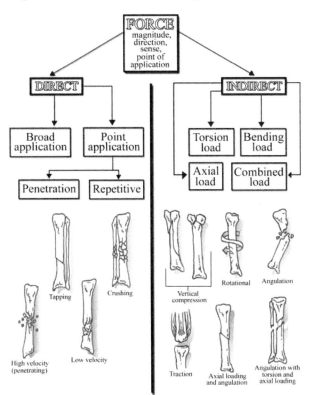

Figure 5.23 Fractures of long bones may occur via direct or indirect loading. Loading mechanisms are matched with fracture patterns. (Courtesy of Rockwood et al. 1996)

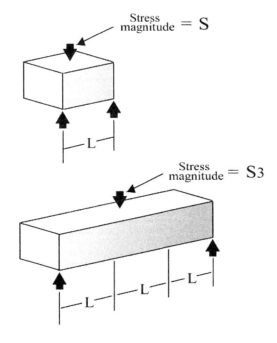

Figure 5.24 When the beam length is tripled, the moment (force × force moment arm) and the coincident compression and tension stresses will increase three fold. (Courtesy of Robert Perry)

I and *S*. It should be noted that the area moment of inertia will change as we move from one end of the long bone to the other. Generally, the open cylinder (like a pipe) is the best representation of the largest portion of the bone shaft (diaphysis). (Figures 5.25 and 5.26)

Resistance to failure of long bones which are subjected to torsion loads (around the bone long axis) is affected by the moment arm which in this case is measured by the radius of the long bone cylinder. When a force is imposed at the periphery of a long bone, the force couple acting at a larger force moment arm results in an increased torque that will increase shear and tension stresses. However, this effect is more than offset in terms of a resistance to a torsion load by what is termed the "polar moment of inertia" (J). (Figure 5.27)

Case Study 5.5

An elderly woman was being transported in a van for the disabled operated by a small municipality. The side door of the van was opened, and the client began to exit holding on to the handrail. At approximately the last step, she collapsed and fell to the pavement below. A supracondylar fracture of the left distal femur consistent with an axial compression load resulted from this fall injury. The treating surgeon opined that this was a spiral fracture of the distal femur due to twisting. Radiography did not confirm this surgeon's opinion. Furthermore, this area of the femur has a large polar moment of inertia and would not have been the weak link in torsion. In fact, in the absence of bone necrosis or a bone tumor in this area, a spiral fracture will not occur at this site and fracture fragment evidence supported the opinion of an axial compression load to the distal left femur from a pavement impact.

It should be appreciated that long bones will form a bony callus during the normal healing process. This callus serves to increase the polar moment of inertia at the

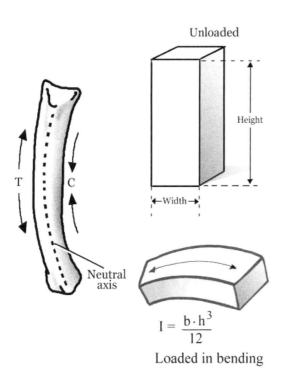

$$I = \frac{b \cdot h^3}{12}$$

Loaded in bending

Figure 5.25 *When a bending load is imposed on a rectangular beam, the area moment of inertia is found by I = base × height³ / 12. The height dimension dramatically increases the area moment of inertia. The elastic section modulus is directly related to the beam's resistance (strength) to an imposed bending load and may be expressed by S = I/c, where c is the centroid of the long beam. (Courtesy of Robert Perry)*

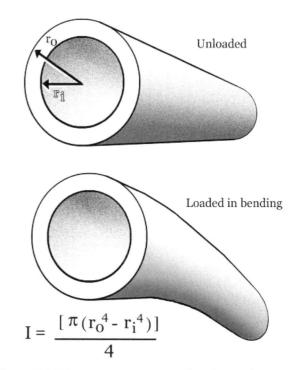

$$I = \frac{[\pi(r_o^4 - r_i^4)]}{4}$$

Figure 5.26 *Stresses to response in bending. When a bending load is imposed on an open cylinder, the area moment of inertia for an open cylinder is found by I = [Pi(r⁴ₒ-r⁴ᵢ,0)]/4). The elastic section modulus (S) is then calculated by: S= I/c, with c being the centroid or radius in our open cylinder example. One must keep in mind that in human bone wall thickness may vary from one side to the other, and structural engineers must be careful to recognize limitations in applying structural mechanics to biological structures. (Courtesy of Robert Perry)*

fracture site. Eventually it becomes smaller and may disappear (resorbed). However, while it is present, it serves to help prevent re-fracture due to bending or torsion loading which may occur before the healing process is complete.

5.13 Failure at the Epiphyseal Growth Plate

In individuals who have not attained skeletal maturity, failure at the epiphyseal sites of long bones may occur. Many times these areas represent weak points because they are composed of hyaline cartilage which has a lower ultimate

failure point under all types of loading. In immature humans, these growth plate areas may be loaded commonly in shear and compression during falls to the ground. In the United States, it is common to classify these fractures as Salter-Harris fractures I-V of the epiphyseal plate. (Figure 5.28)

Case Study 5.6
During the early part of the school year, a seven-year-old girl at school was playing on the playground on a geodesic dome-like jungle gym structure. She was hanging in an inverted position inside the dome, holding on with her extremities.

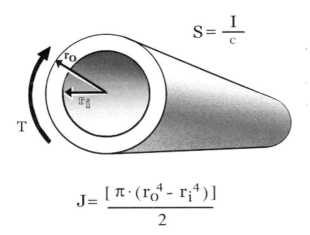

$$S = \frac{I}{c}$$

$$J = \frac{[\pi \cdot (r_o^4 - r_i^4)]}{2}$$

Figure 5.27 Hollow cylindrical shaft with resistance to applied torque. The polar moment of inertia for a hollow cylinder is calculated by $J = [Pi \times (r_o^4 - r^4)] / 2$. Therefore, the most dramatic increase in the polar moment of inertia is achieved by the largest radius (r_o^4) rather than bone wall thickness. Of particular importance in resisting torsion loads is the amount of shear stress and shear strain that result from a torsion load. Compact and trabecular bone is weakest in shear and significant shear stresses are generated in torsion loading. This is illustrated by the equation of $t = (T \times r) / J$ where although the torque is greater with a larger cylinder radius, this is more than offset by the beneficial effect of the larger radius to the fourth power used to calculate the polar moment of inertia (J). Note that t and J are inversely related, and therefore a larger long bone radius will dramatically increase its resistance to shear stresses resulting from a torsion load. Therefore, spiral fractures almost always begin in the region where J is the smallest due to a torsion load. (Courtesy of Robert Perry)

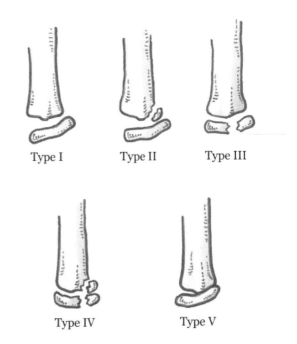

Type I   Type II   Type III

Type IV   Type V

Figure 5.28 Epiphyseal fractures. In Salter-Harris types I–IV, shear plays a significant although not an exclusive role in the failure mechanism. In these cases, there is a slip failure that occurs at the interface of the bone-cartilage line. Furthermore, shear and/or cantilever bending may take place and result in bony fractures of the epiphysis and/or diaphysis of the long bone. A type-V Salter-Harris fracture results in compression of the epiphyseal plate with resulting damage. The type-V Salter-Harris fracture is difficult to diagnose because gross slippage of bony components is absent. In all Salter-Harris fractures, the concern is that growth at the damaged epiphyseal line will be arrested with one upper or lower extremity developing shorter than the non-affected side. Fortunately, with a good reduction, growth of the long bone is usually normal. (Courtesy of Robert Perry)

Before her fall she lost her hand grips and leg hooks and started falling with her back and head towards the ground. She was able to reach back with one hand and break her fall with the left side upper extremity. This resulted in bringing the left elbow into pronounced hyperextension and a Salter-Harris type-II fracture at the distal end of the humerus. In this case, an open reduction-internal fixation intervention resulted in good alignment and a very satisfactory result some six years after the injury with continued long bone growth at the proximal epiphyseal plate area of her left humerus.

Irregular, short, and flat bones will also exhibit characteristic fracture patterns depending upon the type of loading. For example, the skull and face are composed of many flat bones that may fracture because of a direct impact strike resulting in a depressed fracture in much the same way that the shell of a hard-boiled egg may fracture when it is struck against a hard surface. In similar fashion, breaks will occur at selective "weak points" when a

broad-based blunt force is applied to various areas of the face resulting in Le Fort fractures types I, II, and III. (Figure 5.29a and 5.29b) In some cases an impact to the skull may produce indirect loading and result in a basal skull fracture (i.e., commonly the sphenoid bone).

Case Study 5.7

One side of the victim's skull was completely caved in due to the compression load, resulting in a depressed fracture of temporal, parietal, and occipital bones of the skull. Linear cracks extended to the other side of the skull. This type of fracture of flat skull bones demanded a high loading blunt impact with a large implement such as a baseball bat at high velocity or a head strike during rapid deceleration.

5.14 Other Fractures

Vertebral (irregular bones) fractures and wrist and foot (short bones) fractures are described in the respective chapters. The fracture pattern and the degree of comminuted fragments will clarify the loading and will help dictate to the surgeon the treatment protocol as well as clarify the loading etiology for the biomechanist.

5.15 Stress Risers and Open Section Defects

In a stress riser or an open section defect, the discontinuity in the bone wall may lead to fracture. The fracture is initiated at the site of the defect due to a stress concentration. Stress risers and open section defects may occur as

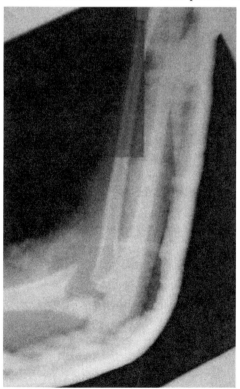

Figure Case Study 5.6 *Example of Salter Harris Type 2 fracture. (Courtesy of Patrick Hannon)*

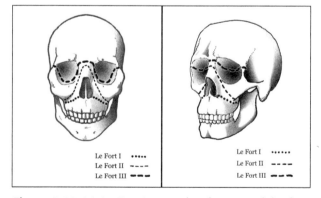

Figure 5.29 *(a) Le Fort I, II, and III fracture of the face are illustrated. In (b) Le Fort I, II, and III fracture of the face are illustrated. (Courtesy of Robert Perry)*

the result of penetrating injury but are more commonly produced during a bone biopsy or surgical intervention. An open section defect is produced when the entire wall thickness is breached and remains open (e.g., a hole or slot going completely through the long bone shaft wall), whereas a stress riser occurs when an induced defect in the bone cylinder wall is less than the wall thickness or when a screw is first inserted through the bone shaft wall.

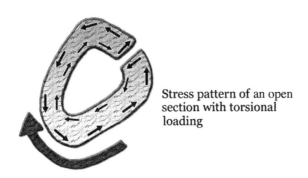

Stress pattern of closed section with torsional loading

Stress pattern of an open section with torsional loading

Figure 5.30 In the stress riser, stress may be conceptualized as being concentrated at the defect point. Material strength properties around the defect are reduced due to microscopic deformation induced by the damage or the inserted bone screw and the resulting excessive strain at the defect point, resulting in crack development and propagation. In an open section defect pictured above, the discontinuity of the bone wall leads to even greater strain and a crack is initiated and proceeds through the bone. Bone is especially susceptible to torsion loads that produce a shear stress. Stress risers are most significant when bone screws are first inserted. When bone remodels adequately around bone screws, stress risers disappear only to reappear as open section defects if bone screws need to be surgically removed at some time. In time bone will "fill in" as bone remodels and the open section defect is eliminated. (Courtesy of Robert Perry)

Bone may decrease in strength by 60% for a stress defect (Nordin and Frankel, 2001) or up to 90% with an open section defect (Nordin and Burnstein, 1970) during an applied torsion load. (Figure 5.30)

This same mechanism plays an important factor in fracture fixation implants that are introduced during open reduction internal fixation (ORIF) in the surgical repair of a bone fracture. For example, when a screw hole is present in a fracture fixation metal plate, there is an abrupt change in the plate's cross-section and this along with other geometric effects results in strains and stresses adjacent to the hole to elevate much beyond other plate areas remote to the "stress concentration" hole. Fracture failure of a plate is most common in hardware which has been utilized to treat non-union bone fractures. In these cases, the stabilizing metal plate bears the load and fatigue failure may occur over many months or years (Burstein and Wright, 1994).

5.16 Bone Unloading

Bone may be unloaded by active muscle elements. A good example of this mechanism is when the femoral neck is unloaded by the abductor muscles (especially gluteus medius) of the hip joint. When the hip abductors are active, they actually produce a bending load that acts opposite to the cantilever bending load at the femoral neck during body weight support. The effect is to reduce the tension

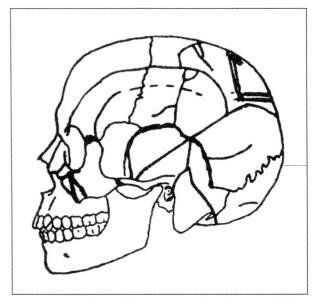

Figure Case Study 5.7 Medical examiner's drawing of skull damage. (Courtesy of Robert Perry)

stress on the upper surface of the femoral neck and the compression stress on the lower surface of the femoral neck. Reducing the tension stress is most important, and in this way the femoral neck upper surface experiences less net tension stress. It has been hypothesized that part of the problem of hip failure in the elderly due to cantilever bending at the femoral neck is that hip musculature is in a "detrained" state and is therefore not able to effectively unload the femoral neck when the foot is put into abrupt weight bearing. (Figure 5.31)

5.17 Chronic Loading Bone Failure

These injuries are commonly called overuse injuries and occur when relatively small loads are imposed upon various tissues, including bone. The chronic stress can out-pace the remodeling process of bone with resulting fracture failure. Because this process is slow, most commonly small cracks develop in bone with a resulting non-displaced fracture. Bone pain signals the problem, and the activity is

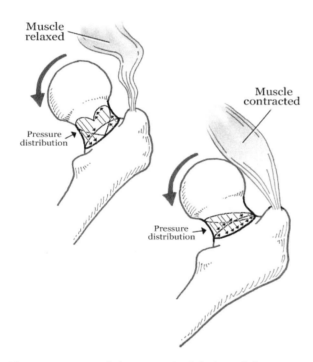

Figure 5.31 *Hip abductors, which help stabilize the pelvis during standing or in single limb support during walking, are able to "neutralize" the cantilever bending effect produced by weight bearing and therefore protect this area from loads that could produce fracture in an individual with osteoporosis. (Courtesy of Robert Perry)*

stopped. However, sometimes, for example in the foot, a displaced fracture may occur (e.g., march fracture) during continued marching or hiking while carrying loads.

5.18 Degenerative Changes in Bone Caused by Aging

The structure of compact bone and cancellous bone changes over several decades. Compact bone which surrounds cancellous bone may thin and amount to only 25% of its original mass at a specific site. Cancellous bone may reduce to 50% of its original mass (Frankel and Nordin, in Nordin and Frankel, 2001). In cancellous bone, this results in increased porosity (i.e., the derivation of the term "osteoporosis"). Bone loss is greatest in women over the age of forty. This decrease in mass density in both types of bone necessarily results in changes in the mechanical properties of bone, with a decrease in ultimate strain and ultimate stresses. The lumbar spine (multiple lumbar bodies) and the neck of the femur are especially susceptible to fracture with advanced osteoporosis. Exercise stress at the appropriate level seems to be therapeutic (micro-motion stimulates bone remodeling) in addition to pharmacological intervention. (Figure 5.32)

5.19 Fracture Fixation and Healing: Biomechanical Considerations

Many times fractures require only a cast to restrict movement and sometimes only a sling (common clavicle fracture). In other cases such as fractures of spinous or transverse processes of vertebra or some rib fractures, nothing is done and healing progresses without complication. Furthermore, research findings indicate that the

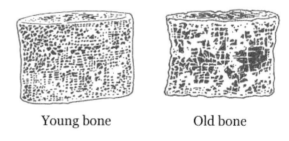

Young bone   Old bone

Figure 5.32 *Vertebral cross sections from autopsy specimens of young and old vertebral bodies showing a significant reduction in bone mass in the old specimen with obvious increased porosity. (Courtesy of Robert Perry)*

small amounts of motion produced by small forces may actually aid in healing, and therefore restriction of movement is contraindicated. This is the rationale for treating fractures that do not heal with ultrasound stimulation. The micro-motion produced by the ultrasound appears to induce small electrical currents in bone (bone is an example of a piezo-electric material) and therefore promote healing. Alternatively, the small motions of displaced rib fractures in adults may significantly prolong the healing of a rib or ribs (i.e., costae). Therefore, displaced rib fractures in some adult patients are treated with ORIF with inserted metal plates spanning the fracture site in order to minimize rib motion and promote healing.

Unstable fractures require external or internal fixation with multiple transcutaneous pins, screws, wires, plates, and rods. Good bone end or bone fragment approximation are important for optimal healing (a satisfactory fracture reduction). A good blood supply is also very important, and this can be accomplished by preserving the soft tissue adjacent to the lesion site to ensure the continued blood supply to the outer layers of bone (two layers of periosteum). Bone screws alone may be sufficient to bring displaced bone fragments together and may be specifically designed for compact bone or for cancellous bone. (Figures 5.33a and 5.33b)

Sometimes metal plates are also attached by means of bone screws and are most critical on the side of the bone that is exposed to tension stresses as the result of bending loads but may be applied to both sides of the bone for better fixation. These plates or rods are also made from similar metal alloys. These plates can also protect the bone during torsion loads and the shear, tension, and compression stresses that result from these torsion loads discussed earlier. These same stresses are also applied to intramedullary devices inserted into the long bone medullary cavity. The hardware itself may also fail, and Kummer states that "sometimes there is a race between healing of the bone and fracture, usually by fatigue, of the device" (Kummer 2001, p. 393).

Hardware is also sometimes applied after an invasive surgical procedure which damages a bone. For example, the sternum may be bisected along its long axis by the cardiothoracic surgeon with a bone saw in order to expose the heart and pericardium as required for some procedures such as multi-artery bypass or some heart valve replacements. In closing reduction of the induced injury, sometimes metal plates (e.g., titanium) are fixated to the sternum body in addition to wire placement. This procedure is said to provide increased stability of the sternum halves, less pain during recovery, and more rapid patient

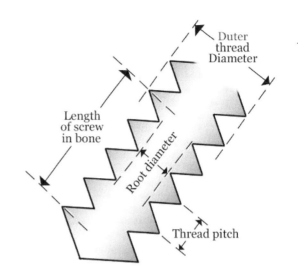

Figure 5.33a *Screw parameters. (Courtesy of Robert Perry)*

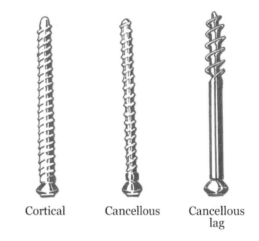

Figure 5.33b *Types of bone screws. Bone screws may be made from stainless steel, titanium alloy, or cobalt-chromium alloy. The thread pitch is greater in cancellous bone screws in similar fashion to "deck screws" used in carpentry. The holding capability of a bone screw is dependent upon the thread diameter times the thread length inside the bone (Kummer, 2001). Sometimes the screw holes are pre-tapped to minimize the micro-damage of screw insertion. The most important variable in screw fixation is the quality (density) of the compact (cortical) or cancellous bone. Those individuals with marked osteopena (lower bone density) are more likely to have screw loosening and inadequate fixation. Bone screwdrivers are also equipped with a force limiting mechanism (i.e., similar to a torque wrench) to prevent the stripping of bone caused by too much torque during screw insertion (Kummer, 2001). (Courtesy of Robert Perry)*

healing.

In some cases, internal hardware is designed to stay in permanently, while in other cases the hardware may be removed later after satisfactory reduction, fixation, and healing has occurred. (Figure 5.34) One concern of the physician is that stress shielding may take place with hardware in place. Stress shielding results during fracture fixation when the inserted hardware absorbs the stresses that would normally be applied to the bone. In accord with Wolff's law, stress shielding can lead to bone atrophy (becomes thinner) through bone resorption and a concomitant significant loss in strength. When the hardware is removed, the bone under a plate may be significantly weaker. Coupled with the bone micro-damage involved in pulling out pins and bone screws, and leaving "stress concentration(s)," bone will be more susceptible to refracture after these surgical procedures. Within weeks, in most cases, the bone will remodel sufficiently to become much stronger, and re-fracture is much less likely (Hannon, 2016).

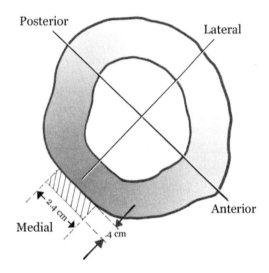

Figure 5.34 The "area moment of inertia" or "polar moment of inertia" (closed cylinder) may be increased with fracture fixation hardware. This example illustrates how a metal plate is much more rigid (resistant to bending) in anterior-posterior bending because of the increased height (2.4 cm³) of the metal plate. (Courtesy of Robert Perry)

References

Burstein, A and Wright, T., (1994) Fundamentals of Orthopaedic Biomechanics. Williams & Wilkins. Baltimore.

Connolly, John, *Fracture Complications: Recognition, Prevention, and Management* (Chicago: Year Book Medical, 1998)

Frankel V.H. and A.H. Burnstein, *Orthopaedic Biomechanics* (Philadelphia: Lea & Febiger, 1970)

Gibson L.J. and M.F. Ashby, *Cellular Solids* (Oxford: Pergamon Press, 1998)

Hannon, P. (2016) A brief review of current orthopedic implant devise issues: biomechanics and biocompatibility. *Biology, Engineering and Medicine,* v. 1 (1) pp. 1–2.

Hayes, W.C., *Bone Biomechanics: From Tissue Mechanical Properties to an Assessment of Structural Behavior in Frontiers in Biomechanics*, Schmid-Schonbein, Woo and Zweifach, eds. (NY: Springer-Verlag, 1985)

Keaveny, T. M. and W.C. Hayes, "Mechanical Properties of Cortical and Trabecular Bone," *Bone* 7:285–344 (1993)

King AI. Fundamentals of Impact Biomechanics: Part I à Biomechanics of the Head, Neck and Thorax." *Annual Review of Biomedical Engineering.* 2:55–81. (2000)

King AI. "Fundamentals of Impact Biomechanics: part II à Biomechanics of the Abdomen, Pelvis and Lower extremities." *Annual Review of Biomedical Engineering.* 3:27–55. (2001)

Kleinman, P. and Schlesinger, A. (1997) Mechanical factors associated with posterior rib fractures: laboratory and case study. Pediatric radiology, v. 27, pp. 87-91.

Kleinman PK, Marks, SC, Spevak MR, et al. (1992) Fractures of the rib heads in abused infants. Radiology; 185(1):119-23

Kummer, F.J., "Introduction to the Biomechanics of Fracture Fixation," in Nordin M. and V. Frankel, *Basic Biomechanics of the Musculoskeletal System* (Philadelphia: Lippincott Williams & Wilkins, 2001)

Martini, F.H., *Fundamentals of Anatomy and Physiology* (Upper Saddle River, NJ: Prentice Hall, 1995)

Mow, V.C. and W.C. Hayes, *Basic Orthopaedic Biomechanics*, Second edition. (Philadelphia: Lippincott Williams & Wilkins, 1997)

Nordin, M. and V. Frankel, *Basic Biomechanics of the Musculoskeletal System* (Philadelphia: Lea & Febiger, 1989)
Nordin, M. and V. Frankel, *Basic Biomechanics of the Musculoskeletal System* (Philadelphia: Lippincott Williams & Wilkins, 2001)

Rockwood, C.A. et al., eds. *Rockwood and Green's Fractures in Adults*, Fourth edition (Philadelphia: Lippincott-Raven, 1996)

Whiting, W.C. and R.F. Zernicke, *Biomechanics of Musculoskeletal Injury* (Champaign, IL: Human Kinetics, 1998)

Chapter 6

Biomechanics of Articular Cartilage

Patrick Hannon

6.1 Introduction

Cartilage tissue develops from mesenchymal tissue embryologically. Cartilage then differentiates into one of three types: elastic cartilage found within the nose and external ear for example; fibrocartilage, found within the intervertebral discs of the spinal column and fibrocartilaginous discs of some freely moveable joints; and hyaline articular cartilage that covers the ends or sides of bones. The temporal mandibular joint of the jaw is a notable exception, with fibrocartilage covering the bone surfaces of the mandible and the temporal bones at the joint interface. Fibrocartilage structures are addressed in this text in the cervical and lumbar spine.

6.2 Elastic Cartilage

Elastic cartilage, as the name implies, has a long elastic zone within the stress/strain curve. As an example, the external ear can be bent and twisted and is still able to return to its original shape. Elastic cartilage structures are not a principal concern in this text because this material is not weight bearing and therefore the loading is minimal under most circumstances. It can however be subjected to laceration/abrasion trauma in face trauma. A common injury of the external ear is hematoma auris, perichondrial hematoma or traumatic auricular hematoma, all commonly known as cauliflower ear. This condition may occur to the external ear during wrestling, boxing or mixed martial arts competitions resulting from a collection of clot-

ted blood or other fluid under the perichondrium. This fluid separates the elastic cartilage from the overlying perichondrium resulting in the formation of fibrous tissue which short of cosmetic surgery is considered permanent. Timely evacuation of an acute external ear hematoma may prevent or reduce this deformity of the external ear.

6.3 Articular Cartilage

Articular cartilage has a unique structure that enables it to function in a way that dramatically reduces friction drag between joint surfaces and at the same time enables it to endure large compressive forces that occur during weight bearing and muscle contraction. Articular cartilage may reduce compressive contact stresses by 50% within the joint cavity compared with bone on bone (Weightman and Kempson, 1979).

A. Overview of the structure of articular cartilage

Articular cartilage is 60 to 80% fluid, the vast majority of which is located outside the cartilage cells (i.e., chondrocytes). The chondrocytes are very sparse, making up less than 10% of articular cartilage. These cells are responsible for manufacturing all the macromolecules that inhabit joint cartilage tissue, including the collagens, proteoglycans, glycoproteins, noncollagenous proteins, and lipids. Both fluid and the manufactured macromolecules contribute to the functional material properties of articular cartilage in addition to the semipermeable membrane at the external surface of articular cartilage. In similar fashion to bone, articular cartilage is a composite material with collagen, water, and other macromolecules, contributing to articular cartilage strength in resisting tension, shear, and compression loads.

Articular cartilage is a relatively simple tissue. It lacks a blood supply and neural enervation, and because of sparsely distributed cells, the metabolic demand is relatively low compared to other tissues. Three zones occur within the articular cartilage thickness: the superficial tangential zone (STZ), the middle zone, and the deep zone. (Figure 6.1)

B. Articular cartilage components and material properties

1. Collagens

Articular cartilage collagen is primarily type II collagen with minor amounts of types V, VI, IX, and XI (Hou and Jung, 2001). These type II collagen molecules aggregate to form microfibrils and finally fibrils within the 1 to 6 mm thickness of human articular cartilage. This is accomplished by cross linking of tropocollagen molecules in a 75% overlap fashion. (Figure 6.2)

Type II collagen fibrils are responsible for the strength of articular cartilage during imposed tension and shear loads that occur when one articular surface moves across another. This is accomplished in the uppermost surface area of articular cartilage called the superficial tangential zone (STZ), where the collagen fibrils are highest in density and arranged parallel to the surface. When the surfaces of articular cartilage slide over each other, for example, tension stresses result at the cartilage surfaces due to friction drag, and therefore collagen fibrils are put on stretch.

Articular cartilage is anisotropic. Therefore, when subjected to tension or shear loads, articular cartilage is strongest in resisting the resulting tension stresses in the same direction as the type-II collagen strand orientation.

For example, a braided rope pulled from its two ends is able to resist a tension stress. Pulling perpendicular to the length of rope will produce a rope failure (unraveling). In the same way, if a tension load is in a direction not in line (parallel) with collagen strands, then split lines may develop in the articular cartilage surface in the same way that a braided rope would have its strands pulled apart. While it is tempting to believe that collagen fibrils are arranged parallel to the specific surface direction in response to the typical tension stresses imposed, the evidence in this regard is not strong. The specific direction of collagen fibrils in the STZ is still functionally undetermined excepting that the "parallel to the surface" arrangement clearly has functional value (Figure 6.3)

In the middle zone the collagen fibrils are arranged in more random fashion with decreased density. Here they interact with other macromolecules to resist compression, shear, and tension. Finally, in the deep zone, the collagen fibrils are arranged as roots, which anchor articular cartilage to the cartilage-bone articular lamina interface (tide-

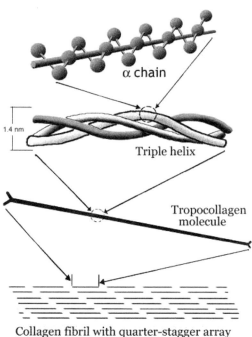

Figure 6.2 Composition of collagen from the alpha chains to the fibril. Three alpha chains spiral to form the tropocollagen molecule. These molecules aggregate in a parallel fashion outside the chondrocytes to form type II collagen fibrils in articular cartilage. The quarter stagger overlap of the fibrils serves to increase the strength in tension. (Courtesy of Robert Perry)

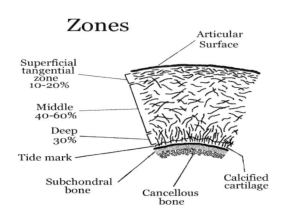

Figure 6.1 In the superficial tangential zone the collagen fibrils form sheets of strands that are roughly parallel to the surface, but typically in one predominant surface direction in specific areas. In the middle zone these fibrils are randomly arranged, while in the deep zone these fibrils act like small roots to anchor the articular cartilage to the subchondral bone. (Courtesy of Robert Perry)

mark). Because they are very slender upright strands, they do not assist in resisting compression loading in articular cartilage.

Articular cartilage exhibits a toe zone at the beginning of its stress/strain curve indicating that a large strain is produced with a relatively small tension stress. This characteristic toe zone is primarily due to undulations or waves in the type II collagen fibrils. When articular cartilage is first stretched, this "slack" is taken up. As increased tension strain takes place, articular cartilage stiffens (i.e., higher tension modulus) and responds in a more linear fashion. Everyday loading will keep articular cartilage within the elastic zone. In engineering tests, articular cartilage samples can be taken to progressive and complete failure. Such extreme loading seldom occurs in vivo during human activity (Figure 6.4).

2. Proteoglycans

Proteoglycans are large protein-polysaccharide molecules that form a core with attached glycosaminoglycans (GAGs). They differ in size and composition and include biglycans, decorin, and the largest class, termed aggrecans (or PG monomers). The GAGs of aggrecans fall into two classes of sulfate chains: (1) chondroitin sulfate, which is present in higher relative concentration at birth and progressively declines as we age and (2) keratan sulfate GAGs which progressively increase as we age into adulthood.

Aggrecans look like a test tube brush in three dimen-

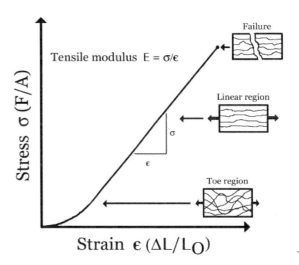

Figure 6.4 A stress/strain curve for articular cartilage in uniaxial tension. The slack in the toe zone is taken out during an initial stretch with increasing tension deformation bringing the collagen fibrils to a taut configuration until the sample reaches ultimate failure. (Courtesy of Robert Perry)

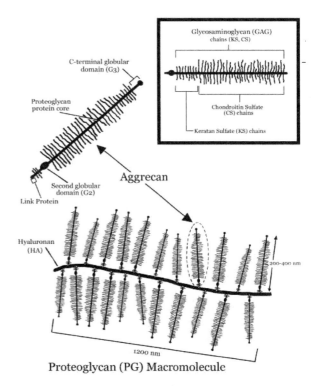

Proteoglycan (PG) Macromolecule

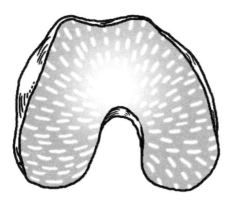

Femoral condyles

Figure 6.3 An example of articular cartilage anisotropy is observed in split lines across the surface of the femoral condyles when a small indenter is repeatedly pressed against the cartilage surface producing these split lines. (Figure adapted from Hultkrantz, 1898.) (Courtesy of Robert Perry)

Figure 6.5 (a) A schematic illustration of an aggrecan with its attached chondroitin and keratin sulfate chains bound to the protein core. (b) A schematic proteoglycan macromolecule (PG aggregate) with its hyaluronic acid core and attached aggrecans. (Courtesy of Robert Perry)

sions and are attracted to and bind with a large hyaluronic acid molecule strand to form a proteoglycan aggregate (PG aggregate). These structures, and to a lesser extent the free (unbound) proteoglycans, are responsible for resisting compression loads in articular cartilage. (Figures 6.5a and 6.5b)

Weight bearing acts to compress articular cartilage. The PG aggregates act much like air-filled balloons packed together in an enclosed rigid container. As a compressive load is applied, the PG aggregates become smaller (e.g., smaller balloons) and the joint cartilage becomes stiffer and thinner. When the load is relieved, the PG aggregates and the cartilage layers return to their unloaded status. (Figure 6.6) Additionally, articular cartilage as previously discussed is 60 to 80% water, and fluid flow occurs within the three layers of the cartilage thickness as well as movement of fluid out through the porous cartilage surface during compressive joint loading.

6.4 Lubrication of Articular Cartilage Surfaces

Healthy articular cartilage is extremely smooth. However,

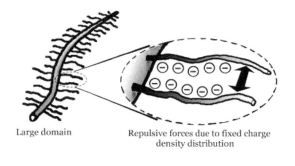

Large domain   Repulsive forces due to fixed charge density distribution

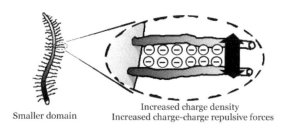

Smaller domain   Increased charge density Increased charge-charge repulsive forces

Figure 6.6 PG aggregates. This structure, and to a lesser extent the free proteoglycans, is responsible for resisting compression in articular cartilage. The PG aggregates, which may be up to 4 micrometers long, form domains that are compressed because of compressive loads that are imposed on diarthrodial joints during weight bearing and active muscle loading. (Courtesy of Robert Perry)

the smoothness of articular surfaces is not the only factor that governs the ability to minimize frictional forces. Fluid lubrication is the predominate factor in reducing diarthrodial joint (freely moveable joint) friction, with "boundary lubrication" (see Figure 6.7) playing a lesser role. Boundary lubrication is hypothesized to involve substances that act like a stick free coating in a modern frying pan. This coating consists of hyaluronan, lubricin, and phospholipid molecular components within synovial joints (Jahn, S., Seror, J. and Klein, J., (2016). Fluid lubrication occurs as the synovial membrane within diarthrodial joints produces a thin layer of synovial fluid that coats the articular surfaces. The quality of this fluid lubricant is affected by its material properties. Viscosity is one such property, and synovial fluid has the approximate viscosity of raw egg white. Synovial fluid is always being produced and reabsorbed in a healthy synovial (diarthrodial) joint. The result is a joint that moves under very low friction loads, improving mechanical efficiency and with minimal wear imposed upon the articular cartilage surfaces. The coefficient of friction may be as low as .005 to .01 (Soderberg, 1996). More recent research efforts indicate that the coefficient of friction of sliding cartilage surfaces may be as low as 0.001 up to pressures of 100 atm (atmospheric pressure) (Jahn, S., Seror, J. and Klein, J., (2016). Jahn, et al. (2016) also indicate that no man-made material can match this low limiting friction F_L. The authors also discuss the increased importance of boundary lubrication

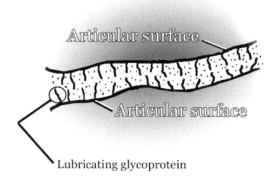

Articular surface

Articular surface

Lubricating glycoprotein

Figure 6.7 Boundry lubrication is not dependent upon fluids or fluid flow and instead is a lubrication that is due to a coating of the articular cartilage surfaces with surface adhering molecules. Lubricin (Swann et al., 1985) and/or dipalmitoyl phosphatidylcholine (Hills, 1989) have been implicated as the lubricating substance(s) responsible for boundry lubrication. (Courtesy of Robert Perry)

and the synergy of boundary effects in aqueous media and fluid lubrication.

Fluid lubrication falls into two modes: 1) hydrodynamic and 2) squeeze film lubrication. Each occurs under a different loading mechanism. Hydrodynamic lubrication occurs when one articular surface moves over another surface and when a thin wedge of fluid is pulled into an ever decreasing space at the apex of the wedge formed by the moving bones. Fluid, being non-compressible, helps keep the moving joint surfaces apart, preventing or reducing wear. (Figure 6.8a)

The second type of fluid lubrication is squeeze film lubrication, which occurs when predominant compression loads occur without joint movement. An example would be standing in a relatively still position. At the ankle joints, for example, body weight and muscular forces combine to produce significant joint reaction forces wherein one joint surface is pressed onto the other (e.g., inferior tibia into the superior surface of the talus bone). This is analogous to pushing two flat glass plates together with an oil film placed between the surfaces. The synovial fluid is loaded (hydrostatic loading), and pressures produced by the compression load are uniformly distributed throughout the fluid. With continued pressure, the fluid layer is thinned as fluid moves towards the edges of the compressive load area. (Figure 6.8b) Nevertheless, protection is provided by this thin fluid film due to the load distribution. The synovial (diarthrodial) joint is a closed system, and therefore when a compressive load is taken off the joint bearing surfaces, some synovial fluid returns to the joint surfaces and film thickness increases to its previous non-compressed state. During unloading some fluid also moves back into the articular cartilage in a process termed "imbibition," similar to a sponge absorbing a fluid.

During prolonged compressive loading, it is suggested that the viscosity of synovial fluid increases as the water component and small solutes are pushed through the small pores of articular cartilage surface into the cartilage tissue. However, large hyaluronan macromolecules (0.22 to 0.65 micrometer long) which formed outside the articular cartilage are too large to flow into articular cartilage tissue (Mow and Hung, 2001). Therefore, they become trapped at the surface and collect in valley asperities on the cartilage surfaces. The resulting increased viscous fluid may be able to provide some margin of continued protection. This mechanism has been termed boosted lubrication (Walker et al., 1968; 1970). (Figure 6.9)

6.5 Effect of Loads and Stresses

One factor which will serve to increase a normal stress

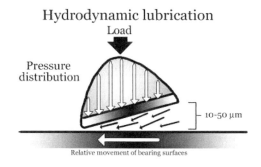

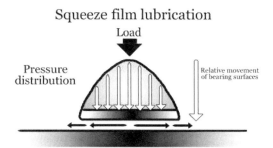

Figure 6.8 (a) In hydrodynamic lubrication, the relative movement of joint surfaces produces a wedge of fluid that is drawn into the ever decreasing space. This lubrication is very important in joint rotation, rolling and sliding motions. (b) squeeze film lubrication, a force couple is applied perpendicular to the joint surfaces. A fluid film acts to maintain some space between the two surfaces illustrated. Adapted from Nordin and Frankel, 1989. (Courtesy of Robert Perry)

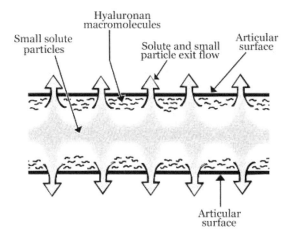

Figure 6.9 Boosted lubrication under prolonged loading with a concomitant increase in fluid viscosity. (Courtesy of Robert Perry)

is that of load distribution (normal stress = load/area). If an incongruity exists between joint surfaces or if a fibro-cartilage spacer such as one of the menisci in the knee has been surgically removed, then the area over which the load acts will be decreased with a resulting increase in stress. If the medial and lateral menisci are removed, then increased compressive stresses act to accelerate the degenerative articular cartilage process. (Figure 6.10)

Impact compression forces applied directly to a joint may be significant, and indirect axial loading through an upper or lower extremity may also occur as the result of impact. Finally, it should be appreciated that joint reaction forces that occur during joint motion (e.g., stair climbing) can be significant. In the knee for example, the force that pulls the bones together over the joint contact area (femur and tibia) may exceed 10 times body weight in single limb deep squat support. Stair climbing may produce a joint reaction force at the knee (tibiofemoral joint) exceeding four times body weight in a single limb step support (Nordin and Frankel, 2001).

The actual mechanism of injury from compression loads is not fully elucidated for articular cartilage, and a complete discussion is beyond the scope of this text. However, several contributing factors probably play a part in this process which include a degradation of the PG aggregates with more free aggrecans, collagen damage, a concomitant decrease in charge density, and decreased swelling pressure in the PG aggregates. Furthermore, altered loading may result in altered stimuli to chondrocytes and high levels of stress to subchondral bone (Mow et al., 1992).

Finally, articular cartilage exhibits several viscoelastic properties. Stress relaxation occurs in articular cartilage in a matter of seconds during prolonged loading. This mechanism in articular cartilage is fluid flow dependent and results from a redistribution of fluid within the three zones of articular cartilage. Very rapid loading may override this protective mechanism. Therefore, during quick impact loading, damage is more likely to occur. (Figure 6.11)

Direct trauma to a diarthrodial joint may result in a laceration of the cartilage surface. A defect in articular cartilage produced in this way will result in an exacerbation of the degenerative process as joint shear motion and compressive/tension stresses are introduced.

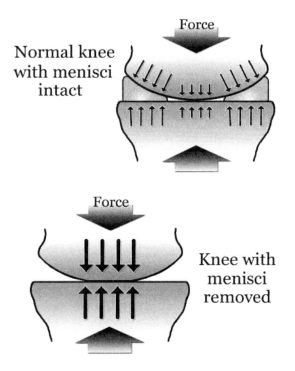

Figure 6.10 The load distribution is much smaller with the menisci removed from the knee joint as contrasted with a normal joint. The resulting compressive stress with this reduced area is necessarily at a much higher level at the joint surface contact area, leading to an acceleration of articular cartilage degeneration. (Courtesy of Robert Perry)

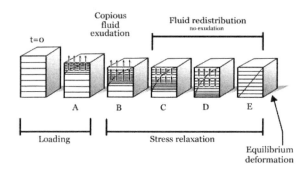

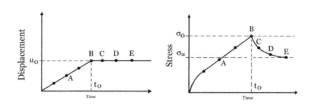

Figure 6.11 Stress relaxation which occurs in 2 to 5 seconds will be beneficial in terms of reducing peak stresses within articular cartilage by means of fluid redistribution (i.e., stress relaxation; Hou et al., 1992). (Figure adapted from Mow and Hung, 2001.) (Courtesy of Robert Perry)

6.6 Deformable Bearings and Stress Relaxation

Articular cartilage surfaces act much like deformable bearings when they are loaded in compression during sliding, rolling, spinning or during static axial loads. They will deform in such a way as to increase the contact surface area of the joint and therefore decrease the compression stress over the adjoining joint surfaces. This process also helps to attenuate the decrease in fluid film thickness that occurs with prolonged compressive loading during squeeze film fluid lubrication (Hou et al., 1992). (Figure 6.12)

6.7 Biomechanical Factors Involved in Articular Cartilage Degeneration

Normally, articular cartilage is a white, smooth glass-like surface. However, with age and repetitive loading, these surfaces may develop splits that will eventually progress to the bone articular lamella and may sustain erosion in similar fashion to a stream bed eroded down to bedrock. Splits (fibrillations) are thought to develop due to tension stresses that result from surface friction loads. The fail-

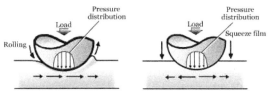

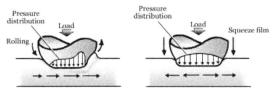

Figure 6.12 Deformable bearings result in what is termed elastohydrodynamic lubrication in diarthrodial joints. Each side of the joint surfaces will deform to decrease compressive stresses. (Courtesy of Robert Perry)

ure occurs in the collagen fibrils within the STZ layers initially. However, as the split propagates into the middle layer of cartilage, the PG aggregate-collagen matrix is disrupted as well, and the split continues into the deep layer zone and finally to the bone articular cartilage interface. This process is usually accompanied by the erosion process (smooth surface destructive thinning) with principally two underlying mechanisms. The first mechanism is adhesion, whereby surface areas in contact with each other adhere and are torn off the STZ. The second

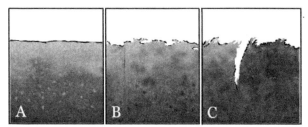

Figure 6.13 Representations of vertical sections through the surface of articular cartilage: (a) normal, (b) eroded, and (c) vertical split that will eventually reach the full thickness of the sample. (Courtesy of Robert Perry)

process is abrasion, whereby one joint surface area is harder than the opposing articular cartilage joint surface and will actually scrape off fragments of the STZ zone in the softer opposing joint surface. A combination of both mechanisms may result in an osteoarthritic joint with progressing chondromalacia and finally the sloughing off of the cartilage from the subchondral bone (stage IV chondromalacia). (Figure 6.13)

Case Study 6.1

A woman driver occupant in her fifties and grossly obese was involved in a minor passenger's side impact and claimed that her left knee moved sideways and struck the steering wheel column during this impact. Within weeks she underwent surgery to address chondromalacia (grades III and IV) of the medial femoral condyle (weight-bearing surface). The short time frame between this event and this pathology was not a match. Additionally, it was pointed out that the loading to the medial femoral condyle would have been exponentially greater in stair climbing activity compared to the loading in the subject motor vehicle accident, and therefore this accident event was not responsible for her articular cartilage pathology. Furthermore, any left knee impact loading imposed during this accident would not have produced significant stresses to the medial femoral condyle weight-bearing surface within the joint.

Figure Case Study 6.1 *(Courtesy of Robert Perry)*

References

Benjamin D. Ward, M.D. and James H. Lubowitz, M.D. (2013) Basic Knee Arthroscopy Part 4: Chondroplasty, Meniscectomy, and Cruciate Ligament Evaluation. Arthrosc Tech. 2 (4): pp. e507-e508.

Brand, R.A. "Joint Lubrication." In J.A. Albright and R.A. Brand, eds. *Scientific Basis of Orthopedics* (NY: Appleton Century Crofts, 1987), 373–386 (1987).

Ewers, B.J. et al. "Rate of Blunt Impact Loading Affects Changes in Retropatellar Cartilage and Underlying Bone in the Rabbit Patella." *J. of Biomechanics* 35:747–755 (2002)

Hills, B.A. "Oligolamellar Lubrication of Joints by Surface Active Phospholipid." *J. Rheum.* 1–6, 82–91 (1989)

Hou, J.S. et al. 1992. "An Analysis of the Squeeze-film Lubrication Mechanism for Articular Cartilage", *J. of Biomechanics*, Pergamon Press. Great Britain.

Hultkrantz, W. "Ueberdie Spaltrichtungen der Gelenknorpel." *Verhandlungen der Anatomischen Gesellschaft* 12:248 (1898)

Jahn, S., Seror, J. and Klein, J. (2016) Lubrication of Articular Cartilage, Annual Review of Biomedical Engineering, 18, pp. 235-258.

Mow, V.C., S.P. Amoczky and D.W. Jackson. *Knee Meniscus: Basic and Clinical Foundations* (NY: Raven Press, 1992)

Mow, C. and C. Hung. 2001. "Biomechanics of Articular Cartilage." In M. Nordin and V. Frankel, eds. *Basic Biomechanics of the Musculoskeletal System* (Philadelphia: Lippincott Williams & Wilkins, 2001)

Nordin, M. and V. Frankel. *Basic Biomechanics of the Musculoskeletal System* (Philadelphia: Lea and Febiger, 1989)

Nordin, M. and V. Frankel. *Basic Biomechanics of the Musculoskeletal System* (Philadelphia: Lippincott Williams & Wilkins, 2001)

Soderberg, G.L. 1996. *Kinesiology: Application to Pathological Motion* (Baltimore: Williams & Wilkins, 1996)

Swann, D.A. et al. "The molecular structure and lubricating activity of lubricin from bovine and human synovial fluids." *Biochem. J.* 225:195 (1985)

Walker, P.S. et al. "Boosted lubrication in synovial joints by fluid entrapment and enrichment." *Ann. Rheum. Dis.* 27:512 (1968)

Walker, P.S. et al. "Mode of aggregation of hyaluronic acid protein complex on the surface of articular cartilage." *Ann. Rheum. Dis.* 29:591 (1970)

Weightman, B. and E.G. Kempson. "Load carriage." In M.A.R. Freeman, ed. *Adult Articular Cartilage* (London: Pitman, 1979)

Williams, P.F., G.L. Powell and M. Laberge. "Sliding friction analysis of phosphatidylcholine as a boundary lubricant for articular cartilage." *Proc. Inst. Mech. Engrs.* 207:59 (1993)

Woo, S. L-Y, and J.A. Buckwalter. *Injury and Repair of the Musculoskeletal Soft Tissues* (Park Ridge, IL: American Academy of Orthopaedic Surgeons, 1987)

Chapter 7

Soft Tissue Biomechanics: Tendons, Ligaments, Muscle and Skin; Blood Fluid Dynamics

Patrick Hannon

7.1 Introduction

Injuries to tendon, ligament, muscle, and skin are often overlooked in favor of injuries considered to be more debilitating. However, damage to these soft tissues can be serious, influencing one's ability to perform physical work and adversely affecting one's quality of life. Resulting patho-mechanics from damage to soft tissues may also result in damage to other tissues such as articular cartilage and bone. Damage to vasculature may be life threatening.

7.2 Tendon and Ligament Development, Structure, and Physiology

Ligaments and tendons develop from mesenchymal tissue embryologically which differentiates into dense regular connective tissue. Ligaments connect bone to bone. Tendons connect muscle to bone or muscle to aponeuroses (sheet-like connective tissue). The collagen fibers and fiber bundles are parallel (tendons) or nearly parallel (ligaments). Elastin strands make up approximately 1% of tendons and a higher but variable percentage of ligaments. The collagen is responsible for the strength of these tissues in tension, and the elastin enables the connective tissue to stretch and then return to its original shape (elasticity). Fibroblasts (collagen producing cells) are relatively sparse, and their bodies do not directly contribute to the material strength properties of tendon and ligament.

Type I collagen is the primary solid component of tendons and ligaments with type III collagen comprising approximately 10% of ligamentous tissue and from 1–5% of tendinous tissue (Nordin, Lorenz and Campello, 2001). Type I and III collagen are formed from fibroblasts found between the fibers that secrete a larger precursor molecule called procollagen. Outside the fibroblast, procollagen is cleaved into the smaller units of collagen, and these units then aggregate into larger microfibrils, fibrils, fibers, and bundles of fibers. (Figure 7.1)

Tendons receive their blood supply from muscle, the bone attachment at the periosteum layer, and from a paratenon or a tendon sheath. In tendons where there is a surrounding vascular paratenon, the blood supply is extensive throughout the structure and the tendon is able to grow and remodel. (Figure 7.2) Some tendons are surrounded by a tendon sheath rather than a paratenon, and here the blood supply is limited to select areas along the sheath and tendon. Many areas under this tendon sheath do not have a vascular supply and therefore depend solely on a diffusion gradient through synovial fluid for nutrition and oxygen.

Ligaments receive their blood supply from the periosteum covering of bone at their attachment sites. Ligament vascularity is uniform hypo-vascular, and yet ligament insertion sites are of primary importance in maintaining the viability of ligaments (Woo et al., 1994). Ligaments may

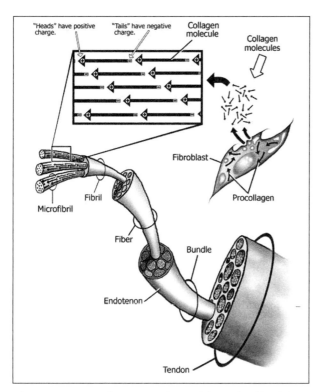

Figure 7.1 *Procollagen is released from the fibroblast and cleaved into collagen molecules which aggregate in an overlapping fashion to form microfibrils and fibrils. Fibrils combine to form fibers which also aggregate to form bundles of fibers and finally whole tendon or ligament. (Courtesy of Robert Perry)*

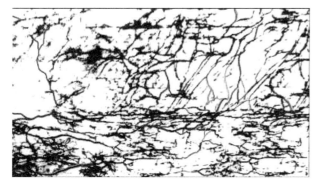

Figure 7.2 *Tendons with paratenon. Note the extensive vascular network. (Courtesy of Robert Perry)*

also derive oxygen and nutrition through synovial fluid diffusion gradients.

A. Tendon and ligament tissue healing

Tendons and ligaments may be torn under tension or cut during penetrating injury. Complete ruptures in tendons require reattaching the two ends surgically. In ligaments, complete tears may also involve reattachment, but under some circumstances ligamentous structures will reattach of their own accord. A complete tendon rupture will cause the muscle to concentrically shorten, and prompt surgical reattachment is usually advised. Injury accelerates the remodeling process of ligaments and tendons, and fibroblasts will increase their production of glycosaminoglycans (GAGs) and procollagen. Some scarring may also take place after an injury event, and this scar tissue differs from normal ligament and tendon tissue to a variable degree (Woo, 1985). Tendons and ligaments do not remodel as quickly as muscle, and stable cross links between collagen molecules and between collagen fibrils take time to become established.

B. Material properties of ligaments and tendons

Loading to ligaments and tendons is most appropriately tested with tension loading. Ligaments hold bones together and resist the distraction of moveable (diarthrodial) joints. Therefore ligaments must be strong in tension yet flexible and compliant enough to allow for changing joint positions during motion. Muscles and tendons transmit pulling forces upon bone or connective tissue.

The stress/strain curve for tendons and ligaments is very different from bone and usually largely dependent upon the collagen content of these tissues. Initially a toe zone develops as the collagen fibers begin to straighten out tendons and ligaments. When the slack is taken out of microstructures, they become markedly stiffer and enter into a linear elastic region on the curve. Finally, at extreme lengthening, past the physiological range of the joint and ligament, the proportionality limit (P point) is reached and microfailure begins to occur. Finally, with increased loading, the yield point on the stress-strain graph is reached and finally ultimate failure may occur, usually coincident with a complete rupture of the tendon or ligament.

Tendons may rupture due to external loads or internal loads when muscle force exceeds the breaking point. These soft tissues may therefore rupture within the normal range of motion (ROM). However, ligaments will only reach the failure point when joints are taken beyond their normal ROM. This is an important concept often overlooked by attorneys, and it should be appreciated that human motions produced by an external load but within an individual's normal ROM (a.k.a. physiological range) may load ligaments but will not produce injury trauma to these structures unless some other pathology is also present (Nordin et al. in Nordin and Frankel, 2001).

Ligaments that have a high percentage of elastin function differently and have different material properties: principally an extended elastic zone on the stress/strain curve. These ligaments act like stretched rubber bands and are able to apply pretension loads to some structures. One example is ligamentum flavum which spans the posterior spine just posterior to the spinal cord. Even in an erect standing position, this structure, because of its high elastin content, serves to compress vertebral bodies against each other and therefore increase the posterior joints' integrity of the spine. When flexion of the spine occurs, this ligament structure is further stretched within the posterior spinal canal and becomes somewhat stiffer to produce increased tension offering more protection to spinal elements. (Figure 7.3)

7.3 Skeletal Muscle Development, Structure, and Physiology

Skeletal muscle develops from mesenchymal tissue embryologically which differentiates into mesoderm in the embryo. Along the spine, this mesenchymal tissue in the form of somites develops, with one component being the myotome which develops into most of the spinal musculature. (Figure 7.4) Generalized mesoderm develops ultimately into musculature in the extremities of the fetus.

In humans, muscle cells (i.e., muscle fibers) may have hundreds of nuclei and generally range from approximately 1 to 30 centimeters in length. These cells fire (termed a muscle fiber action potential) and will produce tension with an attempt to shorten when they fire repeatedly. (Figure 7.5) Skeletal muscle fibers are recruited by the nervous system by stimulating "motor units." A more detailed discussion of motor units is presented in Chapter 19 of this text. Strong evidence indicates that the sliding filament theory is the best explanation for how muscle cells shorten or attempt to shorten. The mechanics of this

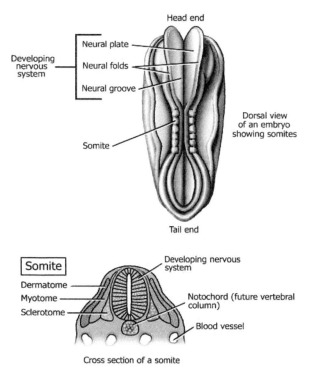

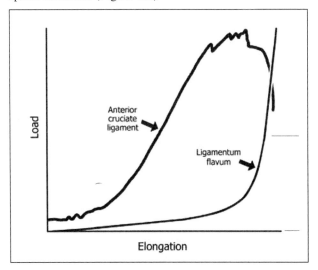

Figure 7.3 Ligamentum flavum of the human spine is contrasted with the anterior cruciate ligament of the interior human knee. The anterior cruciate bundles are much stiffer than the elastic ligamentum flavum which is much more flexible. (Courtesy of Robert Perry)

Figure 7.4 A cross-section and dorsal view of somites which are comprised of three regions: sclerotome developing into vertebrae, dermatome developing into connective tissue, and myotome developing into skeletal muscle tissue along the neck, spine, and torso. (Courtesy of Robert Perry)

muscle shortening involve myofilaments composed of actin and myosin and two other protein strands (titin and nebulin). Actin and myosin interaction is thought to be principal in this process. The reader is referred to Lorenz and Campello (2001) for a complete discussion of the mechanics and physiology of this process.

When muscle cells shorten to produce tension, they transfer tension to the connective tissue that runs through skeletal muscles. This tissue includes endomysium which surrounds the muscle fibers, perimysium that surrounds the bundles of muscle fibers, and epimysium that surrounds the entire individual muscle. This connective tissue forms the tendon previously discussed, and therefore one may think of the tendon as running through the entire muscle as it pulls on its two or more attachment points. (Figure 7.6)

A. Muscle tissue healing

Muscle tissue is able to store oxygen, glucose, and fatty acids, but the supply is very limited, and therefore muscle tissue requires a rich blood supply for oxygen and food substrates in order to continue active muscle contraction. The rich blood supply also facilitates muscle healing after damage such as muscle tears (e.g., a muscle strain). However, skeletal muscle healing is limited by the formation of scar tissue and by stem cell tissue regeneration. Stem or myosatellite cells in muscle tissue lie dormant until they are recruited into action by an injury mechanism and begin to mature and fuse together to form whole new muscle fibers. The extent of this regeneration process in the mammalian system is limited in skeletal muscle. Therefore large lacerations or the destruction of large numbers of skeletal muscle fibers results in significant scar connective tissue formation which can affect muscle extensibility (decreased range of motion) and decrease muscle tension production.

B. Material properties of skeletal muscle tissue

Muscles produce active tension and the muscle tendons transmit this tension to the bone or the connective tissue. The forces that occur during voluntary muscle activity are considerable and may approximate as much as 44 lbs. per square inch (psi) (Alexander, 1992). A more recent study indicates that mammalian muscle can be calculated by multiplying the physiological cross-section area (PCSA) by 22.5 Newtons/centimeter^2 (Lieber et al., 2011). These muscle-produced tensile forces may actually bring a muscle or muscle group to failure within the central portion of the muscle (muscle belly), at the muscle-tendon junction,

or at the muscle-tendon-bone attachment site (i.e., avulsion bone fracture). In these cases, a forceful voluntary muscle contraction is initiated and results in injury at one of these three sites. Sometimes high external loads are applied to the neck, torso, or extremities. In response to these loads, muscle elements are brought into play and voluntarily or reflexively produce muscle tension forces that may produce injury at these same sites. Once failure occurs at one site, the energy is released, and other sites are usually spared from injury. This failure may occur even if the joint(s) stay within the normal range of motion.

Muscle may also be subjected to external loading when relaxed (loading to passive muscle). This passive stretch may occur in high speed automobile accidents and in any passive joint movement that occurs very rapidly

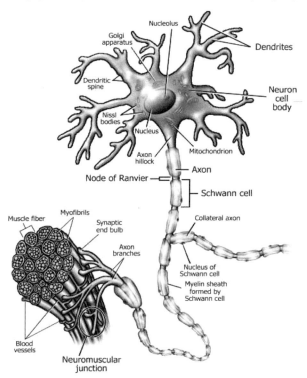

Figure 7.5 The motor neuron housed in the anterior horn portion of the spinal cord serves to stimulate skeletal muscle fibers at the periphery. One alpha motor neuron may stimulate (enervate) up to roughly 1,500 muscle fibers. When the motor neuron fires, generally all of the muscle fibers of this unit will also fire (i.e., action potential). Repeated firing at six or seven pulses per second will produce a sustained active contraction of the muscle fibers of a motor unit. A large human muscle may have hundreds or thousands of motor units and these units may fire within a range of 5 to 40 Hz. (Courtesy of Robert Perry)

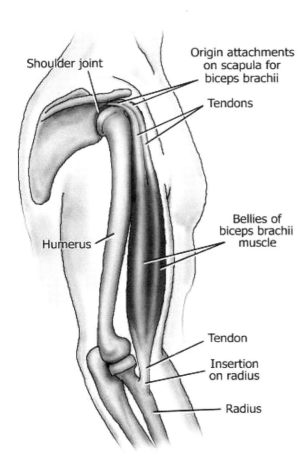

Figure 7.6 *The muscle-tendon complex. Muscles pull rather than push and therefore operate by producing a tension force on bone or connective tissue. (Courtesy of Robert Perry)*

(less than 75–100 ms) so as to eliminate the effect of the muscle stretch reflex (i.e., myotatic stretch reflex). In these instances, muscle and tendons may be brought to failure if the ROM in joints is exceeded, in addition to possible failure of joint ligaments.

Muscle stress/strain curves incorporate active, passive, and total tension stress components. The passive component curve starts to rise beginning at normal resting muscle length in response to an externally applied load in much the same way as typical tendons and ligaments. (Figure 7.7) The active component, however, must be tested using live stimulated animal muscle tissue in vitro (live excised muscle tissue). This inverted U-shaped curve illustrates the relative maximal force that muscle tissue may produce at different muscle lengths. This principle is important to the biomechanist in terms of estimating voluntary muscle forces during specific human positions or movements.

Muscle tissue may also be exposed to compression loads and with significant compression stresses over time,

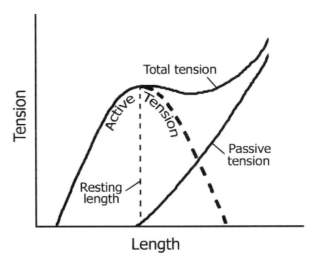

Figure 7.7 *The active, passive, and total tension stress curves at various lengths of skeletal muscle. Note that muscle length is determined by the angle of joint(s). (Courtesy of Robert Perry)*

muscle damage may result from decreased blood perfusion or, more rarely, from extreme mechanical compression strain of muscle fibers. These compressive stresses may lead to muscle cell death in addition to peripheral nerve and vascular damage within muscle tissue.

7.4 Skin Development, Structure, and Physiology

The skin comprises the integumentary system and forms from ectoderm embryologically. Its purpose is to protect deeper tissues from the outside environment. The skin provides a barrier to pathogens and sunlight, helps to maintain body temperature, and provides resistance to external loading. External loading of skin is our primary focus in biomechanics. The skin may be breached by impacts producing abrasions, lacerations, and punctures.

Skin consists of two major components: a cutaneous membrane and accessory structures. The cutaneous membrane consists of outer epidermis layers (four to five) and a deeper inner dermis consisting of two layers. Accessory structures such as hair, nails, and exocrine glands are found in both the epidermis and the dermis of the cutaneous membrane. The nature of skin varies considerably depending upon the area of the body. Skin on the palms of the hand and bottom surface of the foot is thick and tough with ridges that are thought to increase friction when grabbing objects or walking on smooth surfaces. These ridges on the fingertips are genetically determined, and biological diversity enables forensic experts to identify individuals from fingerprints. Chronic loading of these skin areas during hand labor or barefoot locomotion will increase the thickness of the epidermis layers of skin (specifically the stratum germinativum layer component), and stem cells within this layer divide more rapidly due to the external mechanical stresses. (Figure 7.8)

A. Skin tissue healing

When skin injury is limited to the epidermis, this organ has a great capacity for self repair. Stem cells from the stratum germinativum within the epidermis rapidly multiply and migrate to the epidermis injury site. If the damage is widespread within the epidermis or if injury extends into the dermis, then repair takes place with variable scarring. Large lacerations, very deep abrasions or burns such as water scalding which occur during trauma may produce considerable scarring. Keloid scars may also develop in some individuals with scarring that extends deeper into the dermis layer and/or beyond the area of the injury site. Hypertrophic scarring (raised scarring without an increase in the total cross section area) is even more common than keloid scarring and both types of scarring may occur in partial thickness or full thickness burn trauma. In addition to a poor cosmetic appearance, the material properties are different in scar tissue as compared to normal healthy skin (less extensibility and elasticity).

B. Material properties of skin tissue

Human skin is subjected to tension forces during body movements. It is composed of primarily type I collagen and elastin. Its relatively high elastin content enables skin to stretch and then return to its original length and form.

(Figure 7.9)

These collagen and elastin fibers exhibit small undulations and therefore are not taut in relaxed skin. The fiber orientation within skin is predominantly parallel to the skin's surface (within the membrane thickness) but varies in direction in the other two dimensions within layers and within regions. (Figure 7.10) When skin is brought to ultimate failure point in tension, it should be appreciated that other deeper structures may have also reached their elastic limits and have exceeded their ultimate failure points. Skin may also be taken gradually into the plastic zone and may experience micro-failure followed by scarring. This sometimes happens during pregnancy or rapid excessive weight gain (muscle or fat tissue) and results in what are commonly known as stretch marks.

Cyclic loading of skin has been shown to increase the collagen fibril diameter and decrease fibril density (Sanders and Goldstein, 2001). The formation of calluses on the bottom surface of the feet or on the palms of the hands is one example of skin adaptation that acts to protect. However, in other skin areas, the overall effect of shear, tension, and compression loading is still largely undetermined in terms of gross morphology and strength/stiffness properties.

Skin may also be penetrated, resulting in a laceration or a puncture wound. A sharp instrument that is able to breach the skin may introduce pathogens. A laceration wound may be straight with little skin damage, or it may be a jagged wound resulting in more extensive damage. Puncture wounds tend to close up and may appear rela-

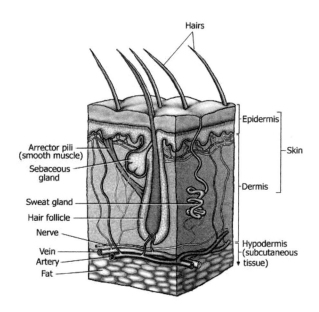

Figure 7.8 A cross-section of human skin. (Courtesy of Robert Perry)

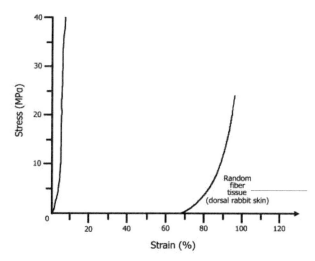

Figure 7.9 Dorsal rabbit skin stress/strain curve. Skin exhibits a very long elastic zone with a concomitant low-tension modulus when subjected to uniaxial tension. Adapted from Woo (1985). (Courtesy of Robert Perry)

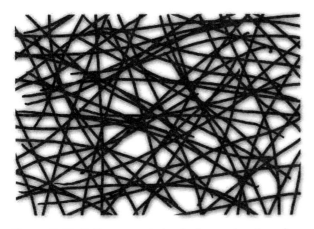

Figure 7.10 Collagen and elastin lie predominantly parallel to the surface of skin within respective layers. However, collagen orientation is responsible for skin anisotropy, and skin in similar fashion to other biological materials does not exhibit identical (failure points in all directions. (Courtesy of Robert Perry)

tively innocuous. In reality, serious damage may exist to deeper structures, and puncture wounds also present an increased risk of infection (Whiting and Zernicke, 1998).

Skin and subcutaneous tissues may also bruise (tissue ecchymosis) when subjected to acute loading (e.g., impact or severe muscle strain). This is largely due to the rupture of the blood vasculature in skin and deeper subcutaneous tissue. Under chronic continuous compression or shear loads, blood and hence oxygen perfusion decrease within the dermis layer, sometimes leading to decubitus ulcerations in skin (e.g., bed sores). The elderly population is especially susceptible to these effects.

Desmoulin, et al. (2011) and Huang, l. (2012) provide an authoritative discussion of the mechanics of acute blunt compressive trauma bruising (ecchymosis) and the stress levels involved in failure of several tissues including capillary tissue. Desmoulin et al. (2011) provides human subject testing of quantified blunt force trauma to the upper and lower extremities of one 34-year-old male with the dependent measure being bruising.

In the SCALP of the head, swelling and ecchymosis result from trauma to capillary tissue within the connective tissue of the SCALP (i.e., "C" in scalp) or from the clamping of the skin's dermis, hypodermis and deeper tissues to include muscle and bone mid to lower face due to lateral clamp compression against a hard surface. The minimum force required to produce SCALP or face swelling and resulting ecchymosis has not been experimentally established in adults or in infants/children. Furthermore, normal biological individuality and underlying bleeding pathology may affect the development of impact trauma

event bruising.

7.5 Vasculature and Blood

A. Vasculature structure and material properties

Veins return blood to the heart, and arteries transport blood away from the heart by means of the heart pump mechanism. The structure of both of these vessels is composed of three distinct layers termed tunics. From the outer wall inward these layers include the tunica adventitia (tunica externa), the tunica media, and the tunica interna (tunica intima). Within the center of these vessels is the lumen through which blood flow takes place. In veins, this lumen is larger, and there are one-way valves that function to bring blood back to the heart (not present in arteries). In arteries, the lumen is smaller, but the three layers of tunics form thicker walls which contain a higher percentage of elastin fibers (large elastic arteries) so as to permit circumferential stretch during heart pump (left ventricle) expulsion of blood (systoli) and contractility of the walls and lumen during heart left ventricle relaxation (diastoli). (Figure 7.11) Therefore, these large arteries form what is termed a pressure reservoir (Tortora and Grabowski, 1993). Moderately sized arteries also have a larger percentage of elastin than do veins. However, it is the smooth muscle tissue that surrounds these arteries that makes them unique. A constriction of this smooth muscle tissue in response to hormonal factors enables these vessels to increase blood pressure (to maintain adequate blood perfusion), which prevents various forms of "shock" and to distribute blood where it is needed. These arteries may be termed muscular distributing arteries (Tortora and

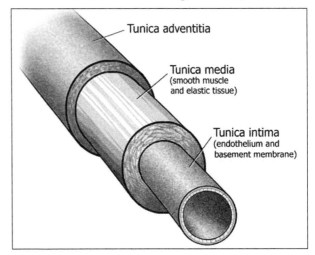

Figure 7.11 Cross-section of veins and arteries. (Courtesy of Robert Perry)

Grabowski, 1993). Smaller arteries, termed arterioles, also exhibit this muscular vasoconstriction property and a coincident affect upon blood pressure.

Veins and venules (small veins) serve as blood reservoirs holding approximately 60% of the body's blood, and once activated, smooth muscle will again serve to constrict these vessels, which results in an expulsion of this blood from these venous reservoirs with a concomitant increase in blood pressure and increased availability of blood for working muscle during exercise or during a fight or flight response (Tortora and Grabowski, 1993).

This ability of the cardiovascular system to bring more blood into the arterial system from the venous reservoir, coupled with arterial regulation of arteries to constrict to produce additional increases in blood pressure and dilation of other arteries to better distribute oxygenated blood is considered protective in most cases. However, if body trauma involves a laceration of moderate or large arteries, then this condition may lead rapidly to hypovolemic shock due to a loss of blood volume and an inability of the cardiovascular system to maintain adequate perfusion regardless of increased heart rate or stroke volume. Tissues are damaged and may die due to a lack of oxygen (anoxia). The reader is referred to Landry and Oliver (2004) for a more detailed discussion of shock and its treatment.

Veins and arteries may be punctured or lacerated or may burst due to blunt force trauma. Smaller vessels and capillaries that are close to the skin in the torso and extremities when brought to failure will produce characteristic bruising (ecchymosis). Larger vessels will produce a more extensive hematoma. In general, a laceration, puncture, or blunt force rupture of venous vasculature is not as serious as the failure of arterial vasculature. The arterial system will permit much more perfuse bleeding because of higher fluid pressures, and therefore exsanguination (removal of blood leading to death) becomes a major immediate concern if significant large arteries fail. For example, rupture of the thoracic aorta due to blunt force trauma against the steering wheel in a motor vehicle accident is immediately life threatening (see torso and abdomen chapter). Venous bleeds may also result in significant blood loss but over a longer time frame depending upon the size of the vein(s) that have failed. In general, arteries are better protected from trauma than veins due to their deeper location within the body in addition to the material properties than make them tougher. The reader is referred to Chuong and Fung (1985) for a more detailed discussion of stress and strain in arteries.

B. Blood fluid dynamics
The study of non-Newtonian fluids (e.g., blood or paint)

in terms of fluid deformation, flow characteristics, and drop separation is termed rheology. Blood is a non-Newtonian, viscoelastic liquid composed of some substances in solution (e.g., glucose) and some suspended cells and particles. Plasma proteins and red blood cells are responsible for blood's non-Newtonian, viscoelastic properties (Wonder, 2001). Blood composition becomes important in blood spatter analysis in criminal forensics. Although water is a primary component of blood, blood behavior is more complex due in large part to blood viscosity (which is variable) and "adhesion" between the transport mechanism and blood. As an example, a high hematocrit (percentage of red blood cells per unit volume) will increase the elasticity and viscosity of blood, resulting in an elongated spatter pattern (from source to spatter) along a surface rather than allowing blood to separate into droplets as would water (Wonder, 2001). Blood is also determined to be a thixotropic fluid rather than a rheopectic fluid (Huang, C., Pan, W., Chen, H., and Copley, A., 1987). In thixotropic fluids such as many gels and human blood, a time-dependent characteristic is that when a significant stress is applied for a relatively long time, there is a concomitant increase in the fluid state with less viscosity. As an example, when Ketchup (also a thixotropic fluid) is about to be poured out of a glass bottle with a narrow neck (best at about 30°), a palm hand impact load to the bottom of the bottle results in shear stresses which increase the fluid state of the Ketchup and temporarily decrease its viscosity and now the Ketchup flows very rapidly out of the bottle. whereas initially without the shear stress application, the Ketchup does not flow out due to gravity alone. Once the stress is removed from a thixotropic non-Newtonian fluid such as Ketchup or human blood (e.g., after blood spatter has come to stop on a wall), these fluids return to their more viscous state and fluid flow is reduced or stops.

Rheopectic fluids on the other hand, such as dairy cream, increase their viscosity in a time-dependent manner and become thicker when stresses are applied by shaking or stirring (University of Wakato, 2010. www.Sciencelearn.org.nz). Dilatant fluids act in much the same way as rheopectic fluids in that fluid viscosity is increased with applied stresses but not in a time-dependent manner.

C. Blood spatter analysis
Finally, the angle of impact, the area of origin or convergence, and the directionality of the blood spatter pattern may all be determined from a blood spatter analysis. Additionally, forward projection spatter versus backward projection spatter versus cast-off spatter may be determined in many cases involving gunshot trauma. Recently, programs such as Hemospat 1.11 or BackTrack eliminate

the need for a string analysis at the crime scene (directionality and area of origin) if good photographic data is available of the blood spatter pattern. These software programs have been further validated with traditional string pattern analysis.

Blood analysis involves both impact biomechanics and chemical analysis. The reader is referred to Wonder (2001) and Bevel (2008) for a discussion that extends beyond this basic introduction.

7.6 Anisotropic and Viscoelastic Behavior

A. Anisotropic behavior

All these soft tissues discussed exhibit differences in strength depending upon the direction of the force applied. This anisotropic effect is directly dependent upon the direction of the collagen and elastin strands within soft tissues. In muscles, tendons, and ligaments, the collagen strands are oriented parallel to the direction of pull so as to most effectively transmit the force or resist the tension/shear loading. In skin, these strands are parallel to the skin's surface but more random in terms of surface direction. Therefore, skin is less anisotropic and able to handle shear loads from many directions. Nevertheless, skin has lines of cleavage which represent a dominant direction of collagen and elastin strands as represented in Figure 7.10. A collagen helical fiber array in arteries helps prevent kinking as these vessels are bent during body movements (Wainwright, 1985). Collagen fiber orientation is therefore adapted to the tissue and serves to protect the tissue from failure.

B. Viscoelastic behavior

The soft tissues all exhibit time-dependent viscoelastic properties, in most cases becoming stronger and stiffer (increased viscosity) when the loading rate is rapid. This effect in soft tissues may prevent injury in many cases during rapid loading. However, if the soft tissue is brought to the breaking point, an increased amount of energy will have been stored during rapid loading which when released may result in increased disruption of these tissues. Furthermore, all tissues do not exhibit identical rate-dependent viscoelastic properties. Cortical bone tissue exhibits increased strength and stiffness to a greater degree than do ligaments and tendons during very rapid loading. Therefore, bone may fail at a relatively low loading rate during a forceful muscle tendon pull and at higher rates of loading, the muscle or tendinous tissue may rupture instead due to cortical bone's increased ultimate failure point.

References

Alexander, R.M. *Exploring Biomechanics: Animals in Motion*. Scientific American Library, (1992).

Bevel, T. (2008) Bloodstain Pattern Analysis 3rd Ed., CRC Press.

Chuong, C.J. and Y.C. Fung. *Residual Stress in Arteries in Frontiers in Biomechanics*. Eds. Schmid-Schonbein, G. W. Woo and Zweifach, B.W. New York: Springer-Verlag, (1985).

Desmoulin, G., and Anderson, G. (2011) Method to investigate contusion mechanics in living humans, Journal of Forensic Biomechanics, vol. 2, doi: 10.4303/jfb/F100402

Huang, C., Pan, W., Chen, H., and Copley, A., (1987) Thixotropic properties of whole blood from healthy human subjects, Biorheology, 24 (6), pp. 795-801.

Huang, L., Bakker, N., Kim, J., Marston, J., Grosse, I., Tis, J., and Cullinane, D. (2012) A multi-scale finite element model of bruising in soft connective tissues. Journal of Forensic Biomechanics. Vol 3, doi: 10:4303/jfb/235579

Landry, D.W. and J.A. Oliver. "Insights into Shock." *Scientific American* February; 36–41. (2004)

Lieber, R. and Ward, S. (2011) Skeletal muscle design to meet functional demands. Philos Trans Soc London B Biol Sci, vol. 366 (1570): pp. 1466–1476.

Nachemson, A. L., and J. H. Evans. "Some Mechanical Properties of the Third Human Lumbar Interlaminar Ligament (Ligamentum Flavum)." *Journal of Biomechanics* (1968); 1:211–220.

Norden, Lorenz, and Campello. In Nordin M. and V. Frankel, *Basic Biomechanics of the Musculoskeletal System*. Philadelphia: Lippincott Williams & Wilkins, (2001).

Sanders, J.E. and B.S. Goldstein. "Collagen Fibril Diameters Increase and Fibril Densities Decrease in Skin Subjected to Repetitive Compressive and Shear Stresses." *Journal of Biomechanics* (2001); 34:1581–1587.

Soderberg, G.L. *Kinesiology: Application to Pathological Motion*. Baltimore: Williams & Wilkins (1996).

Tortora, G.J. and S.R. Grabowski. *Principles of Human Anatomy.* 7th ed. New York: Harper-Collins College Publishers, (1993).

Wainwright. "Fibrous Skin Mechanics: Superstructure and New Problems." In *Frontiers in Biomechanics.* Eds. Schmid-Schonbein, G.W. Woo and B.W. Zweifach. New York: Springer-Verlag, (1985).

Whiting, W.C. and R. F. Zernicke. *Biomechanics of Musculoskeletal Injury.* Champaign, IL: Human Kinetics, (1998).

Wonder, A.Y. *Blood Dynamics.* San Diego: Academic Press, (2001).

Woo, S.L.Y. "Biomechanics of Tendons and Ligaments in Frontiers." In *Biomechanics eds.* Schmid-Schonbein, G.W. Woo and Zweifach, B.W. New York, Springer-Verlag, (1985).

Woo, S. L. Y. and J. A. Buckwalter. *Injury and Repair of the Musculoskeletal Soft Tissues.* Park Ridge, Ill.: American Academy of Orthopaedic Surgeons, (1987).

Woo, S.L.Y. et al. "Anatomy, Biology and Biomechanics of Tendon, Ligament and Meniscus." In S. R. Simon (Ed.). *Orthopaedic basic science.* Rosemont, Ill.: American Academy of Orthopaedic Surgeons (1994).

Chapter 8

Biomechanics of Spinal Cord, Nerve Roots, and Peripheral Nerve

Patrick Hannon

8.1 Introduction

The function of the nervous system includes acquiring information from the environment, processing this information (interpretation, synthesis, and decision making), and motor execution by means of muscle contraction. This communication network involves two broad interrelated systems: the central nervous system and the peripheral nervous system, both of which are neuron based. Neurons (nerve cells) that are wholly within the brain, brain stem, or spinal cord are considered central nervous system neurons. Neurons that are wholly or partially outside the brain, brain stem or spinal cord are termed peripheral neurons. This chapter addresses the anatomy and biomechanical behavior of groups of neurons and related cells within the spinal cord (central nervous system) and within the peripheral nervous system (nerve roots and peripheral nerve).

Chapter 19 addresses neurophysiology and muscle activity in more detail for the reader who desires additional information on this subject.

8.2 Anatomy of the Spinal Cord and Nerve Roots

The spinal cord forms at the inferior end of the brain stem (medulla oblongata) and consists of ascending (sensory) and descending (motor and gland) tracts at the circumferential periphery. The interior section of the cord is gray matter primarily composed of the cell bodies of neurons and glial cells. In the spinal cord, this interior section forms a butterfly shape, with the tails of the butterfly wings corresponding to the back of the spinal cord gray matter. (Figure 8.1) The spinal cord ends at approximately the first lumbar vertebra in the adult, and this level marks the beginning of the cauda equina (horse's tail). The spinal cord is enveloped with the same three meninges that cover the brain's cerebral cortex, which include the pia mater, arachnoid membrane, and the dura mater. Twelve cranial nerves are peripheral nerves (excepting the optic nerve) and span from brain stem structures to the head and neck and sometimes beyond as in the case of the vagus nerve (cranial nerve; number X). These nerves may be motor or sensory or both and may enervate rather large muscles such as trapezius and sternocleidomastoid (accessory nerve; number XI). (Figure 8.2)

Thirty-one nerve roots extend outward from the intervertebral foramina, and these nerve roots are also encased in these three meninges. These connective tissue membranes funnel down distal to the joining of motor and sensory nerve root branches, and thirty-one peripheral nerves begin as they exit from the spinal foramina (a.k.a., intervertebral foramina). (Figure 8.3) Spinal nerves are peripheral nerves that exit from the intervertebral foramina as mixed (motor and sensory) and are labeled from C1 to C8 in the cervical spine. In the cervical spine, the cervical and brachial plexuses are formed as peripheral nerves join together as they move laterally from the spinal column. In the thoracic spine, plexuses are not formed as peripheral nerves extend outward. In the lumbar and sacral spine, spinal nerves once again form plexuses and radiate outwards from the spinal cord or the cauda equina.

8.3 Anatomy of Peripheral Nerve

Spinal peripheral nerves are covered with three connective tissues which differ in their location and in terms of their biomechanical properties. The epineurium covers the entire peripheral nerve; the perineurium covers nerve bundles (fasciculi); and finally the endoneurium covers individual neuron axons. (Figure 8.4) Furthermore, a nerve plexus, such as the brachial plexus, has a periradicular sheath that covers the majority of nerve roots of C5-8 and T1 during their course along the side of the neck. This structure continues downward to form the epineural sheath of the brachial plexus.

8.4 Microanatomy and Physiology of Neuron Axons

Peripheral nerves are made up of neuron axons that transmit sensory, motor, or autonomic impulses (sympathetic and parasympathetic). The vast majority of peripheral nerve axons are covered with a myelin sheath formed by Schwann cells which wrap themselves around individual axons at one millimeter spacings. Myelin serves as an insulating material and speeds the conduction of electrical impulses (ionic current). In humans, this peripheral nerve transmission can be as high at 70 meters/second for large diameter myelinated axons and as slow as one-half meter/second for some type IV unmyelinated nociceptive (pain)

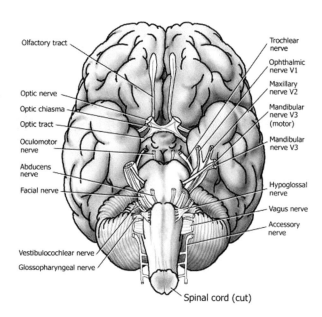

Figure 8.2 Inferior view of the brain. The cranial nerves have many motor and sensory functions and autonomic functions (e.g., heart rate control). (Courtesy of Robert Perry)

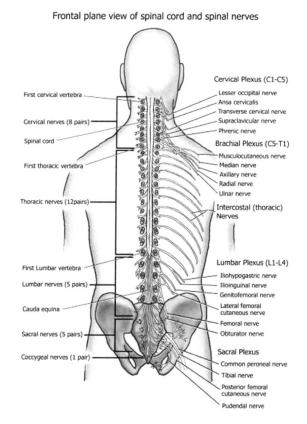

Figure 8.3 Frontal plane view of spinal cord and spinal nerves. Nerve roots exit the intervertebral foramina and form peripheral nerves. (Courtesy of Robert Perry)

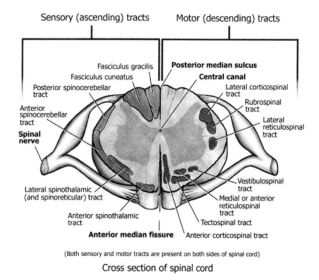

Figure 8.1 A cross-section (horizontal plane) of the spinal cord and exiting nerve roots. Sensory and motor tracts are indicated. (Courtesy of Robert Perry)

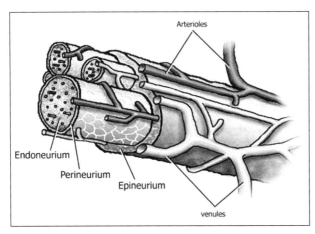

Figure 8.4 Three connective tissues form around a peripheral nerve. The epineurium surrounds the whole nerve; the perineurium surrounds nerve bundles; and the endoneurium surrounds individual axons. (Courtesy of Robert Perry)

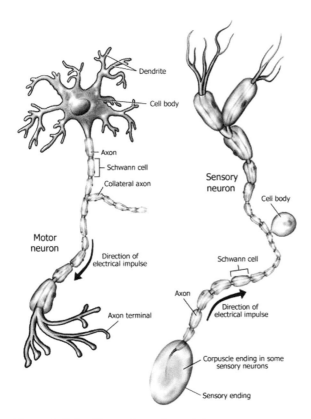

Figure 8.5 An illustration of an alpha motor neuron (an efferent neuron) responsible for muscle activation and a sensory neuron (an afferent neuron) responsible for skin sensation or body segment information. (Courtesy of Robert Perry)

receptor axons. Motor nerves transmit from cranial nuclei or from the anterior horns of the spinal cord to the periphery. Sensory nerves transmit from the periphery to the cell body and beyond (unipolar neurons of dorsal root ganglia) in spinal nerves responsible for skin sensor reception and body segment position information. (Figure 8.5)

8.5 Spinal Cord Loading

The spinal cord may be loaded in tension, compression, or shear. Although protected by the bony spinal column, the spinal cord is subject to penetration and laceration injuries. Bending, tension, and torsion loads are usually minimal within the elastic zone and therefore unlikely to produce mechanical injury. Some concern has been expressed in terms of high head link angular accelerations which may produce tension within the brain stem or at the brain stem and spinal cord interface (See Chapter 9). The dura mater (tough mother) is the only membrane that provides significant structural strength to resist significant tension loading within the spinal cord.

A. Penetration

Penetration injuries can occur to the cord when a sharp instrument or a high velocity projectile penetrates the spinal column. A partial or complete laceration or a highly comminuted fracture that drives bone fragments into the spinal cord or cauda equina can be catastrophic. Even in a partial penetrating compromise of the neural canal, subsequent swelling, inflammation, and ischemia may exacerbate the original spinal cord or cauda equina injury. Neurons and their axons do not appear to regenerate in the mammalian spinal cord as they do in most peripheral nerves. Furthermore, once a lesion has occurred within the cord, healing in the true sense does not take place. Neuron axons within the cord that have been severed will no longer conduct impulses. Whole nerve tracts may be completely obliterated with all function lost. This may result in hemiplegia, paraplegia, or quadriplegia (tetraplegia) as well as sensory loss depending upon the level and extent of the neural lesion. Once mechanical deformation has occurred, some of the damage is done and not recoverable given current medical science. Corticosteroid treatment (e.g., methlprednisone) and other new agents are helpful however in reducing the acute swelling and edema which can exacerbate the pathological changes that occur within the spinal cord as the result of trauma.

Please note however that recent evidence clearly

indicates that stem cells within the upper CNS do form new neurons during adulthood. Furthermore, many investigators have reported regenerating spinal tracts. Both motor and sensory axons have been found to grow spontaneously in contused (blunt trauma) spinal cords, crossing glia cell tissue and white matter surrounding the blunt injury site. Sensory axons grow long distances in injured dorsal (sensory) columns of the spinal cord toward the upper CNS after peripheral nerve lesions. Cell transplants and treatments increase cyclic adenosine monophosphate (i.e., cAMP) and neurotrophins stimulate motor and sensory axons to cross glial scars and to grow long distances in white matter. Therefore, hope remains that spinal tract regeneration in humans may one day be possible (Young, 2014).

Possible spine injury always indicates the need for immobilization prior to determining the stability of the spine by imaging. Movement of an unstable spine at the lesion site may produce additional mechanical penetration primarily through shear loading as vertebral body fragments, end plates/discs of vertebral bodies, or posterior vertebral elements move in many possible directions. (Figure 8.6)

B. Compression

The spinal cord or cauda equina may also be compressed

as the result of a bony stenosis within the neural canal of the spinal column. Most vulnerable are the areas of C3 to T2 and from T9-10 to L1-2 which result from a fusiform thickening of the cervical and thoraco-lumbar spinal cords, and therefore more space is occupied within the neural canal (Hyde, 1992). Biological individuality dictates that some individuals have congenital stenosis defects most typically in the cervical spine. The stenosis usually involves radial compression (i.e., around the entire spinal cord). Relatively small movements of the spinal column in shear may produce compressive stresses applied to the thecal sac surrounding the spinal cord in these individuals. These individuals may be predisposed to cervical spine trauma due to biomechanical loading. Usually, this only becomes evident after a traumatic episode when appropriate imaging of the cervical spine neural canal takes place. (Figure 8.7)

The spinal cord, cauda equina, and intervertebral nerve roots may also be compressed by a disc protrusion or a frank herniation of the intervertebral disc. In these cases,

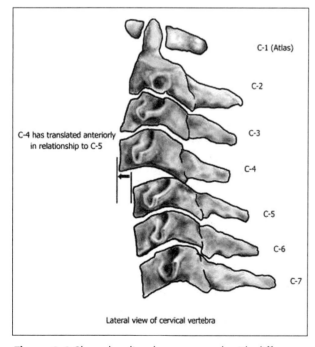

Figure 8.6 *Shear loading has occurred with differential movement occurring between two vertebral bodies. (Courtesy of Robert Perry)*

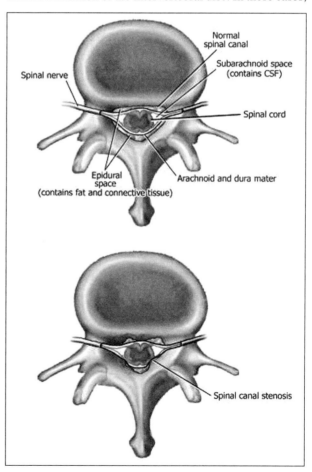

Figure 8.7 *Spinal stenosis of the spinal canal. Less room is available within the canal due to a congenital stenosis. (Courtesy of Robert Perry)*

a direct compressive force is applied to the spinal cord by a disc bulge, disc fragments, or the extruded nucleus pulposus (high viscosity fluid within the intervertebral disc). Alternatively, gradually developing intervertebral disc bulges, protrusions or frank herniations may result from the natural aging process, biological individuality, activity level and obesity. These conditions may remain asymptomatic even when MRI imaging is positive. See chapters 11 and 12.

The onset of symptoms is usually gradual due to increasing mechanical deformation of nerve roots at the intervertebral foramina and chemical irritation at the lesion site. The lesion is not a radial compression but instead involves the application of force at the bulge/protrusion/frank herniation site which explains why the symptoms are different in spinal cord stenosis versus nerve root compression. (Figure 8.8)

C. Shear

One example of chronic shear is spondylolisthesis: a condition where a superior vertebral structure can slip forward over the vertebrae below and therefore may impinge upon the spinal cord or cauda equina during this shearing motion displacement. This condition is most common in the lumbar spine (L4-5) and at the lumbar-sacral union

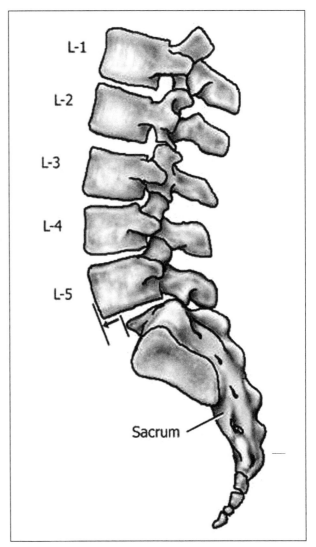

Figure 8.9 *Spondylolisthesis in this subject case has resulted in a forward slip due to gravity of L5 on top of S1 (spondylolisthesis of the lumbo-sacral union). (Courtesy of Robert Perry)*

(L5-S1) due to the force of gravity and an "accelerated curve" at these levels. This condition may result in an impingement of the neural canal. (Figure 8.9)

8.6 Specific Spinal Cord Injuries

A. Anterior cord syndrome

Anterior cord syndrome is perhaps the most common of spinal cord lesions. It is commonly caused by a fractured vertebral body resulting in retropulsing the body or body fragments backwards. However, it may occur without fracture, and x-rays may not reveal a subluxation (Reid

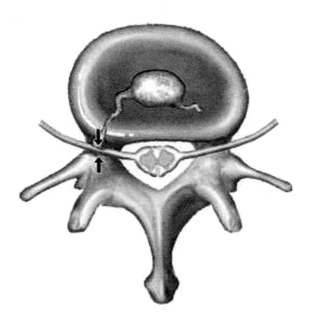

Figure 8.8 *An intervertebral nerve root is compressed by a frank herniation of the intervertebral disc (a.k.a. disk). (Courtesy of Robert Perry)*

and Reid, 1984). Additionally, a protruding vertebral disc may press against the anterior spinal cord. The loading mechanism usually includes compression or shear. Symptoms include a loss of motor control and may involve complete paralysis from the lesion site and below when anterior cord syndrome is severe. In survivors, sensory functions are preserved as cutaneous, and proprioceptive sensory information enters through the posterior roots into the posterior spinal cord.

B. Central cord syndrome

Central cord syndrome is more frequent in patients who have a preexisting spondylosis in the cervical spine (Yashon, 1986). Calcification of the posterior longitudinal ligament has also been found in some central cord syndrome patients. In the somatic peripheral nervous system, the symptoms in the upper extremities predominate. There may also be some loss of autonomic peripheral nervous system control (e.g., bladder control) in these trauma patients. The hands, which are distal, are more affected than the proximal portions (shoulders) of the upper extremities. Yashon (1986) states that hyperextension is the most common etiology for central cord syndrome in the cervical spine, with a compressive intrusion into both the anterior and posterior surfaces of the spinal cord occurring during hypermobility, due to the high energy effects of the moving bone (kinetic energy $= 1/2mv^2$) with energy waves that disrupt cord tissue and surrounding blood vessels.

Death is common when a transecting cord injury occurs between the skull occiput and C5. Injury site levels below C5 lead to better end results as the injury site descends to lower levels.

Spinal cord transections at lower levels of the cervical spine may produce flaccid paralysis and loss of the sensory tracts. In the cervical spine, quadriplegia (tetraplegia) may occur. Lower levels of partial or complete transection of the cord will produce lesser symptomology. Paraplegia involves the loss only of the lower extremities. Hemiplegia resulting from a lesion in the cervical, thoracic, or lumbar spine affects only one side of the body.

Treatment with corticosteroids has been effective in reducing those spinal cord injuries that are associated with edema and with changes in spinal cord chemistry when the lesion is incomplete. Complete lesions, if survived, result at present in permanent loss of motor and sensory response below the site of the lesion. Drug therapy may, however, reduce the secondary deleterious effects that would otherwise occur above the lesion site.

8.7 Nerve Root Loading—Tension, Compression, and Shear

Spinal nerve roots are subjected to tension during normal neck and limb movements. Excepting the thoracic spine region, this stretch can be significant. This stretch or tension stress is first imposed upon the proximal spinal nerve roots. A common example of injury that may occur is that of a brachial plexus injury (C5- T1 spinal nerves; some anatomists also include part of C3 and C4) in water skiing. When the skier is pulled out of the water, the tension load imposed upon the arms of the water skier is significant, especially at the beginning of the ski run. This may produce a stretching injury at the nerve root exit points or within peripheral nerve trunks that extend away from the spinal cord. (Figure 8.10)

The intervertebral foramen may also develop a stenosis through hypertrophy of bone tissue (e.g., osteoarthritis/spondylosis), or excessive connective tissue may form around the area of the opening of the intervertebral foramen, which in turn may produce compressive stresses upon nerve roots. Interestingly, because nerve roots normally adhere to tissues superior and inferior to the verte-

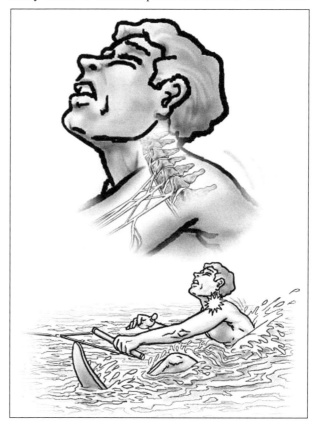

Figure 8.10 *The water skier is pulled abruptly out of the water, and a close-up view of the brachial plexus indicates a significant stretch. (Courtesy of Robert Perry)*

bral disc, a compression stress may produce consequent increased intraneural tension (Rydevik, Lundborg, Olmarker, and Myers, 2001). A soft tissue bulge may produce a stretching of an attached nerve root. Furthermore, if the opening of the intervertebral foramina is reduced, there may be more friction and irritation produced as nerve root sliding takes place within this opening during normal neck, limb, and trunk movements (tension displacements). Finally, the exit position of spinal nerve roots varies in terms of biological individuality, and when the spinal nerve exits from the bottom or top of the foramen rather than the middle portion, shear loading results. (Figure 8.11)

As previously stated, nerve roots may be subjected to compression stresses by a prolapsed disc. At the disc prolapse site, there may be contact with connective tissues that press into the nerve root, which may result in sensory and motor loss within that peripheral nerve's distribution. Nerve roots are more commonly compressed than the spinal cord due to prolapsed discs, because the largest percentage of protrusions and frank disc herniations occur posteriorly and laterally to the disc adjacent to nerve root

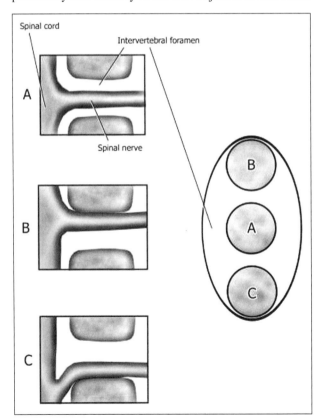

Figure 8.11 Three exit positions of intervertebral nerve roots are illustrated. An opportunity for shear loading in figure c is evident in this example. (Courtesy of Robert Perry)

exit points, as per Figure 8.8, as opposed to large central protrusions into the spinal cord or cauda equina.

Compression along nerve roots at more than one level may augment the nerve root pathology. Olmarker and Rydevik (1992) found that compressing nerve roots at more than one level in pigs (cauda equina region) within the neural canal resulted in a greater disruption of neural impulses even when compared to a significantly elevated pressure at a one-site application. Therefore patients with multiple levels of compression may experience increased symptoms, and furthermore, a surgical approach at one level is likely to produce a less than optimal result. These findings are not to be confused with "transitional syndrome" where levels above or below a vertebral fusion may lead to increased degeneration of the superior or inferior vertebral discs due to the vertebral bodies fusion effect upon adjacent spinal elements. In this latter case, new levels of root compression may develop because of and subsequent to the initial single level spinal functional unit fusion surgical procedure.

8.8 Peripheral Nerve Loading

A. Tension

A peripheral nerve may be loaded in compression, shear, or tension and is subject to penetration/laceration injuries. In similar fashion to the spinal cord and for some of the same reasons, a peripheral nerve is unlikely to experience trauma as the result of bending and torsion. Spinal peripheral nerve distal to the nerve roots is also resistant to tension loads due to the strength and elasticity of the connective tissues surrounding the nerve. The strongest of these tissues is the perineurium which surrounds the nerve bundles within spinal nerve and spinal nerve branches (Sunderland, 1978). Peripheral nerve and connective tissue have relatively long elastic zones due to nerve axon, myelin, and connective tissue elasticity. Furthermore, spinal nerves and their branches have many small undulations as they course through the neck, trunk, and extremities. When a stretch is applied, the undulations straighten out initially before the tension load is transferred to the nerve connective tissues. These undulations are the major basis for the long "toe zone" in the stress/strain curve of peripheral nerve. A nerve can be stretched approximately 8% without any problems and may go to 15% for short time periods without deleterious consequences. (Figure 8.12)

In similar fashion, the small vessels that transport blood to and from the nerve are arranged in coils similar to a coiled telephone cord (land line) to permit considerable stretch before they become occluded and blood flow stops. (Figure 8.13)

Case Study 8.1

This case study involved an Erb's palsy infant. The plaintiff's claim was that the obstetrician was pulling too hard and had produced the shoulder dystocia in the newborn infant. In this pathology, a torticollis (tilted head) is common, and this case fell into the severe category as it eventually required a peripheral nerve graft to reduce the torticollis. One medical expert witness had opined that the physician must have been pulling at approximately 100 lbs. to produce this result, and he further negated the possibility that this Erb's palsy could have simply been produced as the infant proceeded down the birth canal during the normal birth process. A review of the literature indicated that forces on the order of 100 lbs. are not produced by trained ob/Gyns even in cases of difficult delivery or shoulder dystocia. Twenty-five pounds of tension is a more probable result in cases of more difficult deliveries. Furthermore, the natural birth process can produce significant tension forces on the head and

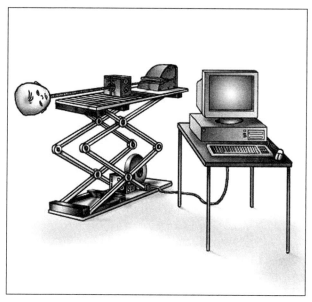

Figure Case Study 8.1 *Trained ob/gyn physicians (during a conference proceeding) were asked to perform infant head pulling during what they perceived to be normal, difficult, and shoulder dystocia birth deliveries. (Courtesy of Allen R. H. , Bankoski B.R., Butzin, C.A. and Nagey, D.A. 1994)*

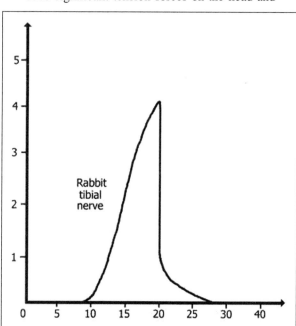

Figure 8.12 *Peripheral nerve exhibits a long toe (flattened curve) at the beginning of the elastic zone. Approximately 8% elongation may take place before physiological functions of the nerve are compromised. (Courtesy of Robert Perry)*

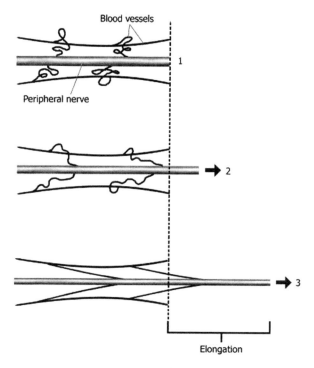

Figure 8.13 *Microvasculature forms coiled vessels that may be stretched without damage or occlusion when a peripheral nerve is lengthened. (Courtesy of Robert Perry)*

neck during the delivery process, especially in cases of shoulder dystocia.

B. Compression

Spinal peripheral nerve is also resistant to compression loads in that it is usually well protected within hard or soft body tissues. Second, peripheral nerve maintains a significant positive pressure within the perineurium (nerve bundles) relative to surrounding body tissues. Therefore, this positive intraneural pressure helps to maintain the nerve diameter dimensions. Nevertheless, when an entire limb is subjected to a radial compression load, such as a surgical tourniquet during a limb extremity surgical procedure or when a focal point application of compressive force is applied to a body region where a peripheral nerve is relatively superficial as in an orthopedic fracture table perineal post applying external pressure to the perineum (groin) area, compression stress can compromise the nerve function (Schulak et al., 1980).

The two types of compression in peripheral nerve are radial compression (uniform circumferential compression) and lateral clamp compression. In radial compression, a uniform pressure outside the nerve is applied around the entire circumference of the peripheral nerve. Examples include carpal tunnel syndrome involving the median nerve at the anterior wrist and lateral compartment syndrome involving the peroneal nerve within the lateral compartment below the lateral portion of the knee joint. In these examples, pressures are applied by fluid-filled tissue which surrounds the peripheral nerve. The diameter of the nerve is decreased, and nerve function is impaired. This first example of carpal tunnel syndrome is almost always due to chronic overuse due in part to inflammation of tissues surrounding flexor tendons that pass through the small carpal tunnel space. The last example is typically the result of acute injury involving a fracture of the lateral plateau of the superior tibia or a superior fibula fracture. The lateral leg compartment internal pressure may involve serious compromise to vasculature as well as to the peroneal nerve which courses through the lateral compartment and may result in acute tissue death below the lateral compartment lesion site.

Experimentally, we are able to study peripheral nerve compression by means of isolating the nerve (animal models) and applying the circumferential compression stress in an enclosed air chamber. (Figure 8.14)

Such experiments are useful and have revealed that not only is the amount of compressive stress important (i.e., pressure expressed as millimeters of mercury {Hg}), but also the time duration of the pressure application has

an important bearing on the short- and long-term outcome of peripheral nerve function, with long duration pressures contributing to increased pathology. When the pressure outside the nerve rises to a level which significantly exceeds the intraneural pressure of the nerve, the circumference of the nerve decreases. This deformation is roughly uniform on all sides (uniform circumferential compression). However, interestingly, the tissues at the edge of the applied compressive stress are stretched (moving away from the compressive site) to a greater degree with a greater percentage strain. This has been termed the "edge effect" (Ochoa et al., 1972). (Figure 8.15)

Large fibers which course through the nerve (e.g., median nerve) and carry motor impulses are affected first with small fibers including type IV unmyelinated axons (type IV pain receptors) preserved intact, and therefore these pain receptors continue to conduct impulses from the compression site back to the spinal cord (an undesirable result for the most part).

Uniform clamp compression of peripheral nerve is a second mechanical means of applying a compression stress. This type of loading involves clamping the nerve between a hard surface (e.g., leaning on a table) and a bony structure within the body. One example involves a compression of the ulnar nerve branch between a hard external surface and the medial epicondyle of the humerus of the upper arm. Leaning on a table in this manner may produce numbness and pain which occur at the compression site and extends to the ring and little finger of the hand. Most of us are familiar with the acute consequences of striking the inside surface of the elbow against a hard object. In both of these cases, a uniform clamp pressure is

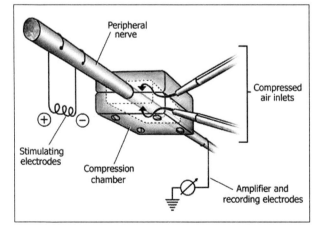

Figure 8.14 *A peripheral nerve is isolated and compressed in a small air compression chamber. Nerve conduction and other physiological tests may be run concomitantly under a radial nerve compression load. (Courtesy of Robert Perry)*

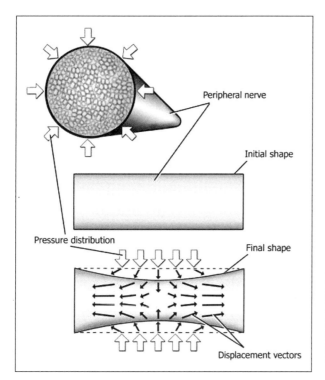

Figure 8.15 *At the edge of the compression site, the nerves and their myelin sheaths are displaced toward the site adjacent to the compression, and the strain damage is greatest at these points. In the middle area of compression, in spite of a relatively large decrease in circumference, the damage to peripheral nerve is less. (Courtesy of Robert Perry)*

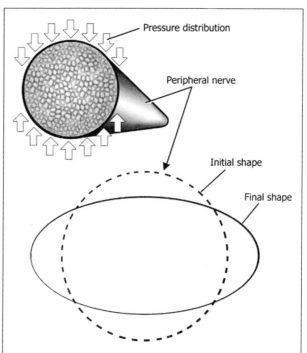

Figure 8.16 *A uniform clamp compression results in the nerve trunk becoming shorter and wider without a significant change in the cross-section area. Note if uniform clamp pressure is excessive, then the cross-sectional area of the nerve will be reduced. (Courtesy of Robert Perry)*

being applied to the ulnar nerve. The shape of the nerve is changed, but the overall change in the cross-section area of the ulnar nerve is usually minimal in prolonged lateral clamp compression. (Figure 8.16)

This uniform clamping can adversely affect neural transmission and axonal transport of the nerve fibers that make up the nerve, and this may become a chronic condition necessitating surgery involving an ulnar nerve branch relocation to a site where uniform clamp pressure is reduced or eliminated.

Case Study 8.2

Lateral clamp compression was applied to the dorsal branch of the radial nerve in a case involving the handcuffing of a woman during her arrest. It also appeared that the woman struggled after the handcuffs were applied. The handcuffs resulted in a clamping pressure on the dorsal surface of the hand close to the thumb side. A temporary injury (mild neuropraxia) of the radial nerve resulted from this pressure, with more se-

vere vascular and thumb extensor tendon damage. The trauma to the extensor tendon subsequently required surgical intervention.

Case Study 8.3

A serious recreational bicyclist complains of erectile dysfunction due to a single bout of exercise (approximately a 35 mile ride). The seat manufacturer was sued based on the premise that the seat failed during the ride. A crease was evident in the foam over the rear portion of the saddle nose of the saddle. Plaintiff's claim was that this defect occurred without warning and resulted in subsequent pain and erectile dysfunction. We opined, as did plaintiff's expert, that if this defect was due to riding, it did not occur from a single riding bout. Furthermore, the claim was made that the saddle was improperly mated with a seat post that allowed the tip of a bolt on the top of the mounting post to protrude through the bottom surface of the padded seat by approximately 1/8 inch. Approximately 3/4 inch thickness medium density closed cell foam cov-

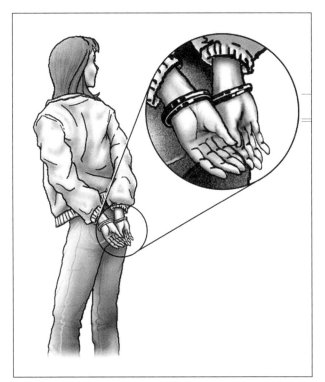

Figure Case Study 8.2 *Handcuffing this woman resulted in temporary radial nerve damage to the right hand and wrist. (Courtesy of Robert Perry)*

ered the bolt tip in this area of the bicycle padded seat. We were suspicious because the crease and the bolt tip protrusion were close to the anatomical anus. Even if pressure was high in this area due to bolt protrusion, this area of the perineum anatomy is medial to the pudendal neurovascular bundles that run adjacent to the right and left ischial tuberosities. Therefore, loading from a bolt tip in the middle of the saddle nose is not a mechanism that would produce uniform clamp compression against the ischial tuberosities of the pelvis (Hannon, 2016).

Another potential site of uniform clamp compression of the pudendal neurovascular bundles is where the right and left trunks of these bundles join at the approximate base of the penis. If a rider leans too far forward or if the saddle nose is inclined upwards (upward pitch), compressive stress may disrupt the neurovascular bundle. However, this area of the plaintiff's actual saddle was without a defect. A complete discussion of erectile dysfunction related to trauma loading or bicycling may be found in the torso and thorax chapter (Chapter 10).

8.9 Peripheral Nerve Injury

A. Categories of peripheral nerve injury

Peripheral nerve injury is usually limited to a "neuropraxia," where there is only a degradation of myelin covering around axons, and therefore transmission of impulses is impaired. However, a more serious injury disrupting individual axons may also occur (axonotmesis). In this peripheral nerve injury, the axons within peripheral nerve are able to grow back within nerve fasciculi tubes which have not been disrupted. After stabilization of the peripheral nerve injury, this growing back process may proceed at about one millimeter each day in human peripheral nerve and may delay the return nerve function for weeks or months depending upon the distance required for target reinnervation. The most serious peripheral nerve injury is the neurotmesis which usually involves a complete disruption of fasciculi and sometimes whole peripheral nerve. Reinnervation is not as good with neuron axon regrowth blocked by various other body tissues during attempted regrowth, and sometimes motor axons will grow from the proximal nerve stump to the wrong muscles.

B. Multiple levels of peripheral nerve compression

It has been hypothesized that spinal peripheral nerve may exhibit greater pathology when compression is applied at two sites (Upton and McComas, 1973). One example often cited is that of compression applied to brachial plexus nerve roots and, secondarily, pressure applied to the median nerve under the transverse ligament of the wrist. The resulting carpal tunnel syndrome in this example results from two compression sites which sum in an undetermined way to create more extensive symptoms. This has been termed double crush syndrome. In this instance, a carpal tunnel release at the wrist will typically not eliminate the entire pain pathology.

A more complex triple compression may result from compression sites at the C6-8 nerve root, the thoracic outlet, and within the carpal tunnel. Again, the elimination of only one of these compression sites usually does not eliminate the median nerve symptoms. Nerve conduction studies at specific sites are one common way of attempting to discern where peripheral nerve compression site(s) exist prior to surgical intervention.

References

Allen R. H. , Bankoski B.R., Butzin, C.A. and Nagey, D.A. "Comparing Clinician-applied Loads for Routine, Difficult, and Shoulder Dystocia Deliveries." *American Journal of Obstetrics/Gynecology,* Dec. pp.1621–1627 (1994)

Hannon, P. (2016) Forensic biomechanics/functional anatomy/physiology analysis of erectile dysfunction: A defense perspective in a product liability case, v. 7(1)

Hyde, A.S. *Crash Injuries: How and Why They Happen.* Hyde Associates, Inc. Key Biscayne, Fl. (1992)

Ochoa, J., Fowler, T. J., and Gilliatt, R. W. "Anatomical Changes in Peripheral Nerves Compressed by a Pneumatic Tourniquet." *Journal of Anatomy, 113,* 433 (1972)

Olmarker K. and Rydevik, B., "Single versus Double level Compression. An Experimental Study on the Porcine Cauda Equina with Analyses of Nerve Impulse Conduction Properties." *Clinical Orthopedics, 279,* 3539 (1992)

Reid, S.E. and Reid S.E. Jr. *Head and Neck Injuries in Sports.* Charles C. Thomas Pub. Springfield, Illinois (1984)

Rydevik, Lundborg, Olmarker, and Myers, "Biomechanics of Peripheral Nerves and Spinal Nerve Roots" in Nordin and Frankel eds. (2001) *Basic Biomechanics of the Musculoskeletal System.* Lippincott, Williams & Wilkins, Philadelphia (2001)

Schulak DJ, Bear TF, Summers JL "Transient Impotence from Positioning on the Fracture Table." *Journal of Trauma, 20,* 420 (1980)

Sunderland S, *Nerves and Nerve Injuries,* Second edition. Churchill Livingstone, Edinburgh, Scotland (1978)

Upton R.M.,and McComas, A.J. *The Double Crush in Nerve Entrapment Syndromes.* Lancet, 2, pp.359 (1973)

Yashon, D. *Spinal Injury* Second Ed. Appleton-Century-Crofts. Norwalk, Conn. (1986)

Young, W., (2014) Spinal cord regeneration. Cell Transplant, v 23 (4-5), pp. 573-611.

Additional Reading

Cherington M: *Hazards of Bicycling: From Handlebars to Lightning. Seminars in Neurology,* Vol. 20, No 2; 247–253 (2000)

Desai KM, Gingell JC. "Hazards of Long Distance Cycling" (letter). Br Med J 1989; 298: 1072–73 (1989)

Chapter 9

Head, Face, and Brain

Patrick Hannon

9.1 Introduction

Head, face, and brain injuries that come to litigation can range from mild facial disfigurement to catastrophic brain injury and death. Brain injury may include permanent loss of some sensory modalities, loss of movement capabilities, and loss of normal mentation. These types of injuries occur frequently in traffic accidents, industrial accidents, falls from considerable height, and in beatings or shootings. The incidence of these injuries is high, with some 31% of vehicular injuries occurring to the head and face as shown in Figure 9.1. Finally, it should be appreciated that face and head injuries account for the greatest number of motor vehicle injuries at each abbreviated injury scale level 1–6. (Figure 9.2) Furthermore, in regard to beatings,

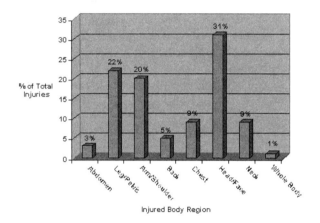

Figure 9.1 *Injuries in different body locations. Data from the NASS crashworthiness Data System (CDS) for 1988–1997. (Adapted from Allsop and Kennett, 2002)*

American cinema presents action films which represent blows to the head as trauma resulting in only a temporary headache with full recovery. Real life head trauma is much different, and beatings involving impact to the head frequently result in death or brain injury that changes someone's life forever and frequently results in death.

In Chapter 5, general bone biomechanics are discussed with reference to specific types of fractures, including depressed flat bone fractures that are not uncommon in face and skull bones. In this chapter, specific fractures of facial and skull bones are addressed. Furthermore, injury to the brain that results from impact and non-impact injury to the head are discussed.

9.2 Structural Anatomy of the Head

A. Scalp anatomy

The head link is superficially composed of scalp and elastic cartilage that comprise the external ear and part of the nose. The scalp is approximately 0.25 inch thick and is composed of the skin, connective tissue (subcutaneous), the aponeuromuscular layer (galea or helmet), loose connective tissue, and the periosteum. (Figure 9.3) The acronym "SCALP" also serves as a mnemonic, with each letter representing the five layers of the scalp. Skin is discussed in more detail in the soft tissues chapter. Beneath the scalp lies bone, three meninges, and the brain. (Figure 9.4)

B. Face and skull anatomy

The head link is composed of the "skull bones" which include eight flat cranial bones and fourteen facial bones. The calvarium is a term used to denote the top half of the cranium. The facial bones do not include the frontal bone (forehead) which is a part of the cranium and the

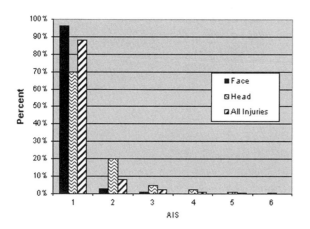

Figure 9.2 Abbreviated Injury Scale (AIS)- face, head, and other injuries. (Adapted from Allsop and Kennett, 2002)

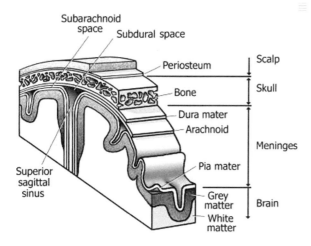

Figure 9.3 Layers of the scalp. (Courtesy of Robert Perry)

calvarium. In the face and skull, flat and irregular bones predominate. The bones of the adult skull are composed of relatively thick compact bone with some minimal core trabecular bone. Facial bones will vary in terms of composition with thicker bones exhibiting a significant core of trabecular bone filled with red marrow.

Eight specific bones at the cranium surface include one frontal bone, one occipital bone, two parietal bones, and two temporal bones. Additionally, one ethmoid and one sphenoid bone comprise the base of the cranium. Fourteen facial bones include left and right maxilla, nasal, lacrimal, zygomatic, palatine, and inferior nasal concha. Additionally, one mandible and one small vomer bone are included as facial bones. (Figures 9.5a ,9.5b and 9.5c)

C. Brain anatomy

The central nervous system is composed of the brain and spinal cord. The adult brain has an approximate mass of 1,100 to 1,700 grams and fills the skull cavity. For the purposes of this text, the brain is divided into the forebrain or cerebrum (telencephalon and diencephalon), the midbrain (mesencephalon), and the hindbrain (rhombencephalon). The reader should be aware that alternative approaches exist. For example, in mammalian brain, the hindbrain structures may be divided into the metencephalon (pons and cerebellum) and myelencephalon (medulla oblongata).

The brainstem is a component of the brain and includes the midbrain and the pons and medulla oblongata of the hindbrain. Some authors also include the diencephalon in the brainstem instead of including it within the forebrain. The brainstem is a structure that is similar in appearance to a stalk with a bulbous fruit at its superior end. Table 9.1 and Figure 9.5c should help the reader to simplify this complex organization and is one way to categorize brain anatomy.

The brain telencephalon is surrounded by three membranes, termed meninges, that include the outer dura mater, the arachnoid membrane (spider web), and the pia mater (very thin membrane closely attached to the cerebral cortex). The dura mater is a tough membrane and has

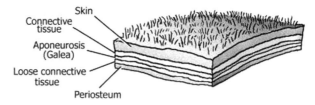

Figure 9.4 Scalp skull, meninges, and brain (Courtesy of Robert Perry)

substantive biomechanical value. The arachnoid membrane is richly supplied by blood vessels and also serves to contain cerebral spinal fluid. The pia mater is very thin and is closely fixed to the outer layer of cerebral cortex. The cerebrum mass includes the approximate 0.25 inch thick cerebral cortex consisting of neuron cell bodies. Very briefly this cerebral cortex structure is important for mentation, sensory perception, and motor control. Deeper structures within the forebrain, midbrain, hindbrain, and the large hindbrain ccrebellum structure also have important roles in learning, memory, sensory perception, and motor control. The reader is referred to Nolte, The Human Brain, for a more detailed discussion of neuroanatomy and the functional significance of brain structures.

9.3 Loading to Head, Face, and Brain

A. Scalp loading

Scalp or skin lacerations may result from blows to the face and cranium. Sharp bony edges in facial areas such as the lower eye orbit (zygomatic ridge) or upper eye orbit (frontal bone) present points of maximum compressive stress to both broad based and focal point loads applied to the face. Skin injury in these cases involving blows to the face is common, with lacerations paralleling the bony ridges. These lacerations are an example of a clamp compression wherein an external compressive stress can clamp soft tissue over these bone ridges.

The subcutaneous connective tissue (second layer) of the scalp (a.k.a. SCALP; an acronym) is supplied with an extensive network of blood vessels, and a laceration that occurs through this layer results in a bleed that is somewhat more extensive because the blood vessels in this area are strongly supported and therefore are not able to retract once severed (Pike 1990). The third layer (aponeuromuscular layer) serves as a protective layer for the two layers above if it remains intact. Muscle and membrane are within this layer, and this layer is able to prevent additional separation of a wound that breaches the first two outer layers. However, if this aponeuromuscular layer is breached, then it tends to pull apart along with the upper two layers of the scalp, leading to increased scarring in areas of skin covering the calvarium (Pike 1990).

To some small degree, a blow to the head can be absorbed by the scalp. This soft tissue is able to deform and absorb some energy with some small increase in time of impact to decrease reaction force levels. In high level loading, the beneficial effects are negligible.

Please note that fractures to the face and cranium do not occur without evidence of skin or scalp trauma includ-

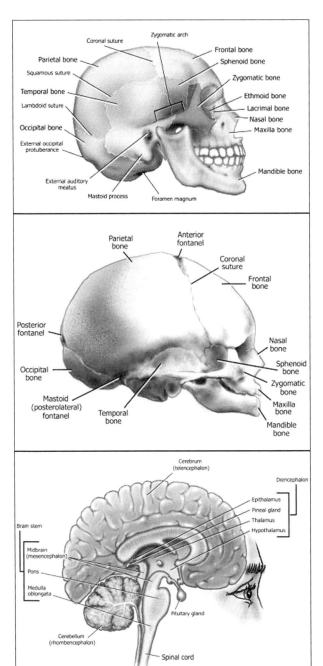

Figure 9.5a (top) Bones of the skull (cranial and facial bones). (Courtesy of Robert Perry)
Figure 9.5b (middle) Bones of the infant skull. (Courtesy of Robert Perry)
Figure 9.5c (bottom) Brain and brain stem structures. (Courtesy of Robert Perry)

Table 9.1

Forebrain
    Telenephalon (cerebrum)
        cerebral cortex—divided into two hemispheres
        white centrum
        basal ganglia (deep)
        limbic lobe (deep)
        corpus callosum

    Diencephalon
        Two football-shaped thalami (left and right)
        hypothalamus
        epithalamus
        subthalamus

Brainstem
    midbrain (mesencephalon)
        tectum
        superior and inferior colliculi (small hills)
        paired cerebral peduncles
    hindbrain structures (rhombencephalon)
        pons
        medulla oblongata

Other Hindbrain (rhombencephalon)
    cerebellum

(See Figure 9.5c)

ing but not limited to scalp swelling which is visible using several imaging modalities.

B. Loading of the face and skull

Recall that compact bone is much stronger under all types of loading than is cancellous bone. Cranium bones have relatively thick layers of compact bone on the inside and outside surfaces. Blows to the face or skull may result in a single linear crack, a stellar pattern fracture, or depressed skull-face fractures that result in variable inward displacement. One key variable is the area of impact. Experimental procedures manipulate the impact area upon cadaver skulls with a striking implement in order to examine the differences between focal point and broad based impact loading. The human skull acts as a hard hat and is able to distribute focal point loads. However, failure points may be reached at more moderate load levels for focal impacts. An example of focal versus broad-based impact is presented in Allsop, Perl and Warner (1991). In this research effort, intact cranium parietal bones of cadaver specimens were impacted with a flat circular disk (1.0 inch diam-

eter) versus a flat rectangular plate. As one can see from the data presented in Figure 9.6a and 9.6b, fracture of the skull was produced at lower levels of loading and generally resulted in increased bone depression when the focal impactor was the striking implement. This is of course intuitive, as a small impactor with the same load level will produce the highest compressive stress (compressive stress = load/area). In real-world accidents, impact occurs along a continuum of focal point versus broad-based impacts ranging from high-speed bullets or a small-diameter club (e.g., tire buddy) impacts to head-ground impact (flat ground surface). The SAE J885, 2011(Section 5.1.2) considers an area of 2.0 square inches as the transition point from distributed to concentrated loading (a.k.a. focal point versus broad based). One should keep in mind, however, that a flat pavement head strike may involve only a relatively small portion of the skull with a skull curve that is relatively abrupt such as the mid-lateral portion of the frontal bone. Such a head strike will result in a small area of the skull contacting the pavement, and therefore the compressive stress level will increase to a much higher level as in striking a hardboiled egg on a flat surface. One of the functions of a helmet discussed later in this chapter

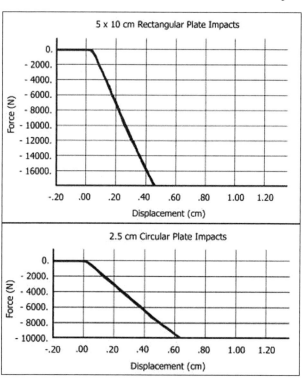

Figure 9.6a and **b** Focal point loading versus broad based impact. Failure occurs at lower levels in focal point impact. Allsop D.L., Perl, T, and Warner C. (1991). Force/deflection and fracture characteristics of the temporo-parietal region of the human head. (Courtesy of Society of Automotive Engineers 912907)

is that of load distribution. The helmet is able to spread an impact load over a larger area, and therefore compressive stress is reduced.

When failure points are reached for various bones, a fracture occurs. Please note that there is considerable variation in these values based on biological individuality, age, and gender differences. Furthermore, load distribution as previously discussed, significantly affects the ultimate failure point for facial and cranial bones. These factors indicate a strong cautionary note to the attorney and biomechanist when examining published data regarding tolerance limits which by no means represent exact figures.

Focal point fractures to the face may occur in any area, and the damage is dependent upon the energy level. Blows to the front or side of the face may produce local injury at the site of impact. Linear cracks may propagate across the suture lines of the cranium bones of infants, children and young adults although they may occur in older adults (e.g., diastatic fractures). Blows to the mandible of the face are many times limited to mandible fracture because the mandible will not effectively transmit force to the maxilla and temporal bones unless the teeth are tightly clenched. However, there may of course be significant stress at one or both of the temporomandibular joints, with consequent damage as the result of a significant impact.

High speed projectiles that pierce the head and face bones will produce highly comminuted fractures due to the extremely high energy levels. Note, as discussed in the bone biomechanics chapter, there have been cases where bullet projectiles (at a shallow angle) have not been able to penetrate cranium bones. This again serves as an example of biological individuality, with some individuals having stronger and thicker skulls. A good contemporary summary of the research and tolerance of the bones of the skull excluding the mid-face and lower face may be found in Yoganandan et al. (2004).

C. Energy absorption during facial fracture

Another issue of import is that of energy absorption resulting from facial fracture. Some controversy exists in terms of facial fractures being a protective mechanism for brain injury. On the one hand, when facial bones deform, this deformation represents the absorption of energy, and therefore less energy is transmitted to the brain (i.e., a protective effect). A blow to the mandible, for example, that results in failure of this jaw bone will attenuate the acceleration impulse transmitted to the brain. On the other hand, in theory, forces applied to facial bones may transmit force inward to the brain. Such transmission requires

a good bone conduit for energy wave propagation. An example of this mechanism is when a basal skull fracture (e.g., sphenoid bone) occurs due to facial blows (e.g., Le Fort III fractures) and may result in brain damage due to significant bone fracture displacement (note: many times this fracture results in minimal bone-brain displacement). It should also be appreciated that any time there is a direct displacement of skull bone fragments that are retropulsed into the brain, significant brain damage occurs. In a sense, these fragments enter like shrapnel into the cranium, destroying brain tissue and brain vasculature with additional complications such as bleeds and brain tissue edema following. Little epidemiological evidence has addressed this controversy regarding protective versus adverse effects of facial fractures. However, in regard to motor vehicle accidents, Davidoff (1988) offers some epidemiological evidence that facial fracture may result in an increased incidence of closed head injury (CHI).

D. Classification of facial fractures

Fractures of the face may be classified as Le Fort I, II, or III fractures as illustrated in Figure 9.7. These fractures result from frontal loading to the face as may occur during a steering wheel strike or a fall to the ground (face first). Fractures to the lower face are outlined along the maxilla and are indicative of a Le Fort I fracture pattern. This fracture normally occurs when there is a strike to the lower face. In experimental testing, the forces have ranged from 623 newtons (140 lbs) to 1,980 newtons (445 lbs) for the maxilla (6.5 cm² impactor) (Allsop and Kennett, 2002).

A Le Fort II fracture results from a more superior impact to the face, with fractures of the nasal, zygomatic, and maxilla bones. A Le Fort III fracture may result in fracture of the nasal, frontal, and zygomatic bones which are exposed to the impact blow. Other bones that make up part of the eye sockets may be disrupted (e.g., ethmoid, sphenoid, lacrimal) in this serious facial fracture. Impact blows to the nose may also fracture bone regions within the nasal cavity, including the vomer bone, nasal concha, and nasal septum. The medial eye orbit walls represent the thinnest most delicate bones of the face and cranium and may fracture easily depending upon the load vector direction. Additionally, a Le Fort IV fracture has been described as a fracture across the frontal bone above the eye orbits (supraorbital) (Manson, 1987). With regard to possible brain injury, increased risk parallels the numbering classification, with type III and IV Le Fort fractures being the most likely to produce serious brain injury.

E. Other facial injuries

Facial fractures and soft tissue injury can lead to disfigure-

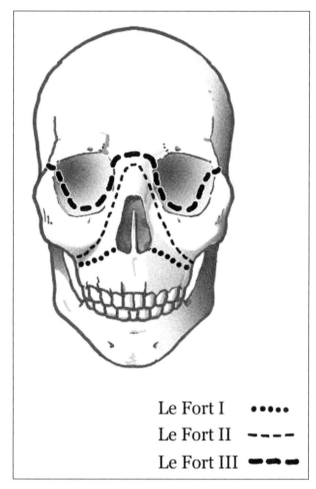

Le Fort I   •••••
Le Fort II - - - -
Le Fort III ▬ ▬ ▬

Figure 9.7 *Le Fort I, II, and III fractures of the skull and face. (Courtesy of Robert Perry)*

ment, but many times these bone failures are managed well by plastic reconstructive surgery. Furthermore, skin in the face area enjoys a relatively good blood supply and regenerative capacity. Still, scars may develop, including the more noticeable hypertrophic or keloid scarring in some individuals, and every attempt is made to minimize scarring and to perform possible revision of scar tissue (e.g., surgical revision, CO_2 laser, topical corticosteroids, and so on). Nerve injury may also result in facial numbness and more importantly loss of motor control of facial muscles (e.g., facial nerve). Partial loss of facial muscle control can result in loss of facial expression or in an abnormal facial expression. Usually, but not always, facial nerves regrow and reinnervate the appropriate musculature.

Finally, severe soft tissue facial injury may involve a rupture of one or both globes (eyeballs). Normally the globes are well protected in the recessed bony eye sockets, and broad-based blows to the face may not significantly impact the globes to produce compressive rupture. However, in massive facial impacts or explosions, if globe

rupture does occur, then blindness in that eye results. Focal point loads applied to the eyes may produce varying degrees of damage, ranging from corneal abrasion or a small retinal detachment to a scooping/shearing blow or explosion that takes the eye (globe) out of its socket.

F. Skull and facial bone loading and brain injury

Strikes to the head in regions excluding the face occur to flat bones that are in close proximity to the cerebral cortex, cerebellum, or brainstem (inferior cranium). These bones in general have higher failure points which again will vary with age, gender, and load distribution. Strikes to these bones may not result in a bone fracture or may result in a simple linear non-displaced fracture resulting from bending loads applied to the skull, or may result in a more serious highly comminuted fracture and/or deeply depressed fracture with intrusive bone shrapnel imploding into brain tissue. Interestingly, when the focal point area is small and the load is high, such as a hammer strike to the calvarium, a punch fracture may occur with little caving in of adjacent bone fragments (SAE J885, 2011). Furthermore, lateral strikes to the skull may propagate energy waves through the cranial sphenoid bone to produce a basal skull fracture as discussed previously. Another example of energy wave transmission is the contrecoup skull fracture (Hirsch and Kaufman, 1975). These uncommon fractures may occur when a strong stiff bone is exposed to a high magnitude direct impact (e.g., occipital bone) and bones at the approximate counterpole within the skull, such as the thinner (more fragile) middle or anterior fossae areas or the floor of the eye orbit, may fracture (i.e., indirect loading).

Two other issues should be appreciated that relate to bone and brain interaction during trauma. One issue relates to the inside surface of cranium bones that surround the brain. There are protrusions and ridges that can produce tissue damage due to shear and tension stresses when the cerebrum and cranium bones experience differential motion. This differential motion occurs when the cranium moves one way and the brain, because of Newton's first law of motion, wants to remain stationary (law of inertia). The base of the cranium is more complex in terms of ridges and blood vessel orifices, and significant differential displacement of brain and bone is more likely to produce vessel and brain tissue damage in this area. This can result in lacerations and tearing of neural and vascular tissues due to tension and shearing stresses. The damage may be superficial, with damage to the cerebral cortex or in the case of a basal skull fracture (e.g., near the foramen magnum) important blood vessels may be severed. Please note that in the case of the brain, superficial structures are no less important than deep structures. Finally, damage at the cerebral cortex may produce brain bleeds that can have an overall depressive effect upon brain function as intracranial pressure increases.

The second issue of importance is the fact that very small compressive strains in bone tissue that occur very rapidly may transmit a high energy wave into the brain of considerable depth. It has been estimated that a 0.125 inch elastic displacement inward of a cranial flat bone (rapid movement) may produce a brain bruise and resultant hematoma that extends deep into the brain.

Case Study 9.1

This medical malpractice case involved a young man who was struck with a golf ball at high velocity on the side of the head. The velocity of the golf ball could have been as high as 100 to 125 miles per hour. However, the mass of a golf ball is small, and a fracture did not result from this head impact. Furthermore, the head will not experience a significant change in velocity from this impact because of the relatively small change in the momentum of the young man's head. However, the parietal bone clearly would have been quickly depressed (then returned to its original position), and the underlying brain tissue was rapidly impacted, resulting in a brain tissue hematoma that developed over three days that extended approximately two inches deep through gray and white brain tissue and into deep sulci (fissures on the cerebral cortex). At emergency room presentation, a goose egg on the head was evident due to scalp swelling. The x-rays were unremarkable for fracture, and the patient was due to be released. At the insistence of one of the parents, a CT scan was performed with a brain tissue window. This series indicated a small subdural hematoma at the impact site. A neurosurgeon was consulted. However, it was not possible to transmit the digital image to the neurosurgeon at his home due to technical transmission problems. The neurosurgeon advised the parents that they could go home with their son but with the usual precautions and instructions that are always administered after a head injury. It was felt that because of the subdural hematoma's small size, serious brain injury was not a genuine concern. Without warning some three

days later, this young man experienced a serious brain seizure during the early morning hours. He was admitted to his local hospital, and in spite of efforts to stabilize his condition, he died within two days of admission. Autopsy revealed that the tissue damage to the brain (a deep penetrating contusion) was present from the time of impact with the golf ball.

G. Infant skull and brain injury

Cranium bones in the neonate are quite thin in comparison to adult bones. The flat bones form from membranes, and an ossification center is already present at birth. However, neonatal cranium bones are very flexible, with a thin and flexible layer of compact bone over the cranium bones. The two layers of compact bone of the calvarium develop later during early childhood. The flexibility of the membrane bones coupled with the fact that the anterior and posterior fontanels permit much deformation of the baby's head makes possible a less difficult birth during vaginal delivery.

In cases involving infant child abuse, the skull of the young infant is more flexible but fragile, and shake and strike motions that are one form of infant child abuse may produce fractures in the compact bone shell of the calcified cranium membranes. In many cases involving skull fracture, the infant is shaken while she is on her back, resulting in impacts with the floor or a table surface. Because these bones are not fused, the fracture lines and fontanels in these bones will tend to expand and become more evident over time. In many cases with reluctance and only when behavioral abnormalities develop will the infant be brought to the medical practitioner's office or to a hospital setting. A cranial burst fracture may also result in a diastasis of the fracture line and a concomitant extrusion of the cerebral brain tissue beyond the outer bone table of the cranium, but underneath an intact scalp may occur. This usually occurs in infants less than one year of age. Finally, leptomeningeal cysts filled with cerebral spinal fluid may also result from trauma that has produced a linear skull fracture. Usually this relatively rare development occurs in young children (toddlers and younger) whose fracture has resulted in a tear of the duramater membrane coupled with the rapid brain growth of the young child resulting in the growth of the fracture line.

Swelling and ecchymosis (bruising) result from trauma to capillary tissue within the connective tissue of the SCALP (i.e., the "C" in SCALP) or from the clamping of the skin's dermis, hypodermis and deeper tissues to include muscle and bone mid to lower face due to lateral clamp compression against a hard surface. The minimum force required to produce SCALP swelling and the resulting ecchymosis has not been experimentally established in adults or in infants/children. Furthermore, normal biological individuality and underlying bleeding pathology may affect the development of this impact trauma event bruising. Moderate or high loads applied to an infant's or toddler's head would also necessarily result in SCALP swelling within minutes at the impact point and an acute skin/SCALP bleed. Acute TBI due to "impact" loading does not occur without concomitant SCALP swelling of the human head link with the only exception being helmeted heads (e.g., contact sports such as American football or ice hockey; providing a large head load distribution). Desmoulin, et al. (2011) and Huang, l. (2012) provide an authoritative discussion of the mechanics of bruising and the stress levels involved in failure of several tissues including capillary tissue. Desmoulin et al. (2011) provide human subject testing of quantified acute blunt force trauma to the upper and lower extremities of one 34-year-old male with the dependent measure being bruising. However, testing of blunt force trauma to the head does not exist in live human subjects at present. The best evidence that we have in both biomechanics and in medicine at present is that SCALP swelling and bruising (regardless of biological individually) is most usually the weak link in head and face blunt impact trauma. This is confirmed by case study evidence rather than true experimental research as experimental research involving volunteer ex-

perimental and control groups does not exist to date in terms of head impact and bruising/swelling in adults or in children for obvious reasons. Nevertheless, the case study evidence is strong. This bruising is not always apparent and in some cases may not become apparent until autopsy exposes the SCALP underside. Furthermore, the dating of blunt force trauma based upon the breakdown of hemoglobin and color changes is subject to biological individuality and is no longer considered a very accurate method of the dating of this skin/SCALP trauma.

Buadu, L. et al. (2004) in regard to face and SCALP swelling discuss that this bruising may not be readily apparent by observation. However, CT scans are well suited to the evaluation of fluid collections of the SCALP including subcutaneous hemorrhage or edema (caput succedaneum), subgaleal hemorrhage or a subperiosteal hemorrhage (cephalhematoma). Furthermore, MR imaging has superior soft tissue resolution and provides a very clear picture of SCALP swelling (See Figures 9.8a and 9.8b).

The absence of visible soft-tissue swelling in inflicted or non-inflicted TBI reflects the absence of a head strike. Ewing-Cobbs et al. (1998) state that: "Most head injuries involve both contact and inertial forces. Contact forces [i.e., impacts] which occur either when the head is struck or strikes an object, produce focal injuries to the scalp, skull, and brain such as lacerations, fractures, contusions, and epidural hematomas" (p. 300). The authors go on to state that inertial forces result in movement of the

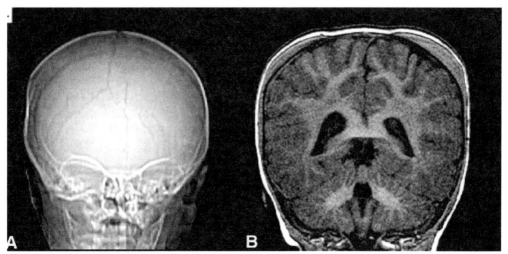

Figure 9.8ab *SCALP Swelling: A. Scout image from a CT scan of an eight month old male with suspected non-accidental head injury shows left and right soft SCALP tissue swelling; B. Coronal T1 gradient echo images show the left and right subgaleal hematomas to a better degree (Bauda, L. et al., 2004 by permission).*

brain via acceleration and deceleration forces (p.300). It is the relative movement of the brain/skull interface and/or movement between brain/brainstem regions which are responsible for concussion (i.e., mild TBI) or at higher levels, subdural hematoma and diffuse axonal injury. Please note however, that these higher levels of rotational acceleration most usually are produced by head impact rather than only shaking even in young children under one year of age. Ewing-Cobbs et al. (1998) found no statistically significant differences in what they termed soft tissue swelling and in skull fractures between "Inflicted TBI' versus "Noninflicted TBI" (p. 303). However, they did find individual cases in both inflicted and noninflicted injury groups where no soft tissue swelling within one week of trauma was present via the head imaging analyses. Reasons for this last finding may have included the absence of a head strike, a very soft load distributed head impact and/or inertial head loading without head impact in infants under 14 months of age.

Weber (1984) was the first to examine skull fracture in infants (without force measurements). His work included 82 cm (32.3 inch) drops of 15 infant cadavers to surfaces of 1) stone 2) carpet and 3) foam backed linoleum. In all 15 cases, "dome" (a.k.a. calvarium) fractures were created in the postmortem infant skulls from this 32.3 inch vertical fall: 5 falls to stone, 5 falls to carpet and 5 falls to foam backed linoleum. Subsequently, Weber (1985) conducted an additional 35 infant postmortem falls from 32.3 inches vertical displacement above the floor. Twenty-five of these 35 falls involved a landing surface of a double folded 8 mm thick camel hair blanket and 10 falls involved a landing surface of a foam mat. In 5 cases of these 35 falls to these soft surfaces, similar dome skull fractures occurred, all to the parietal bones of the infant skulls (Weber, 1985).

Ibrahim, N. and Margulies, S. (2010) dropped an 18 month anthropometric toddler dummy directly on its head in 1, 2 and 3 foot falls to concrete and additionally to a carpet pad. As one might expect, the force and decelerations were significantly higher when the child dummy impacted the concrete (stiff) surface. In fact both the greater height (1 versus 3 feet falls) and the concrete surface in a 2-factorial (height and surface) ANOVA found an increase in height and surface stiffness to significantly increase the impact force (p < 0.0001) (Ibrahim, N. and Margulies, S., 2010, p. 60). The overall results of the six different conditions (fall height and floor surface type) yielded forces of between 2.0 and 9.5 kNewtons (449.6 and 2135.7 pounds). Recent data involving measured forces in cadaver pediatric skulls

ranging from 33 weeks gestation to 16 years of age is now available (Loyd et al., 2019). One important implication for young pediatric head injury patients in short falls is that three of the four pediatric skulls, ages 5 months and 22 months, sustained fractures from drops of only 15 cm (5.9 inches) and 30 cm (11.8 inches). Adult skulls fracture at 11.9 +-.9 kNewtons (2,675 lbs +- 202 lbs) and facial fractures in adults can range from 2 to 4 kNewtons (449.6 to 899 lbs) (Nyquist, G. et al., 1986). Coats, et al. (2007) used radiological serial images of infants (<6 weeks old) and recent published material property data for children to develop a computer finite element model (FEM) of the infant head to study skull fracture from occipital impacts. Validation of this FEM model against published infant cadaver drop research (Weber, 1984) found good agreement with the prediction of fracture for falls onto hard surfaces. Coats, Margulies and Ji (2007) reported a fracture force as low as .28 kNewtons (63 lbs) (50% probability of fracture) in infant skulls. Toddlers at 18 months to 2 years have similar bone material properties as young infants with an elastic modulus of E= 321 Megapascals. However, toddler skulls are approximately 1.67 times thicker and therefore significantly more rigid than the infant skull (Ibrahim, N. and Margulies, S., 2010). A child of approximately 10 months would fall somewhere in between the 63 lbs for a young infant and the estimated 290 lbs for an 18-month-old toddler.

Anthropometric infant/toddler surrogate heads falling on floor surfaces indicate that stiffer surfaces result in increased head decelerations and an increased lateral clamp compression mechanism to the skin and SCALP compared to softer (less stiff) surfaces (e.g., concrete versus a carpeted floor) (Ibrahim and Margulies, 2010). The 22-month-old toddler's fracture was audible and confirmed by a CT scan (Loyd et al., 2019). A complete discussion of abusive TBI versus short accidental falls resulting in significant life threatening TBI is beyond the scope of this text. However, the best evidence (albeit limited) is that of a one meter fall or above upon carpeted flooring depending the head strike point is sufficient to result in a TBI fatality even in approximate 2-year-old toddlers (video taped case study documentation; Van Ee et al., 2009).

H. Brain loading and traumatic brain injury (TBI)

Two issues are important for the personal injury attorney in regard to the biomechanics of brain injury. First, is whether the level of loading (e.g., angular acceleration, linear acceleration) is sufficient to produce brain injury.

Defense and plaintiff's attorneys need to differentiate the client with psychogenic disorders after head trauma from the client with real organic brain injury due to a trauma event. To underscore this problem, Sheftell et al. (2007) report that "In litigious cultures, when there can be active solicitation by attorneys of injury-related cases and patients being coached by attorneys, assessment of malingering may present a challenge even to experienced clinicians and neuropsychologists (Hayes, J., 1999)." Malingering as a diagnosis should not be made by exclusion. Observation of tasks not able to be performed, performance on forced choice tests worse than chance, Cluster B personality disorders (e.g., anti-social), prior work history, prior injury claims and excessive endorsement of symptoms may indicate feigning of symptoms (Young, W. et al. 2005 and 4th ed. Diagnostic and Statistical Manual of Mental Disorders, 1994). Certainly, there are instances where both organic and non-organic etiologies will interact with one another (Solomon, S., 2005). These opinions are reported here, but are normally not within the domain of the biomechanics/functional anatomy or neurosciences expert unless this expert is also a qualified clinical mental health licensed professional.

Acknowledging biological individuality, brain injury tolerance limits in regard to loading are important to examine. Second, the use or nonuse of protective measures to reduce brain injury, such as the use of seat belts or helmets during particular activities, may be an issue. The biomechanist plays an important role in cases where protective measures were not taken by the plaintiff and injury has resulted. The issue in brain injury then becomes one of comparing the level of loading to the head link without protective measures (actual loading) versus with protective measures in place. Each case needs to be examined on its own merit and circumstances, which include variables related to the type of loading, the magnitude of loading, and the direction of the loading vector.

In the area of medical malpractice, two other issues become important with regard to brain injury. One is regarding the diagnosis of head injury based upon the patient's history of the trauma event. Patient event history does play a part in brain injury diagnosis, and medical practitioners should recognize a serious trauma event based in part upon the event description. This is especially true in closed brain injury where the seriousness of the brain injury (small contact site or noncontact brain injury) is not always appreciated. Certainly, medical specialists must be aware of brain loading biomechanical mechanisms and general mechanisms of injury in order to make the best decisions regarding the ordering of tests and making diagnoses.

1. Primary insult

Regardless of the underlying mechanism of injury, brain tissue becomes distorted or deformed in the process of traumatic brain injury. Some evidence indicates that lesser degrees of injury may still occur even if brain tissue stays within its elastic zone and returns to its original shape. The momentary deformation is enough to produce brain injury. In other cases, the elastic zone is exceeded, and a permanent deformation including disruption of brain tissue and vasculature may occur. These elastic and plastic deformations resulting from differential motion of brain tissue as the result of trauma are termed "primary injuries" to the brain. They include concussions, contusions, small and massive bleeds, and diffuse axonal injury (DAI) of varying degrees.

2. Secondary insult

Secondary insult to the brain may result from a rise in intracranial pressure, possible brain extrusion via herniation of brain tissue, and a decreased blood perfusion to the brain. The Monro-Kellie doctrine dictates that any increase in any fluid (blood, cerebral spinal fluid, extracellular fluid, or intracellular fluid) within a closed system, such as the central nervous system, must be accompanied by a decrease in another fluid or the intracranial pressure will increase, leading to a decrease in blood perfusion of brain structures. Cerebral (blood) perfusion pressure equals mean arterial blood pressure minus intracranial pressure. Blood perfusion of the brain/brainstem must be maintained in order to keep sensitive central nervous system tissues alive. Intracranial pressure is monitored and may be treated in several ways, some non-invasive, such as simply raising the head and torso of the patient by the neurosurgeon. If intracranial pressure continues to increase in spite of pharmacological measures, head positioning or surgery, brain tissue deformation and extrusion may occur as the internal pressures exceed the containment capabilities of the container skull.

Examples include extrusion of the cerebellar tonsils through the foramen magnum or extrusion of cerebral cortex and underlying brain tissue through a surgically induced skull defect or penetration trauma. These conditions are all secondary to the primary trauma insult and must be managed appropriately by the medical care team to provide the best probability of a good result. Malpractice litigation with a focus on secondary trauma and appropriate medical care is usually beyond the scope of the biomechanist and therefore requires medical opinion exclusively.

From a clinical medical perspective, upper central nervous system injury may be classified and graded as described in Tables 9.2 and 9.3.

9.4 Mechanisms of Traumatic Brain Injury

The biomechanist focuses on a mechanistic approach to traumatic brain injury. Static loading is much less common in traumatic brain injury (TBI), and when it does occur, its effects are usually localized. In static loading, little or no movement occurs to the head link in relation to a ground reference during the loading mechanism. For ex-

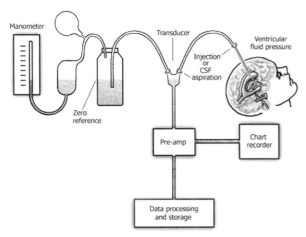

Figure 9.9 *A technique for the continuous measurement of intracranial fluid pressure. (Courtesy of Kandel et al., 1991)*

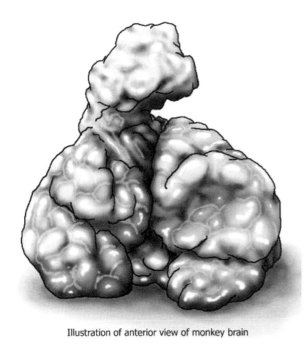

Illustration of anterior view of monkey brain

Figure 9.10 *An example of acute brain swelling that creates a mushroom structure after a surgical defect is produced in a monkey skull. (Courtesy of Dacey et al., 1987)*

ample, if the skull is caught in a compressive vice or press which slowly applies a compressive stress and consequent strain, this would be an example of static loading. Similar situations do occur, and this author has been involved in one of these cases that resulted in the death of a laborer. Much more common however is dynamic loading (producing motion) that results in contact (impact) or alternatively non-impact loading (i.e., inertial loading). Impact and non-impact loading set our framework for examining dynamic loading to the brain.

A. Penetration

Direct impact to the skull involves contact phenomena. Penetration (e.g., depressed skull fracture or missile penetration) may result with direct deformation and/or loss of brain tissue underlying a skull bone. Other examples include missiles and are most common in gunshot wounds in this country. High velocity missiles (greater than 320 meters/second) due to KE = 1/2 mass x velocity^2 produce the most significant brain damage and may result in significant energy wave transmission and cavitation within brain tissue.

Brain tissue lacks the strength and integrity of other biological tissues, and is not able to retard and absorb a bullet's energy as well as other soft tissues; therefore more widespread brain damage is likely to occur.

The neurological result of penetrating brain injury is dependent upon the specific brain tissue damaged. One famous example of this type of injury is that of Phineas Gage, a young American railroad construction worker who during the mid-1800s was tamping explosives in a hole which had been drilled in rock. An explosion occurred, and the thirteen-pound, one-meter-long iron tamping rod entered the left cheek of Phineas and drove through his anterior superior cranium. He was still awake and cognizant of his surroundings after this accident. Phineas Gage was able to survive this event, and his motor and basic language skills were unaffected. However, with the loss of significant frontal lobe brain matter, his social and reasoning skills were adversely affected in a progressive manner, making him much less functional during the remainder of his life (Damasio, 1994).

B. Linear head acceleration: coup and contrecoup contusions

Impact loading may produce significant inertial loading to the head link. A strike to the head may produce both linear accelerations (translation) and angular acceleration (rotation).

Table 9.2
Level of Consciousness: Classification and Grading Systems

(Becker et al., 1982)
I—Transient loss of consciousness; now alert and oriented w/o neurological deficit; may have headache, nausea, or vomiting
II—Impaired consciousness but able to follow at least a simple command; may be alert, but with focal neurological deficit
III—Unable to follow even a single command because of disordered level of consciousness; may use words, but inappropriately; motor response varies from localizing pain to posturing or nothing
IV—No evidence of brain function (brain death)

(Ransohoff and Fleischer, 1975)
I—Alert; responds immediately to questions; may be disoriented and confused; follows complex commands
II—Drowsy, confused, uninterested; does not lapse into sleep when undisturbed; follows simple commands only
III—Stuporous; sleeps when not disturbed; responds briskly and appropriately to mildly noxious stimuli
IV—Deep stupor; responds defensively to prolonged noxious stimuli
V—Coma; no appropriate response to any stimuli, decorticate and decerebrate responses included
VI—Deep coma; flaccidity; no response to any stimuli

(Grady Coma Scale)
1.) Drowsy, lethargic, indifferent, uninterested or belligerent and uncooperative; does not lapse into sleep when left undisturbed
2.) Stuporous, will lapse into sleep when not disturbed; may be disoriented to time, place and person
3.) Deep stupor; requires strong pain to evoke movement
4.) Does not respond appropriately to any stimuli; may exhibit decorticate or decerebrate posturing; retains deep tendon reflexes
5.) Does not respond to any stimuli; flaccid

(Glasgow Coma Scale)
E—Eye Opening
    4-spontaneous
    3-to speech
    2-to pain
    1-nothing
M—Best Motor Response
    6-obeys
    5-localizes
    4-withdraws
    3-abnormal flexion
    2-extensor response
    1-nothing
V—Verbal Reasoning
    5-oriented
    4-confused conversation
    3-inappropriate words
    2-incomprehensible words
    1-nothing
(Coma Score: E+M+V = 3 to 15)

Linear acceleration may produce focal brain effects such as contusions (coup and contrecoup) due to compression and tension brain tissue strains. Diffuse effects from linear acceleration, excepting extremely high linear accelerations, are not common.

Coup contusions are the result of linear acceleration or deceleration driven contacts. If the skull experiences minimal deformation due to an impact, then the head link can be described in accord with rigid body laws. However, brain tissue and vasculature within the rigid skull container will still experience compression, tension and shear deformation and disrupted vasculature bleeds which may lead to ischemia in brain tissue at the site of impact and a rise in intracranial pressure as previously described. The compression and tension stresses under these conditions are due to the application of Newton's first law of motion which dictates that the brain tends to remain stationary during the time in which the skull moves, thereby producing brain skull inner surface impact. Blunt loads applied to a stationary head link tend to produce coup contusions via inertial impact (Dawson et al., 1980), and the lesion occurs at the impact site. An example of this loading would be a strike to the head link by a broad-based implement (without skull penetration) or a broad-based pedestrian head impact to the windshield of a motor vehicle.

Contrecoup contusions result in a lesion at what is termed the counterpole or opposite side of the skull. Some evidence indicates that these lesions are most common in the temporal and frontal lobe regions (Dawson et al., 1980) and therefore result from contralateral side impact or impact to the posterior occipital bone. These contusions are most likely the result of a moving head being

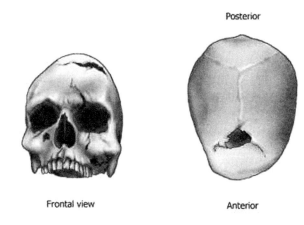

Figure 9.12 An artist's depiction of the skull of Phineas Gage. (Adapted from Damasio Descartes' Error: Emotion, Reason, and the Human Brain. New York: Grosset/Putnam 1994).

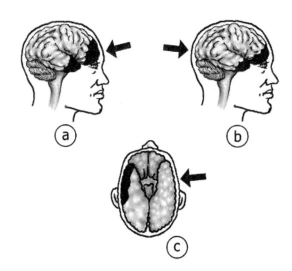

Arrows indicate contact point and direction of applied force. Shaded areas show location of contusion.

Figure 9.13 (a) sagittal view of a coup mechanism brain injury; (b) sagittal view of a contrecoup mechanism brain injury; (c) horizontal view of contrecoup mechanism brain injury. (Courtesy of Robert Perry)

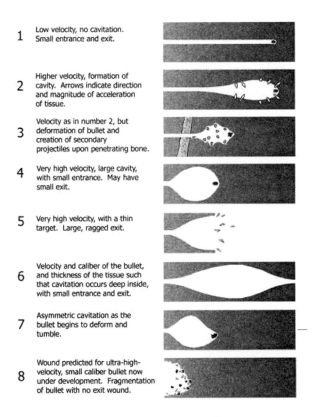

Figure 9.11 Ballistic effects on animal tissue. (Adapted from Swan and Swan, 1989 in Zernicke and Whiting, 1998.)

Table 9.3
Concussion Classifications

(Torg, 1982)
Grade I—"Bell Rung", short-term confusion, unsteady gait, dazed appearance, loss of consciousness, post-traumatic amnesia

Grade II—Post-traumatic amnesia, vertigo

Grade III— Post-traumatic amnesia, retrograde amnesia, vertigo

Grade IV—Immediate, transient loss of consciousness

Grade V—Paralytic coma, cardiorespiratory arrest

Grave VI—Death

(Kulund, 1982)
Mild—Stunned, dazed; no confusion, dizziness, nausea or visual disturbance; feels well after 1–2 minutes; coordination

Moderate—Loss of consciousness; mental confusion, retrograde amnesia; Tinnitus, dizziness; skill recovery may be very rapid

Severe—Longer loss of consciousness; headache, confusion; posttraumatic amnesia, retrograde amnesia

(Nelson et al., 1984)
Grade 0—Head struck or moved rapidly; not stunned or dazed initially; subsequently reports headache and difficulty in concentrating

Grade I—Stunned or dazed initially; no loss of consciousness or amnesia; "bell rung"; sensorium quickly clears (<1 minute)

Grade II—Headache, cloudy sensorium < 1 minute; no loss of consciousness; may have tinnitus, amnesia; may be irritable, hyper-excitable, confused and dizzy

Grade III—Loss of consciousness > 1 minute; not comatose (arousable with noxious stimuli); demonstrates Grade II symptoms during recovery

Grade IV—Loss of consciousness > 1 minute; not comatose (arousable with noxious stimuli); demonstrates Grade II symptoms during recovery

rapidly decelerated—as, for example, when an occupant's moving head strikes a stiff surface in a fall from height. The actual mechanism of injury in a brain contrecoup lesion is not yet well defined. However, one hypothesis has been ruled out. The brain does not bounce back and forth inside the skull to produce this counterpole damage. The brain tissue viscosity and low coefficient of restitution make this explanation erroneous. A viable hypothesis for some contrecoup lesions includes the previously discussed angular acceleration effects that may occur at remote brain surface sites that are directly under bony projections (inside), resulting in a laceration of brain tissue at that site during differential angular motion. In the authors' opinion, a more important mechanism for most contrecoup lesions (especially those which involve deeper tissue destruction) is that of cavitation that is thought to occur due to linear deceleration of a moving head. At the counterpole site of an impact, the brain continues to move in the same previous direction in spite of the deceleration of the skull (Newton's First Law of Motion). This motion of the brain results in a pulling away from the brain-skull interface at the counterpole site which in turn results in a negative pressure in relation to brain pressure in other areas. In effect, the brain arterial vasculature may drop from normal operating systolic and diastolic blood pressure to near zero pressure at the counterpole site in high linear acceleration impacts resulting in a vacuum effect (Watts, 1999). Under these conditions, viscous liquid-like brain tissue and vasculature deform easily and in turn will move to fill that vacuum site, resulting in significant tissue damage in that region. Blood vessels may expand and burst due to this negative pressure, with resulting bleeds. Cavitation is the term that describes this process involving the creation of this relative negative pressure zone. However, this is an over-simplification of the mechanics. A more detailed explanation is that cavitation occurs with a skull impact and a counterpole effect and is one way to produce an area of liquid local pressure that is below the vapour pressure in that area. This lower local pressure in relationship to the vapour pressure leads to liquid evaporation in the area and the consequent formation of cavitation bubbles which continue to enlarge. As the larger bubbles move into an area where the local pressure exceeds the vapour pressure, the vapour condenses and at the weakest spot of the bubble, collapse begins. The rapid collapse or implosion of bubbles progresses with the coincident release of high energy over a very small area resulting in significant brain tissue damage.

Experiments in fluid filled containers lend evidence for cavitation playing a part in both coup and contrecoup

injuries. Although cavitation theory at present has the most biomechanical proponents in terms of a contrecoup mechanism, a competing theory is the shear strain theory which addresses both coup and contrecoup contusions. An academic discussion of these competing theories is beyond the scope of this text. Suffice it to say that we know that most contrecoup contusions result from an impact to a moving head producing a significant deceleration as the head link is brought to an abrupt linear motion stop.

1. Tolerance limits for linear acceleration

The skull is assumed to act as a rigid body, but with brain contents that are deformable due to loading. In reality, some deformation (albeit in some cases very small) occurs to the skull any time a force or an acceleration is imposed to the head link. The experimental data defining brain tissue tolerance limits come from varied sources including animal model data, human cadaver data, and human volunteer data at lower levels including most recently head injury telemetry (i.e., HIT) measuring contact sport athletes during practice and competition events. Furthermore, anecdotal and epidemiological data have expanded our knowledge of tolerance limits for loading. However, these latter data must rely on estimates of the loading that were imposed upon the head link.

It is important to remember that biological individuality applies to brain injury tolerance limits in similar fashion as to other tissues. However, this does not suggest that head loading that normally occurs on a very frequent basis to the population at large should be viewed as injury producing in some individuals based upon their biological individuality. A minimum magnitude loading level must be met for mild TBI and the notion that a percentage of this minimal level (e.g., 50%) results in a 50% mild TBI does not have any genuine scientific support. The short answer for a tolerance limit in terms of linear acceleration

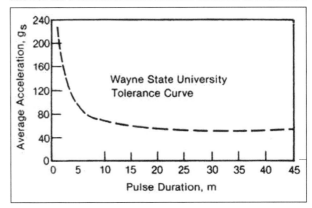

Figure 9.14 *Wayne State tolerance curve. (Courtesy of Robert Perry)*

is demonstrated historically by the Wayne State tolerance curve.

This curve is based on linear acceleration data from a limited set of human skull cadaver data and anesthetized animal data. These data involve linear accelerations of very short duration (3–5 ms). Still this early attempt to develop linear acceleration tolerance data incorporates two important variables that help one to understand the concepts involved in TBI. First is the acceleration (or deceleration) level, which is expressed in gs. One g is the acceleration of gravity and is approximately 32.2 ft/sec/sec or 9.81 meters/sec/sec. In other words, over a brief interval of time, the head link and the enclosed brain may experience a change in velocity (e.g., in ft/sec or meters/sec). The rate at which this change in velocity occurs is the acceleration or deceleration and is simply determined by dividing the change in velocity by the time over which this velocity change occurs (e.g., 10 ms or 100 ms). This figure is then converted to a measure in gs as per the appropriate conversion factor. For example:

Delta velocity (V) = final velocity (V_f) – initial velocity (V_i)
V = 0 ft/sec – 18 ft/sec = 18 ft/sec

Time over which the delta velocity takes place = 10 ms

Average linear acceleration = V /t = 18ft/sec divided by 10 ms
= 1800 ft/sec/sec or 1800 ft/sec^2
Average g level = 1800 ft/sec/sec divided by 32.2 ft/s^2
= 55.9 gs

Second, time comes into play in terms of the duration of the acceleration. Note that the Wayne State tolerance curve slopes downward dramatically at 5 ms. Head impacts with hard solid stiff structures such as a vehicle B pillar are normally within this range of time duration (3–5 ms peaks). At time durations longer than 5 ms, tolerable average g levels are approximately 50–60 gs. Some more recent evidence indicates that minimum concussion levels should be dropped to approximately 45 gs over duration time frames of 5–15 msec. When a *constant* acceleration is imposed over a *longer* period of time for a single head impact, there is an increased probability of TBI, and therefore acceleration levels must drop if one is to avoid injury.

It is the interaction of both the acceleration (or deceleration) and the time over which the acceleration acts. The Gadd Severity Index (GSI) represents an effort to exam-

ine average head accelerations over a much longer time frame. A GSI over 1,000 is indicated as an approximate tolerance limit for serious head injury. Historically, other data support a GSI of 1,500 for serious human head injury, which corresponds to approximately 125 average gs over a duration of 10 ms.

2. Head injury scales—Linear Acceleration

More recently is the development of the head injury criterion (HIC) score, with any value over 1000 representing failure. This score is used in automobile crash testing in the United States (FMVSS 208). It is expressed in the formula below:

$$\frac{1^{2.5}}{(t_1 - t_2) \times (t_2 - t_1) \int a(t)dt} < 1000$$

Originally developed from the Wayne State tolerance curve, t_1 and t_2 are two time points during the impulse that maximize the left side of this function. Furthermore, the accelerations at these time points are always equal numerically, and multiplying t_1 or t_2 by 1.6 will always yield the average acceleration. Conceptually, the HIC determines the severity of a head impact producing a linear acceleration by looking at a portion of the loading history to the head. In very long impacts such as those that could occur in a padded dashboard impact or head impact into an airbag, the HIC is inflated and does not represent a realistic injury scale as pointed out by Newman (1998). Although it may seem counter-intuitive, the most recent revision of the HIC involves limiting the t_1 to t_2 interval to a shortened time epoch of 15 ms. This reduction in the integrated time period of head deceleration seems to yield a more predic-

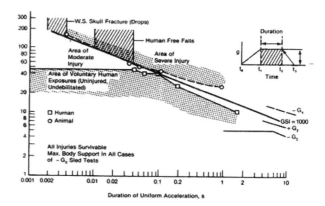

Figure 9.15 Tolerance curve for sled tests, cadaver, and human falls. Adapted from Eiband, A.M. Human tolerance to rapidly applied accelerations: A summary of the literature, NASA Memo 5-19E, 1959. (Courtesy of Robert Perry)

tive injury scale for longer impact times involving lower decelerations (e.g., head-air bag interactions). In this approach, the original equation (flawed as it may be) with a revised 15 ms time epoch gives us the best approximated prediction of linear acceleration loading to the head link. No other head injury calculated criterion for linear acceleration has replaced the HIC in the present. A complete discussion of this topic is addressed in Newman (1998, Appendix C pp. 213–214). Good scores in new 2018–19 automobile vehicles with air bags or air bags combined with pre-tensioning seat belts usually yield HIC scores under 500 and many times under 400 in federally funded New Car Assessment Performance (NCAP) frontal impact testing. Biomechanical studies and safety engineering are responsible for these improvements. However, keep in mind the earlier points discussed in Chapter 4 relating to fixed belt restraints versus adjustable restraints. Therefore, in this case, fixed restraints (which are safer) were largely abandoned in passenger vehicles in the 1970s in favor of adjustable three-point restraints which had the highest probability of increasing occupant compliance (increased convenience and comfort).

A second approach in assessing brain injury from linear acceleration is the use of lumped parameter models. Stalnaker et al. (1971), based on cadaver subject and animal experimental data, developed the *mean strain criterion* (MSC). The concept relates to the relative displacements of two masses divided by the diameter displacement of the human cranium. Real-world injuries involving cranium and brain strain can then be compared with the model when known loads are applied to produce

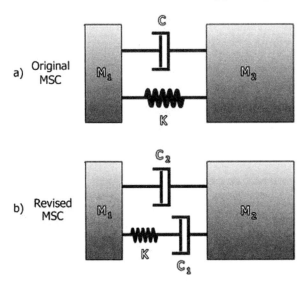

Figure 9.16 (a) The original mean strain criterion; (b) the revised mean strain criterion (Newman, 1998). (Courtesy of Robert Perry)

specific amounts of strain in the model. In this way, strains resulting from stresses can be compared in the experimental model and in actual injuries. Correlations are then calculated based upon these two sets of data. The rationale for the MSC and lumped parameter model in part is based upon the notion that the primary underlying mechanism of brain tissue injury is one of deformation regardless of means of deformation. Therefore, linear acceleration, angular acceleration, pressure (energy) waves, penetration or pressure gradients may all result in brain or brain stem deformation (albeit different types of deformation insults) (Vetter, D., 2000). Nevertheless, it is the deformation that results in TBI.

The original model mean strain criterion (MSC) incorporated two masses, a spring and a dashpot. The spring in a model such as this behaves in accord with Hooke's law and deforms (shortens or lengthens) directly proportionally to the force or load imposed. The dashpot acts as a damping mechanism for energy and also acts to affect the motion of the two masses. In a revised "new mean strain criterion" a second dashpot was added in series with the spring mechanism (Newman, 1998).

Further development led to the Translational Head Injury Model (Stalnaker, 1987) and iterative refinement of this model. At present, this approach has not gained wide acceptance, but it does represent an energy approach to the head injury problem and bases brain injury prediction upon energy imposed and resulting strain of brain tissue (i.e., deformation). Furthermore, it appears to be especially applicable to bullet projectile head trauma.

C. Angular head acceleration

Angular accelerations (impact and nonimpact) commonly produce widespread diffuse effects as the skull and brain or brainstem experience differential accelerations.

Significant loading does occur during rotational motions. Angular acceleration of the head link may occur without impact as per a whiplash mechanism. Usually, more significant levels of angular acceleration occur as the result of a tangential impact to the head, and because the head link is tethered by the neck, a centric impact in line with the center of gravity of the head will result in significant rotation around a generalized cervical spine axis. One strong criticism of the HIC and lumped parameter models is that they do not account for TBI produced by angular acceleration which may occur around one or more of the three principal neck axes: (1) mediolateral, (2) anterioposterior, and (3) longitudinal (ML, AP, and L respectively).

Newton's first law of motion helps to explain how

and why angular accelerations are able to produce shear and tension stresses within brain tissue and differential fluid flow within the cranium. In an impact circumstance, an area of the skull is struck and rotates around the generalized cervical spine axis. The contents within the skull possess angular inertia (I = mass x k²) and in accord with Newton I, want to stay in place. Therefore, the cranium moves, and the brain experiences a differential movement. Shear loads develop at the cranium (skull)-brain interface. In similar fashion, if the cranium is experiencing angular motion and then this angular motion is brought to an abrupt stop, a rapid angular deceleration occurs with similar deleterious effects. Furthermore, brain morphology dictates that structures within the brain differ somewhat in terms of angular inertia, and the interface between these structures can in some circumstances represent a weak link allowing for differential movement of these various brain structures. This results in offset parallel movements of brain tissues. Axons may reach their failure point as they are maximally loaded in shear. These shear loads will produce shear and tension strains of axons within the brain (Graham et al., 1987). These insults can result in mild, moderate, or severe brain injury. The salient variables are the angular acceleration level and the time over which the angular acceleration takes place. When significant angular accelerations are applied to the head regardless of the mechanism, a more diffuse injury pattern will occur. Animal experimentation as well as epidemiological human research suggests that a loss of consciousness occurs when angular acceleration is predominant in an event as opposed to linear acceleration (although, both linear and angular accelerations usually occur in concert with one another). Angular acceleration is thought to result in upper central nervous system pathology dependent upon the level and duration of the angular acceleration impulse. The clinical result begins with varying degrees of concussion, progressing to acute subdural hematoma, and finally progressing to *diffuse axonal injury* (DAI), which in the absence of petechial hemorrhages, can only be seen microscopically (Graham et al., 1987). Finally, experiments with gels and vinyl bags of gels with surrounding water placed in brain model containers show that fluid movement may be significant and complex during physical model iterations of various internal configurations (Aldman, Thorngren and Ljung, 1983).

Furthermore, during high angular acceleration, the axons of neurons may be traumatized due to these stresses and consequent strains, and therefore function (i.e., neural transmission) will be impaired. Thibault (1993) indicates

that this is accompanied by an influx of calcium (Ca++) which leads to an increased osmotic pressure swelling within the neuron axon (transmitting component of the neuron) and finally axolemma rupture. Furthermore, there is increased potassium (K+) efflux from the neuron with brain trauma. Calcium influx and K+ efflux across the neuron membrane lead to increased firing (depolarizations) and an increase in the neurotransmitter glutamate in some central nervous system neurons. These alterations lead to an energy crisis within neurons with increased adenosine triphosphate (i.e., ATP) requirements for metabolism (i.e., active membrane pumps) to re-establish relative ion concentrations inside and outside the neuron cell. Additionally, within the cell, brain trauma initiates the pathophysiology cascade with altered proteolysis, abnormal proteins, intracellular and extracellular toxicity, inflammation, axonal injury and altered neurotransmitter release (Giza and Hovda, 2014).

However, focal brain injury may also result from angular acceleration insults in areas that are weak and vulnerable. One example of a vulnerable site is the region of the bridging veins that pierce the dura mater at the brain-skull interface. These vessels will rupture relatively easily during shear loading (tension stresses) applied during high angular acceleration resulting from an impact as per a shake and strike mechanism (applied to an infant head). Secondly, ridges on the inside surface of the skull present sharp projections which may lacerate brain tissue at various specific interface sites during skull-brain differential rotational (angular) motion as previously discussed.

Experimentally, isolating angular acceleration in the laboratory animal model required that the animal's head be placed tightly (bone secured) in a jig mechanism such that when activated, it produces only angular acceleration (around a single axis). This is not analogous to real-world accidents that coincidently produce linear and rotational accelerations around non-principal axes. However, this experimental procedure is necessary to parcel out any concomitant linear acceleration that may occur with a head impact to the animal. It should also be noted that during the 1970s and early 1980s, when most of these animal experiments took place, it was clear that much higher angular acceleration levels were required, especially in smaller live primate models. This was due to the fact that non-sapiens primate brains are smaller than the human brain (less mass) and with smaller radii of gyration. To achieve the same shear stresses and strains as one should expect in adult humans, angular accelerations in some cases approaching 50,000 radians/sec² were required using experimental primate models (e.g., squirrel monkeys). Extrapolating these findings to humans then required scaling down the angular acceleration levels applied to non-sapiens primates to tolerance limits that would be most appropriate for adult humans. A further difficulty in this approach is that lower primate brains represent some differences in gross structure (morphology). This presents a limitation to any scaling procedure.

One line of evidence suggests that lateral flexion of the neck as would most probably occur in a side impact motor vehicle accident has the highest probability of producing grade 3 DAI by means of angular acceleration (Gennarelli, 1982).

1. Tolerance limits for angular acceleration

It is important for the attorney to understand that while we have a relatively good estimate of linear accelerations required for moderate and severe brain injury, angular accelerations required for these same levels of injury are not well defined. Estimates over the past thirty years have ranged from approximately 600 radians/sec^2 for mild concussion to over 16,000 radians/second^2 or above for severe angular acceleration injury (Ommaya and Gennarelli, 1974 and Margulies, Thibault, and Gennarelli, 1990). Lowenhielm (1975), based on cadaver tests and his mathematical model, established human tolerance levels at 4,500 radians/second^2. Ommaya (1984) proposed angular acceleration tolerance limits related to the Abbreviated Injury Scale (AIS) (Newman, 1998). Depreitere et al. (2006) repeated a similar methodology of Lowenhielm (1975) and subjected ten adult cadaver specimens to occipital (back of head) impacts of varying magnitude. Thitry-three percent of the impacts resulted in bridging vein failure detected at brain autopsy.

More recently other authors such as Thibault and Gennarelli (1990) have (based on primate experiments) ascribed angular acceleration loading up to 15,000 radians/sec^2 over 10 ms to the most serious angular acceleration insult responsible for diffuse axonal shearing.

Early human work also expands the literature. Muzzy (1976) reports the data on five male volunteers who during sled tests were subjected to head link inertial loading forward peak linear accelerations ranging from 29.38 gs to 40.95 gs without injury. Angular velocities of the head link from on the order of 1,500 radians/ second^2 were not uncommon, yet did not produce injury (Muzzy, 1976).

Boxing also presents a good model for studying angular acceleration in humans because boxing head injuries (and knockouts) are predominantly the result of angular

acceleration impulses applied during boxing training or a boxing match. In this regard, Pincemaille, Trosseille, Mack and Tarriere (1989) instrumented volunteer boxers with triaxial accelerometers in their head gear and concomitantly recorded with video at 500 fields/second. Five boxers, aged nineteen to twenty-seven, fought three round bouts. Forty-five blows to the head were selected for analysis, and interestingly, all the blows produced head acceleration levels which exceeded 3,500 radians/second^2 in these boxers. Three-millisecond duration angular accelerations were in many cases over 6,000, 7,000, and 8,000 radians/second^2. Linear accelerations of the head link also reached levels of 130–159 peak gs in some selected cases without injury (linear acceleration measurements). Although one test was suggestive of mild temporary impairment, the overall picture was unremarkable for TBI. In explanation of these data, it should be clarified that the durations of these high peak accelerations were very short, and therefore extremely high angular velocities of the head link were not achieved in these boxers (Pincemaille et al., 1989). This is not to suggest that boxing over the longer term is harmless. Pugilistic dementia and Parkinson's disease in boxers is well documented in the literature and usually occurs gradually over many fights. Chronic Traumatic Encephalopathy (CTE) is also certainly a concern based upon published clinical and autopsy literature in American football activity.

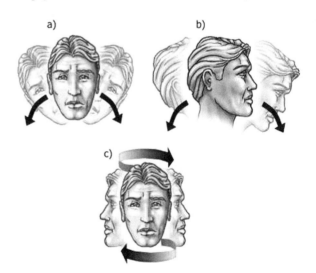

Figure 9.17 *Angular motion velocities and accelerations around one or more of the three principal axes of rotation. The cervical spine serves as the primary point for the axes of rotation: (a) anterioposterior axis, (b) mediolateral axis and (c) longitudinal axis. (Courtesy of Robert Perry)*

Finally, the literature also documents many case reports of boxing deaths with 75% of these deaths being in association with acute subdural hemorrhages. In four fatal boxing match cases reported by Lechowski (1965), there was cerebral edema and severe hemorrhagic necrosis in some of the basal portions of the cerebrum and within basal ganglia structures (Unterharnscheidt, 1985). These are deep structures and illustrate that acute brain injury (more often without protective head gear) may occur in deep structures as well as superficial areas in amateur and professional boxing participation. Furthermore, there is unquestionably increased concern over the more recently popular mixed martial arts (i.e., MMA) where blows to the head of an opponent come from the bare feet, shanks, elbows and minimally padded fists.

This discussion leads to the conclusion that much is yet to be determined in establishing angular acceleration tolerance limits for brain injury for adults, let alone children. Limits are not well established, and there is a need for additional non-sapiens primate experiments for high magnitude angular acceleration research in this author's opinion. Additionally, the new HIT technology will continue to provide additional valuable brain injury data in regard to the minimal level of loading magnitude and in terms of protective equipment for adult and youth contact sports.

9.5 Mild Brain Injury

The head link presents a number of protective mechanisms. The brain is extremely well protected from impact trauma. Nature has devised an excellent system that incorporates a scalp padding, a hard compact bone shell, a dura mater membrane, and cerebral spinal fluid which acts to reduce linear and angular accelerations to the brain. Furthermore, it must be emphasized that in addition to these brain impact protective factors, the undulations and elasticity in brain neuron axons within the central nervous system provide significant protection against these shear stresses and strains that result from angular acceleration. Therefore, for example, striking the head against a padded head rest in a rear-end collision in the absence of another impact will not result in brain injury because the level of loading is extremely low in comparison to other more significant events that do not produce traumatic brain injury. Furthermore, although transient headaches have been produced in recent human subject rear low impact experimental studies, they disappear within seconds, minutes, or hours of the event without consequence (Brault et al., 1998). Other accident events involving head impact may

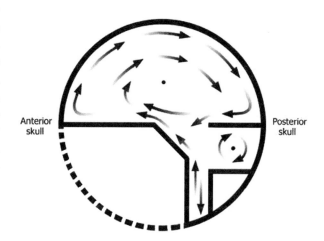

Figure 9.18 A forward acceleration of the head link in the sagittal plane where the gel sticks to the sides and structures of the container meant to simulate the skull. (Courtesy of Aldman, Thorngren, and Ljung, 1983)

also be found upon close examination not to represent significant loading to the brain or brain stem. One problem may be that early imaging data including standard CT scans that may be administered to patients are not sensitive enough to detect mild brain injuries without bleeds or brain contusions. Therefore, emergency department clinical signs are of the utmost importance to physicians along with cautionary notes to the patient that even with normal mentation and other normal clinical measures, head injury patients may deteriorate rapidly, as discussed previously in Case Study 9.1.

Dacey et al. (1993) indicate that mild brain injury is one of the most common of hospital admissions due to physical trauma and therefore deserves more attention. Examples of mild brain injury include small brain contusions due to linear acceleration or energy wave propagation. These brain insults can usually be managed without surgical intervention if intracranial pressures can be managed with coincident adequate brain blood perfusion. The end result is very good, usually without permanent neurological damage. Dacey et al. (1993) indicate, however, that some small minority of patients will experience ongoing symptoms and neuropsychological deficits after this type of brain trauma. Brain injury does appear to occur across a broader continuum compared to other tissues such as cortical bone for example (fracture versus no fracture). In the great majority of minor head injury cases, behavioral deficits are absent or temporary in nature (Dacey et al., 1993). However, in some cases, recovery after mild brain injury is not complete. Dacey et al. (1993) indicate that 1 to 3% of patients with an initial normal neurological clinical examination or mild altered consciousness will require a neurosurgical operative procedure. Identifying these patients who will have serious complications following a seemingly minor head injury and therefore warrant an initial CT scan or follow-up CT scans over the following hours or days remains a formidable medical diagnosis problem. A larger minority (yet undetermined) of minor head injury patients will suffer from varying degrees of post-concussive syndrome (PCS) or posttraumatic syndrome symptoms (PTS symptoms) for an extended period of time. Dacey et al. (1993) state that "despite the fact that these symptoms occur in a predictable pattern and are quite similar from patient to patient, very little is understood about their etiology or persistence" (p. 173). More recently, clinical observation markers for concussion have improved in the acute diagnosis of concussion, and the development of biochemical markers for concussion are expected in the near term future.

Documenting post-concussive syndrome (PCS) in patients requires neuropsychological and electrophysiological testing as well as patient history after TBI. Furthermore, new imaging techniques such as positron emission tomography (PET scans), single positron emission tomography (SPECT scans), diffusion tensor Imaging (DTI), Functional MRI and Magnetoencephalography (MEG) may be promising in documenting organic brain injury. Obviously, these scans/procedures are not performed prior to an injury and many times are not performed until some significant time period after the head injury because of their expense and the low expectation of significant brain injury. Therefore, intervening history is a

possible confounding variable in determining the etiology of a brain lesion. Patients with persistent PCS symptoms continue to be the subject of medical controversy in terms of organic (neurological) versus somatoform disorder, clinical depression, and other forms of mental illness or simple aging etiology. Finally, it must be emphasized that when loading is applied to the head that is at or near what most humans normally experience on a daily or weekly basis, then the rationale for mild TBI is simply absent. The best evidence that we have to date in late 2019 based upon several lines of evidence including the HITS data is that linear acceleration magnitude levels must exceed an average level of 40–50 gs in a single exposure as a minimum level in adults to produce a concussion (i.e., mild TBI). However, once this minimal level is met or exceeded (e.g. 40–50 gs linear acceleration), then the question becomes, what is the expected outcome for an acute single concussion exposure and perhaps more importantly, the probable outcome resulting from many repetitive concussion insults over years. Some recent anecdotal but increasing evidence from the National Football League raises the suspicion that hundreds of head impacts on the order of 15–25 gs experienced by American football lineman may lead to chronic traumatic encephalopathy in later years (Funk et al., 2012).

Clearly, in this author's opinion, the possibility of brain injury must take into account the mechanism of injury. Several lines of evidence support mild brain injury due to an angular acceleration mechanism if the level and

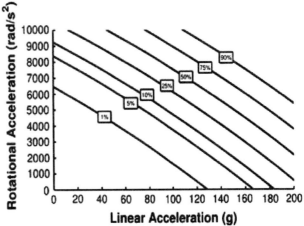

Figure 9.20 *Combined probability of concussion contours relating overall concussion risk to linear and rotational head acceleration. Adapted from Rowson, S. and Duma, S. (2013) Brain Injury prediction: Assessing the combined probability of concussion using linear and rotational head acceleration. Annals of Biomedical Engineering.*

Chronic Cumulative Pathology

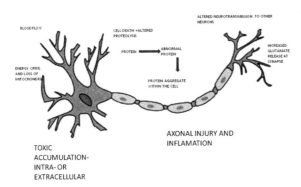

Figure 9.19

duration of the angular acceleration exceeds the protective factors previously discussed. Oppenheimer (1968) examined brain samples from fifty-nine TBI cases ranging from mild concussion (subsequent death due to other causes) to complete decerebration with survival times that exceeded twelve hours and up. Results indicated that diffuse microscope lesions were seen in a high percentage of human brains for many months after injury. Oppenheimer (1968) stated that mechanical lesions "are seen, not only after severe trauma, but also in cases of 'concussion'." In the mild brain injury cases, a possible underlying mechanism for injury is that minor damage to axons within the brain may inhibit axonal transport which may lead to axonal swelling at the point of injury (Graham et al., 1987). Animal studies support axonal shearing during minor head injury or simple concussion. Jane, Steward, and Gennarelli (1985) tested male Macaque fascicularis monkeys in an angular acceleration jig. The primate heads were taken through a 60° displacement arc (sagittal plane motion) over (1) 25 ms or (2) 5 ms, respectively. These two levels of angular acceleration were designed to produce minor head injury. In some cases, the animal did experience loss of consciousness (LOC) during the experimental procedure. The animals were cared for and then sacrificed at time points between seven and thirty days. The sacrifice occurred under general anesthesia with a circulation perfusion of 10% formalin solution. The formalin perfused brains were removed and examined by Fink-Heimer and

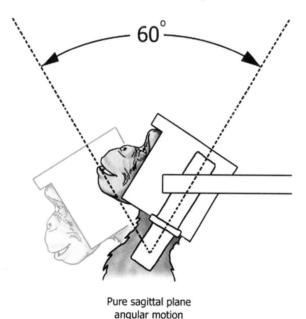

Pure sagittal plane
angular motion

Figure 9.21 A 60° excursion occurred to the primate head over 5 or 25 ms. (Courtesy of Jane et al., 1985)

Nauta techniques to examine evidence of degenerating axons (silver impregnation methods). Degenerating axons have a decreased affinity and therefore reduced uptake of silver. Two control groups (no trauma) of monkeys were also sacrificed, and their brains were prepared and examined using the same procedures. The results in this study indicated very few lesions in the cerebrum (telencephalon, forebrain) of the animals exposed to angular acceleration trauma, and when lesions were found, they developed in subcortical white matter below the cerebral cortex (axon tracts). The majority of these degenerating axon lesions were found in the mid-brain (mesencephalon) or in the crossing fibers of the pons. These are deep structures, and shear stresses in these regions would not be expected to be as high in comparison to the cerebral cortex regions at the surface of the cerebrum. Not all degenerating axons were ruptured. Damage had occurred due to the experimental trauma, but sometimes the degenerating axons were intact yet dysfunctional. In other cases, the axons had retracted (within hours of trauma) into what has been termed as "retraction balls." This line of evidence points to temporary brainstem dysfunction, normally with recovery but with some microscopic morphological changes that occur principally in these brainstem structures (Jane, Steward and Gennarelli, 1985). However, in cases where angular acceleration was predominant, organic brain damage given current medical diagnostic technology cannot always be visualized or detected initially.

Most recently Mouzon et al. (2018) have investigated single exposure concussion and repetitive (5 spaced impacts) concussions using male C57BL/6J mice at time point 2–3 months of age. The traumatic insult was administered under general anesthesia(s) and included control groups with repetitive sham (anesthesia only—no impact insult). Mentation behavioral measures during recovery of the single mTBI exposure group and repetitive five mTBI exposures group was degraded during the recovery period compared to the control groups, but improved over 15 months to the point of similar performance of the single exposure (s-mTBI) impacted mice and the single exposure (s-sham-no impact control groups). However, at 18–24 months, objective behavioral measures were observed by blinded investigators (double blind study) and findings indicated a gradual deteriorating behavioral performance was found in the s-mTBI group of mice with the implication being that the consequences of even a single mild TBI may reappear in the context of normal aging at late timepoints. Interestingly, both the single and 5 repetitive r-mTBI groups of mice exhibited increased microgliosis and astrocytosis in the corpus callosum (post-mortem histology). However, the authors provide a cautionary note that "although diffuse traumatic axonal injury has been increasingly documented in studies acquired at autopsy from patients in all severities of TBI, the question of whether white [brain] matter pathology is a lifelong condition remain to be established in humans" (Mouzon et al., 2018). The extrapolation of findings from "mice to men" and using the mouse animal model to investigate human pathology has long been a problem in acute trauma and in many disease states such as Type I diabetes. Mice are not the best model for human head injury and aging.

Additionally, some sport activities indicate a relatively high rate of mild brain injury. Concussive brain injury was found to occur at a surprisingly high rate of 19/100 high school football players per year (Gerberich et al., 1983). Alves et al. (1986) and Barth (1989) examined 2,350 football players from ten universities prior to the season and after concussive head injury with and without a loss of consciousness during the season. Neuropsychological testing revealed impairment of cognitive skills and information processing capabilities. These symptoms resolved over the next ten days. However, evidence exists that repeated concussive head injury may lead to a cumulative effect in terms of post concussive syndrome symptoms (loss of attention, irritability, mild confusion, memory deficits) or chronic traumatic encephalopathy over the long term.

A loss of consciousness or an immediate stupor after an angular acceleration event would argue for a minimum of a mild brain injury. In this regard, Levin et al. (1986) reported on ninety-four closed-head injury patients (varying degrees of injury) who were examined by magnetic resonance imagery (MRI) with an approximate 88% of the MRIs being positive for an abnormality. There was a positive correlation between brain lesion depth and the time duration of impaired consciousness (Dacey et al., 1993). In contrast, Leininger et al. (1989) found no significant differences in neuropsychological scores between minor head injury patients who had suffered a brief loss of consciousness versus no formal loss of consciousness (dazed only). Both of these subgroups scored at a lower overall level on the neuropsychological testing battery administered on average several months after the head injury compared to a control group sample of human subjects without brain injury.

Over the past approximate twenty years, Head Impact Telemetry (HIT; a.k.a. HITS i.e., Head Impact Telemetry System) has provided a wealth of human data in contact sports including American football, soccer and ice hockey with over 2 million impacts being recorded in American football alone. These research efforts are aimed at reducing concussions (mild brain injury) and more severe TBI in children and adults during sport and recreational activities. Furthermore, contact sports such as American football at all competitive age levels has come under attack in terms of the acute effects of one or more concussions and also in terms of chronic traumatic encephalopathy (CTE). Rowson et al. (2009) estimate that between 1.6 million and 3.8 million concussions occur each year in the United States as the result of athletic sport activity and about 3 hundred thousand of these concussions result in a loss of consciousness.

During the early part of this present century, several authors recreated concussions experienced by NFL professional football players through the use of game competition videos and applying these kinematics to head impacts of Hybrid III dummies (Newman et al., 1999, Newman et al., 2000; and Pellman et al., 2003). These data resulting from the recreated impacts were estimated at 79 peak gs, a Severity Index of 300, a Head Injury Criterion (HIC) of 250 and peak angular acceleration of 5,757 rads/s^2 (Pellman et al., 2003 and King et al., 2003). Naunheim et al. (2000) directly measured head impacts in human subjects wearing instrumented helmets (including the soccer players). Non-injurious (no concussion) g linear acceleration levels (average of peak gs for three sports) were reported to have ranged from 29.2 peak gs (football) to 54.7 peak gs (heading a soccer ball with an instrumented helmet worn by players). Naunheim et al. (2000) used the indices of the Gadd Severity Index and the HIC score (i.e., value). However, neither of these indices took into account angular acceleration and both of these measures were derived from linear acceleration only.

Alternatively, Head Impact Telemetry (HIT) has been used to directly measure both the linear and angular accelerations applied to football players. This system of instrumented accelerometer football helmets is available through Simbex, Lebanon, NH and involves football players wearing the instrumented helmets during practice or game play. The six accelerometer data are recorded for each minimum threshold impact and linear acceleration data are measured, angular acceleration data are estimated, and both outputs are quantified using a mathematical algorithm (Crisco, et al., 2004). Guskiewicz et al. (2007) extended the HIT data collection with over 100,000 football activity head impacts from 88 college/university level football players. Of the more than 100,000 head impacts, only 13 concussions occurred based upon clinical diagnosis. Similarly, Greenwald et al. (2008) collected close to 290,000 head impacts from both high school and university level football players (17 concussions) and found that weighted measures present a better prediction of concussion diagnosis than any other biomechanical measure. Greenwald et al. (2007) included weighted measures of *linear* acceleration and *angular* acceleration magnitudes and the duration of these acceleration impulses. Greenwald et al. (2008) were able to develop a composite injury metric, weighted principal component score (wPCS). This weighting was derived from the measures of instrumented players and also included the location of the impact, the Gadd Severity Index (GSI) and the Head Injury Criterion (HIC).

Funk et al. (2012) examined the Virginia Tech data along with data from other schools from 2010–2016. At Virginia Tech alone, some 37,128 head impacts over the threshold criterion of 10 gs were recorded in football game play. Peak linear acceleration exceeded 100 g levels in 516 of these impacts (0.014 or 1.4%). Furthermore, the Head Injury Criterion (HIC) score exceeded 200 in 468 (0.013 or 1.3%) of these over 37,000 head impacts. One can see that in terms of the college level adult American football population, significant concussion events only take place in a small percentage of the total impacts. The overall game head injury rate was 2.97 concussions per 1,000 athletic exposures. Funk et al. (2012) indicate that "the average head impact severity associated with concussion was 145 peak g, SD of +- 35 g and a HIC of 615, (SD of +- 309)" (p. 82).

Another interesting finding was that football linemen received the highest overall number of game day head impacts while the skill positions such as running backs, receivers and others received head impacts that were more severe but fewer in number. For example, "quarterbacks actually sustained 1.3–1.5 times more impacts of higher severity (> 100 [Peak] g or HIC > 200 per athlete exposure than offensive linemen (Funk et al., 2012), p 83). Furthermore, when only impacts over 100 g were considered, there was much better agreement between the predicted and actual concussion rates compared to previous studies (Funk et al., 2012). Nevertheless, there is anecdotal evidence based upon NFL findings that the increased number of impacts to linemen over their careers in football has led to CTE during their later years post retirement.

In a more recent study, Potvin et al. (2019) discuss epidemiological data that indicates that concussions are most prevalent in Canada in elite ice hockey players with the most common mechanism resulting from upper limb

impacts to the head via the shoulder, elbow and hand. Shoulder impacts account for the greatest number of concussions during "checking." Potvin et al. (2019) conducted a study and reported on 11 elite male ice hockey players (N= 11; age 21–25) who were asked to deliver checks at as "high a level as comfortable" and measurements of both linear and angular acceleration were recorded. Peak g levels for shoulder checks to the head of another player averaged 20.35 gs and the peak angular accelerations averaged 1097.9 rad/s^2 in these non-concussion events. However, this research effort shows the potential for concussion and also indicates that play in ice hockey has the potential to result in many sub-concussive impacts over a long period of time with unknown consequences.

Finally, a cautionary note is that the HIT data and ascribed tolerance limits applied to elite contact sport athletes may not fully apply to the general population. Age and gender differences most probably do exist and present a limitation in applying these data to younger and older age groups and certainly to females. This must be acknowledged. However, arguments such as that neck strength is much greater on average for elite athletes and therefore the HIT data does not apply to age matched males is not a viable argument as the neck strength is accounted for in the data collection with the final measure being head link linear and angular acceleration regardless of neck strength. A final criticism is that HIT measures of linear and angular acceleration are inflated for the helmet rather than the head itself. This is a legitimate criticism and because the helmet is not always tightly coupled to the head as it should be, slippage may occur which would lead the scientific community to conclude that higher acceleration levels are tolerable when in fact the actual acceleration applied to the head link may have been at a lower magnitude. It is anticipated that over the next few years, research methodology in human research efforts will solve this problem and more accurate tolerance limits for linear and angular acceleration will be forthcoming.

Case Study 9.2

The plaintiff, a lady in her mid-fifties, was a visitor to the city and attending a convention. She and a friend had entered a restaurant for dinner soon after arriving at the hotel. The plaintiff was seated in a long padded bench and her friend was seated in a chair on the other side of the table. The plaintiff indicated that she sat down and had placed her order and a little later she was hit on the back of her head by a full bottle of Champagne and rack that had been placed upon the ledge of her seatback behind and over her head. The total weight of the bottle was 3.24 pounds and the bottle's center of gravity dropped a maximum displacement of 10.5 inches to the back of the plaintiff's head in accord with her approximate sitting height. In discussing the sequence of events, the plaintiff indicated that "when it hit my head, I don't remember it hitting my head right away because the impact was so hard that when it hit my back it knocked all the breath out of me." The bottle and metal display ended up on the bench seat next to the plaintiff. Her friend did not observe this accident event as she indicated that she was looking away at the time that the bottle fell. The plaintiff indicated that much of the evening was not well remembered although she did remember being given a free night's lodging at the hotel by a staff member. The plaintiff did indicate that her head was not bleeding, but indicated there was a huge lump in the spot where she was struck on the head and someone brought her a cloth and some ice for her head. The plaintiff indicated that a significant horizontal force (i.e., a push) must have occurred to the bottle for it to have hit so hard on her upper back to take her breath away. She sought medical attention two days after the incident in her home city at a hospital emergency medical department. Her head was found to be normocephalic and her neurological exam and a head/brain CT scan were without any positive findings. The plaintiff indicated at ER that she did not have a loss of consciousness and she denied any nausea/vomiting, neck pain or ataxia/syncope. One week later after her ER visit, she was administered a MRA with contrast which found a normal and robust blood flow in key arterial systems within her brain and brainstem. In subsequent months and years, the plaintiff's mental health declined and some symptoms were consistent with traumatic brain injury with an alternative diagnosis of simply aging and some form of somatoform disorder.

We were retained to investigate and analyze the probability of moderate TBI resulting from this accident. Our investigation concluded that the most probable scenario was that one of the larger loop base supports of the bottle rack was moved over the edge of wall top when the plaintiff or someone else bumped up against the one side of the seatback wall causing the rack and bottle to fall. The area in back of the seat was occupied by restaurant staff. At our inspection we were able to produce some horizontal vibration motion sufficient to move the large loop base support of the bottle rack over the edge of the seatback top causing the rack and bottle to fall. The wire metal rack was not tightly coupled to the bottle and therefore the rack mass (approximate .1 slug) was not to be added in our momentum equation calculation in this subject accident. Our inspection included using an exemplar subject, (same stature as the plaintiff), taking measurements, photographs, and finally video recordings of the falling bottle and rack to the bench seat without the exemplar human subject present (Hannon, 2018).

The 10.5 inch drop of the approximate center of gravity was modeled as a free fall rather than using an inverted pendulum model and the vertical velocity of bottle was found to be approximately 7.5 ft/second at head contact. The momentum equation was utilized and a worst case scenario assumed that the momentum of the Champagne bottle was brought to zero at contact with the top of the plaintiff's skull calvarium. In our view, the testimony of the plaintiff of a glancing blow to the back of her head and a subsequent second significant strike to the right side upper back (close to her right scapula) indicated that only a small fraction of the linear momentum would have been absorbed during the actual head impact. Nevertheless, we assumed this worst case scenario and when realistic time frames were calculated and bracketed to determine the average reaction forces and consequent potential accelerations applied to the plaintiff's head, we estimated levels of 1.5 up to 3.0 average g loads. Peak g levels would necessarily have been higher. It was our opinion that a focal point contact of a bottle edge striking the head could have resulted in a "goose-egg" swelling of the posterior SCALP. However, medical records two days after the accident did not provide support for the plaintiff's report of such a swelling or lump (Hannon, 2018).

Finally, the literature describing mild traumatic brain injury (MTBI) was summarized and we opined that even mild TBI or other central nervous system pathology was not the result of this accident. Necessarily, the diagnosis and treatment of this woman was beyond the scope of our expertise and was deferred to the appropriate physician and neuropsychology experts.

9.6 Closing Comments—Brain Injury

Based on the previous discussion regarding brain and brain stem injury, Figure 9.22 is presented below. This type of analysis is valuable to the biomechanist in evaluating the mechanism of injury and the potential for differing levels of traumatic brain injury. Biomechanical research in head injury is absolutely required in order to improve head injury prevention or reduction of the severity of head injuries. Much effort over the last fifty years has been made in terms of avoiding advanced primate species research in favor of human cadaver subjects or computer modeling with such programs as the Generalized Acceleration

Model for Brain Injury Tolerance (GAMBIT) which accounts for both linear and rotational motions. Certainly every effort should be made to seek other forms of experimental research to answer important biomechanical and medical questions without the sacrifice of the more advanced primates. This includes a more careful analysis of vehicle and other head loading events (epidemiology) coupled with medical diagnosis and treatment outcome. However, some research with advanced primates (e.g., chimpanzees) may be required to advance important issues in head injury biomechanics and medical treatment of head injury especially in infant and toddler accidental and non-accidental head injury.

9.7 Protection of the Skull, Face, and Brain—Using the Appropriate Helmet

A. Helmet protection—general comments

Helmets may provide protection to the skull, face and brain. This protection is the result of (1) preventing penetration, (2) load distribution, and (3) cushioning an impact

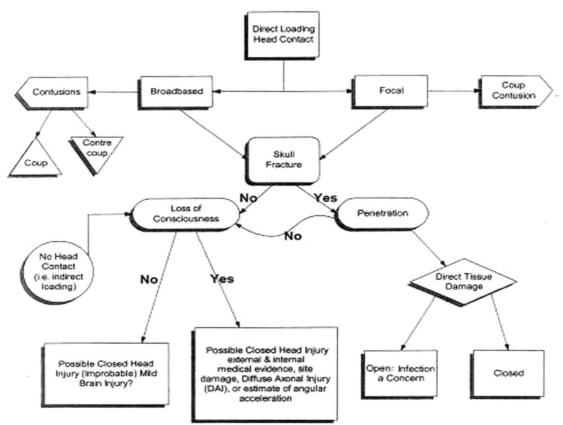

Figure 9.22 *Mechanisms of Injury. (Courtesy of Robert Perry)*

blow. The first two factors are related to one another, and the third factor (cushioning) is in part dependent upon the second factor (load distribution).

It is easy to see how some helmets may help prevent the penetration of a projectile or a penetrating implement. Helmet material properties directly affect the functional effectiveness. Plastics, metals, or composites are generally used in the outer shell to prevent penetration. The helmet outer shell should have a high bulk stiffness (high rigidity) with a high ultimate failure point (strength) and high surface strength (hardness) (Newman, 1998). The outer shell surface should also minimize tangential forces at impact (i.e., frictional forces). This is usually accomplished by using low friction materials. By minimizing frictional forces, bending and twisting forces applied to the cervical spine may also be reduced. Finally, outer shells which cover a large area intuitively provide more protection as in the example of a full face motorcycle helmet. Face guards on football helmets also provide increased head link protection but with an increased vulnerability of the cervical spine to injury resulting from face mask violations. Motorcycle helmet face guards provide protection to soft tissue structures of the face and protect against Le Fort I and II fractures discussed previously. Full face coverage helmets are unfortunately heavier and trap heat in sometimes already hot environments. Furthermore, in some circumstances such as high performance military aircraft, the increased helmet mass (inertia) and wind drag forces of larger helmets with a large cross sectional surface area in regard to relative air flow are also significant, which can be a deleterious factor in regard to cervical spine injury during high performance aircraft ejection.

The second function of the helmet is to distribute a focal point load over a larger area (load distribution). Given that a compressive stress is the load divided by the area (compressive stress = load divided by area), a larger area results in a smaller compressive stress. Load distribution with decreased stress makes penetration much less likely (i.e., the relationship between the first and second variables). Therefore, an industrial helmet (hard hat) without webbing, padding, or other energy-absorbing material is still minimally effective in mitigating head trauma from a focal point projectile with a small energy level. Examples of such impacts would include small hand tools dropped from one or two stories in a construction area. Impacts which incorporate larger momentums and energies will necessarily require helmet liner materials such as expanded bead polystyrene that will absorb momentum and energy.

The third factor is the cushioning effect. Padding enables a helmet to provide protection against what is termed fast rise times in the force level. Average force levels are reduced as the time to bring a mass momentum (e.g., skull and brain mass momentum) to zero is increased as expressed: average force = -momentum divided by time (see Chapter 4 for a more detailed discussion). Similarly, impact to a stationary helmeted head will be brought to final average and peak linear and angular momentums over a longer time frame due to helmet padding. Average and peak reaction forces to these delta momentums will be coincidently reduced. Energy is also absorbed as the liner deforms plastically or elastically (relatively slow elastic reformation rate).

Foams such as expanded bead polystyrene (EBP) have a large plastic zone, are lightweight, and allow manufacturers to vary the foam density easily. They are one use (one crush) helmets, and then they must be discarded because the EBP foam has been permanently deformed and has lost much of its energy absorbing (AE) capability. Motorcycle and bicycle helmets make use of EBP or similar deforming foams. Other helmets, such as football or ice hockey helmets, must withstand many impacts and still retain their energy and momentum absorbing characteristics. Ensolite and other similar closed or open cell foams are used for these helmet applications. Please note

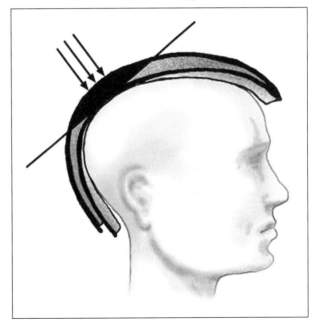

Figure 9.23 A focal point impact produces a larger area of helmet liner crush as the hard helmet shell distributes the force (load). (Courtesy of Robert Perry)

that some motorcycle helmets also incorporate an additional layer of low density open cell foam that aids in heat and moisture dissipation, and provides increased comfort to the wearer. The energy absorbing quality of this low density open cell foam is usually very minimal.

In terms of padding, there are some important concepts to consider. One is that when a material is crushed it absorbs energy, and the absolute limit of this energy absorption cannot exceed the original thickness of the padding material. If and when the padding material bottoms out, the force level rises dramatically. One solution is to make the padding material as thick as possible. Obviously, there are some practical helmet size considerations in terms of what people are willing to wear, helmet weight, and aerodynamic drag problems that arise with a large helmet. Therefore, a helmet with a thick (but reasonable) liner is desirable. A second concept is to maximize the amount of padding that is deformed for a given head impact (more material strain = work = more kinetic energy {KE} absorbed {AE}). This can be accomplished by the hard shell that surrounds the outside of the helmet. Even in the case of a relatively focal point impact to the helmet, through the load distribution previously discussed, the helmet's hard shell will produce a padding liner deformation over a relatively large area where the padding meets (interfaces) with the head. Therefore, the padding does not just deform at the impact site, but rather it is deformed in the padding surrounding the impact site (more AE).

Finally, the type of padding material that is used will affect the energy absorbed and the load time (force time) history. We ideally want a material that will either permanently deform with relatively little reformation (single use helmets) or materials that will deform and then reform relatively slowly (e.g., ensolite or similar foam). A weaker material (usually a lower density) may provide optimal protection at low impact levels but may bottom out before a significant portion of the kinetic energy has been absorbed and therefore will be the worst choice in terms of moderate or severe impacts (unless of course we make the padding much thicker). A material that is too strong (stiffer and usually higher density) will result in a fast force rise time with peak forces producing brain injury before the material can reach its limit of energy absorbing deformation. Additionally, a material that reforms too quickly, such as some densities of ethafoam used in tumbling mats, would not be a good choice in this regard. This has also been the criticism of helmets in the past that made use of air bladders within the lining. Peak forces closely approached the end of safe limits (NOCSAE Standard) because air bladders tend to reform quickly. Furthermore,

in some cases, helmet impact has resulted in rupture of these bladders (Nesbitt, 2002). Football helmet manufacturers still incorporate custom inflatable air bladders in some of their models and have improved the air bladder response during impact. However, proper snug fit of any football helmet is always important, and helmet air bladders can lose air pressure over time due to the diffusion gradient and are affected by altitude at game time in a city at a lower or higher elevation. Both factors can affect the energy absorbing capacity and the fit of the helmet. Energy-absorbing padding with some increased weight avoids these problems. In helmets, an effective approach has been to select a padding material with a uniform crushing strength so as to result in a load deformation curve that keeps the loads at a manageable level throughout the entire loading event (time history). This is illustrated in Figure 9.24. In November of 2018, the NOCSAE standards for newly manufactured football helmets have gone into effect and the standard for football faceguards went into effect in February of 2019.

An optimal approach would be to develop a helmet liner material that will be weaker during the first part of its deformation to handle low energy impacts and then become stiffer during the remainder of the liner deformation time history for moderate to severe impacts without completely bottoming out. In this regard, some progress has been made by using a padding liner with two or more separate materials (e.g., a dual density foam now used in some football helmets). Finally, some specialized needs of head protection have arisen as the result of combat trauma. For example, solders in military vehicles may be

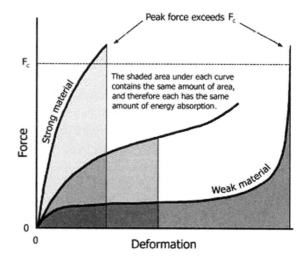

Figure 9.24 *The inner lining of a football helmet with dual density foams. Courtesy of Mike Nesbitt—Athletic Trainer, Northern Arizona University.*

Figure 9.25 Example of a dual density foam football helmet (Courtesy of Patrick Hannon and Mike Nesbitt—Athletic Trainer, Northern Arizona University)

subjected to underbelly blasts as the result of explosive devices triggered under the vehicle which can accelerate the solder's head to approximately six meters/second to the vehicle's interior padded roof (Franklyn and Laing, 2016). Both the roof liner and the padding incorporated into the helmet may have a major affect upon brain injury and/or survival outcome. Recent testing utilizing the Hybrid III headform has indicated that military interior roof padding with rigid IMPAXX foams outperform the semi-rigid ethylene vinyl acetate (EVA) foam (Franklyn and Laing, 2016).

Please also note that temperature effects and the rate of loading (lining material viscoelasticity) also play a part in selection of the energy absorbing mechanism and selected material properties. All these considerations represent formidable challenges to the helmet designer and manufacturer. Furthermore, one must always remember that the helmet only has benefit in mitigating face, cranium, and brain injury if it is worn by the child or adult. Public awareness, public acceptance, and public law will dictate a helmet's usefulness. The reader is referred to helmet development and standards by the Snell Foundation 2010 Standard for Protective Headgear: For Use with Motorcycles and Other Motorized Vehicles.

B. Bicycle helmet protection

1. Experimental bicycle helmet biomechanics research

A common helmet worn by many Americans is the bicycle helmet. Therefore, bicycle helmets are discussed in more detail in this text.

The Consumer Products Safety Commission (CPSC) standard is a legal requirement for any bicycle helmet manufactured in the United States. It requires a 2 meter drop on to a flat anvil. The most current Federal Register is the 1998 Part II CPSC 16 CFR Part 1203 Safety Standard for Bicycle Helmets; Final Rule. These standards went into effect on March 11, 1999. The CPSC standard for bicycle helmets requires testing on three types of impact anvils: i) flat anvil, ii) hemispherical anvil and iii) curbstone anvil. Impact velocities of the uniaxial accelerometer instrumented headform and helmet must reach 6.2 meters/second +- 3% (13.9 mph) on the flat anvil and this usually requires a drop of the helmet of about 2.0 meters (6.56 ft). The hemispherical and curbstone anvil drop heights are reduced to 1.2 meters (3.9 feet). The vertical velocity for the hemispherical and curbstone anvil must be approximately 15.85 ft/second (10.8 mph). In all specified environmental conditions, anvil types and specific helmet impact sites, the Peak g level must not exceed 300 gs in adults (using a 5.0 kg head form mass) (Federal Register is the 1998 Part II CPSC 16 CFR Part 1203 Safety Standard for Bicycle Helmets; Final Rule). Finally, dynamic retention strap standards are also regulated for bicycle helmets by the current CPSC Standards. The American Society for Testing and Materials (ASTM) has similar standards as the CPSC in terms of retention strap dynamic testing and impact attenuation, and the work of this organization formed much of the early basis for the CPSC Standards. Furthermore, the Snell Memorial Foundation has its own bicycle helmet standards, some of which exceed that of the CPSC (e.g., the B-95 standard).

The majority of adult bicycle helmets manufactured in the USA use expanded bead polystyrene of varying densities as an impact absorber typically of 20–30 mm thick (Gilchrist and Mills, 1996). Consumer Products Safety Commission helmets do a very good job of covering the calvarum of the skull. However, facial areas at or below the external auditory meatus of the ear are usually not covered in a CPSC adult bicycle helmet. The CPSC bicycle helmet does not cover the zygoma bone or the zygomatic arch of the face. However, it does cover a good portion of the left and right temporal bones, the entire area of the bilateral parietal bones and a good portion of the frontal bone. Recently, new technologies are developing and materials science may be able to provide significant improvements in bicycle helmets. The Bontrager company is now manufacturing helmets using what they term "wavecel" (layered collapsible cellular structure) materials in addition to traditional expanded bead polystyrene which may signficantly improve the energy absorbing qualities of bicycle helmets and reduce the impact acceleration levels while maintaining a low mass helmet (Bliven et al., 2019).

Numerous biomechanics research studies have demonstrated a significant reduction in local contact head injuries in addition to reducing the magnitude of Peak linear accelerations: Gilcrest et al., 1996; Mills et al., 2008; Pang et al., 2009; McIntosh et al., 2013; and Cripton et al., 2014 and others. More recent studies have additionally addressed brain and brain stem injuries due to angular acceleration head link loading. McIntosh et al. (2013) conducted drop tower tests using a validated anthropomorphic test headform (i.e., the Hybred III) to produce oblique head impacts. Tests were conducted at 0.5, 1.0 and 1.5 meters drops to address vertical velocity impacts. Additionally, a force plate coincidently moved horizontally at 0 km/second, 15 km/second and 25 km/second during the vertical drop impacts. This moving force (striker) plate resulted in an oblique head impact that examined the effect of the horizontal velocity (15 and 25 km conditions) resulting in a head angular velocity simulating a bicyclist sliding across the pavement (e.g., neck injury concerns). The authors state that, "The study confirmed that bicycle helmets certified to a national standard are effective from a biomechanical perspective in reducing linear and angular head accelerations, as well as impact force" (p. 507).

Cripton et al. (2014) performed biomechanical testing of paired helmeted and unhelmeted head impacts using a range of drop heights between 0.5 and 3.0 meters. The Hybred III headform Peak acceleration and Head Injury Criterion (HIC) score were the dependent variables. At the highest end of the continuum for bicycle accidents (the CPSC Bicycle Helmet Standard), a 2.0 meter drop resulted in a vertical velocity of 6.3 meters/second. A bicycle helmet reduced the Peak accelerations in this 6.3 meters/second delta velocity at impact from 824 Peak gs (unhelmeted) to 181 Peak gs (helmeted) and the HIC was reduced from 9667 (unhelmeted) to 1250 (helmeted). At lower more realistic drop heights for bicycle occupant falls of 1.0 meters (4.4 meters/second velocity) to 1.5 meters (5.4 meters/second velocity), bicycle helmets were also very effective in reducing the Peak g levels and the

HIC scores. In the 1.0 meter drops, the Peak g level for helmeted drops was 125 Peak gs and the HIC score was 552 compared to the unhelmeted 1.0 meter drops which resulted in a Peak g level of 471 and a HIC score of 2968. In the 1.5 meter drops, the Peak g level for helmeted drops was 154 Peak gs and the HIC score was 865, compared to the unhelmeted 1.5 meter drops which resulted in a Peak g level of 601 and a HIC score of 5305. Low HIC scores indicate a reduced level of impact loading.

2. Epidemiology studies—use of a bicycle helmet

Several epidemiology studies from the 1980s forward have examined the frequency and severity of head injury in helmeted and unhelmeted bicyclists involved in vehicle crashes. These research efforts provide strong support of helmet use and that helmets are highly effective in terms of mitigating head injury: Thompson et al., 1989, 1996, 1999, 2000, 2010; Maimaris et al., 1994; Attewell et al., 2001; Bamback et al., 2013 and others. Thompson et al. (1989) conducted a case-control study with the cases consisting of individuals who sought emergency hospital care after bicycle accidents which resulted in head injury in the bicyclist. Helmeted bicyclists had an 85% reduction in head injury risk and an 88% reduction in brain injury risk. A similar research effort was subsequently conducted by Thompson et al. (1996) with a large number of subjects. Their research found that the protective effect of bicycle helmets for any head injury, brain injury, and severe brain injury was 69%, 65%, and 76%, respectively. Furthermore, it was determined that bicycle helmets were equally effective in crashes with and without motor vehicle involvement.

Maimaris et al. (1994) collected data on all bicycle casualties that were treated at the Accident and Emergency Department of Addenbrooke's Hospital in Cambridge, UK in one year and reported a head injury incidence over three times higher in unhelmeted compared to patients who had worn helmets. Attewell et al. (2000) conducted a meta-analysis epidemiology study with an examination of some 63 published research efforts worldwide up to August of 1999. Two independent reviewers assessed the papers for inclusion and extracted data. Sixteen of these 63 papers met the selection criteria and the actual data collection for these studies occurred between 1980 and 1995. The authors found that using the upward bounds of the 95% confidence intervals provided "conservative risk reduction estimates of at least 45% for head injury, 33% for brain injury, 27% for facial injury and 29% for fatal injury (p. 350). Bambach et al. (2013) conducted a retrospective, case-controlled study using linked police-reported road crash, hospital admission and mortality data in New South Wales, Australia during the years of 2001–2009. Bambach et al. (2013) found that "There were 6,745 cyclist collisions with motor vehicles where helmet use was known. Helmet use was associated with reduced risk of head injury in bicycle collisions with motor vehicles of up to 74%, and the more severe the injury considered, the greater the reduction [i.e., percentage reduction]. This was also found to be true for particular head injuries such as skull fractures, intracranial injury and open head wounds" (p. 78). "Furthermore, the odds of sustaining a head injury was found to 1.98–3.89 times greater without a bicycle helmet. Similarly, the odds of sustaining an intracranial injury increased 1.60 to 3.52 times greater without a bicycle helmet" (Bambach et al. p. 84).

9.8 Air bag protection in automobiles

Air bag protection in automobiles is governed as a passive restraint mechanism by FMVSS 208. Early development began for driver's side air bags in the 1960s. In this section, the focus is on the prevention of head, face and brain injury by the use of air bags in frontal or side impact collisions. Air bags are intended to be used in conjunction with belt restraint systems. Interestingly, they are not at present used in the automobile racing industry for a number of reasons. Most importantly is the fact that a five point restraint system with an additional HANS device (Head and Neck Support) protects the head link better than an air bag system in a frontal crash. Please note that the 2001 fatal accident suffered by NASCAR participant Dale Earnhart was in part the result of a five point restraint anchor failure coupled with the fact that the HANS device was not installed in Mr. Earnhart's vehicle. The HANS device, developed by Robert Hubbard, Ph. D., is a force limiting, displacement limiting device consisting of a collar and yoke system that attaches to the racing helmet and reduces the loading to the head link even in situations where non-contact angular acceleration is the predominant loading mode (Hubbard and Downing, 2003). The point is that restraint systems in racing automobiles are usually able to prevent head contact and high levels of acceleration in head link contact and non-contact loading because they are superior to the three-point restraint systems employed in passenger vehicles. Three-point restraints however are more convenient to use and are more likely to be used by passenger car operators (operator and passenger compliance) compared to five point restraints, helmets, or the HANS device. Head airbags and air curtains combined with belt restraint systems in passenger vehicles to a de-gree help close the gap in protection between passenger and racing automobiles.

Front air bags are designed to deploy before forward head and body movement within the vehicle and furthermore to limit head translation and cervical spine angular motion. Air bags will prevent head and face contact with stiff interior compartment structures and will decrease the linear and angular accelerations applied to the head, face and brain. They are designed to deploy within 16 ms (some side air bags) or up to 65 ms (some front passenger frontal air bags) and therefore will fill a space that is not normally occupied by the driver or passenger occupants at the onset of impact loading. For example, in a frontal crash, air bags are generally designed to deploy within a 60° window (plus or minus 30° from a frontal head-on principal direction of force) and at an equivalent barrier impact of 10 to 15 mph (Reinhardt, 2001). Please note that the airbag trigger mechanism algorithm is much more complicated than simply sensing a delta velocity and varies among manufacturers. The crush of the vehicle in a frontal impact takes place before the occupant moves any significant amount forward. When the occupants do move forward in response to the vehicle deceleration loading, the air bag has already fully deployed, and therefore the air bag does not produce an acceleration impulse to the occupant's head. The air bag instead will absorb the energy and momentum of the forward moving head link with corresponding decreases in deceleration and reaction force loading to the face, skull, and brain. This translates into decreased loading to the brain and coincidently to the cervical spine. Frontal air bags are then vented and deflate rapidly. Obviously, if an occupant is unaware of an impending collision and is leaning forward into the space to be occupied by a deploying air bag at the time of the collision, the air bag will produce an acceleration impulse that may well be injurious or fatal to the occupant. Frontal air bags should not malfunction and experience a delay in deployment. Side air bags are also designed to deploy fully before the occupant reaches the side door panel. If a vehicle occupant is leaning against the side door panel at the time of impact, injury may result. This author has investigated one such case where the side curtain air bag produced a serious left eye injury (a rare event). In many new vehicles, inflatable side air curtains are triggered to deploy in both side impact and vehicle rollover events. Furthermore, side air bags and side air curtains are designed to remain inflated for a longer length of time because these collision events may be more complex (e.g., rollovers) and because driver visibility during the remaining accident loading history is not normally a concern.

It may be argued that it is the frontal deploying air bags that are responsible for HIC scores previously discussed routinely falling below 500 in 35 mph barrier frontal collisions when combined with belt restraint systems. Current air bag injury statistics are summarized by Hu and Blower (2013) and at the Insurance Institute of Highway Safety.

References

AConsumer Product Safety Commission, Safety Standard for Bicycle Helmets: Final Rule, 16 CFR Part 1203, Federal Register, Vol.63 No.46, Tuesday March 10, 1998.

Diagnostic and Statistical Manual of Mental Disorders-Fourth Edition (1994) (DSM-IV). American Psychiatric Association, Washington, DC.

Highway Safety. Highway Loss Data Institute at www.hwysafety.org/safety-facts/airbags/stats.htm.

SAE J885 Feb2011 (2011) Human tolerance to impact conditions as related to motor vehicle design. Surface Vehicle Information Report

Aldman B., L. Thorngren, and C. Ljung. "Patterns of deformation in brain models in rotational motion." In *Head and Neck Injury Criteria, A Consensus Workshop*. US Dept. of Transportation, National Highway Traffic Safety Administration, (1983)

Allsop D.L., T. Perl, and C. Warner. "Force/deflection and Fracture Characteristics of the Temporo-parietal Region of the Human Head." *Society of Automotive Engineers*; 912907. (1991)

Allsop, D.L., and K. Kennett. "Skull and Facial Bone Trauma." In Nahum, A. and J. Melvin, *Accidental Injury: Biomechanics and Prevention*, Second edition. New York: Springer Pub., (2002)

Alves W.M., R.W. Rimel, and W.E. Nelson. "University of Virginia Prospective Study of Football Induced Minor Injury: Status Report." *Clinical Sports Med.*; 6:211. (1986)

Amoros, E., Chiron, M., Martin, J-L., Thelot, B., Laumon B., (2012). Bicycle helmet wearing and the risk of head, face, and neck injury: a French case-control study based on a road trauma registry. Inj. Prev. 18, 27-32.

Attewell, R., Glase, K., and McFadden, M. (2001) Bicycle

helmet efficacy: A meta-anlaysis. Accident Analysis and Prevention. 33, pp. 345-352

Bambach, M., Mitchell, R., Grzebieta, R. and Olivier, J. (2013) The effectiveness of helmets in bicycle collisions with motor vehicles: A case-control study. Accident Analysis and Prevention, 53, pp.78-88.

Barth, J.T., W.M. Alves, and T.V. Ryan, et al. "Mild Head Injury in Sports: Neuropsychological Sequelae and Recovery of Function." In Levin H.S., H.M. Eisenberg, and A.L. Benton (eds). *Mild Head Injury*. New York: Oxford University Press, (1989)

Becker, D. P., J.D. Miller, and H.F. Young, et al."Diagnosis and Treatment of Head Injury in Adults." In Youmana, J.R (ed)2. WB Saunders Philadelphia, vol 4, pp. 1938. (1982)

Becker, E. "Helmet Development and Standards." In *Frontiers in Head and Neck Trauma*, N. Yoganandan et al. (Eds). IOS Press, (1998)

Becker E. 2010. Executive Director, Standard for Protective Headgear: For Use with Motorcycles and Other Motorized Vehicles., Snell Memorial Foundation

Beckwith, J.G., Greenwald, R.M., Chu, J.J., (2012). Measuring head kinematics in foot-ball: correlation between the head impact telemetry system and Hybrid III headform, Ann, Biomed. Eng. 40, 237-248.

Benz, G., McIntosh, A., Kallieris, D., Daum, R., (1993). A biomechanical study of bicycle helmets effectiveness in childhood, Eur. J. Pediatr. Surg. 3, 259-263.

Blevin, E., Rouhier, A., Tsai, S., Willinger, R., Bourdet, N., Deck, C., Madey, S., and Bottlang, M. (2019) Evaluation of a novel bicycle helmet concept in oblique impact testing. Accident Analysis and Prevention. V 124, pp. 58-65.

Brault J.R., J.B. Wheeler, G.P. Siegmund, and E.J. Brault. "Clinical Response of Human Subjects to Rear-end Automobile Collisions." *Arch Phys Med Rehabil*. Vol 79, January (1998)

Buadu, L., Ekholm, S., Lenane, A., Mortiani, T., Hiwatashi, A. Westesson, P. (2004) Patterns of head injury in non-accidental trauma, University of Rochester Medical Center, Rochester, New York.

Coats, B., Margulies, S. and Ji, S. (2007) Parametric study of head impact in the infant. Stapp Car Crash v.51, pp.1-15.

Cripton P, Dressler D, Stuart C, Dennison CR, and Richards, D. (2014) Bicycle helmets are highly effective at preventing head injury during head impact: head-form accelerations and injury criteria for helmeted and unhelmeted impacts Accident Analysis and Prevention. 70, pp. 1-7.

Crisco, J., Wilcox, B., Beckwith, J., Chu, J. Duhaime, A., Rowson, S., Duma, S., Maerlender, A., McAllister, T., Greenwald, R. (2011) Head impact exposure in collegiate football players, Journal of Biomechanics 44, (15) pp2673-2678

Dacey, R.G., D. Vollmer, and S. Dikmen. "Mild Head Injury." In *Head Injury,* Second edition. Editor Paul Cooper. Baltimore: Williams and Wilkins, (1993)

Damasio, A.R. *Descartesí Error: Emotion, Reason, and the Human Brain.* New York: Grosset/Putnam, (1994)

Davidoff, G., P. Thomas, Johnson, S. Berent, M. Dijkers, and R. Doljanac. (1988) "The Spectrum of Closed Head Injury in Acute Traumatic Spinal Cord Injury-Incidence and Risk factors." *Arch Phys Med Rehab.* (1988).

Dawson, S.L., C.W. Hirsch, F.V. Lucas, and B.A. Sebek. "The Contrecoup Phenomenon: Reappraisal of a Classic Problem." *Human Pathology*; 11:155–66. (1980)

Depreitere, B., Van Lierde, C., Sloten, J., Van Audekercke, R., Vander Perre, G. et al. (2006) Mechanics of actute subdural hematoma resulting from bridging vein rupture. *Journal of Neurosurgery*, v. 104, pp. 950-956.

Desmoulin, G., and Anderson, G. (2011) Method to investigate contusion mechanics in living humans, Journal of Forensic Biomechanics, vol. 2, doi: 10.4303/jfb/F100402

Duhaime AC, Gennarelli, TA, Thibault CE, Bruce DA, Margulies SS, Wiser R. (1987) The shaken baby syndrome. A clinical, pathological and biomechanical study. Journal of Neurosurgery 66:409-15.

Duhaime, A, Margulies, S, Durham, S., O'Rourke, M and Golden J, Marwaha, S., and Raghupathi, R, (2000) Maturation-dependent response of the piglet brain to scaled cortical impact. J of Neurosurgery, 93, pp. 455-462.

Eiband, A.M. "Human Tolerance to Rapidly Applied Accelerations: A Summary of the Literature." NASA Memo 5-19E, (1959).

Foster, K.J., Kortge, J.O., Wolanin, M.J., (1977). Hybrid III—a biomechanically-based crash test dummy. In: SAE International 770938.

Franklyn, M., and Laing, S. (2016) Evaluation of military helmets and roof padding on head injury potential from vertical impacts. Traffic Accident Prevention, v. 17(7).

Funk, J., Rowson, S., Daniel, R., and Duma, S. (2012) Validation of concussion risk curves for collegiate football players derived from HITS data, Annals of Biomedical Engineering. V. 40(1) pp. 79-89

Gennarelli, T.A., Thibault, and A.K. Ommaya. "Pathophysiological Responses to Rotational and Translational Accelerations of the Head." SAE Paper 720970 in *Biomechanics of Impact Injury and Injury Tolerances of the Head-Neck Complex.* Ed. Backaitis, S., SAE Pub. PT-43; (1993)

Gennarelli, T.A. et al. "Diffuse Axonal Injury and Traumatic Coma in the Primate." Ann. *Neurology*; 12:564–574. (1982)

Gerberich, S.G., J.D. Priest, and J.R. Boen. "Concussions, Incidence and Severity in Secondary School Varsity Football Players." *American Journal of Public Health*; 73:1370. (1983)

Gilchrist and Mills (1996) Protection of the side of the head. Accident Analysis and Prevention, v. 28 (4), pp. 525-535.

Giza, C. and Hovda, D. (2014) The new neurometabolic cascade of concussion. Neurosurgery, v. 75(4), pp. S24-S33. doi: 10.1227/NEU.0000000000000505

Graham, D.I. "Pathology of Brain Damage." In Head Injury, Second edition. Editor Paul Cooper. Baltimore: Williams and Wilkins, (1987)

Greenwald, R., Gwin, J., Chu, J. and Crisco, J. (2008) Head impact severity measures for evaluating mild traumatic brain injury risk exposure. Neurosurgery, v. 62 (4), pp. 789-798. doi: 10.1227/01.neu.0000318162.67472.ad.

Guskiewicz, K., Marshall, S., Bailes, B., McCrea, M., Harding, H., Matthews, A., Mihalik, J., and Cantu, R. (2007) Recurrent concussion and risk of depression in retired professional football players Medicine and Science in Sports & Exercise. DOI: 10.1249/mss.0b013e3180383da5

Hadley, MN, Sonntag, VH, Rekate, HL, and Murphy, A. (1989) The infant whiplash-shake injury syndrome: A clinical and pathological study. Neurosurgery, vol 24, Number 4. Pp 540

Hannon, P.R. and K.L. Knapp. "Causes of Injury: A Review of the Low-Impact, Human-Subject Literature." In Watts, A. Low Speed Automobile Accidents: Accident Reconstruction and Occupant Kinematics, dynamics, and biomechanics. Tucson: Lawyers & Judges Publishing Company, Inc., (2003).

Hannon, P. R. (2018) Forensic Biomechanics/Neuroscience of Alleged Brain Injury (TBI): A Restaurant Defense Case, Journal of Forensic Biomechanics, April, 2018.

Hu, J. and Blower, D. (2013) Estimation of seatbelt and frontal airbag effectiveness in trucks: U.S. and Chinese perspectives. University of Michigan Transportation Research Institute, UMTRI-2013-2, January.

Huang, L., Bakker, N., Kim, J., Marston, J., Grosse, I., Tis, J., and Cullinane, D. (2012) A multi-scale finite element model of bruising in soft connective tissues. Journal of Forensic Biomechanics. Vol 3, doi: 10:4303/jfb/235579

Hayes JS, Varney NR, Roberts, RJ. (1999) Malingering traumatic brain injury: current issues and caveats in assessment and classification. The evaluation and treatment of mild traumatic brain injury. Lawrence Erlbaum Associates, Mahwah, NJ. pp.249-290.

Hirsch, C. and Kaufman, B. (1975) Contrecoup skull fractures. Journal of Neurosurgery. v. 42, May, pp. 530-534.

Hodgson, R. and Voigt (1967) Tolerance of the facial bones to impact. American Journal of Anatomy v 120, pp. 113-122.

Hubbard, R. and Downing, J. Information Sheet at www.hansdevice.com/information-sheet.htm.

Ibrahim, N., and Margulies, S. (2010) Biomechanics of the toddler head during low-height falls: an anthropomorphic dummy analysis. Journal of Neurosurg Pediatrics, v. 6(1), pp. 57-68.

Jane. J.A., O. Steward, and T. Gennarelli. "Axonal Degeneration Induced by Experimental Noninvasive Minor Head Injury." J. of Neurosurg; 62:96–100. (1985)

Kandel, E.R., J.H. Schwartz, and T.M. Jessell. Principles of Neural Science, Third edition. East Norwalk, CT: Appleton & Lange, East Norwalk, (1991)

Kunlund, D.N. The Injured Athlete. Philadelphia: JB Lippincott Co., (1982)

Kushner, D., (1998) Mild traumatic brain injury. Toward understanding manifestations and treatment. Review, Arch Intern Med., v. 158, pp. 1617-1624.

Lechowski, S. and J. Jedlinski. "Subdural Hematoma in Pugilists (Polish)." Pol Tyg Lek.; 20:185. (1965)

Leininger, B.E., S.E. Gramling, and A.D. Farrell, et al. "Neuropsychological Deficits in Symptomatic Minor Head Injury Patients after Concussion and Mild Concussion." J. of Neurol Neurosurg Psych; 33:293–96. (1990)

Levin, H.S., D. Williams, and M.J. Crofford, et al. "Relationship of Depth of Brain Lesions to Consciousness and Outcome after Closed Head Injury." J of Neurosurgery; 69:861–866. (1988)

Lowenhielm. "Brain Susceptibility to Velocity Changes, Relative and Absolute Limits for Brain Tissue Tolerance to Trauma and their Relation to Actual Traumatic Situations." Proceedings of an International interdisciplinary Symposium on Traffic Speed and Casualties held at G1 Avernaess, FUNEN, April 22–24, 1975, Denmark.

Loyd, A., Nightingale, R., Luck, J., Bass, C., Cutcliffe, H., Myers, B. (2019). The response of pediatric head to impacts onto a rigid surface. In Press—accepted June 29, 2019, Journal of Biomechanics.

Maimaris, C., Summers, C.L., Browning, C., Palmer, C.R., (1994). Injury patterns in cyclists attending an accident and emergency department: a comparison of helmet wearers and non-wearers. British Medical Journal, 308. 1537-1540.

Manson. P.N., J.H. French, and J.E. Hoopes. "Management of Midfacial Fractures." In Giorgiade, G.S., R. Riefkohl, and W.J. Barwick. Eds. Essentials of Plastic, Maxillofacial and Reconstructive Surgery. Baltimore: Williams and Wilkins, (1987)

Margulies, S.S., L.E. Thibault, and T.A. Gennarelli. (1990) Physical model simulations of brain injury in the primate. Journal of Biomechanics v. 23(8), pp. 823-836.

Maxwell, W. Povlishock, J., Graham, D. (1997) Journal of Neurotrauma. July,1997, 14(7): 419-440. doi:10.1089/neu.1997.14.419.

Martini, D., Eckner, J., Kutcher, J., and Broglio, S., (2013) Med Science Sports Exercise, v. 45(4) pp. 755-761.

McIntosh, A, Lai A, Schilter E. (2013) Bicycle helmets: head impact dynamics in helmeted and unhelmeted oblique impact tests Traffic Inj Prev. 2013;14(5), pp. 501-508.

Mertz HJ, Irwin AL, Prasad P. (2003) Biomechanical and scaling bases for frontal and side impact injury assessment reference values . Stapp Car Crash Journal 47, pp, 155·188.

Mills, N. and Gilchrist, A. (2008) Oblique impact testing of bicycle helmets. International Journal of Impact Engineering, 35, pp. 1075-1086.

Mouzon, B. , Bachmeier, C., Ojo, J. Acker, C., Ferguson, S., Paris, D., Ait-Ghezala, G., Crynen G., Davies, P., Mullan, M. Steward, W. and Crawford, F. (2018) Lifelong behavioral and neuropathological consequences of repetitive mild traumatic brain injury., Annals of Clinical and Translational Neurology, 5(1) pp.64-80.

Muzzy, William, and Leonard Lustick. "Comparison of Kinematic Parameters between Hybrid II Head and Neck System with Human Volunteers for -Gx Acceleration Profiles." 20th Stapp Car Crash Conference. Warrendale, PA: Society of Automotive Engineers, Inc., (1976)

Nahum, A., and J. Melvin. *Accidental Injury: Biomechanics and Prevention*, Second edition. New York; Springer Pub., (2000)

Nelson, W.E., J.A. Jane, and J.H. Gieck. "Minor Head Injury in Sports: A New System of Classification and Management." *Physician Sports Medicine*; 12:103. (1984)

Nesbitt, M. Personal Communication. Oct. 6, 2002.

Newman, J. "Kinematics of Head Injury." In *Frontiers in Head and Neck Trauma*, N. Yoganandan et al. (Eds). IOS Press, (1998)

Newman, J. "Kinematics of Head Injury." In Frontiers in Head and Neck Trauma. Eds. Yoganandan, N., F. Pintar, S. Larson, and A. Sances. IOS Press. Amsterdam, The Netherlands: IOS Press, (1998)

NOCSAE (2018) November, Standard Performance Specification for Newly Manufactured Football Helmets, Effective, November 1, 2018. NOCSAE Doc (ND) 002-17m17a.

NOCSAE (2019) November, Standard Method of Impact Test and Performance Requirements for Football Faceguards, Effective, Feb 1, 2019. NOCSAE Doc ND087-18m18.

Nolte J. *The Human Brain: An Introduction to its Functional Anatomy*. St. Louis: The CV Mosby Company, (1988)

Ommaya and Gennarelli "Cerebral Concussion and Traumatic Unconsciousness: Correlations and Experimental and Clinical Observations on Blunt Head Injuries." *Brain*; 97:633–654. (1974)

Ommaya, A.K. "Head Injury Biomechanics." George G. Snively Memorial Lecture, Association for the Advancement of Automotive Medicine. Denver, Colorado, (1984)

Oppenheimer, D.R. "Microscopic Lesions in the Brain Following Head Injury." *J. of Neurol Neurosurg Psych* ; 31:299–306. (1968)

Pang, T, Thai, K., and McIntosh, A. (2009) Head and neck dynamics in helmeted hybred III impacts IRCOBI Conference0 York, United Kingdom, Sept.

Pappachan, B. and Alexander, M J (2012) Biomechanics of Cranio-Maxillofacial Trauma Maxillofacial Oral Surgery v. 11 (2): pp. 224–230.

Pellman, E., Viano, D., Tucker, A., Casson, I., Waeckerle, J., (2003) Concussion in professional football reconstruction of game impacts and injuries. Neurosurgery, v. 53(4) pp. 799- 814.

Pike, J.A. *Automotive Safety, Anatomy, Injury, Testing and Regulation*. Warrendale, PA: Society of Automotive Engineers, Inc., (1990)

Pincemaille, Y., X. Trosseille, P. Mack, and C. Tarriere. "Some New Data Related to Human Tolerance Obtained from Volunteer Boxers." In Proceedings 33rd

Stapp Car Crash Conference. Washington, DC, 1989, pp. 177–190.

Potvin, A., Aguiar, O., Komisar, V., Sidhu, A., Elabd, K., and Robinovitch (2019) A comparison of the magnitude and duration of linear and rotational head accelerations generated during hand, elbow, and shoulder-to-head checks delivered by hockey players. Journal of Biomechanics, May in Press-online https;//doi.org/10.1016/jbiomech.2019.05.002

Prange and Margulies, (2002) Regional, directional, and age-dependent properties of brain undergoing large deformation. Journal of Biomechanical Engineering, 124, April, pp.244-252.

Ransohoff, J., and A. Fleischer. "Head Injuries." *JAMA*; 234:861–864. (1975)

Reinhardt, K. at www.asashop.org/autoinc/dec2001/collision. cfm. (2001)

Rowson, S., Brolinson, G., Goforth, M., Dietter, D. and Duma, S. (2009) Linear and angular head acceleration measurements in collegiate football. Journal of Biomechanical Engineering. ASME v. 131.

Rowson,, S. and Duma, S. (2013) Brain Injury prediction: Assessing the combined probability of concussion using linear and rotational head acceleration. Annals of Biomedical Engineering, v. 41 (5), pp. 873-882.

Sheftell F., Tepper, S, Lay, C., Bigal M. (2007) Post-traumatic headache: emphasis on chronic types following mild closed head injury. Neurol Science v. 28: S203–S207 DOI 10.1007/s10072-007-0777-1

Solomon, S. (2005) Chronic post-traumatic neck and head pain. Headache, v. 45: pp. 53-67.

Stalnaker, R.L., J.H. McElhaney, and V.L. Roberts. "MSC Tolerance Curve for Human Head Impacts." In Proceedings ASME Biomechanics of Human Factors Conference, (1971)

Stalnaker, R.L., and V. Rojanavanich. "A Practical Application of the Translation Energy Potentials." In Proceedings International IRCOBI Conference on the Biomechanics of Impacts. Lyon, France, (1990)

Swan and Swan, Variations of Ballistic Effects on Animal Tissue. (Incomplete reference) in Zernicke. (1989)

Tarriere, Claude. "Risk of Head Injury if there is no Direct Head Impact." In *Head and Neck Injury Criteria: A Consensus Workshop*. NHTSA. U.S. Dept. of Transportation, (1983)

Thibault, L.E., and T.A. Gennarelli. "Brain Injury: An Analysis of Neural and Neurovascular Trauma in the Nonhuman primate." 34th Annual Proceedings Association for the Advancement of Automotive Medicine. Scottsdale, Arizona, (1990)

Thibault, L.E. "Isolated Tissue and Cellular Biomechanics." In Frontiers in Head and Neck Trauma. N. Yoganandan et al. Eds. IOS Press, (1993)

Thompson, R.S., Rivara, F.P., Thompson D.C., (1989). A case-control study on the effectiveness of bicycle safety helmets. N. Engl. J. Med 320, 1361-1367.

Thompson, D.C., Rivara, F.P., Thompson R.S., (1996). Effectiveness of bicycle safety helmets in preventing head injuries. A case-control study. JAMA 276, 1968-1973.

Thompson, D.C., Rivara, F., Thompson, R., (1999). Helmets for preventing head and facial injuries in bicyclists. In: The Cochrane Collaboration, Rivara , F. (Eds.). Cochrane Database of Systematic Reviews. John Wiley & Sons, Ltd. Chichester, UK.

Thompson DC1, Rivara FP, Thompson R. (2000) Helmets for preventing head and facial injuries in bicyclists Cochrane Database Syst Rev. Issue 2 :CD001855; John Wiley & Sons LTD.

Thompson DC1, Rivara FP, Thompson R. (2010) Helmets for preventing head and facial injuries in bicyclists Cochrane Database Syst Rev. Issue 4 :CD001855; John Wiley & Sons LTD.

Torg, J.S. *Athletic Injuries of the Head, Neck and Face.* Philadelphia: J.B. Lippincott, (1982)

Torg, J.S. *Athletic Injuries of the Head, Neck and Face.* 2nd ed. St Louis, Mosby Year Book (1991)

Stalnaker, R.L., C.A. Lin, and D.A. Guanther. "The Application of the New Mean Strain Criterion (NMSC)." In *Proceedings International IRCOBI Conference on the Biomechanics of Impacts.* Goteborg, Sweden (1985)

Unterharnscheidt, F. "Boxing Injuries." In *Sports Injuries: Mechanisms, Prevention and Treatment.* Schneider, R.C., J.C. Kennedy, and M.L. Plant, eds. Baltimore:

Williams and Wilkins, (1985)

Van Ee, C., Davis, R., Thibault, K., Hardy, W. and Plunkett, J. Child ATD Reconstruction of a fatal pediatric fall, Proceedings of the ASME 2009 International Mechanical Engineering Congress & Exposition IMECE2009, Nov. 13-19, Lake Buena Vista, Florida.

Watts, A. Low Speed Automobile Accidents: Accident Reconstruction and Occupant Kinematics, dynamics, and biomechanics. Tucson: Lawyers & Judges Publishing Company, Inc., (2003)

Weber, w. (1984) Experimental studies of skull fractures in infants, , *Z Rechtsmed. [In German] translated* 92(2):PP. 87-94.

Yoganandan (1989) "Epidemiology and Injury Biomechanics of Motor Vehicle Related Trauma to the Human Spine." #892438, Stapp. Warrendale, PA: Society of Automotive Engineers, Inc., Oct.

Yoganandan, N. and Pintar, F., (2004) Biomechanics of temporo-parietal skull fracture. Clinical Biomechanics. V. 19, pp. 225-239.

Young WB., Khoury JB., Ramadan NM., (2005) Headaches associated with head trauma (postconcussion headache). Chronic daily headache of clinicians. pp.185-197.

Zernicke, R.F., and W.C. Whiting. Biomechanics of Musculoskeletal Injury. Champaign, Il: Human Kinetics, (1998)

Recommended Reading

Ghista, D.N. *Human Body Dynamics: Impact, Occupational and Athletic Aspects.* Oxford: Clarendon Press, (1982)

Goldsmith, W. *Some Aspects of the Physical and Mathematical Modeling of Loading to Head/Neck Systems and Implications of Current DOT Injury Criteria-Head and Neck Injury Criteria.* United States Government Printing Office, (1983)

Head and Neck Injury Criteria: A Consensus Workshop. Washington DC, March 26–27, (1981). US Government Printing Office (1983)

Hodgson, Voigt, and L. Thomas. "Acceleration Induced Shear Strains in a Monkey Brain Hemisection."

(1979) In *Biomechanics of Impact Injury and Injury Tolerances of the Head-Neck Complex.* Ed. Backaitis, S. SAE Pub. PT-43; (1993)

Hodgson, Voigt. I*njuries Involving the Head and Neck: Experimental and Biomechanical Aspects in Sports Injuries.* PSG Publishing Co., (1986)

Kreighbaum, Ellen. "Anthropometric Parameters." *Biomechanics.* Macmillian Pub. Co., (1990)

Langwieder. "Comments in Injury Biomechanics SP-731." *Society of Automotive Engineers* (1987)

Lighthall, J. "Toward a Biomechanical Criterion for Functional Brain Injury." (1989) SAE Paper 896074 in *Biomechanics of Impact Injury and Injury Tolerances of the Head-Neck Complex.* Ed. Backaitis, S., SAE Pub. PT-43; (1993)

McElhaney, J., COPE 1988, October 31–Novmeber 2 Presentation, Toronto, Canada. (1988)

Ommaya, A. K, and A.E. Hirsch. "Tolerances for Cerebral Concussion from Head Impact and Whiplash in Primates." *Journal of Biomechanics* Vol 4 (1971); pp. 13–21.

Reid, Stephen, Sr., and Stephen Reid, Jr. *Head and Neck Injuries in Sports.* Springfield, Il: Charles C. Thomas Publisher, (1984)

Ricci, L. National Crash Severity Study, University of Michigan. (1980)

Rowland, Lewis, Matthew Fink, and Lee Rubin. "Cerebrospinal Fluid: Blood-Brain Barrier, Brain Edema, and Hydrocephalus." In *Principles of Neural Science*, Third edition. Editors: Kandel, Eric, Schwartz, James and Jessell. Norwalk, Ct: Thomas Appleton & Lange, (1991)

Sances, Anthony. "Biomechanics and Accident Investigation." From *Handbook of Biomedical Engineering.* Section on cervical spine, pp. 533–538.

Simula Inc. Report in Automotive Engineering, October 1996. Society of Automotive Engineers.

Snell, R.S. *Atlas of Clinical Anatomy.* Boston: Little Brown and Company, Inc., (1978)

Vetter, D., Seminar: Biomechanik und Dummy-Technik, TU-Berlin., In Schmitt, K, Niederer, P., Muser, M., and Walz, F (2010) *Trauma Biomechanics-Accidental Injury In Traffic and Sports*, 3rd ed. Springer-Verlag, Berlin

Viano, D. "Biomechanics if Head Injury—Toward a Theory Linking Head Dynamic Motion, Brain Tissue Deformation and Neural Trauma." (1988) SAE Paper 881708 in *Biomechanics of Impact Injury and Injury Tolerances of the Head-Neck Complex*. Ed. Backaitis, S., SAE Pub. PT-43; (1993)

Yarnell and Rossie. "Minor Whiplash Head Injury with Major Debilitation." *Brain Injury*; Vol 2: No 3: pp. 255–258. (1988)

Chapter 10

Torso and Thorax

Patrick Hannon and Michael Iliescu

10.1 Introduction

It is difficult to distinguish the biomechanics and injury mechanisms between the abdomen and thorax. While they are very different in their functional anatomies, their physical anatomies have some overlap. Serious injuries will frequently involve both regions, indicating a close relationship of the injury causing criteria affecting the area. Collectively, they are referred to as the ventral body cavity or the "trunk." The trunk is of great importance in that a large percentage of injuries are a result of blunt trauma, which can range from minor to a fatality and are not always obvious at the time of injury. Consequently, it is not uncommon even for serious trunk injuries to remain undiagnosed for some time, complicating both the treatment and recovery in ways that may have been avoided. In addition, a mechanism of injury can vary according to age, gender, and other physiological states such as muscle tension or level of intoxication. It is therefore essential that the biomechanist understand the different injury mechanisms and proposed tolerance limits of the various organs, soft tissues, and bony structures within the trunk so that these incidents and injuries may be properly evaluated.

10.2 Classifying Injury Severity

Before discussing the various trunk injuries that can occur, it is necessary to give a brief explanation of the injury scales that are used by biomechanists and physicians to classify injuries. These classifications allow for a better common identification of the severity level of an injury. The scale and tables most commonly used today for both abdominal and thoracic injuries is the 2015 Abbreviated Injury Scale (AIS), available through and copyrighted by the Association for the Advancement of Automotive Medicine. Injuries are classified in terms of severity on a 1–6 Likert scale with one being minor and six being maximum injury, virtually non-survivable.

10.3 Thorax

From a biomechanical standpoint, the thorax is less complicated than the abdomen in that it does not have the overwhelming number of organs, and injuries are more easily predicted. However, apart from the brain, injuries to the thorax tend to be the most life threatening and deserve close attention. The thorax is the superior portion of the ventral body cavity, separated from the abdominal cavity by the diaphragm, and is itself divided into left, right, and medial (mediastinum) sections. In general, the thorax is the hard shell that contains the following components: the heart, lungs, trachea, esophagus, aorta, and other major blood vessels. The ribs and sternum surround the entire cavity, providing a protective shell and, along with the diaphragm and intercostal muscles, facilitating respiration. The thorax is generally more difficult to injure due to the protected nature of the cavity, and 75% of all thoracic injuries occur along with injuries to other cavities, mainly the skull or abdomen (Ghista, 1982). The two lateral divisions of the thoracic cavity contain the lungs, enclosed within the two-layered pleural membrane, which is very similar to the peritoneal membranes in the abdomen. (Figure 10.1) The parietal pleura attaches to the inner wall of the rib cage and the deeper visceral pleura forms the outer lining to the lungs. There is a small, air-tight intra-pleural cavity between the two membranes, filled with a lubricating pleural fluid that allows the lungs to slide with very low friction across the ribs during respiration, and maintains the negative pressure. The trachea and bronchi sit outside the pleurae in the mediastinum and the esophagus lies posterior to the trachea; the aorta and superior vena cava also lie posterior to the trachea, with the aorta to the left of the esophagus and the vena cava to the right.

The heart occupies the bulk of the mediastinum and is enclosed by a two-layered membrane called the pericardium. (Figure 10.2) The structure of the pericardium is identical to the pleurae and the peritoneum; a parietal

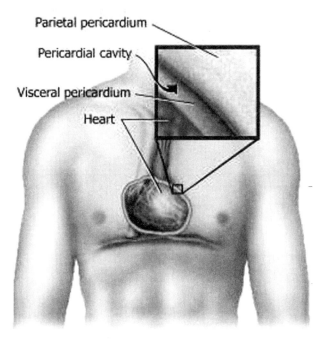

Figure 10.2 The heart and pericardium. (Courtesy of Robert Perry)

pericardium forms the outside of the mediastinum and a visceral pericardium (i.e., epicardium) lines the outside of the heart, with a small parietal cavity between where pericardial fluid provides a lubricating surface for the heart to move during pumping contractions.

10.4 Thorax Anatomy and Mechanisms of Injury

The impact mechanisms for blunt trauma injuries of the thorax are essentially identical to the abdomen. Fracturing of the bony structures can cause compression and coincident puncture of the organs beneath, and shear forces resulting from deceleration and consequent tissue tension and/or shear strain may cause tearing at fixed attachment points. Furthermore, an increase in external loads applied to the thoracic cavity can result in an increase in internal pressure within, resulting in a consequent burst or rupture.

A. Ribs and Sternum

The sternum is a flat bone with three segments connected by strong connective tissue and cartilage. The manubrium is the widest, most superior portion, attaching to both the clavicle and first rib. The sternal angle connects the manubrium to the sternum body, which is the longest part of the sternum, providing the attachment for bilateral ribs 2–10. The xiphoid process is the small tuberosity on the inferior sternum that serves as an attachment site for many

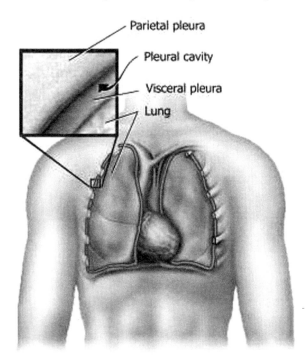

Figure 10.1 The lungs and the two-layered pleural membrane. (Courtesy of Robert Perry)

abdominal muscles. Sternal fractures can result from either direct or indirect loading and have the potential to puncture the heart and major arteries. A fairly common injury is a direct narrow impact to the inferior sternum that causes a detachment of the xiphoid process into the thoracic cavity and internal organ damage. Shoulder belts can cause transverse fractures (bending load of the sternum) such as this at high velocities (Ghista, 1982).

There are twelve sets of ribs. Ribs 1–7 articulate directly with the sternum via the costal cartilages of the stern costal joints and are called "true ribs." They also articulate posterior with the thoracic vertebrae in a tight, ligamentous, synovial joint (still termed diarthrodial joints). Ribs 8–10 attach only to the costal cartilage of rib 7, for which reason they are called false ribs. Ribs 11–12 are completely "floating," with no connection at all to the sternum. The cartilaginous component of the rib structures allows for a large amount of bending strain before fracture failure. Ribs 1–2 are particularly difficult to fracture, as they are well protected by the shoulder girdle bones (i.e., scapulae and clavicles). When these ribs do fracture, there are almost always additional injuries. Ribs 11–12 are also quite difficult to fracture, as their lack of a second attachment site allows for ample bending excursion without fracture-failure. The most frequently fractured ribs are ribs 5–9 (Schneider et al., 1985) which have the longest moment arms and are therefore more susceptible to bending loads.

There are two types of bending rib fractures: a direct bending where fracture occurs at the impact site and an indirect bending where a load is transmitted to a weaker part of the rib and fracture occurs remote to the source of impact during slow loading. (Figure 10.3)

Forced axial rotation of ribs (torsion) can lead to long, splintered fractures along the length of the ribs. These torsion fractures typically occur in ribs 5–9. A rib fracture that does not damage any surrounding tissue will almost always heal itself without consequence, although in adults, complete healing may take months depending upon the displaced status of the fracture. Breathing requires movement and these small movements are thought to prolong the complete process of stabilization, bony cuff formation and finally bone remodeling. In severe rib fractures, broken bone pieces can be pushed into the thoracic cavity and may cause potentially fatal damage to the soft tissue of the lungs, heart, and vessels. These conditions will be discussed along with the lungs. In addition, intercostal arteries, veins, and neurovascular bundles lie between each rib and may also become severed by a rib fracture.

When there are four or more complete displaced rib fractures, the chest wall becomes unstable, a condition that is termed "flail chest." (Figure 10.4) This causes a paradoxical movement upon patient inhalation, where the unstable ribs collapse inward against the increasing pressure of the expanding lung and prevent the lung from properly filling with air, as seen in (Figures 10.5a and 10.5b). A serious flail chest can be fatal unless respiratory assistance is provided in a timely manner.

Posterior rib fractures near the transverse processes of vertebral posterior elements are usually the result of levering (first class lever system) where the rib fractures occur over the point of the fulcrum (i.e., transverse process). Kleinman and Schlesinger (1997) indicate that such fractures are strongly associated with non-accidental pediatric trauma with anterior-posterior compression of the thorax

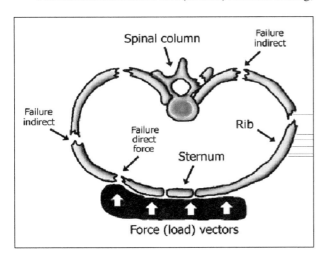

Figure 10.3 *Etiology of rib fracture failure. (Courtesy of Robert Perry)*

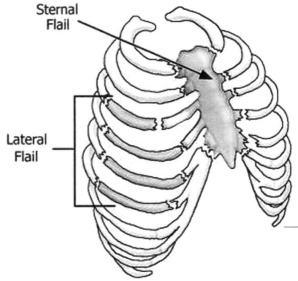

Figure 10.4 *Lateral and sternal flail chest. (Courtesy of Robert Perry)*

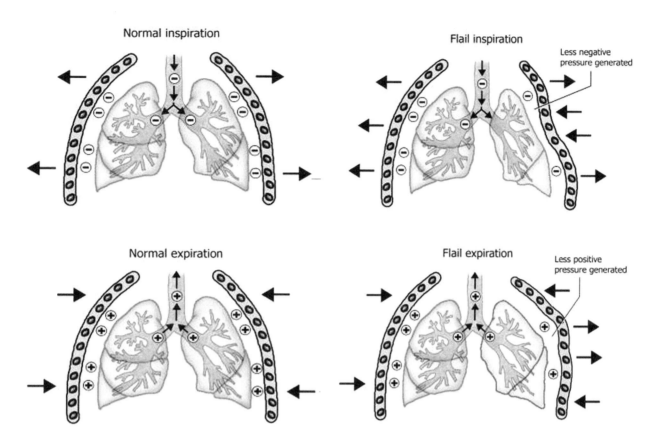

Figure 10.5a *Normal breathing. (Courtesy of Robert Perry)*

during assaults. However, accidental trauma that mimics this same mechanism may occur as well. When due to an assault, these rib fractures may result from a lateral clamp compression of the hands of the perpetrator in child abuse (i.e., bimanual manipulation). Grabbing an infant under the armpits and simply shaking adds an inertial mechanism to the already present compression force couple produced by the hands alone. Fingertip pattern contusions may be present on the skin of the infant's anterior and posterior thorax. The prevalence of posterior rib fractures during manual thoracic compression (bimanual manipulation) is explained by the force applied in the posteriorly located ribs' neck and head regions, as well as the costovertebral articulations. When the thumbs are located on the front of the thorax and the fingers are on the back of the infant, the force (load) vectors result in rib bone failure at the ribs' head, neck, and failure of the costovertebral articulation, and less frequently at the posterior and lateral arc of the ribs (Figure 10.6).

Fractures of the ribs may occur at any point along the rib arc, from the anteriorly located costal chondral junction (CCJ) to the posteriorly located costovertebral articulation. Posterior rib fractures that appear some significant displacement from the transverse processes are not the result

Figure 10.5b *Flail inspiration—decreased negative and positive pressure are produced. (Courtesy of Robert Perry)*

of this first class lever mechanism discussed previously and instead are the result of direct compression loading or of bending loads. These fractures may be either accidental or abuse assaults. However, posterior rib fractures in young children may also occur during motor vehicle accidents as the result of direct compression blows to the posterior thorax. When a chest is compressed on a flat surface (as in CPR), posterior rib fractures will not occur. However, both sternal and anterior rib fractures can occur during the resuscitation maneuvers. However, in abusive shaking when the thumbs are located on the front and the fingers are on the back of the infant, the force (load) vectors result in rib bone failure at the rib's head, neck, and failure of the costovertebral articulation and, less frequently at the posterior, and lateral arc of the ribs. (Figure 10.6)

In a forensic assessment of a child abuse death, radiologic-pathologic correlations should be performed in identifying injuries specific to child abuse. Furthermore, the pathologist will have the important role of processing the ribs and confirming the radiological findings. After radiology imaging and fixation of the ribs in formalin solution, the ribs will be placed in a decalcifying solution. A decalcification log book should be maintained to include the strength and type of the decalcification solution and the duration of decalcification process, because many times aggressive decalcification of bone may create fracture artifacts. Histologic sections will be obtained, preferably following the area where radiology shows suspected injury.

The evaluation of rib fractures needs to be made in conjunction with the histological examination of long bone metaphysis to validate the ongoing abuse. Since classic metaphyseal lesions (CML) are common in infant abuse, sampling of the contralateral metaphysis is necessary for a better comparison of normal versus abnormal, though rarely performed in forensic pathology practice. Because most of the CMLs in infants involve distal femur, proximal and distal tibia and humeri, sampling of these regions should be performed during the forensic autopsy in which rib fractures are noticed. The section through the bone should be done with care in order to avoid artifacts. The ribs should be resected and retracted from their ventral attachments. Furthermore, resection of the entire vertebral body and vertebral posterior elements should also be performed.

B. Heart

The heart has two major anchor points: the diaphragm at the apex and the major vessels at the superior end. The heart is a strong muscle, whose function is to pump blood throughout the body by means of regular electrical stimulation. The bulk of the heart lies just posterior to the sternum, although roughly two-thirds of the heart lies to the left of the midsagittal plane of the body. Penetrating trauma directly to the heart causes extensive bleeding and death. Blunt trauma can include temporary electrical ir-

regularities, complete myocardial infarction, contusions, lacerations, embolism from thrombosis, partial tearing of tissue, or rupture. The mechanisms for these injuries can include puncture from a rib or sternum fracture, compression of ribs and adjacent organs without rib fracture, or tension loads resulting from lengthening deformation of the heart. Any injury in which the heart bleeds openly and is unable to continue circulating blood is usually fatal.

C. Thoracic aorta

DiMarco et al. (2013) state that: "traumatic rupture of the thoracic aorta is a life-threatening lesion and it occurs in 10 to 30 percent of fatalities from blunt thoracic trauma and is the second most common cause of death after head injury. Immediate surgery is often characterized by a high mortality and morbidity rate" (p. 117). The aorta is the primary high pressure artery that carries oxygenated blood from the heart (left ventricle) to be systemically circulated. The thoracic aorta arches posterior-superior and then descends into the abdominal cavity through a hole in the diaphragm. (Figure 10.7)

The most common site of rupture is the rigid descending ramus or aortic isthmus just below the relatively mobile ascending aortic arch. (Figure 10.9) At this site, the relatively mobile thoracic aorta joins the fixed arch and the insertion of the ligamentum arteriosum. (Figure 10.8) Eighty-five to 90% of these injuries lead to immediate death. A small minority of victims remain alive due to ligament structures holding the vessel together just enough to circulate blood (Schneider et al., 1985). It is

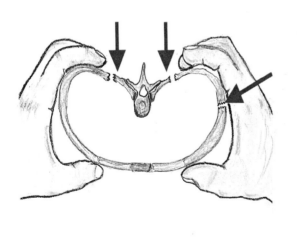

Figure 10.6 Etiology of rib fracture failure Adapted from Kleinman PK, Marks, SC, Spevak MR, et al. (1992) Fractures of the rib heads in abused infants. Radiology185(1):119-23

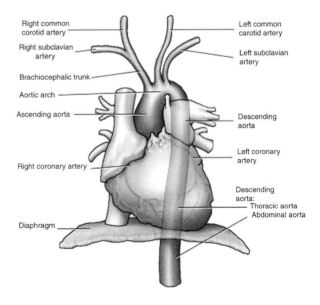

Figure 10.7 The thoracic aorta and its superior branches. (Courtesy of Robert Perry)

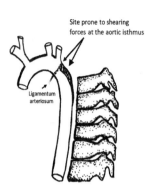

Figure 10.8 *Site prone to shearing forces at the aortic isthmus in deceleration chest injury. (Courtesy of Michael Iliescu)*

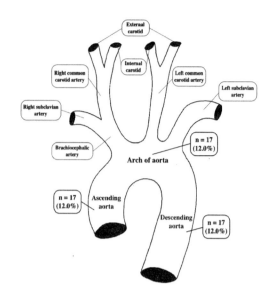

Figure 10.9 *Mechanisms of Injury: Shearing forces may cause tears at the aortic isthmus (site of attachment or ligamentum arteriosum) due to inflexibility of the aorta at this site. Direct compression of sternum (osseous pinch) can compress aortic root and cause retrograde high pressure on the aortic valve. Water-hammer effect: Simultaneous occlusion of aorta and sudden elevation of blood pressure." Adapted from Berger FH, et al. Eur J Radiol. 2010 Apr;74(1):24-39. Epub 2009 Aug 8. Neschis DG, et al. N Engl J Med. 2008 Oct 16;359(16):1708-16. Legome, E. Upto-date, 2010.]*

possible as well that there may only be a partial tear which causes some bleeding and a possible aneurism, with some potential for survival. However, if the partial tear is within the pericardium, there will be an increase in imposed pressure upon the heart itself, known as cardiac tamponade, leading to serious circulation problems (Ghista, 1982). Cardiac tamponade is the result of hemodynamic instability due to heart compression by accumulation of fluid resulting, in an impaired right heart filling pressures and subsequent cardiogenic shock (low blood pressures).

Biomechanically, there are several factors that may contribute to a traumatic thoracic aortic rupture. These include: (1) a sudden and violent compression causing an increase in blood pressure and expansion within the thoracic aorta, (2) shear loads, (3) extension and vibration of the aortic arch, (4) torsion loads and (5) longitudinal tension loads of the thoracic and abdominal aorta produced by descending abdominal organs, or an anterior dislocation of the thoracic aorta produced by a frontal automobile collision (i.e., possible inertial loading) (Ghista, 1982).

Although the thoracic aorta has a high percentage of elastic tissue compared to other soft tissues, its extent of elasticity before failure is limited. While these biomechanical factors offer some explanation of the biomechanics of this injury, aortic rupture is the most difficult fatal injury to repeat in experimental conditions (Ghista, 1982). In high velocity motor vehicle collisions (MVCs), there has been an increased incidence of traumatic aortic injuries which are associated with rapid deceleration in MVCs or falls when the thorax and the thoracic aorta experience rapid deceleration (DiMarco et al., 2013). Three point restraints have reduced the magnitude of the trauma impact to the thorax that leads to aortic injury (DiMarco et al., 2013). However, DiMarco et al. (2013) still ques-

tion the value of front and side air bags in conjunction with three point restraint use in substantively reducing the magnitude of the loading to the thoracic aorta and state that "the frequency of lethal injuries in head-on collisions is lowered by the mandatory use of restraints, which protect the victim from thoracic and head lesions, but not from the mechanism producing aortic injury" (p. 118). Furthermore, there is relatively little empirical evidence present for the precise mechanism of injury in any one specific case of thoracic aortic dissection.

D. Thoracic vena cava (inferior and superior)

The purpose of the inferior and superior vena cava is to return deoxygenated blood to the heart for re-oxygenation in the lungs and finally the recirculating of oxygenated blood by the left ventricle of the heart to arterial systemic circulation. The inferior vena cava is the largest vein in the body and also the most frequently injured major vessel. It travels inferior and posterior from the base of the heart. Most injuries are only partial ruptures and are not serious.

The superior vena cava, with the same origin but traveling superior, is more stable, and injuries are less common in this region. (Figure 10.10)

Venous tissue in general is more flexible and is under a lower fluid pressure load. Compared to the arterial system, injuries are most commonly a result of tension strain rather than compression stresses and strains. Intima inner lining ruptures of the vessel are perpendicular to the long axis of the vena cava vessels and are the most common. Circumferential or complete ruptures of vena cava vessels occur less frequently. Injuries are also dependent on the direction of impact: a dislocation of the heart to the upper left will cause a tension strain on the inferior vena cava, while a dislocation of the heart to the lower left will produce a tension strain on the superior vena cava. (Voigt {in German} in Ghista, 1982). Penetrating wounds may also sever the inferior and superior vena cava.

E. Trachea, bronchi, and lungs

The trachea provides a pathway for inhaled air into the body and bifurcates into the bronchi which direct the inhaled air, along with more than twenty additional branches, into the lungs. (Figure 10.11)

The lungs function by means of the airtight pleural cavity previously discussed which moves air into the lungs by the vacuum created upon elevation and widening of the rib cage. The branches of bronchioles end in delicate alveolar sacs, where a one cell width separation from the blood stream allows for gas exchange of oxygen and carbon dioxide (a diffusion gradient mechanism).

Injuries to the lung are the most frequent thoracic injury and can range from minor to fatal. Injuries to the trachea and bronchi are not as common and are the result of either a shearing against the spinal column, tension from lateral displacement of the lungs or direct puncture or laceration injuries from fractured ribs. If the laceration is substantial, the cavity may develop a pneumothorax. A pneumothorax is the condition in which a puncture of the pleural space allows for the entrance of air, which prevents the lungs from fully expanding upon normal inhalation. The pneumothorax may be classified as primary (unknown etiology), or secondary. Secondary pneumothorax may be traumatic or may be the result of primary lung disease (emphysema and pleural blebs for example).

In terms of air entrapment in the pleural cavity, a simple pneumothorax occurs when the amount of air in the pleural cavity remains stable, and although breathing is compromised, the situation will eventually get better as the pleural cavity membranes heal.

The much more serious 'tension pneumothorax' is the progressive build-up of air within the pleural space, usually due to a lung laceration which allows air to escape into the pleural space but not out again. Medical intervention using positive pressure ventilation may exacerbate

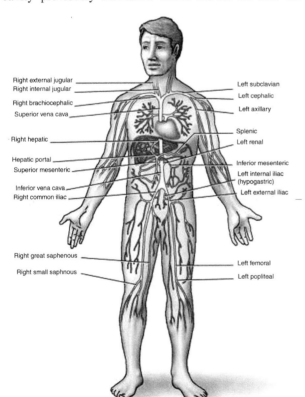

Figure 10.10 Principal veins of the torso, neck, and thighs. (Courtesy of Robert Perry)

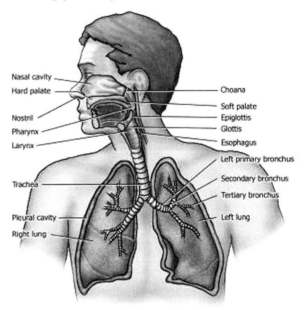

Figure 10.11 The respiratory system. (Courtesy of Robert Perry)

this 'one-way-valve' effect. The most common cause of tension pneumothorax is penetrating trauma of the chest. Whether from a stabbing injury or a gunshot, the injury to the pleural membrane can cause the lung to collapse. The intra-pleural pressure continues to build with each inhalation until the pleural cavity expands towards the mediastinum and compromises blood flow and the cardiac output.

A similar, but slightly more complicated lung injury that occurs from either penetrating trauma or rib puncture is the hemothorax. A hemothorax is caused by a rupture of the intra-pleural space where blood leaks into the cavity upon respiratory inspiration. This ultimately has the same effect as a tension pneumothorax by preventing the full expansion of the lung with a continuously increasing intra-pleural volume pressure due to excess fluid (i.e., blood). It is also possible to have a hemo-pneumothorax, where both blood and air invade the pleural space. Without treatment, hypoxia, acidosis, and death will ensue rapidly.

F. Diaphragm

As previously stated, the diaphragm is the major muscle of inspiration. It is a very strong, dome-shaped muscle that depresses upon concentric contraction, which increases the size of the thoracic cavity and creates an internal negative pressure within the lungs that pulls air inward. This is one of the few skeletal muscles in the body that is controlled by both voluntary and involuntary mechanisms. Exhalation occurs primarily passively as the diaphragm relaxes and returns the thoracic cavity to its original size, forcing out any additional air. Death is not due to diaphragm injury itself but rather is due to pelvis and abdominal trauma that produces extensive organ damage or bleeding. The most common injury of the diaphragm is a laceration due to compression that may result in a hernia of abdominal viscera into the thoracic cavity. This herniation may be on the left or right side of the thorax. When this occurs the expansion of the thoracic cavity in turn may compress the abdominal cavity upon contraction, and expulsion of the urinary bladder and rectum may result. One explanation for this is that the abdominal viscera act as a hydrodynamic fluid, and fluid pressure is imposed in all directions. On the other hand, it is difficult to tear such a strong, thick muscle, and diaphragm herniation injuries are almost always associated with additional and more severe injuries. It is those concomitant injuries that lead to fatalities (Yoganandan et al., 2001).

10.5 Iatrogenic (medically induced) injuries of the torso organs

The following internal organ or structure injury may occur during medical interventions: pneumo and hemothorax during lung biopsy or acupuncture, pneumomediastinum, laceration of liver or spleen during a laparoscopic intervention, trachea laceration during tracheal intubation, CPR induced rib and sternum fractures many times accompanied by contusions and laceration of the lung parenchyma. In other cases CPR has led to lacerations of the liver. In such cases, the left lobe is more frequently involved during the resuscitation procedure versus the right.

10.6 Biomechanics and Injury Tolerance of the Thorax

Despite the fact that the thorax is a complicated and highly variable region of the body, there has been a great deal more research investigating the tolerance limits for the thorax than there has been for the abdomen. In general, there are three common injury criteria used to predict thoracic injury tolerance. Linear acceleration of the cavity was employed by Stapp (1970), who found that human volunteers could withstand up to 45 gs when restrained with a four-point belt system. The current Federal Motor Vehicle Safety Standard (FMVSS 208, 1977) is a tolerance limit of 60 gs not to exceed a 3 ms time frame.

A second criterion for thoracic injury tolerance limits involves measuring the displacement or compression of the chest. Neathery (1975) stated that a chest compression of 76 millimeters is associated with an AIS 3 injury. This is still the current FMVSS 208 standard (2017). Stuhmiller et al. (1996) hypothesized that the chest wall deflection into the lungs is responsible for a compression wave that can cause lung rupture or laceration. Mertz et al. (1991) found a good correlation between sternum deflection and shoulder belt load, where 5 mm of sternal deflection equated to an approximate 1 kilonewton (kN) of belt load and, toward the other end of the continuum, a 50 millimeter sternal deflection creates a 40 to 50% chance of thoracic injury greater than or equal to AIS 3. The current (2017) FMVSS 208 specifies that the sternal deflection displacement inward should not exceed 2.5 inches.

Cesari and Bouquet (1990) also correlated chest injury to belt load, indicating that a 10 kN belt load is sufficient to cause up to six displaced rib fractures and thus a flail chest. Other authors suggest that only a minimum of three to four displaced rib fractures may be sufficient to produce this condition (Keel et al. 2007). Foret-Bruno et al. (1978) identified chest injury in cadaver subjects with respect to age where thorax loads up to 1,650 lbs. did not cause injuries in subjects less than thirty years old, while subjects older than fifty years were injured at approximately a minimum of 950 lbs. of thoracic belt loads.

Viano and Lau (1983) developed a third injury criterion that has been the most effective for thoracic injury predictions. It is V $_X$ C, the instantaneous product of chest wall velocity (V) and chest wall compression (C) expressed as a percentage of total chest wall depth. They found that a product that is greater than 1.0 m/s resulted in a thoracic injury of AIS 4 or 5. In addition, with compression-deformation levels greater than 32%, injuries as serious as flail chest (AIS 4) can occur regardless of the compression velocity.

A flail chest occurs when multiple adjacent ribs sustain displaced fractures and therefore this condition initiates paradoxical respiration where the fractured portion of the chest wall moves inward instead of outward during inhalation. (Figure 10.12) This effect is the result of the now moveable fractured portion of the rib cage moving inward due to the negative pressure within the lung lobe(s) and therefore the air exchange is markedly compromised resulting in less oxygen delivery. This is a life threatening condition and may be further compromised by a commonly associated trauma insult termed a pulmonary contusion or bruise of lung tissue which also compromises O_2 and CO_2 exchange across the lung alveoli.

Finally, fractured ribs with a large displacement may result in a pneumothorax when the chest wall is punctured allowing air to enter into the thorax and into the pleural cavity. (Figure 10.13) External air now accumulates between the chest wall and the lungs (i.e., pleural cavity) causing lung lobe(s) to collapse and preventing O_2 and CO_2 exchange within the lungs or a portion of the lungs. Excepting a very small pneumothorax, a needle is inserted through the chest wall into the air filled pocket to remove the air and allow for normal inhalation and exhalation of the patient.

A similar situation occurs in a hemothorax resulting from displaced fractured ribs or a stab wound where blood enters into this pleural cavity space and the lungs, again with the result of collapsed lung lobe(s) and a concomitant decrease in O_2 and CO_2 exchange. (Figure 10.14) This blood may come from several sources, especially in the case of penetrating injury such as a stab wound, to include the chest wall, the heart, large vessels or the lung parenchyma. In this case, blood is removed by the insertion of a chest tube with suction. This suctioning chest tube may remain in place within the pleural cavity for several days to remove the old and new blood during tissue healing. In some severe cases, video assisted thoracoscopic surgery or a thoracotomy may be performed in exploring a significant hemothorax.

These various criteria provide an understanding of potential injuries involving the ribs, lungs, and heart. However, King et al. (2000) found that aortic rupture was the most difficult injury to reproduce in experimental situations, due to the inability of the aortic tissue in cadavers to simulate the high-pressure system of a live human. Injury tolerances are still not well understood. This lack of understanding, coupled with the fact that traumatic aortic rupture is still responsible for some number of motor vehicle fatalities, indicates that it should still generate research in motor vehicle safety including motorcycle use as well as in combat activity within our armed forces. However, increases in three-point restraint use and automobiles equipped with front air bags have been of significant benefit in reducing traumatic aortic rupture in adults.

10.7 Restraint Systems and Experimental Modeling

The overwhelming number of accidents, injuries, and deaths that occur in motor vehicles has resulted in substantial research in an attempt to provide the maximum amount of safety to the inevitable motorist at risk. Three-point seat belts are a standard in modern cars and have proven to prevent significant life threatening injuries in comparison with the two point lap belt or no restraint. Restraint systems have several functions. They prevent ejection, decrease secondary impact to the inside of the vehicle, and help to transmit the deceleration energy to the occupant in the early stages of impact so that the vehicle and the occupant remain near the same velocity. Newtonian physics and the forces of collision show that even the slack in a seat belt can significantly amplify the force transmission from the vehicle to the occupant upon impact (Ghista, 1982).

There have been several studies to compare the possible injuries sustained while wearing a seat belt versus the injuries without one. Seat belts can cause blunt trauma to both the thoracic and abdominal cavities. Hematomas, rib fractures, and visceral ruptures due to both direct impact and submarining under the lap belt have all been documented in the past in frontal impact collisions. Conversely, air bags also provide additional safety measures by padding the head and thorax and reducing deceleration magnitudes in frontal and side impacts.

One problem with restraints is that many injuries are caused by improper use. The National Highway Traffic Safety Association (NHTSA, 1996) stated that in frontal crashes driver air bags in conjunction with three-point seat belts are as much as 60% effective against serious injury and three-point seat belts alone provided roughly

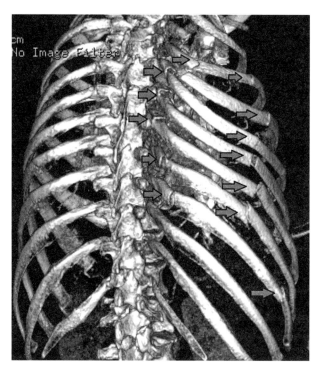

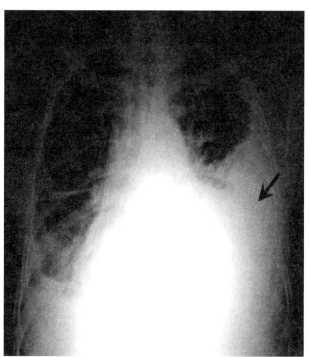

Figure 10.12 *Computer generated reconstructed 3-D imaging (CT scan) of a flail chest involving multiple posterior and lateral rib fractures. Arrows indicate the fracture sites. Some fractures are displaced more than others. (Courtesy of James Heilman, MD, 2016)*

Figure 10.14 *Massive left-sided pleural effusion later shown to be hemothorax. (Courtesy of S. Salim MD, 2008)*

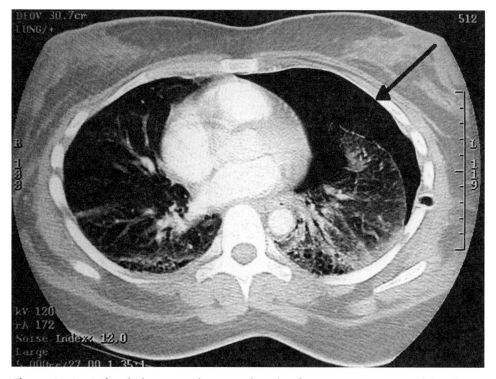

Figure 10.13 *Left-sided pneumothorax (right side of image) on CT scan of the chest with chest tube in place. August, 2006"*

43% injury reduction. However, the decrease in overall injury with an air bag alone was not statistically significant. On the other hand, air bags alone did reduce the risk of fatality by 13% (NHTSA, 1996).

Information regarding the effectiveness and safety of restraint systems has come largely from experiments performed on human surrogates such as BioSID (side impact and the Hybrid III frontal impact). More recently, experiments using computer modeling and mathematical methods have produced fairly accurate results without the use of expensive equipment or test subjects (Huang, S.C. et al., 1999; Huang, Y. et al., 1994; and Stuhmiller et al., 1996). This evolving technology may be the answer to the research restrictions of motor vehicle injuries and may ultimately contribute to making us safer behind the wheel. A more extensive discussion of restraint systems and air bags is presented in Chapter 4.

10.8 Abdomen

The diaphragm describes the upper border of the abdomen, as previously discussed. The lower border of the abdomen is more difficult to describe, as there is no clear physical separation between the abdomen and pelvis, and the two are frequently grouped together. The abdominopelvic inferior boundary is then defined as the bony pelvis and the pelvic diaphragm, specifically the levator ani and superficial transverse perinea muscles. Figures 10.15a and 10.15b show the location of both the abdominopelvic and thoracic cavities. In general, the abdomen lacks the load distributing protection of the rib cage that surrounds the thoracic cavity. It is bounded both laterally and anteriorly by the abdominal muscles and posteriorly by portions of the ribs and vertebrae. The most superior organs, the liver and spleen, are enclosed by the lower rib cage and are often incorporated into the "hard thorax" when describing potential injury mechanisms.

The abdomen is the largest cavity in the body, called the peritoneal cavity. The walls of the peritoneal cavity are lined with peritoneum, a serous, two-layered membrane that provides a low friction lubrication between the abdominal wall and the organs within. The parietal peritoneum provides the outer wall and separates the cavity into anterior and posterior compartments. The visceral peritoneum covers the individual organs within the cavity. Although rare, the peritoneum may be torn by shearing forces. More commonly the peritoneum is breached by penetrating trauma such as a knife wound. This may be a minor injury but can be serious if the tear is large and involves either highly vascular or organ tissue. Most major organs sit anterior to the parietal peritoneum, including the liver, spleen, stomach, most of the small intestine, and

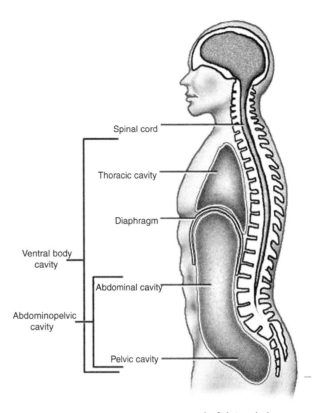

Figure 10.15a Thoracic, abdominal and pelvic cavities. (Courtesy of Robert Perry)

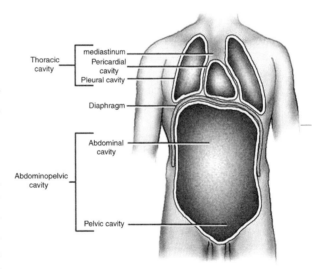

Figure 10.15b Thoracic, abdominal and pelvic cavities. (Courtesy of Robert Perry)

the colon. The pancreas, kidneys, and most of the duodenum lie in the posterior compartment and are described as the "retro peritoneal" organs. This distinction is important in that an examination of the peritoneal organs may not always reveal a retro-peritoneal injury.

Figures 10.16a and 10.16b illustrate the organization

of the two layers of peritoneum. The organs are connected to the peritoneum via either ligaments or additional layers of peritoneal tissue called mesentery. The lesser and greater omenta are the large mesentery that connect the stomach to its adjacent organs, mainly the liver and spleen, as well as the small intestine to the abdominal wall itself. The connection between the organs and the peritoneum is relatively lax, providing a great deal of mobility among the individual organs.

The organs of the abdomen are loosely classified as either solid or hollow. They must all be considered individually, as their differing densities, structures, and the materials contained within all contribute largely to both biomechanical properties and trauma tolerances. In addition, blood flow to each organ is different, making the rupture and subsequent hemorrhage of some organs more life threatening than others. The solid organs of the abdomen include the liver, spleen, pancreas, kidneys, adrenal glands, and ovaries (female). In general, the upper abdomen, which houses the most prominent solid organs, has less tolerance to impact than the lower abdomen. These organs are more susceptible to compression injuries and substantial blood loss. Hemorrhage due to organ rupture is the most common fatal abdominal injury but is frequently preventable if detected and treated immediately (Schneider et al., 1985).

A traumatic rupture of the highly vascularized organs like spleen or liver may result in massive intra-abdominal bleeding and should therefore be treated as a medical emergency. The bleeding will result in hemorrhagic shock (a circulatory failure caused by intravascular volume loss), which presents with tachycardia and hypotension. Rupture of the spleen may be delayed, in which case symptoms may not present until days to weeks after trauma.

The hollow organs include the stomach, small and large intestines, gall bladder, urinary bladder, and uterus. Due to their compressible structure, these organs have higher impact tolerances and are injured less frequently. Although the hollow organs are less likely to result in a bleeding hemorrhage, they have the potential to spill their "contents" into the peritoneal cavity, which can result in infection or peritonitis, a very serious condition.

For a better understanding of the overall anatomy of the abdominal organs, the region is split up into nine sections, as seen in Figures 10.17a and 10.17b. The heterogeneous nature of these organs, coupled with their asymmetrical abdominal locations and differing forms of attachment within the cavity are what make the abdomen a complex structure. Not only does the abdomen exhibit a large variation in impact vulnerability, but in-

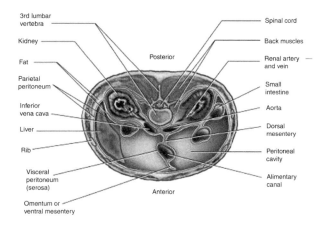

Figure 10.16a *Horizontal section through the abdominal cavity indicating the peritoneum and peritoneal cavity (most abdominal organs omitted). (Courtesy of Robert Perry)*

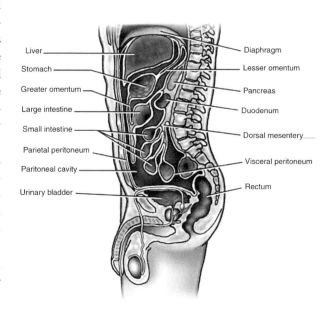

Figure 10.16b *Left lateral view through the thoracic, abdominal, and pelvic cavities (male). (Courtesy of Robert Perry)*

jury mechanisms are also very different depending on the direction of impact, the velocity of impact, and whether the trauma insult is blunt or penetrating. Unfortunately, with so many variables relating to injury severity, it is difficult to accurately model or simulate abdominal impacts and present a detailed analysis of the tolerance limits of each organ. Injury tolerances of the abdomen are by far the least understood. This chapter discusses which organs are more likely to be injured, as well as how and why they are injured. Ultimately, however, individual responses to abdominal trauma must be considered according to the individual event.

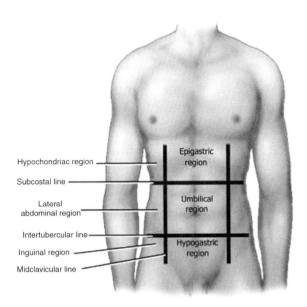

Figure 10.17a Nine external divisions (regions) of the abdominal cavity. (Courtesy of Robert Perry)

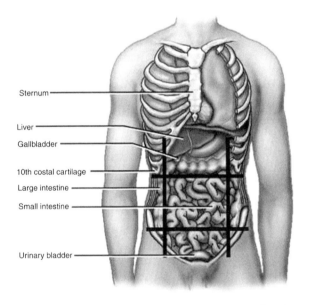

Figure 10.17b Internal anatomy. (Courtesy of Robert Perry)

10.9 Abdominal Anatomy and Mechanisms of Injury

The following section describes each organ individually, its functional anatomy, biomechanical characteristics, and injuries that can occur. Figures 10.18a, 10.18b, and 10.18c illustrate the locations of the thoracic and abdominal organs from anterior to posterior. Blunt trauma injuries to abdominal organs can be described by three major impact mechanisms: (1) impact with bony structures (e.g., spine or ribs) causing compression or puncture, (2) shear-

ing at attachment points due to strain or deceleration, and (3) bursting due to an increase in internal pressure (Pike, 1990).

The liver, spleen, and kidneys are the most frequently injured organs and also present the most serious and life threatening consequences. They are discussed first.

A. Liver

The liver is the largest gland in the body, as well as the largest abdominal organ. It sits in the right hypochondriac and epigastric regions of the abdomen and is partially protected by the lower ribcage. Structurally, the liver is divided into two major lobes, the right lobe much being larger than the left. The hepatic artery provides each lobe with its own blood supply. The liver is responsible for a large number of essential body functions, including metabolism of carbohydrates, lipids, and proteins, blood plasma synthesis, vitamin and mineral metabolism, digestion, and the removal of certain drugs, toxins, hormones, and bacteria from the body. To perform all these functions, the liver requires roughly 27% of the body's blood flow. Since the liver is involved in so many different functions, injury is usually quite serious and requires immediate diagnosis for survival. Although the ribs, previously discussed, shield and help distribute impact loads to the liver, they can compound a liver injury if fractures occur and there is rib bone displacement into the abdominal cavity, causing penetrating lacerations and hemorrhaging of the liver lobes in similar fashion due to the penetrations of the lung lobes discussed previously.

Lacerations and blunt trauma to the liver are the most dangerous abdominal injuries. Lacerations may occur from direct impact compression, puncture from rib fractures, deformation due to compression of other organs, or increased intra-vascular pressure upon impact. An overwhelmingly large percentage of blunt trauma injuries to both the liver and the spleen are related to motor vehicle accidents and to a lesser extent during criminal assaults or military combat.

B. Spleen

The spleen is the most commonly injured organ from blunt trauma. Located primarily in the left hypochondriac region, along the posterior wall of the peritoneum, it is also partially protected by the lower left rib cage. It is the largest lymph organ and is also a site for red blood cell storage. Furthermore, the spleen is responsible for the filtering of bacteria and cellular debris from the blood. The spleen has an extensive vascular structure and will readily cause fatal hemorrhaging when ruptured or damaged if

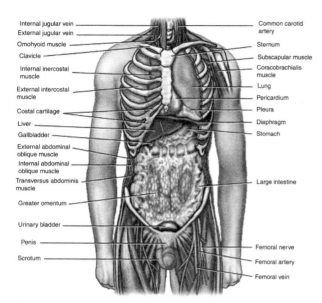

Figure 10.18a *A coronal section of the male at the level of the rib cage and male greater omentum. The rib cage, muscles, and pleura have been removed on the left side of the body. (Courtesy of Robert Perry)*

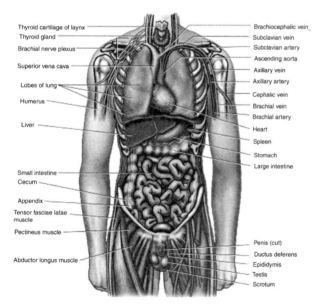

Figure 10.18b *Coronal section of the male with the sternum, ribs, and greater omentum removed. (Courtesy of Robert Perry)*

bleeding is not controlled. A splenectomy is the surgical removal of the spleen due to injury or disease and is medically feasible because the liver and bone marrow are able to take over the spleen's functions after the spleen has been removed in cases of severe trauma. In the past, splenectomies were the most common solution to a ruptured spleen. However, problems with infection and sepsis have

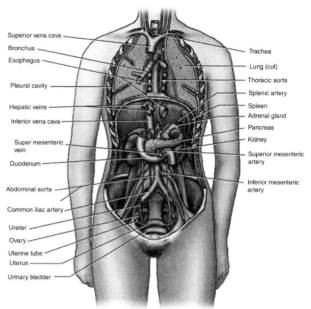

Figure 10.18c *Coronal section of the female at the level of the retroperitoneal organs. The heart has been removed and the posterior portion of the lungs is present. (Courtesy of Robert Perry)*

led to performing only partial splenectomies on injuries that do not involve the spleen in its entirety. Injuries to the spleen can range in order of severity from a minor non-bleeding capsular injury to multiple lacerations and extensive hemorrhage.

C. Kidneys

The kidneys are retro-peritoneal and are located on either side of the spinal column at levels T11 to L3. The right kidney is at a slightly lower position than the left due to the large right lobe of the liver. Because of their location, the kidneys are more susceptible to side and rear direct impacts with stiff structures or implements. The kidneys have no ligament structure to hold them in place; instead the primary attachments or pedicles are the renal veins and arteries that connect them to the abdominal aorta and inferior vena cava respectively. (Figure 10.19) These attachments make the kidney most vulnerable to stretch injuries of the blood vessels and potential detachment from the pedicle. The kidneys are responsible for filtering blood plasma, separating and eliminating waste from the blood stream, controlling blood volume and blood pressure by regulating the amount of water released, and helping to maintain the acid-base and electrolyte balance in the blood. Similar to the liver, the kidneys regulate many body functions that are essential to life and thus demand approximately one quarter of the body's blood supply. Injuries of the kidney can be as minor as a contusion but have the potential to be fatal if there are extensive lacerations or, as previously stated, if a detachment injury at the pedicle occurs. Fortunately, irreparable damage to both kidneys in a single event is less common due to trauma, and people can usually live successfully with the proper function of only one kidney.

D. Adrenal glands

The adrenal glands are endocrine glands that sit on the superior portion of the kidneys. The adrenal glands produce hormones that are important for the regulation of the sympathetic nervous system as well as groups of steroids that promote sexual maturation, fat and protein metabolism, and electrolyte balance within the kidney. Injury to these glands is rare and while hormonal imbalances can cause many problems, hormone replacement therapy makes most of these problems non-life threatening.

E. Pancreas

The pancreas is another retro-peritoneal organ that functions both as an exocrine and endocrine gland. It has an elongated shape with a wider "head" or uncinate process that sits below and behind the stomach in the curve of the duodenum and a "tail" which projects transversely towards the spleen. The pancreas aids in digestion (exocrine function) and produces hormones (endocrine function) that regulate glucose metabolism (insulin, amylin, and glucagon). Other hormones produced by the pancreas include somatostatin and pancreatic polypeptide.

This organ is fairly deep within the abdominal cavity and is thus protected from injury due to the surrounding tissues. Pancreatic injuries account for only 1 to 2% of abdominal injuries (Yoganandan et al., 2001). However, pancreatic rupture can occur in either compression or shear, particularly against the spinal column. This injury is very serious because it is often overlooked, as it almost always occurs with other abdominal injuries that are more immediately recognizable.

F. Stomach

The stomach is a large, hollow organ that is located in the epigastric and umbilical regions. While it is not uncommon to see stomach injury due to a penetrating wound, stomach injury due to blunt trauma is infrequent and typically not life threatening. The stomach is highly compressible and resistant to bursting, although its distention when full may allow for failure of stomach tissues. In addition, the stomach has extremely low levels of bacteria and is unlikely to cause infection in the peritoneum if it does

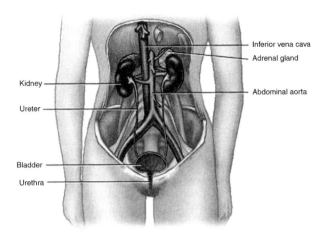

Figure 10.19 The kidneys, urinary system, and major vessels. (Courtesy of Robert Perry)

rupture. It is also possible for stomach contents to explode through the esophagus and mouth during high magnitude blunt impact of the abdomen in a similar fashion to projectile vomiting (a reflexive action), for example in cases of severe food poisoning.

Case Study 10.1

A pedestrian was hit by a compact car moving at approximately 45 mph. It was dark and the driver of the vehicle did not see the pedestrian at impact. The impact was a vault trajectory where the pedestrian proceeded over the vehicle and landed in back of the vehicle (see Chapter 4). The major impact consisted of the victim's torso to the windshield with pedestrian head contact at the roof rail of the vehicle. The impact against the windshield was so violent that the liver, spleen, and one kidney ruptured. Additionally, severe blunt trauma to the head occurred. Subsequently, another vehicle struck the victim but did not roll over the victim. Instead the victim was observed by witnesses to roll over several times (log roll fashion) due to this second vehicle contact.

The authors' opinion was that the initial strike to the windshield produced the major blunt thorax and abdominal trauma in addition to the head injuries due to a significant change in pedestrian acceleration and therefore was responsible for the fatality. Solid organ rupture was evident, and there was evidence that the hollow stomach organ expelled its contents on impact. In contrast, the medical examiner felt that the second vehicle impact may be equally responsible for the abdominal organ rupture due to the subsequent log roll action of the victim (i.e., centrifugal force) produced by a large angular velocity which he was not able to quantify. We explained that there was no basis of support for the centrifugal force mechanism resulting from a sufficiently high angular velocity so as to result in organ rupture in the victim. Road rash was present on the body which certainly may have been due in large part to the second vehicle strike. However, the fatal impact had already occurred at the first vehicle strike.

G. Small intestine

The small intestine travels through most of the central and lower portions of the abdominal cavity and is separated into three sections, running from the stomach to the large intestine: the duodenum, the jejunum, and the ileum. The duodenum is short and wide, containing the pancreatic and bile ducts that help continue digestion of food content. These entering ducts can be severed in cases of extreme external compression loads. Similar to the stomach, the potential for compression or burst injury in the duodenum increases when it is full and blunt trauma injury is possible. These structures are fairly moveable within the cavity and yield well to compressive and tension loads. Once again, some evidence suggests that when the duodenum and/or jejunum are filled with food (i.e., chime), they are more susceptible to deep blunt impact injury.

The most frequent blunt trauma injury to the small intestine is a shearing tear near the bowel (large intestine) attachment due to deceleration or an acute compression tear. These latter tears are often localized and up to one-third of the small intestine can be removed without serious consequences (Pike, 1990). Furthermore, portions of the duodenum may be ruptured by blunt trauma to the abdomen of an infant or toddler resulting in compression and shear stresses as may occur in non-accidental trauma (child abuse) to this area. Commonly, in non-accidental trauma to infants and young children, there is an obvious avulsion of the mesentery at the Ligament of Treitz, which is a point of attachment securing the duodenum. This avulsion failure may occur from a perpetrator fist punch or a foot stomp which applies the high magnitude compressive load to the victim's abdominal area typically when the victim is laying on his/her backside against a hard surface such as the floor. High acceleration motor vehicle accidents may also result in this trauma to infants/toddlers. However, four and five point restraints in current child car seats provide significant protection to infants and younger children in preventing this deep organ trauma.

Many times in adults, it is generally a penetrating wound that results in injury to the small intestine. When a sharp implement or bullet wound is suspected in this organ, careful exploratory surgery is necessary. This involves the surgeon palpating and in some cases manipulating the small intestine in order to examine all sides for a puncture wound. The jejunum and the ileum are the bulk of the small intestine and contain increasing levels of bacteria towards the terminus of the ileum and the beginning of the large intestine (i.e., large bowel).

Case Study 10.2
A young female infant just under a year old was taken to a local medical center and was found to have numerous bruises over multiple parts of her body including the face, flanks, buttocks, perineum and legs. Radiology revealed that she had healing rib fractures and healing metaphyseal fractures of the right distal tibia and fibula. There were also bilateral skull fractures. Importantly, some 500 cc of dark old blood and intestinal fluid was suctioned out and this victim was found to have an avulsion of the mesentery and a complete duodenal avulsion at the ligament of Treitz. This was a life threatening injury although she did recover with intensive medical treatment. The mother was living with her boyfriend (not the child's father) and two young female siblings, ages two and four. The opposing biomechanics' expert opined that rough play on the part of a four-year-old female sibling running over the young infant on the floor could have reasonably resulted in the trauma to the duodenum and the rupture of the ligament of Treitz with consequent significant bleeding over the ensuing days. This other biomechanist's rationale was that in the running step cycle, we usually see two force spikes at ground contact (one at foot strike and one at push-off) as per measured force plate running gait studies, and furthermore, the size of the four-year-old sibling's foot was more consistent with this abdominal trauma than the suspect male defendant's much larger foot. However, we explained that the size of this foot landing upon the infant victim was irrelevant and the biomechanics literature strongly supported that a force of high magnitude, albeit without specific force tolerance limits, must be imposed upon the upper abdomen in order to produce duodenum trauma and rupture of the ligament of Treitz. Our

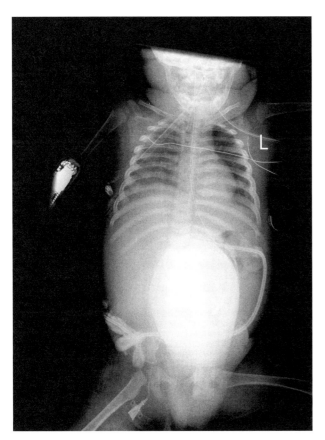

Figure 10.20 Non-contrast study of young infant victim with duodenum rupture detachment and multiple relatively non-displaced rib fractures due to non-accidental trauma by a caregiver (Criminal case). Courtesy of Patrick Hannon and Michael Iliescu.

opinion was that the foot of an approximate 40 pound four-year-old female child running over her sister was not sufficient to produce this large magnitude force. Furthermore, the constellation of injuries to other areas of the head and body strongly implicated the defendant boyfriend.

H. Large intestine

The large intestine consists of the cecum, appendix, colon, rectum, and anal canal and is located around the periphery of the small intestine. It is another hollow organ that is more frequently injured by penetrating trauma, but it also has several anchor points to the abdominal wall and other organs. A rupture of the transverse colon may also occur from compression against the spinal column again as the result of an abdominal blow. However, blunt trauma injury to the colon comprises only about 5% of all injuries reported in adults (Yoganandan et al., 2001). Bacteria levels do continue to climb in the large intestine

and are highest in proximity to the rectum of the colon, affecting potential infection if contents breach the large bowel.

I. Abdominal wall

It is possible to tear the lining of the abdominal wall without injuring any other organs. Blood may collect within a partially torn cavity, causing a rectus sheath hematoma, or a complete tear may lead to a traumatic hernia, where various organs may be pushed outside the cavity itself. Depending upon the degree of extrusion of the traumatic abdominal hernia and the degree to which blood flow to organs is reduced or eliminated (e.g., small intestine pressure ischemia), the severity of the injury will vary. Chronic loading and a weakening of the lining of the abdominal wall over an extended period of time due to aging or a previous breach of the abdominal balloon wall may also result in herniae such as an inguinal or incisional herniae.

J. Gall bladder

The gall bladder is a storage site for the bile that is created in the liver, with a common duct that empties into the duodenum. The gall bladder is well protected from injury, being located inferior and posterior to the liver. Injuries to the bile ducts can occur with a crushing blow to the posterior torso. Another possible injury mechanism described by Yoganandan et al. (2001) suggests that the bile duct may be ruptured upon the rapid emptying of the gall bladder into the common duct coupled with a simultaneous shearing force during distension of the duct. However, it is not probable that these events will occur coincidentally, and therefore this is most likely an uncommon mechanism of injury.

K. Urinary bladder

The urinary bladder is located on the floor of the pelvic cavity. Lying inferior to the peritoneal cavity, the flattened, superior surface of the bladder is covered by parietal peritoneum. (Figure 10.20) The muscle tissue of the bladder is highly distensible. The empty bladder has strong, thick walls that become thinner as the bladder fills. The bladder fills superiorly, pressing on the walls of the peritoneum. The potential for injury increases with its level of filling fluid distension. A sudden increase in intra-abdominal pressure due to a compression load may cause a distended bladder to rupture, similar to a balloon, at the point of least resistance and the incidence of acute urinary bladder injury to include frank ruptures is approximately 60-85%. In addition to internal volume compression loads, shear loading and pelvis fractures may be responsible for the urinary bladder rupture failure (Alhamzawi et al. 2012). Note that internal volume compression results in tension stresses and strains applied to the urinary bladder wall tissue in much the same way as a balloon being filled with air or water results in wall tension stresses and strains which may lead to rupture failure.

L. Female Reproductive organs

The female uterus, a strong thick-walled hollow organ, sits superior to the urinary bladder and, until a woman becomes pregnant, remains very tolerant to blunt impact forces. The location of the uterus can be seen in Figure 10.20. The ovaries are solid organs that are connected by ligaments to the uterine walls. The ovaries are well protected deep in the pelvic cavity and are not often injured. The pregnant uterus, however, effectively changes the biomechanics of the abdomen. In addition, by putting every organ under a constant strain, it is easier to injure other organs through blunt impacts that would, in normal circumstances, be minor. Figure 10.21 illustrates how a full-term fetus occupies much of the abdominal cavity. This is of particular concern in motor vehicle accidents with pregnant drivers. As a woman comes to term in her pregnancy, the abdomen-to-steering wheel clearance decreases by roughly 80 mm and can vary dramatically according to the woman's stature. Upon impact, there is a higher probability of steering wheel contact at a sufficient velocity to cause injury. In addition, between 50 and 80% of the pregnant uterus lies below the lap belt, and the shoulder belt is pushed higher against the sternum, changing the impact mechanism in several parts of the body, (DeSantis et al., 1999). King et al. (1971) utilized pregnant baboons to study the effects of pregnancy in motor vehicle acci-

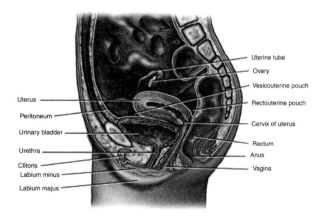

Figure 10.21 *A sagittal view of the urinary system and reproductive organs of the female. (Courtesy of Robert Perry)*

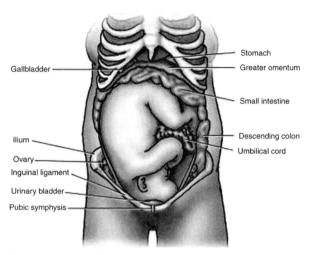

Figure 10.22 *Full-term fetus. (Courtesy of Robert Perry)*

dents. Their findings suggested that modifications could be made to vehicles that would help protect a pregnant woman, such as specialized seat belts. Most recently, new data on three point restraint use and air bag deployment provide significant benefit to pregnant women (Culver, et al., 1990, Pearlman et al., 2000 and Delotte et al., 2006).

M. Major abdominal vessels

Two major blood vessels travel through the abdominal cavity: the abdominal aorta and the inferior vena cava. These two vessels are retro-peritoneal and enter the abdomen through openings in the diaphragm. They are surrounded by the muscles of the lower back, lateral abdomen, and spine, which provide substantial protection. At the level of L4–L5, these vessels bifurcate into the left and right iliac veins and arteries and continue into the lower extremities. The aorta and iliac arteries are highly pressurized vessels with blood flowing away from the heart and are resistant to compression loads. The abdominal aorta is relatively fixed to the spine and injury is therefore a result of direct impact, rather than shearing from a deceleration force. Furthermore, spinal fractures can lead to injuries of the abdominal aorta if pieces of a fractured vertebra are pushed anteriorly into the secured semi-rigid aorta causing an aortic dissection.

An indirect compressive stress wave may cause aortic injury when transmitted from adjacent organs. Yoganandan (2001) estimates that between 1,000 and 2,500 millimeters of mercury of internal pressure are required to cause rupture of the abdominal aorta. Conversely, the inferior vena cava is a low-pressure vessel with a forgiving wall of venous tissue, making rupture extremely rare. Injuries to this tissue are almost always seen in conjunction with various other organ injuries. The most common injury associated with the inferior vena cava is a thrombosis due to either a partial tear in the vena cava wall or a hepatic injury that leaks into the vena cava. A thrombus may be life threatening as blood flow is toward the heart and lungs leading to a pulmonary embolism. Note that smaller thrombi which may form with or without trauma (e.g., long duration automobile or aircraft travel) in smaller diameter lower extremity veins may result in this same condition. This is known as a deep vein thrombosis (DVT) which is a common cause of pulmonary embolisms.

10.10 Biomechanics and Injury Tolerance of the Abdomen

As stated earlier, the liver, spleen, and kidneys are the most commonly injured organs of the abdomen. As the majority of blunt abdominal injuries occur in motor vehicle accidents, much of the data involving abdominal tolerance refers to the liver, spleen, and kidneys in various automobile situations. Yoganandan et al. (2000) found that abdominal injuries to the liver and spleen were most frequent in side impacts. King et al. (2001) describe the primary frontal impact sources as the steering wheel and improperly worn seat belts. In side impacts, the abdomen is also exposed to the arm rest and door, and King opines that injuries to the liver, spleen, and kidneys are more common in this kind of impact. Vock (2001) states that liver rupture can only occur upon impact with a hard-edged or narrow surface. Anecdotal evidence involving cases investigated by the authors lead to statements that are less strong. Augenstein et al. (1999) found liver rupture due to seat belt trauma in frontal collisions between 30–35 mph, and Leung et al. (1980) estimate that the tolerance level of the abdomen with a lap belt is approximately 790 lbs. (3.5 kN), with 1.5 in of deflection. At high force levels, a seat belt can impose a sufficiently stiff and narrow focal load to cause serious injuries as it penetrates into the abdomen. Unembalmed cadaver drop tests (N= 11) revealed that liver injuries were the most serious of blunt abdominal trauma, with AIS injuries up to a level 4 occurring with falls of only 1 meter onto a simulated arm rest. In one drop, the cadaver subject sustained an AIS 4 injury with only a maximum force of 380 newtons (85.4 lbs) (test 209) onto a polystyrene arm rest (Walfisch et al., 1980). Another series of drop tests performed using cadaver subjects at heights ranging from 2.6 meters to 27.8 meters (Yoganandan et al., 2001) found that energies between 36.5 and 46 Joules resulted in minor internal liver lacerations, and energies ranging from 144 to 182 Joules resulted in external tears. Finally, energies of 386 to 488 Joules resulted in complete liver rupture. In addi-

tion, Viano (1994) used the side impact dummy (Biosid) and found that the tolerance of both the thorax and the abdomen is substantially dependent upon upper extremity position during impact. The arm and forearm can act as a buffer upon impact, providing additional protection to the internal organs and therefore providing protection to the abdomen and thorax if shielding takes place.

When predicting the severity of abdominal injury, it is important to realize that the extent of injury is a function of both abdominal cavity compression and the velocity of impact. Cripps (1997) conducted a study comparing intestinal injuries with differing impact velocities. In general, an impact results in a transfer of mechanical energy from one body to another which may be in the form of propagating energy waves. In the human body, these propagating energy waves may cause the displacement of body tissues and organs, which can lead to injury or rupture if substantial movement occurs. In a high velocity impact, such as a bullet penetration or explosion, stress waves are formed: fast high pressure compression waves that cause rapid and small displacements as they propagate through body tissue. Tissue damage may be extensive (See also chapter 4).

A lower velocity impact coupled with a massive compression, such as a motor vehicle accident, will result in the propagation of shear waves: slow moving large amplitude waves that translate into a large displacement of the body wall and thus the organs within. The relatively moveable organs in the abdomen, such as the small intestine, do not resist these shear waves and allow for their propagation by moving along with them, generally without injury. On the other hand, organs such as the colon, with several fairly rigid points of attachment, can become disrupted and torn as the shear wave propagates through the cavity (Cripps, 1997).

10.11 Biomechanics and Injury Tolerance of the Male Reproductive System

A. Accident trauma loading

The organs of the male reproductive system are located outside the abdomino-pelvic cavity. However, they are considered in this chapter as the author views these issues best covered here. Figure 10.22a presents the basic structures of the adult male perineum. Figure 10.22b presents the exposed male perineum.

A number of papers have addressed serious acute trauma to the penis, perineum, or pelvis resulting from falls, motorcycle and automobile accidents, penis fracture during intercourse, and fracture fixation of lower extremities on an orthopaedic fracture table (Schulak et al., 1980). Acute trauma resulting from direct impact to the male perineum does have the potential to produce male erectile dysfunction. Munarriz et al. (1995), based on their nine-year longitudinal study of a research sample of 131 men (from an erectile dysfunction population of 3,989 men) with persistent changes in erectile function following blunt pelvic or blunt perineal trauma, estimate that some 600,000 American men are afflicted by traumatic vasculogenic impotence with some 250,000 of this population segment afflicted by sports injuries which involve blunt impact loading to the perineum or pelvis. Diagnostic tests for the entire sample of 131 men included "a complete pharmaco-cavernosometry/pharmaco-cavernosography study for impotence" (p. 1831–1832). Additional tests administered as needed to the sample of 131 men included "psychological interviews, laboratory testing, endocrine screening, nocturnal penile tumescence testing, penile biothesiometry and duplex Doppler ultrasonography" (Munarriz, 1995, p.1832). Hemodynamics were within normal range for 5 of the 89 patients with a history of perineal trauma, and therefore erectile dysfunction was attributed to psychogenic factors for those 5 men. The remaining 126 men were diagnosed with abnormal hemodynamics (N= 42 pelvic trauma and N= 84 with perineal trauma). The authors report that the most common blunt trauma to the perineum was a fall onto the bicycle frame cross bar (Munarriz, 1995).

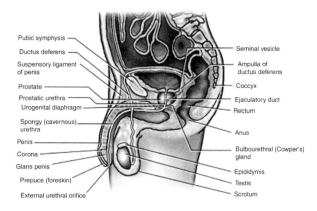

Figure 10.23a *Male reproductive system and adjacent structures. (Courtesy of Robert Perry)*

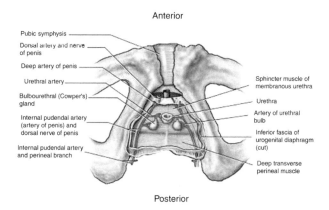

Figure 10.23b *The male perineum area. (Courtesy of Robert Perry)*

B. Loading to the perineum from bicycling activity

A review of the literature indicates that stresses in the perineal area may produce erectile dysfunction in men with prolonged bicycling riding. Trauma may be a moderately frequent cause of impotence, particularly in younger men (Lurie et al., 1987). Penile erection requires adequate arterial flow into the penis, a viable venocclusive mechanism, relaxation of the lacunar musculature of the corpora cavernosa, and physiologically intact pudendal, and greater and lesser cavernous nerves (nerves that course through the perineal area) (Lurie et al., 1987; Solomon et al., 1987). Mellion (1991) addresses the issue of male impotence and bicycling in a review paper in Sports Medicine. Studies cited indicate an occasional problem in serious bicyclists who have lost the ability to attain an erection after repeated multi-day rides. Treatment consisted of eliminating the activity and adding additional padding to the bicycling shorts and/or saddle seat of the bicycle.

Solomon and Cappa (1987) report a case study involving a 55-year-old-male physician who incorporated stationary bicycling into his fitness routine with resulting impotence presumably due to high perineal compression stresses. With continued stationary bicycle activity (20 minutes/day), erectile dysfunction persisted for one year despite lowering the bicycle seat. Eliminating the bicycling activity resulted in a return of normal erectile function within one month and remained so (nine months later at the time of submission of the authors' paper).

Anderson et al. (1997) conducted an epidemiology study on 1,990 participants in The Great Trial of Strength amateur bicycling touring race (540 km) in Oslo, Norway. Two hundred sixty self-completion questionnaires were delivered prior to the race. Sixty-five percent (160 men and 9 women) responded. Results indicated that 21 men (13%) experienced impotence following this Oslo 1990 tour. In 11 of 21 men, this erectile dysfunction lasted at least one week. In 2 men ages 31 and 42 years, erectile dysfunction lasted for 5 and 8 months respectively. Interestingly, "almost nobody had genital symptoms after tours of less than 150–200 km" (Anderson et al., 1997, p.

236) {respondents answering in regard to previous bicycling tours}. Furthermore, the authors reported that impotence experience increased with the number of completed Great Trial of Strength racing tours (P= .001). Two male responders indicated that "they accepted impairment of sexual potency as almost inevitable during the racing season" (Anderson et al., p. 236).

Finally, an experimental study is reported by Nayal et al. (1999) involving measures of penis glans oximetry (transcutaneous penile oxygen partial pressure) in 25 healthy males (repeated measures study design). The measurements were taken during: (1) standing off the bicycle; (2) seated and cycling on the stationary bicycle (2 separated trials for each subject); and (3) cycling in a standing position on the bicycle. Mean partial pressure of oxygen (due to arterial blood perfusion of the penis glans) indicated normal values while standing (mean pO_2 = 61.4 millimeters of mercury) or standing cycling (mean pO_2 = 68 millimeters of mercury). However, cycling in a seated position produced mean values of only pO_2 = 19.4 millimeters of mercury on the first seated trial and a pO_2 = 18.4 millimeters of mercury on the second seated trial. Clearly, vascular perfusion was significantly decreased during the seated cycling position. The authors reported a return to normal penile perfusion pO_2 levels within 10 minutes of recovery. Erectile dysfunction from prolonged and repeated exposure to bicycling with commonly used bicycle seats (with a nose) is supported by the literature. Usually, it is temporary, and normal function returns when the frequency and duration of this bicycling activity is reduced.

More recently, Lowe et al. (2004) found that a traditional saddle with a protruding nose produces on average a greater than double compressive stress in the male perineal area compared to those saddles without a protruding nose (p<0.01). Therefore, stationary exercise bikes without a saddle nose are a logical consideration for males. Conversely, road bicycling requires the increased control of a saddle nose for adequate safety and performance.

References

Alhamzawi, H., Abdelrahman, H., Abdelrahman, K., El-Menyar, A., Althani, H., and Latifi, R. (2012) Delayed Presentation of Traumatic Intraperitoneal Rupture of Urinary Bladder: Case Report in Urology, v. November, Article ID 430746 http://dx.doi.org/10.1155/2012/430746

Anderson KV, Bovim G. "Impotence and Nerve Entrapment in Long Distance Amateur Cyclists." *Acta Neurol Scand.* 95:233–240. (1997)

Augenstein J, Perdeck E, Bowen J, Stratton J, Horton T, Singer M, Rao A. Digges K, Mallaris A. "Injury Patterns among Belted Drivers Protected by Airbags in 30 to 35 mph Crashes." *Society of Automotive Engineers.* 1999-01-1062:77–83. (1999)

Berger FH, et al. Eur J Radiol. 2010 Apr;74(1):24-39. Epub 2009 Aug 8. Neschis DG, et al. N Engl J Med. 2008 Oct 16;359(16):1708-16. Legome, E. Uptodate, 2010.]

Bowen D.A.L., Teare R.D. (1962) Delayed traumatic rupture of aorta. *Thorax.* 17(2):150–153. doi:10.1136/thx.17.2.150

Cesari D, Bouquet R. "Behavior of Human Surrogates Thorax under Belt Loading." *Society of Automotive Engineers.* 90-2310:73–81 (1990)

Cripps NP, Cooper GJ. "Intestinal Injury Mechanisms after Blunt Abdominal Impact." Ann R *Coll Surg Engl.*79(2):115–120. (1997)

Culver CC, Viano DC. Anthropometry of seated women during pregnancy: defining a fetal region for crash protection research. Human Factors. 1990 Dec;32(6):625-36.

DeSantis Klinich K, Schneider LW, Rupp J, Eby B, Pearlman M. "Challenges in Frontal Crash Protection of Pregnant Drivers Based on Anthropometric Considerations." Society of Automotive Engineers. 1999-01-0711:105–127. Federal Motor Vehicle Safety Standard No. 208. (1977). Federal Register, Docket 74-14, Notice 11. 42(128). (1999)

Delotte, J., Behr M, Baque P, Bourgeon A, de Peretti F, Brunet C. (2006) Modeling the pregnant woman in driving position.

Surg Radiol Anat. 2006 Aug; 28(4): 359-63.

Foret-Bruno JY, Harteman F, Thomas C, Fayon A, Tarriere C, Got C, Patel A. "Correlation Between Thoracic Lesions and Force Values Measured at the Shoulder of 92 Belted Occupants Involved in Real Accidents." *Proceedings of the 22nd Stapp Car Crash Conference. Society of Automotive Engineers.* 78-0892. (1978)

Gaines, B., Shultz, B., Morrison, K., Ford, H. (2004) Duodenal injuries in children: Beware of child abuse. J of Pediatric Surgery, v. 39 (4), pp. 600-602.

Ghista DN. *Human Body Dynamics: Impact, Occupational and Athletic Aspects.* Oxford: Clarendon Press. (1982)

Huang SC, Chu JY, Chang CH. "Modeling of Occupant Dynamics During Automobile Rear-end Impacts." *Biomedical Materials and Engineering.* 9(5–6):335–345. (1999)

Huang Y, King AI, Cavanaugh JM. "A MADYMO Model of Near-side Human Occupants in Side Impacts." *Journal of Biomedical Engineering.* 116(2):228–235. (1994)

Keel, M., Meier, C., (2007) Chest injuries—what is new? Current Opinion in Critical Care. 13 (6) pp. 674–679.

King AI. Fundamentals of Impact Biomechanics: Part I à Biomechanics of the Head, Neck and Thorax." *Annual Review of Biomedical Engineering.* 2:55–81. (2000)

King AI. "Fundamentals of Impact Biomechanics: part II à Biomechanics of the Abdomen, Pelvis and Lower extremities." *Annual Review of Biomedical Engineering.* 3:27–55. (2001)

King AI, Crosby WM, Stout LC, Eppinger RH. "Effects of Lap Belt and Three-point Restraints on Pregnant Baboons Subjected to Deceleration." *Society of Automotive Engineers.* 71-0850:69–89. (1971)

Kleinman, P. and Schlesinger, A. (1997) Mechanical factors associated with posterior rib fractures: laboratory and case study. Pediatric radiology, v. 27, pp. 87-91.

Kleinman PK, Marks, SC, Spevak MR, et al. (1992) Fractures of the rib heads in abused infants. Radiology; 185(1):119-23

Leung YC, Mairesse P, Banzet P. ATP Safety of Vehicles, Submarining Criterion. Final Report: Peugeot SA/Renault Association, Contract No. 78-043. (1980)

Lowe BD, Schrader SM, Breitenstein MJ. "Effect of Bicycle Saddle Designs on the Pressure to the Perineum of the Bicyclist." Medicine and Science in Sports and Exercise. 36(6): 1055–1062. (2004)

Lurie AL, Bookstein JJ, Kessler WO. "Post-traumatic Impotence: Angiographic Evaluation." *Radiology.* 165:115–119. (1987)

Mayberry JC, Trunkey DD. "The Fractured Rib in Chest Wall Trauma." *Chest Surgery Clinics of North America.* 7(2):239–261. (1997)

Mellion MB. "Common Cycling Injuries. Management and Prevention." *Sports Med.* 11:52–70. (1991)

Mertz HJ, Horsch JD, Horn, G, Lowne RW. "Hybrid III Sternal Deflection Associated with Thoracic Injury Severities of Occupants with Force-Limiting Shoulder Belts." *Society of Automotive Engineers.* 91-0812:105–119. (1991)

Munarriz RM, Yan QR, Nehra A, Udelson D, Goldstein I. "Blunt Trauma: The Pathophysiology of Hemodynamics Injury Leading to Erectile Dysfunction." *J Urol.* 153:1831–1840. (1995)

National Highway Traffic Administration. "Effectiveness of Occupant Protection Systems and their Use." *Third Report to Congress.* Washington, DC: U.S. Department of Transportation. (1996)

Nayal W, Schwarzer U, Klotz T, Heidenreich A, Engelmann U. "Transcutaneous Penile Oxygen Pressure During Bicycling." *BJU International.* 83:623–625. (1999)

Neathery RF. "Prediction of Thoracic Injury from Dummy Responses." *Society of Automotive Engineers.* 75-1151:295–316. (1975)

Pearlman MD, Klinich KD, Schneider LW, Rupp J, Moss S, Ashton-Miller J. (2000) A comprehensive program to improve safety for pregnant women and fetuses in motor vehicle crashes: a preliminary report. Am J Obstet Gynecol. 2000 Jun;182(6):1554-64.

Pike JA, *Automotive Safety ‡ Anatomy, Injury, Testing and Regulation.* Warrendale, PA: Society of Automotive Engineers, Inc. (1990)

Schneider RC, Kennedy JC, Plant ML.(Eds.). *Sports Injuries ‡ Mechanisms, Prevention and Treatment.* Baltimore, MD: Williams and Wilkins. (1985)

Schulak DJ, Bear TF, Summers JL. "Transient Impotence from Positioning on the Fracture Table." *J Trauma.* 20:420. (1980)

Solomon S, Cappa KG. "Impotence and Bicycling. A Seldom-reported Connection." *Postgrad Med.* 81:99–102. (1987)

Stapp JP. "Voluntary Human Tolerance Levels." In Gurdjian ES, Lange WA, Patrick LM, Thomas LM. (Eds.)

Impact Injury and Crash Protection. Springfield IL: Thomas. (1970)

Stuhmiller JH, Ho KH, Vander Vorst MJ, Dodd KT, Fitzpatrick T, Mayorga M. "A Model of Blast Overpressure Injury to the Lung." *Journal of Biomechanics.* 29(2):227–234. (1996)

Viano DC. "Comparison of Arm Up and Down in Side Impacts with BioSID and Different Armrests." *Journal of Biomechanical Engineering.* 116(3):270–277. (1994)

Viano DC, Lau IV. "Role of Impact Velocity and Chest Compression in Thoracic Injury." Avia. *Space Environ. Med.* 54:16–21. (1983)

Vock R. "Liver Rupture Caused by Isolated Blunt Force Impact: the Result of a Blow, a Kick or a Fall?" *International Journal of Legal Medicine.* 114(4-5):244–247 (2001)

Voigt, G. E. *Die Biomechanik Stumpfer Brustverletzungen Besonders von Thorax, Aorta und Herz (German).* Berlin: Hefte zur Unfallheilkunde Heft 96 Springer. (1968)

Walfisch, G. Fayon, A., Tarriere, C., Rosey, J.P. "Designing of a Dummy's Abdomen for Detecting Injuries in Side Impact Collisions." *Proceedings of the Fifth International IRCBI Conference on the Biomechanics of Impacts.* France: Bryon. (1980)

Yoganandan N, Pintar FA, Gennarelli TA, Maltese MR. "Patterns of Abdominal Injuries in Frontal and Side Impacts." *44th Proceedings of the Association for the Advancement of Automotive Medicine.* 44:17–36. (2000)

Yoganandan N, Pintar FA, Maltese MR. "Biomechanics of Abdominal Injuries." *Critical Review of Biomedical Engineering.* 29(2):173–246. (2001)

Recommended Reading

Absoeif SR, Breza J, Orvis BR, Lue TF, Tanago EA. "Erectile Response to Acute and Chronic Occlusion of the Internal Pudendal and Penile Arteries." *J Urol.* 141:398–402. (1989)

Backaitis SH. *Biomechanics of Impact Injuries and Injury Tolerances of the Abdomen, Lumbar Spine and Pelvis Complex PT-47.* Warrendale, PA: Society of Automotive Engineers, Inc. (1995)

Backaitis SH. *Biomechanics of Impact Injuries and Injury Tolerances of the Thorax-Shoulder Complex PT-45.* Warrendale, PA: Society of Automotive Engineers, Inc. (1994)

Buchsbaum HJ. *Trauma in Pregnancy.* Philadelphia, PA: W.B. Saunders Company (1979)

Cherington M. "Hazards of Bicycling: From Handlebars to Lightning." *Seminars in Neurology.* 20(2):247–253 (2000)

DiMarco, L., Pacini, D. and Bartolomeo, R. (2013) Acute traumatic thoracic aortic injury: Considerations and reflections on the endovascular aneurysm repair. Journal Aorta, July, v 1 (2), pp. 117-122.

Desai KM, Gingell JC. "Hazards of Long Distance Cycling (letter)." *Br Med J.* 298:1072–73 (1989)

Haland Y, Pipkorn B. "A Parametric Study of a Side Airbag System to Meet Deflect Based on Criteria." *Journal of Biomedical Engineering.* 118(3):412–419 (1996)

Hyde AS. *Crash Injuries: How and Why They Happen.* Key Biscayne, FL: HAI. (1992)

Lehman K, Schopke W, Hauri D. "Subclinical Trauma to Perineum: A Possible Etiology of Erectile Dysfunction in Young Men." *Eur Urol.* 27:306–310 (1995)

Lurie AL, Bookstein JJ, Kessler, WO. "Angiography of Posttraumatic Impotence." *Cardiovasc Intervent Radiol.* 11:232–236 (1988)

Martini F. *Fundamentals of Anatomy and Physiology,* Third edition. Upper Saddle River, NJ: Prentice Hall (1995)

Matthews LA, Herbener TE, Seftel AD. "Impotence Associated With Blunt Pelvic and Perineal Trauma: Penile Revascularization as a Treatment Option." *Seminars in Urology,* 8(1):66–72 (1995)

Rouana SW. "Biomechanics of Abdominal Trauma". In Nahum AMMelvinJW.(Eds.) *Accidental Injury ‡ Biomechanics and Prevention.* New York: Springer-Verlag (1993)

Saladin KS. *Anatomy and Physiology: the Unity of Form and Function,* Second edition. Boston, MA: McGraw Hill (2001)

Introduction to Musculoskeletal, Structural, and Functional Anatomy

Patrick Hannon

The human musculoskeletal system is composed of muscles, bones, and joints which permit mechanical energy in one form to be transformed into mechanical energy that is in a more useful form in order to produce force and motion.

Joints are made up of two or more bones and may be classified in terms of their functional characteristics. These classifications include synarthrodial, amphiarthrodial, or diarthrodial joints or articulations.

Synarthrodial joints are articulations that for the most part are considered immovable. Examples would be the sutures in the adult skull and likewise the gomphosis joints where the teeth slip into the sockets within the mandible and maxilla. Amphiarthrodial joints are slightly moveable joints. In some cases, the movement is fairly significant at these joints as per the joints between the vertebral bodies that sandwich a fibrocartilaginous intervertebral disc. In other cases, the amphiarthrodial joint may present fairly minimal movement, such as symphysis pubis where the two pubic bones come together or at the distal tibiofibular union. In this latter example, we have a tight ligament capsule that binds the tibia and fibula together into a relatively immoveable union. Keep in mind that movement can occur even in these relatively immoveable joints if the level of loading is of sufficient magnitude. Finally, we have diarthrodial joints which are freely moveable. They also have a synovial membrane which secretes synovial fluid. Hence, from a structural standpoint they may also be termed synovial joints.

There is a large variability in terms of the range of motion (ROM) of specific joints within the human body. For example, the sacroiliac joints (SI joints) between the sacrum and the ilium of the pelvis are classified generally as diarthrodial joints (left and right side), complete with a synovial capsule. However, in the adult human, these joints are relatively immoveable, bound by tight bony structures that interlock and a number of ligament structures that tie the sacrum tight into the ilium on both sides of the pelvis. Contrasting the SI joints are the shoulder joints (glenohumeral joints) which have a broad range of motion and are able to move around three motion axes (triaxial joints).

Joint motion may be described as linear motion, also termed translation (sliding-gliding), or as angular motion around a relatively fixed axis. Many of the linear and angular motions that take place at diarthrodial and amphiarthrodial joints may result in moving the entire human body from point A to point B (linear motion). Human walking gait for example results principally from angular motion at diarthrodial joints. However, the net result is the entire body ends up moving in a linear fashion.

Osteokinematic Joint Motions

Osteokinematic motions (a.k.a. anatomical or physiologic motions) are described in relationship to a standardized position that we term the anatomical position. Bending the elbow is an example of an angular motion which we term flexion. Angular osteokinematic motions such as flexion or extension of the elbow occur along a plane and around an axis. Flexion begins at zero degrees (anatomical reference position) and ends at full flexion (approximately 140°) within the sagittal plane and around a mediolateral axis. Extension of the elbow moves the forearm back to the anatomical position within this same plane and rotational axis. Osteokinematic motions occur in the coronal and horizontal planes around the anterioposterior and longitudinal axes respectively. More detail is provided for specific joints within the following regional anatomy sections. The reader is also encouraged to refer back to Chapter 3 for a more complete discussion of anatomical planes and axes.

Arthrokinematic Motion

(anatomical machine systems within the body)

Within diarthrodial joints, movements occur to include: 1) sliding, 2) rolling and 3) rotating or spinning. An example commonly used is that of an automobile. When the four wheels are locked up on ice, sliding takes place and when the wheels-tires are moving over the pavement, rolling is occurs. Both motions may occur coincidently as when a freely moving vehicle wheel-tire is rolling and sliding over an icy street surface. Rotation alone (i.e., spinning) takes place in this motor vehicle example when the vehicle is stuck on snow or ice and the wheel and tire just spin without rolling or sliding. The wheel maintains its stable immoveable position over the ground surface as it is rotating. Tight diarthodial joints such as the elbow (humeroulnar joint) operate primarily by rotation or spinning; whereas the shoulder joint (glenohumeral) spins but also exhibits significant rolling and sliding as the head of the humerus also rolls and slides across the glenoid cartilage labrum/bony glenoid fossa of the scapula. Interestingly, when rolling of a convex joint surface takes place over an opposing concave or flat joint surface in one direction, sliding occurs in the opposite direction. Such is the example of the convex humeral head in the shoulder joint rolling across the concave glenoid surface of the scapula. Sliding will take place in the opposite direction. Conversely, if a concave surface moves over a convex surface, sliding is in the same direction. This may be termed the convex-concave rule in arthrokinematic motion.

Muscle Forces

Muscles produce tension forces and do so by shortening or attempting to shorten. When muscles shorten, the contraction is termed concentric as in the example of lifting a weight through flexion of the elbows (e.g., barbell curl). Eccentric contractions are also common as in the example of the quadriceps musculature of the front of the thigh elongating during staircase descent or when one sits down in a chair.

Generally, skeletal muscle is strongest at normal resting length and is not able to produce as much force at significantly shorter lengths. (See Chapter 7.) This is not a concern in resisting submaximal loads but may become a concern in resisting maximal external loads.

Another factor affecting muscle force is the velocity with which a muscle contracts. Generally, when a muscle produces a shortening contraction against a maximal resistance (i.e., weight) at a slow velocity, the force will be greater. An isometric contraction (no joint movement) with maximum effort produces a very high amount of muscle force. As angular velocity of the joint increases during a concentric contraction, the muscle force decreases correspondingly during and only during maximal effort exercise repetitions. This effect can be illustrated when a patient performs a knee extension on an isokinetic device (angular velocity is controlled). At high angular velocities, the amount of muscle force produced is lower. At slower muscle shortening velocities or at zero velocity (i.e., an isometric contraction), the muscle force produced is significantly higher when a "maximal effort" is applied by the subject or patient.

This relationship changes in a forced lengthening muscle contraction termed a "supramaximal eccentric contraction". The muscle in response to an external load becomes longer. This forced supramaximal eccentric contraction has the capability of producing even higher forces than we would normally see in a maximal voluntary contraction (i.e., an isometric contraction). These supramaximal eccentric contractions at high angular velocities sometimes do occur in accident situations and will increase the potential for injury to muscle tissue.

Muscle forces can produce predominant sliding in an arthrodial joint (i.e., sliding joint; subcategory of diarthodial joints). However, more commonly muscles and external loading produce arthrokinematic joint motions that are predominantly rotating in nature, and therefore a force is imposed perpendicular to and some distance away from the axis of rotation of the diarthrodial joint. In this way, a moment arm is created, termed a force moment arm. In handling external loads, a resistance moment arm results which is the perpendicular distance from the line of resistance to the joint's axis. In terms of voluntary human motion, many times these two moments, (i.e., a muscle force moment and a resistance or load moment) must be balanced. The reader is referred to chapter 20 for a more complete discussion of the functional anatomy of bones, joints, muscles, and external loads.

The following chapters address specific anatomical regions to include the cervical and lumbar spine and the upper and lower extremities. The reader is also referred to our CD series which addresses detailed structural anatomy of the upper and lower extremities.

Chapter 11

Biomechanics of the Cervical Spine

Patrick Hannon

11.1 Introduction

The human spine is a complex structure designed to transfer and distribute loads between the head, trunk, and pelvis, as well as to provide protection for the spinal cord. In total, there are thirty-three individual vertebrae comprising the bony elements of the spine. Twenty-four intervertebral articulations permit multi-axial movement while surrounding ligaments, muscles, and intervertebral disks provide stability. The first seven vertebrae comprise the cervical spine (C1–C7), followed by twelve thoracic vertebrae (T1–T12), five lumbar vertebrae (L1–L5), five fused sacral vertebrae (S1–S5), and finally an approximate four fused coccygeal vertebrae (fusing at between twenty to thirty years). As the primary support structure for the skull, the cervical spine also provides multidirectional shock absorption for the head. In addition, the cer-

vical spine surrounds and protects the brain stem, spinal cord, nerve roots, and numerous vascular structures entering and exiting the foramen magnum of the skull and throughout the neck. The structure of the cervical spine offers a wide range of motion to the head and neck that is suitable for the functional negotiation of one's surroundings (Nordin and Frankel, 2001). However, such extensive motion also limits the ability of the cervical spine to protect the many delicate structures contained within. For this reason, an understanding of cervical spine stress tolerance is essential to the biomechanist and attorney in cases of trauma and injury.

11.2 Structural and Functional Anatomy of the Cervical Spine

When viewed in the sagittal plane, the cervical spine has an anteriorly convex curve (lordotic). This lordosis is in part maintained by the shape of the intervertebral disks; wedge-like structures that narrow posteriorly, as seen in Figure 11.1.

From a biomechanical standpoint, the spine can be viewed as a string of individual motion segments linked together to enable complex movements. Each motion segment or functional unit consists of two adjacent bony vertebrae, their connecting intervertebral disk (a.k.a. disc), and the surrounding ligaments holding the functional unit together. The functional requirements of the spine differ throughout its length, resulting in many structural variations within each division.

A. Bony elements

The first two vertebrae are distinctly different from the other vertebrae in the cervical spine. They are known as the atlas (C1) and the axis (C2) and articulate to form the atlantoaxial joint. (Figures 11.2a and 11.2b) The remaining cervical vertebrae C3–C7 are very similar with minor variations in structure and function (Mercer, 2004). Structurally, C1 is a ring of bone resembling a washer with no body or spinous process. The atlas cradles the occiput of the skull and transmits forces from the head to the rest of the cervical spine. In addition, it serves as the attachment site of numerous ligaments and muscles. Laterally, the ring of the atlas widens into two large lateral masses which are vertically aligned below the occipital condyles. Slender arches complete the ring and unite the masses anteriorly and posteriorly. The weight of the head is then transmitted from the occipital condyles via the large lateral masses of the atlas down to the axis (C2). This superior articulation between C1 and the occipital condyles is called the atlanto-occipital joint and is primarily responsible for a good portion of cervical flexion and extension, providing an average total range of ten to twenty-five degrees (Werne, 1959; Porterfield and DeRosa, 1995). It is important to note that although there is significant excursion in flexion and extension at the atlanto-occipital joint, this joint provides little or no rotation around the longitudinal axis (Mercer, 2004).

The axis has an unusual body, spinous process, and the other typical vertebral processes. The axis body also includes the odontoid process (also called the dens), which projects up into the anterior ring portion of C1 creating a trochoid or pivot joint. The dens is actually the missing

body of the atlas, which fuses with the axis during embryonic development. The dens, acting as a swivel pole, provides more than half (about forty degrees in one direction) of all cervical spine rotation. (Figure 11.2b) The atlantoaxial joint also contributes roughly twenty degrees of cervical flexion and extension. Furthermore, there is no lateral flexion permitted at the atlantoaxial joint (Porterfield and DeRosa, 1995).

Cervical vertebrae 3 to 7 have common distinguishing features, shown in Figure 11.3. These four cervical vertebrae consist of a body, two pedicles, two lateral masses, two laminae, and a bifid, or forked, spinous process. The body is oval, broader from side to side than along the anterior-posterior dimension. The C7 vertebra

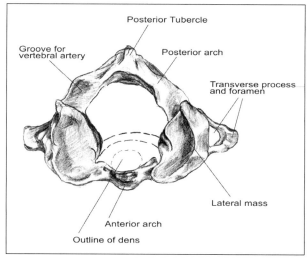

Figure 11.2a A superior view of the atlas (C1) with its lateral masses. (Courtesy of Dave Williams M.F.A.)

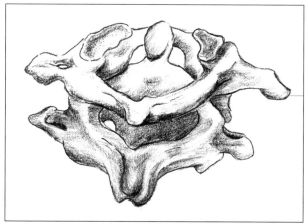

Figure 11.2b Atlantoaxial articulations. A large range of rotation motion exists between these two vertebrae (C1–C2). (Courtesy of Dave Williams M.F.A.)

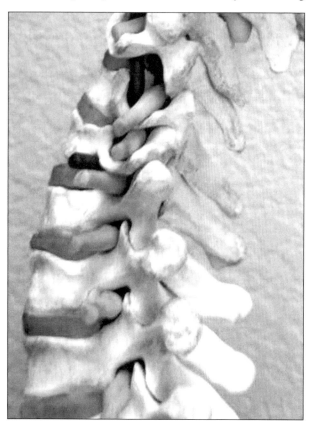

Figure 11.1 Bone elements and intervertebral disks of the cervical spine. (Courtesy of Patrick Hannon)

has the longest and most prominent transverse and spinous processes which serve as attachment sites for part of ligamentum nuchae and several muscles (Mercer, 2004). The C7 spinous process is very prominent and may easily be palpated by placing one's hand upon the back of the lower neck.

The vertebral foramen of the cervical spine are large and generally triangular. Each transverse process contains a transverse foramen through which the vertebral arteries and veins pass to the brain stem. Each transverse process has two projections, the anterior and posterior tubercles, which serve as attachment points for anterior and posterior muscles. The lateral masses project superiorly and inferiorly to become the superior and inferior articulating processes of the zygapophyseal joints, as discussed in the following section.

B. Intervertebral joints

There are two sets of joints that make up the motion segments of the spine: the zygapophyseal joints (a.k.a. apophyseal joints or facet joints) and the joints between the vertebral bodies. There are two lateral zygapophyseal joints and one intervertebral body joint in each motion segment. Together the three joints control movement and provide stability for the interaction of the two vertebrae that make up the functional unit.

The bone-disk-bone interface of the joint between the vertebral bodies sustains the majority of the total compressive load, while the two zygapophyseal joints handle the remaining load. Neck and head position will affect this distribution of loading. However, for any one neck position, disruption of these three loads will in turn affect the efficiency of the entire spine as well as the spinal functional unit.

1. Zygapophyseal joints

Below the articulations of the occiput, C1 and C2, each vertebral body interacts with the body above and below via two lateral zygapophyseal joints. These are synovial joints, with a fluid-filled capsule, ligamentous surroundings, and joint surfaces that are lined with articular cartilage. Within the zygapophyseal joints are fibroadipose meniscoids (Mercer, 2004) which may serve to protect the articular cartilage surfaces of the facets. The zygapophyseal joint alignment of C3–C7 is approximately forty-five degrees to the coronal (frontal) plane. This orientation allows the zygapophyseal joints to effectively resist anterior-posterior shear loads acting at the cervical spine and at the same time provide a facet plane of motion which is very compatible with flexion and extension motions. (Figure 11.1)

a. Motion coupling. Some movements of the cervical spine are coupled due to the alignment of the joint surfaces. Flexion of the cervical spine in the sagittal plane is accompanied by an anterior translation (i.e., linear motion) of the inferior facets (superior vertebra), and cervical spine extension demonstrates a posterior translation of these facets. The zygapophyseal and uncovertebral joints are also responsible for a coupling of motion in the lower cervical spine. Lateral flexion to the right will result in rotation of the spinous processes to the left (and vice versa) due to the gliding of the joint surfaces in C3 through C7. (Figure 11.4)

At the atlanto-axial joint, a coupling of longitudinal rotation and vertical translation is seen, where rotation in either direction is combined with a telescoping axial upward translation and turning the head to one side will very slightly raise one's stature.

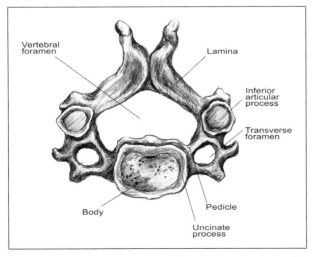

Figure 11.3 Bony structures of C3–C7. (Courtesy of Dave Williams M.F.A.)

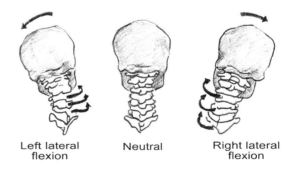

Left lateral flexion   Neutral   Right lateral flexion

Figure 11.4 Lateral bending (lateral flexion) produces rotation of the lower cervical spine around the longitudinal axis of the cervical spine. (Courtesy of Dave Williams M.F.A.)

This telescoping translation occurs because the facets of the cervical vertebrae ride up on each other. (Figure 11.5) These two examples of motion coupling lend some additional mobility (and in turn some decreased stability) to the cervical spine. The cervical spine is thus most stable in a neutral position, where joint surfaces are most congruent.

2. Joints between vertebral bodies

In addition to the zygapophyseal joints, each vertebral body beginning at C2–C3 is connected by yet another articulation. The joints between the vertebral bodies at C2 through C7 are amphiarthrodial, with less movable articulations connected by a fibro-cartilage disk. The disks effectively limit the multi-axial range of motion of the vertebral functional unit. The superior surfaces of the cervical vertebral bodies are unique in that they are somewhat concave. This is due to the uncinate processes, which are bony protuberances that form a ridge along the lateral superior surfaces of the cervical bodies. These processes function to allow each cervical body to sit into the concave surface of the vertebral body below, creating a second articulation called the uncovertebral joint.

Uncovertebral joints are not typically considered true synovial joints but are theorized to contribute to shear force resistance in flexion, extension, and lateral flexion of the cervical spine. The uncinate processes also prevent excessive motion coupling, adding to the stability of each motion segment (Nordin and Frankel, 2001).

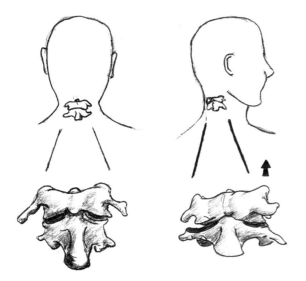

Figure 11.5 *Rotation of the cervical spine around a longitudinal axis will result in upward translation of the head at C1–C2. (Courtesy of Dave Williams M.F.A.)*

Collectively, C1–occiput, C1–C2 and the C3–C7 disks permit about one hundred forty degrees of flexion and extension and about forty-five degrees of lateral flexion to each side. Active rotation (longitudinal axis) may exceed one hundred eighty degrees in some individuals, with passive motion (external load applied) approaching two hundred degrees of rotation in some individuals (Mercer, 2004).

C. The cervical spine intervertebral disk

The intervertebral disks are essential for decreasing and distributing loads across the vertebral bodies. These disk structures create a stable bone-disk-bone interface that is able to resist both compressive and tensile stresses acting on the spine during cervical spine motions. At the same time, the presence of a disk between the bony elements permits a level of mobility and flexibility that would otherwise be impossible. While the overall components of the intervertebral disks are consistent throughout the spine, there are several key differences between the cervical and lumbar disks that require attention. Please refer to Chapter 12 for a detailed anatomical description of the intervertebral disk in the lumbar spine.

The intervertebral disks of the cervical region contain less obvious rings or layers of annular fibers, as well as a smaller proportion of gelatinous nuclear material (or nucleus pulposus) than the disks in the lumbar spine. In addition, cervical disk relative height is proportionally greater than in the lumbar spine, and the disk does not extend to the lateral border of the vertebral bodies due to the presence of the uncinate processes. The seven vertebrae of the cervical spine permit more mobility around all three principal body axes than do the lumbar spine but with less stability.

D. Ligaments of the cervical spine

1. Ligaments of the atlantoaxial-occipital complex

The ligaments of the cervical spine are important for a balance of both stability and motion. Most spinal ligaments have a high type I collagen content, which limits their extensibility during spine motion. The ligaments surrounding the occiput, the atlas, and the axis help dictate the range of motion of the cervical spine. The dense anterior atlanto-occipital ligament (membrane) extends from the superior surface of the anterior arch of the atlas to the anterior margin of the foramen magnum. (Figure 11.6a) It is considered an extension of the anterior longitudinal ligament. The posterior atlanto-occipital ligament (membrane) (not pictured) spans the displacement between the posterior arch of the atlas and the posterior margin of the foramen magnum, similar to the ligamentum flavum in the lower cervical spine. The dense alar ligaments extend from the superolateral aspect of the dens (C2) to the occipital condyles and limit rotation of the cranium at the atlas-skull interface. Human cadaver data indicate that rotation around the longitudinal axis increases in both directions if either the left or right side alar ligament is transected or ruptured (Panjabi et al., 1991).

The cruciform ligament is comprised of a transverse and longitudinal ligament. The transverse component (a.k.a. transverse ligament of the atlas) arches across the atlas posterior to the dens and prevents the dens from moving backward into the spinal cord. The two transverse ligament fiber layers cross at about thirty degrees relative to horizontal in the middle and transition into fibrocartilage at the juncture where they meet the dens (Saldinger et al., 1990). The longitudinal portion of the cruciform ligament plays a much lesser role in preventing posterior translation of the dens but may assist in stabilizing C1 and C2. (Figure 11.6b)

A strong dense ligament fixed to the dorsal surface of the axis is known as the tectorial membrane, which passes posterior to the cruciform ligament and attaches to the anterior border of the foramen magnum. It is also known as the cranial extension of the posterior longitudinal ligament. (Figure 11.6c)

Some lesser ligaments of the cervicocranium region include the apical dental ligament, which is a thin fibrous cord extending from the tip of the dens to the anterior margin of the foramen magnum; the accessory ligaments that extend from near the base of the body of the dens to each lateral mass of the atlas; and the anterior and posterior atlantoaxial ligaments (Harris and Edeiken-Monroe, 1987).

2. Ligaments of the lower cervical spine

The lower cervical vertebrae C3–C7 have ligaments with less specific functions and are present throughout the cervical area. The ligamentum nuchae extends deep into the neck, attaching to the spinous process of the cervical segments which forms a septum between the muscles on each side of the posterior aspect of the neck. A component of the ligamentum nuchae is the supraspinous ligament, a strong fibrous ligament that connects the apices of the spinous process of C6, C7, and sometimes T1 to the external occipital protuberance of the skull. The dorsal raphe component of ligamentum nuchae is comprised of

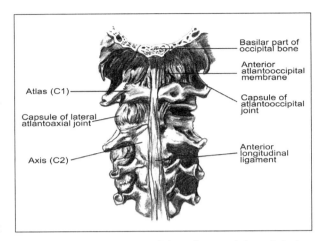

Figure 11.6a *Ligaments of the atlantoaxial-occipital, the anterior longitudinal ligament and the ligamentum flavum. (Courtesy of Dave Williams M.F.A.)*

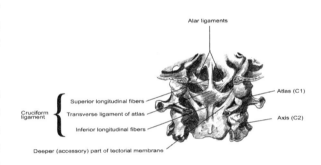

Figure 11.6b *Cruciform and alar ligaments surrounding and stabilizing the dens. (Courtesy of Dave Williams M.F.A.)*

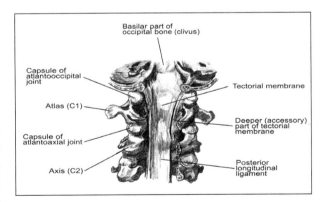

Figure 11.6c *Tectorial membrane—extension of posterior longitudinal ligament. (Courtesy of Dave Williams M.F.A.)*

tendon tissue and serves as an attachment site for several large muscles (Mercer, 2004). Ligamentum nuchae has been postulated to serve to counteract the forward bending moment of the cervical spine produced by the weight of the head link, and tension is increased in this ligament as the neck is flexed forward. The importance of this ligamentum nuchae function has recently been questioned by Mercer (2004). In certain areas, ligamentum nuchae may contain up to 75% elastin fibers which markedly increases ligament elasticity (Frank et al., 1987).

The interspinous ligaments are thin membranous structures that connect adjacent spinous processes, extending from the base of the skull to the tip of each spinous process. The thick, dense, broad structure that connects the laminae of adjacent vertebra is the ligamentum flavum, a highly elastic ligament that allows for flexion and extension without impingement of the spinal cord. There exists a two-to-one ratio of elastin (66%) to collagen fibers in the ligamentum flavum, and this ligament is able to protect the spinal nerve roots from mechanical impingement by pre-stressing the functional unit (motion segment) in compression and therefore providing intrinsic spine stability much in the same way that rebar reinforces stability in tension slab concrete.

Two important ligaments which help to stabilize the cervical spine are the anterior and posterior longitudinal ligaments. The anterior longitudinal ligament (ALL) extends from the anterior inferior surface of the axis to the sacrum, running along the vertebral column on the anterior side of the vertebral bodies. The ALL is the strongest single ligament of the spine. In addition, it attaches loosely to the intervertebral disk and is the only ligament that provides significant resistance to cervical spine extension. The posterior longitudinal ligament (PLL) lies on the dorsal side of the vertebral bodies just in front of the spinal cord extending from the axis to the sacrum. When coupled with the other posterior ligaments, the PLL provides resistance to cervical spine flexion. (Figure 11.7) In addition, the PLL is thickest in the cervical spine region and contributes significantly to protecting the spinal cord from posterior disk herniation and protrusion of nuclear material against the spinal cord thecal sac. Finally, the intertransverse ligaments span between the transverse processes and provide resistance to contralateral lateral flexion.

It is important to understand and fully appreciate that for damage to occur to spinal ligaments, the movement of the spine or its components must exceed the normal range of motion of one or more functional spinal units. This can happen in the cervical spine and is commonly called a lig-

ament sprain. The term sprain is not a biomechanical term. The most appropriate term should be a ligament "strain" as per the engineering and biomechanics disciplines. In a ligament strain, when functional spinal units or portions of these units exceed the normal range of motion, ligament tissue length exceeds the elastic zone and enters into the plastic zone. If the ligament strain increases due to a tension stress, a portion of, or the entire ligament may be brought to the ultimate failure/rupture point as discussed in further detail in chapter 7 of this text. However, in many minor accidents or low speed collisions, the range of motion of joints remains well within the normal ROM and although muscle strain may still occur, ligament strain or sprain will not result.

E. Neurovascular structures in the cervical region

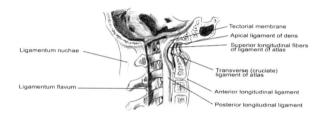

Figure 11.7 *Ligaments of C3-C7. (Courtesy of Dave Williams M.F.A.)*

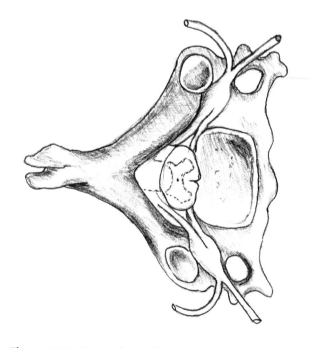

Figure 11.8 *Cervical spinal nerves exiting via intervertebral foramina. Transverse plane view. (Courtesy of Dave Williams M.F.A.)*

1. Spinal cord and spinal nerves

A portion of the central nervous system (i.e., the spinal cord) is enclosed in the vertebral column of the cervical spine. It consists of nerve cells and bundles of nerves connecting all parts of the body to the brain. The spinal cord extends from the medulla oblongata at the upper border of the atlas (C1) to the level of the first or second lumbar vertebra. The spinal nerves are named according to their exit points from the spinal cord. There are eight pairs of cervical spinal nerves (C1 to C8) exiting through the intervertebral foramina between each vertebral body. (Figure 11.8) Each spinal nerve connects to the spinal cord on each side by two roots: the dorsal and the ventral. Each root forms from a series of rootlets that attach along the whole length of the corresponding spinal cord segment. In the cervical spine, the intervertebral nerve roots come together to form a cervical and a brachial plexus (plexi of peripheral nerves). Please refer to Chapter 8 for a more detailed discussion of the structures of the central and peripheral nervous systems.

2. Arteries

The arteries of the cervical spine are more vulnerable to trauma insult because of their proximity to the surface of the neck (versus deep arteries that supply the lumbar spine) and because forced or voluntary motion may damage one set of arteries that supply the cervical spine.

There are three major pairs of arteries supplying blood to the head and neck that run adjacent to or through the cervical spine: the common carotid arteries (which bifurcate into the internal and external carotids), the vertebral arteries, and the thyrocervical-costocervical trunks. The vertebral arteries spring from the subclavian arteries at the root of the neck and ascend through foramina of the vertebral transverse processes of the cervical vertebrae to enter the skull through the foramen magnum. In route, they send anterior and posterior branches to the cervical spinal cord and some deep structures of the neck. (Figure 11.9) These arteries have been injured in cases of hyperextension most commonly combined with rotation resulting from a compression load applied between C1 and the occiput during these neck motions. This has occurred during chiropractic manipulation of the cervical spine. Furthermore, I was retained on one case involving a middle-school wrestler and leading to quadriplegia.

Within the cranium, the right and left vertebral arteries join to form the basilar artery, which ascends along the anterior aspect of the brain stem, giving off branches to the cerebellum, pons, and inner ear structures. The Circle of Willis unites the brain's anterior and posterior blood supplies and is formed by the posterior communicating

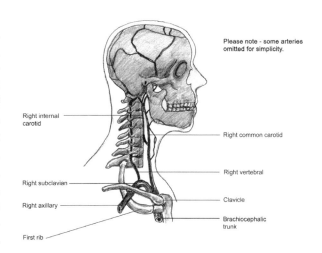

Please note - some arteries omitted for simplicity.

Right internal carotid

Right subclavian

Right axillary

First rib

Right common carotid

Right vertebral

Clavicle

Brachiocephalic trunk

Figure 11.9 Cervical arteries. (Courtesy of Dave Williams M.F.A.)

arteries connecting to the posterior cerebral arteries and the middle cerebral arteries anteriorly.

3. Veins

Most blood being drained from the head and neck is collected by three pairs of veins: the external jugular, the internal jugular, and the vertebral veins. The vertebral veins run adjacent to the vertebral arteries down through the foramina of the cervical transverse processes and join the left and right brachycephalic veins at the base of the neck. (Figure 11.10) These veins principally drain only the cervical vertebrae, the spinal cord, and some small neck muscles.

F. Cervical spine musculature

The strength and control of the muscles along the cervical spine are important in maintaining head and neck posture. These muscles or muscle elements may aid in removing stress from the bony vertebral elements. On the other hand, imbalances in the cervical musculature can effectively contribute to postural problems, pain, and spine degeneration. Many of the cervical muscles work both individually and in concert with each other to produce movements of the cervical spine. During various motions of the neck, bending moments are applied to the vertebral bodies and skull as muscle elements produce flexion and extension, lateral flexion, and rotation.

1. Flexor musculature

Flexor muscles are situated at the anterior and lateral aspect of the cervical spine and include the *sternocleido-mastoid, longus colli, longus capitis*, and the *scalenes*.

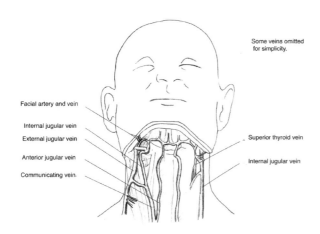

Figure 11.10 Cervical veins. (Courtesy of Dave Williams M.F.A.)

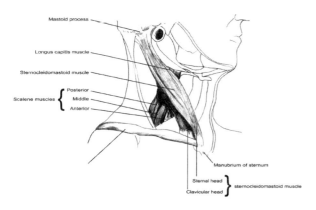

Figure 11.11 Cervical musculature which participates in flexion or lateral flexion. The scalenes also may assist in respiration (inhalation). (Courtesy of Dave Williams M.F.A.)

(Figure 11.11) Anterior musculature will produce flexion in the sagittal plane when active bilaterally. Unilateral activity produces lateral flexion or bending the neck to the left or right side with coupled rotation around the longitudinal axis (horizontal plane motion). The *sternocleidomastoid* (SCM) is a large two-headed muscle with parts on either side of the neck. This muscle passes from the medial clavicle and the manubrium of the sternum to the mastoid process of the lateral half of the superior nuchal line. It is the prime mover of neck flexion and will resist forced cervical spine extension. Contraction of both left and right muscle heads causes neck flexion, and if acting alone each left or right SCM muscle will rotate the chin towards the shoulder on the opposite side (contralateral rotation) and tilt (laterally flex) the head to its own side (ipsilateral flexion).

The *longus colli* and *longus capitis* are located deep in the anterior neck. The *longus colli* has a complicated arrangement. It is a triangular muscle with the inferior fibers passing superiolaterally, while the superior fibers pass superiomedially and the intermediate fibers travel straight from lower cervical levels to upper cervical segments. The *longus colli* flexes the neck and causes ipsilateral lateral flexion and rotation of the cervical spine. The *longus capitis* spans the neck superiomedially from cervical transverse processes (C3–C6) to the basilar part of the occipital bone and serves to produce flexion of the cervical spine and ipsilateral rotation of the head. *Longus colli* and *longus capitis*, in addition to SCM muscles, are also active in protection of anterior cervical spine structures during forced neck extension motions.

The scalene muscles are three deeply positioned muscles on each side region of the neck with their origins on the transverse processes of the cervical vertebrae. This lateral muscle group usually acts together to laterally flex and stabilize the neck. Additionally, the *scalenes* are able to elevate the ribs as accessory respiration muscles by pulling upward on their distal (lower) rib attachments.

2. Extensor musculature

Several small muscles make up the deep extensors of the cervical spine. Deeply situated in the posterior cervical area below the occipital region of the skull are the suboccipital muscles: a group of four muscles that spans the distance from C2 to C1 or to the skull occiput. When acting in concert, their actions are to extend the upper cervical spine with ipsilateral rotation and lateral flexion of the neck. The suboccipital triangle is an anatomical landmark comprised of the suboccipital: deep within this triangle are the vertebral arteries and the suboccipital nerves. (Figure 11.12a) The multifidi muscles are also considered extensors with attachments on the transverse processes and the spinous processes of vertebrae from C2 on down. Unilateral shortening produces ipsilateral lateral flexion and contralateral rotation of the cervical spine.

Finally, the deep rotators (collective term) also attach to the transverse and spinous processes from C2 on down and serve to extend the cervical spine and produce contralateral rotation.

Moving outward (more superficial), the next group of extensor muscles occupies the space between the spinous processes of the cervical vertebrae: the *semispinalis capitis* and *semispinalis cervicis* muscles. (Figure 11.12b) They are considered the prime movers for cervical spine extension. The *semispinalis capitis* inserts centrally on the occipital bone of the skull between the superior and inferior nuchal lines. Bilaterally it produces extension of the cervical spine and accentuates the normal cervical lordosis with minimal lateral flexion when acting unilaterally.

A large flat muscle group that covers the superiomedial aspect of the posterior neck is the splenius muscle group, including the *splenius capitis* and *splenius cervicis*. These muscles extend the cervical spine when acting bilaterally and produce unilateral lateral flexion when acting on only one side.

The erector spinae muscle group also spans and acts to extend the cervical spine. These bilateral muscles consist of three subgroups: (1) *iliocostalis cervicis* and *iliocostalis thoracis*, (2) *longissimus cervicis* and *longissimus thoracis*, and (3) *spinalis cervicis* and *spinalis thoracis*. These muscles, in addition to extending the cervical spine,

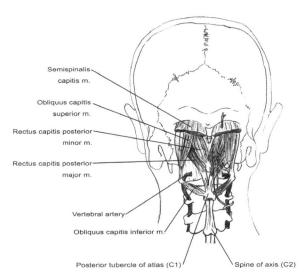

Figure 11.12a *Cervical extensor musculature (deep). (Courtesy of Dave Williams M.F.A.)*

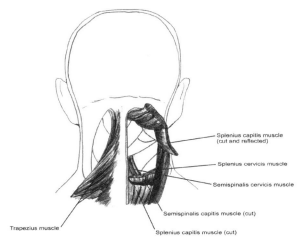

Figure 11.12b *Cervical extensor musculature (superficial and intermediate layers). (Courtesy of Dave Williams M.F.A.)*

will produce ipsilateral flexion when acting on only one side. Finally, the superior portions of left and right side trapezius muscle are able to act as strong cervical spine extensors when the scapulae (shoulder blades) are stabilized on the thorax by contracting muscles.

11.3 Loading to the Cervical Spine Elements

A. Direct impact, crush, lacerations, and penetrations

Direct loading to the cervical spine is a rare occurrence. In most cases of direct crush or laceration, there is extensive additional damage to other parts of the body, particularly the head. However, isolated blunt or penetrating traumas are possible and can result in bone fracture, musculo-tendon rupture, vascular disruption, or neurological compromise.

Criminal acts involving laceration of the neck or strangulation of a victim provide other examples of direct loading to the cervical spine. Hyoid bone fracture is common in strangulation produced by the perpetrator's hands. Furthermore, an anterior neck load applied even for a short duration strangulation or a blunt force-crush trauma applied to the anterior neck may result in swelling and closure of the trachea and consequent suffocation.

B. Indirect loading (forces, moments, and torques)

There are two ways in which loads may be imposed to the cervical spine by an indirect source. Impact to the head may impose a compression or bending load to the cervical spine that places stress on cervical structures. Serious injuries to the cervical spine are usually the result of indirect loading produced by significant impact to the head (Clark et al., 1988). In significant motor vehicle accidents, the neck (cervical spine) may be subject to rotational moments in flexion, extension, and lateral flexion resulting from head impact, as well as linear loads applied to the head that result in compression, tension, and shear stresses within the c-spine. These loads can result in damage to the internal structures of the cervical spine as the result of both linear and angular accelerations. In addition, inertial loading due to a change in angular velocity of the head, such as the case of severe whiplash, has the potential to cause injury without head impact. Injuries from whiplash are most often referred to as cervical sprain, soft tissue injury, flexion-extension injury, or acceleration-deceleration injury (Teasell, 1993) and are sometimes termed whiplash associated disorders or WAD symptoms. In this text, loading due to whiplash associated injury is referred to as inertial loading.

Inertial loading injury may also result in failure of bony elements of the cervical spine in addition to soft tissue trauma. In motor vehicle impacts, at the time of impact, the vehicle and seat are accelerated in one direction while, in accord with Newton's first law of motion, the head and torso links possessing inertia stay where they are located until forces, moments, and torques act upon these links. The torso is normally restrained by the seat back in a rear collision, the restraint system in a frontal collision, or the side door panel in a near side collision. The head however is free to move in frontal and side impact collisions, and a transfer of linear and angular momentum may increase angular and linear accelerations of the head. The function of the head rest is to prevent hyperextension in a rear impact collision as the initial movement of the head is backwards relative to the vehicle. Sports activities involving contact with other players, such as football, rugby, or ice hockey, may expose the cervical spine to very large inertial loads. In addition to cervical spine injury, brain injury may result if the inertial loading approaches a significant level so as to result in high level head link angular accelerations. (Chapter 9)

These injuries due to inertial loading are directly dependent upon the delta velocity, acceleration level, and time duration of the loading. Current experimental research literature indicates that very low impact collisions (regardless of force or acceleration vector direction) do not produce inertial loading that results in any cervical spine injury (Arbogast, K., 2009; Brault et al., 1998; Carlsson, et al., 2010; Castro et al., 1997, Castro et al., 2001; Hannon and Knapp, 2003; Hartwig, et al., 2004; Kaneoka et al., 1999; Kaneoka et al., 2007; Malik et al., 2004; Soloman, 2005; Yang et al., 2003). A review of low impact loading literature and WAD symptoms is beyond the scope of this text. Additionally, there has been considerable debate regarding the epidemiological versus the biomechanics findings regarding acute or chronic whiplash associated disorder in low impact collisions.

1. Hyperflexion resulting from head impact or high magnitude inertial loading

Hyperflexion injuries are caused by forward rotation and translation of a cervical vertebra in the sagittal plane. They result from simultaneous distraction of the posterior columns (structures) and compression of the anterior columns (vertebral bodies) of the spine. Trauma may occur in bony elements as well as within soft tissue. Direct trauma to the head when the cervical spine is in a flexed position causes most flexion injuries. Typically, less severe injuries result when the cervical spine was originally in a neutral position and is then driven into a flexed position. Forced flexion acts opposite that of forced extension, applying compressive loads to the anterior elements and tensile forces to the posterior elements of the cervical spine. The anterior structures resisting flexion are the intervertebral disks and vertebral bodies, whereas the posterior structures stretched in hyperflexion (tension loading) are the zygapophyseal joint capsules, articular pillars, posterior ligaments, and the posterior neck muscles. At the atlantoaxial joint, the transverse component of the cruciform ligament, and to a lesser degree the left and right alar ligaments, will be stressed as the atlas attempts to move anteriorly to the axis during forced cervical flexion. The transverse component of the cruciform may fail, but more commonly a type II dens fracture failure results (the dens usually being the weak link).

Anterior subluxation resulting from neck hyperflexion may produce disruption of the posterior ligament complex and the zygapophyseal joint capsules. A rationale exists for the posterior portion of the annulus fibrosus of the intervertebral disk to be disrupted during high flexion loads due to high level tension stresses. However, most of the disk, the anterior longitudinal ligament, will experience only manageable levels of loading. The disruption of soft tissue structures may allow the vertebra above the injury site to rotate or slide anteriorly over the subjacent vertebra.

2. Hyperextension resulting from head impact or high magnitude inertial loading

Extreme hyperextension may result from an impact imposed upon the face, mandible, or forehead that propels the head backwards or may result from severe inertial loading. When a hyperextension load acting at the upper cervical spine is transmitted to the anterior arch of C1, an avulsion (tension) fracture of the anterior arch of C1 may result. The force will also load the anterior atlantoaxial ligament, which may result in a transverse fracture of the arch or failure of the anterior tubercle of the C1 vertebra. Tension stresses are applied to anterior structures and compression stresses act on the posterior structures during forced cervical hyperextension. The anterior structures include the ALL, the anterior disk, the anterior cervical muscles, and the dens of C2 (due to a bending load imposed by the anterior ring of C1 vertebra).

3. Lateral flexion resulting from head impact or high magnitude inertial loading

Lateral flexion of the cervical spine between C2 and C7 is coupled to rotation around a longitudinal axis at the cervical spine. The normal range of motion (ROM) is approximately forty to forty-five degrees of lateral flexion on each side (Mercer, 2004). Forced lateral flexion of the cervical spine may present a risk of injury in part determined by the extent to which lateral flexion-rotation coupling motion occurs. If physiological lateral flexion ROM is exceeded, the zygapophyseal joint capsules on both sides will be put at the greatest risk from the resulting axial torque. If there is little motion coupling, lateral flexion will compress the ipsilateral zygapophyseal joints (possible fracture/failure) and distract the contralateral zygapophyseal joint (possible ligament capsule strain failure) (Barnsley, Lord, and Bogduk, 1993).

4. Combination loading

Injury can also occur due to a combination of rotation and either extreme flexion or extreme extension. Extreme flexion with rotation (longitudinal axis) causes a distraction of the zygapophyseal joints. The zygapophyseal joints opposite the direction of extreme rotation may become dislocated, or fracture failure of bony elements may occur. Simultaneous extreme extension and rotation will create large compressive and bending loads upon the vertebral arch portion of the posterior elements, resulting in possible fracture failure.

Vertical compression injuries are more likely to result from an axial force delivered to the skull and indirectly to the spinal column when the cervical spine is straightened and the normal lordotic curve of the cervical spine is absent prior to impact. The compression load is transmitted from the vertex of the skull through the occipital condyles to the spine. The vertical forces applied to the head vertex may result from motor vehicle accidents (e.g., vehicle rollovers), sports injuries, and falling objects. Some evidence indicates that a straight cervical spine acted upon by an axial compression load will undergo buckling resulting in significant bone and spinal cord injuries. One reason that football players are told by their coaches to keep their heads up in tackling a ball carrier is to maintain normal cervical lordosis and therefore decrease probability of high compression loads being imposed to the cervical spine during head-helmet impact. Burnstein and Wright (1994) describe a deceleration (Average Deceleration = Velocity^2/2 x distance) occurring when the vertex of the head strikes a barrier with a straight cervical spine orientation. Under such circumstances, the skull restricts the C1 vertebra which in turn is pushed toward the head by the inferior cervical vertebrae ending at C7. The C7

vertebra therefore imposes a force on the torso mass to decelerate its velocity because it is moving slower than the torso (Burnstein and Wright, 1994). Burnstein and Wright estimate that the straight cervical spine is able to compress about 2 centimeters before it will buckle and suffer immediate hyperflexion. The authors further estimate that the compression of 2.0 cm (depending upon biological individuality) will require about 2,000 Newtons (450 pounds) and any force that exceeds this level will result in failure of an intervertebral body or disk or multiple vertebral functional units. A lay term for this mechanism of injury is known at the "pile driver effect." An alternative and less complex explanation for this effect is that a barrier or another mass brings the head and neck to an abrupt stop and a good portion of the body's mass wants to keep moving in the same direction and at the same velocity. The result is that the cervical spine column is compressed between the relatively stationary head (skull) and a good portion of the body's mass below the neck resulting in a "cervical spinal column collapse."

11.4 Cervical Spine Trauma

The cervical spine is susceptible to injury in many events because it is often unrestrained. Injuries that occur to the cervical spine are usually a result of a violent force that causes bending, tension, or compression through either direct or indirect loading. Vertebral fractures or injury to soft tissues may result. Cervical spine injuries can be catastrophic and cause paralysis, or they may only cause mild pain and soreness.

Neck pain is a commonly reported symptom in motor vehicle accidents. Pain reports from patients can range from dull, constant, and aching to sharp and provoked by neck movement. A frequent association due to the inertial loading in whiplash motions is neck stiffness and a decrease in the cervical range of motion. Sometimes the pain radiates to the head, shoulder, arm, or interscapular region. These same symptoms result from delayed onset muscle soreness (DOMS) that one might experience from a good workout. Yet when muscle damage is appreciable, swelling and hemorrhage result, leading to what is sometimes termed a muscle strain. Muscle strain may occur within the normal ROM, while ligament injury is believed to only occur when the normal ROM of the cervical spine is exceeded.

Apart from muscle pain, headaches are frequently reported following cervical trauma. Occipital pain has been reported, radiating anteriorly into the temporal or orbital regions. Visual and balance disturbances are other complaints, leading to dizziness, nausea, or confusion. Important considerations for the biomechanist and the physician are the probable causes for such a wide variety of complaints. Direct head impact clearly represents etiology for these neurological symptoms, but significant very high level inertial (non-contact) loading has also been associated with these same reported symptoms.

The cervical spine is composed of a large number of structures that have the potential for injury and subsequent pain. This author's objective in the following section is to identify and describe different types of trauma, the tolerance limits of specific structures (where data are available), and possible sources of pain in cervical spine trauma.

A. Bony elements

There are several types of bone fractures that are affected by the vertebral structure, rate of loading, and the direction of the loading vector. Bone fractures may occur due to a single loading mode or result from combined loading. An opinion regarding mechanisms of bone injury must be undertaken carefully because observed head motion by witnesses or from video may occur subsequent to the actual injury mechanism (Myers et al., 1994; Whiting and Zernicke, 1998). Documented observed motion does present a line of evidence. However, bone fracture patterns and the magnitude and direction of displaced bone fragments lodged within soft tissue are also important in a biomechanical analysis of the injury mechanism.

1. Classifications of fractures

a. Extreme flexion fractures

i. Wedge fracture

A wedge fracture (Figure 11.13) occurs when a sufficient load is produced upon the anterior portion of two vertebral bodies, resulting in fracture failure. The posterior ligamentous complex will either remain intact or be partially or fully disrupted. In a non-displaced wedge fracture, associated neurologic injury is uncommon. However, in cervical spine displaced wedge fractures, retropulsed fragments of the posterior vertebral body may impinge upon or enter the spinal cord, resulting in anterior cord syndrome, and depending upon the severity of the displacement, quadriplegia may result.

ii. Flexion teardrop fracture

The flexion teardrop fracture is defined by injury to the posterior and anterior ligaments, the disruption of the zygapophyseal joints, and the formation of a large triangular fragment from the anterioinferior portion of the vertebral body (Greenspan, 1992). (Figure 11.14) The mechanism of injury is severe cervical spine hyperflexion, similar to the wedge fracture. However, this injury is

very unstable, and in contrast to the simple non-displaced wedge fracture, a flexion teardrop fracture may result in immediate quadriplegia below the lesion site as the vertebral body is retropulsed backwards into the spinal canal. Acute anterior cord syndrome is a common result, with a loss in peripheral pain and temperature distinction in addition to the quadriplegia. The dorsal column afferent tracts are usually maintained (kinesthesis) (Greenspan, 1992). In children and young adolescents, this same flexion mechanism may result in flexion-produced spinal cord injury without radiographic abnormality (SCIWORA) due to the flexibility of the cervical spine musculature. Under these circumstances, no fractures occur; however neurological damage is present.

iii. Clay-shoveler's fracture

The clay-shoveler's fracture is an avulsion fracture (tension mechanism) of the C6, C7, or T1 spinous processes and is illustrated in Figure 11.15. This fracture occurs due to the interspinous and supraspinous ligaments opposing the extreme flexion of the neck. The ligaments are stretched and pull on the spinous processes, causing enough force to cause vertical or oblique fracture lines in these spinous processes. The neural canal containing the spinal cord is not disrupted and this fracture is considered to be stable.

iv. Flexion bilateral zygapophyseal dislocation

The bilateral zygapophyseal dislocation is the result of an anterior displacement of a superior vertebra over its sub-adjacent inferior vertebra. (Figure 11.16) The inferior facets of the vertebra above pass up and over the superior facets of the vertebra below. Soft tissues (muscles and ligaments) exert strong tension forces to produce an interlocking of facets which is easily observed on a lateral view projection radiograph. Spinal cord damage is probable due to ligamentous injury with tears, either partial or complete, to the posterior longitudinal ligament and the anterior longitudinal ligament. The intervertebral disk may also be disrupted (Greenspan, 1992). There may be small fractures between the zygapophyseal joints, but they are considered clinically insignificant compared to the nervous tissue damage.

b. Hyperextension fractures

i. Atlas (C1) posterior arch fracture

The isolated fracture of the posterior arch of C1 results from compression of the posterior arch of C1 between the occiput and the posterior arch of the axis during extreme hyperextension. (Figure 11.17) This fracture may occur alone or with other fractures. Displacement of fragments is minimal. Neither neurologic deficit nor atlanto-axial instability is associated with a posterior atlantal arch

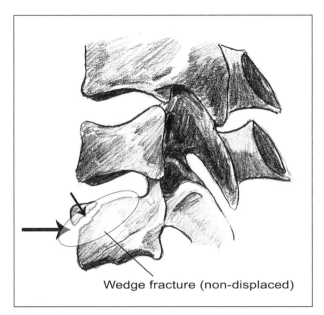

Figure 11.13 *Wedge fracture (non-displaced). (Courtesy of Dave Williams M.F.A.)*

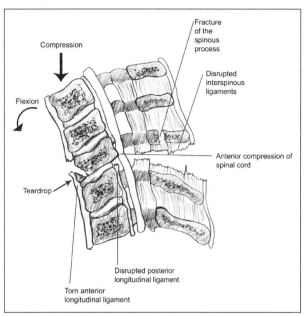

Figure 11.14 *Flexion teardrop fracture of C4. (Courtesy of Dave Williams M.F.A.)*

Figure 11.15 *Clay-shoveler's fracture. (Courtesy of Dave Williams M.F.A.)*

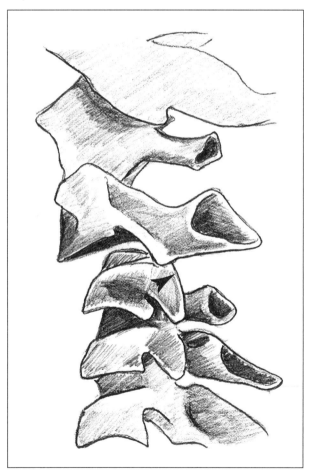

Figure 11.16 *Flexion bilateral zygapophyseal dislocation. (Courtesy of Dave Williams M.F.A.)*

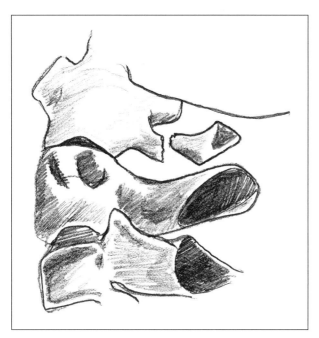

Figure 11.17 *C1 posterior arch fracture. (Courtesy of Dave Williams M.F.A.)*

Figure 11.18 *Extension teardrop fracture (always at C2). (Courtesy of Dave Williams M.F.A.)*

fracture when this fracture occurs in isolation.

ii. Extension teardrop fracture

The extension teardrop fracture involves the anterior inferior corner of the axis (C2) that results in a separate triangular fragment avulsed at the site of insertion of the intact anterior longitudinal ligament during extreme hyperextension. (Figure 11.18) This fracture is more common in older patients with osteoporosis or degenerative disease of the spine. More than one segment of the vertebral body of the axis or C3 may be fractured as well (Greenspan, 1992). This is a stable fracture without neurological complications.

iii. Laminar fracture

A laminar fracture involves the posterior arch portion that is between the articular masses and the spinous process that results from compression of the lamina (bending load) between the lamina of the superior and inferior vertebrae during forced hyperextension of the cervical spine (Harris and Edeiken-Monroe, 1987). This injury is illustrated in Figure 11.19. The mechanism of injury is similar to the described C1 posterior arch fracture but occurs on lower vertebrae and with a greater generated moment due to a much longer posterior element moment arm (spinous process). This uncommon fracture is mechanically stable usually without neurological deficit because the anterior column (vertebral bodies) and the lateral zygapophyseal joints are still intact. However, if laminar fragments impinge upon the spinal cord, neurological complications will result.

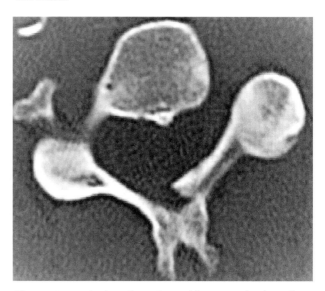

Figure 11.19 *Isolated uni-lateral laminar displaced fracture in the middle cervical spine. Public Domain-Fair Use*

iv. Traumatic spondylolisthesis in the cervical spine

Traumatic spondylolisthesis refers to a bilateral fracture usually of the pars interarticularis of C2 during forced cervical hyperextension. (Figure 11.20) There are three types of traumatic spondylolisthesis (TS) described by Effendi et al. (1981). Type I is an isolated hairline fracture of the C2 ring with minimal displacement and with a normal intervertebral disk. The type II fracture is characterized by an abnormal C2 to C3 disk and displacement of the anterior segment of C2 and is thought to involve a higher hyperextension moment (extension bending load). The force vector that produces this hyperextension mechanism of injury (e.g., forehead to the windshield—MVA) will also produce a compression load to the C2 vertebrae in addition to the bending load imposed upon the upper cervical column (Harris and Edeiken-Monroe, 1987).

The mechanism of injury attributed to the type III may be different or variable (based on case reports). Effendi (1981) ascribes this type III TS to initial hyperflexion followed by rebound hyperextension resulting in anterior displacement of a C2 body component and bilateral zygapophyseal joint dislocation (C2-C3). Some authors ascribe all three types of TS to a hyperextension mechanism only (Harris and Edeiken-Monroe, 1987).

Traumatic spondylolisthesis has also been termed a hangman's fracture. Although the hangman's fracture (human execution) pattern may be similar, a judicial hanging also results in significant distraction of the cervical spine due to the body's initial drop (vertical momentum of the body) in addition to the forced hyperextension produced by the rope knot most commonly placed under the chin. This cervical distraction of the upper cervical spine results in extreme anterior dislocation of the axis with subsequent tearing transection of the spinal cord (invariably a poor prognosis) (Greenspan, 1992).

v. Hyperextension dislocation and hyperextension fracture dislocation

Hyperextension dislocation (HD) is poorly understood because the dislocation reduces spontaneously after the removal of the load. Hyperextension dislocation is thought to occur as the result of backward or backward-upward forces applied to the forehead or mid-face (direct loads). The head is driven backwards, and the cervical spine moves into hyperextension from the backward force. The posterior column of the cervical spine is compressed, acting as a fulcrum for the backward rotation. As seen in Figure 11.21, sufficient force may cause a rupture of the anterior longitudinal ligament, and the intervertebral disk may be either detached or disrupted from the inferior

end plate of the dislocated vertebral body. A shear load may also result in posterior displacement and dislocation of the superior vertebra. Severe displacement will pinch the cervical spinal cord between the posterior cortex of the displaced vertebral body, the dura mater, ligamentum flavum, and the vertebra laminae. Once this bending load is removed, the cervical spine spontaneously reduces, and the lateral x-ray may look normal. However, the spinal cord damage remains (Harris and Edeiken-Monroe, 1987). Acute central cervical cord syndrome is a probable outcome from this kind of compression. The reader is referred to Chapter 8 for a more detailed discussion of central cord syndrome.

A similar mechanism of injury is seen in a hyperextension fracture-dislocation of the cervical spine, usually involving rotation of the head on the longitudinal axis. The hyperextension bending load in this case is sufficient to result in fracture-failure of the posterior column (usu-

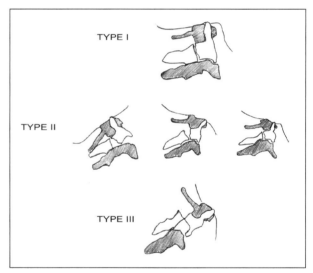

Figure 11.20 *Traumatic spondylolisthesis of the axis (C2). (Courtesy of Dave Williams M.F.A.)*

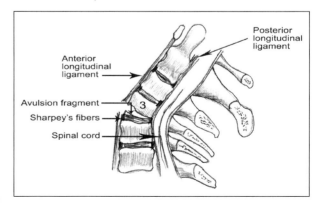

Figure 11.21 *Hyperextension dislocation. Note the rupture of the anterior longitudinal ligament. (Courtesy of Dave Williams M.F.A.)*

ally unilateral due to the rotated head) as compression loads are imposed upon the zygapophyseal joint surfaces. Additionally, there is a rupture of the anterior longitudinal ligament, and there may be an avulsion fracture of the anterior body of one vertebra. Anterior displacement of the vertebra may be 3 to 6 mm (Harris and Edeiken-Monroe, 1987). This is an unstable fracture, and although easily recognized by the trained radiologist as a cervical fracture, it must be differentiated from a flexion injury which can also result in forward displacement of the vertebral body (Harris and Edeiken-Monroe, 1987).

c. Hyperflexion and rotation
i. Unilateral zygapophyseal dislocation and unilateral zygapophyseal fracture dislocation

A unilateral zygapophyseal dislocation (a.k.a. unilateral interfacetal dislocation {UID}) occurs due to simultaneous flexion (mediolateral axis) and longitudinal axis rotation and involves the dislocation of only one zygapophyseal joint. The anterior superior vertebral segment will move over the inferior segment, and the inferior articular process becomes wedged into the intervertebral foramina (Harris and Edeiken-Monroe, 1987) (Figure 11.22) This locks the dislocated facets on one side due to tension elements (ligaments and muscles), and therefore this specific cervical dislocation may be stable. However there is usually damage to the posterior ligamentous complex and the intervertebral disk and non-dislocated zygapophyseal joint may also be disrupted. Foreman and Croft (1988) indicate that when the initial trauma is significant enough to produce neurological injury, the UID should be considered unstable. Sometimes one side of the spinal cord is loaded in shear and compression, with UIDs resulting in Brown-Séquard syndrome which is the result of a trauma lesion on one side of the spinal cord. This condition may result in muscular weakness or even hemiparaplegia on the ipsilateral side of the body with hemianesthesia on the contralateral body side in accord with spinal cord motor and sensory tracts respectively.

Fractures of the dislocated facet surfaces, lamina, and pedicle (unilateral interfacetal fracture dislocation {UIFD}) may also occur, leading to complete structural instability (Harris and Mirvis, 1996).

d. Hyperextension and rotation
i. Pillar fracture

The pillar fracture (Figure 11.23) is a hyperextension and rotation injury that results in a significant compression stress that occurs as the lateral masses on one side of two vertebrae impact each other. This can result in a fracture of the articular mass (a pillar of bone comprising the zygapophyseal facets) between the adjacent counterparts.

Figure 11.22 Unilateral zygapophyseal dislocation (Couresty of Patrick Hannon).

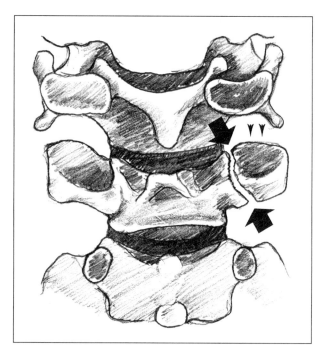

Figure 11.23 Pillar fracture within the cervical spine. (Courtesy of Dave Williams M.F.A.)

This fracture will usually be in a vertical or oblique vertical orientation and usually occurs as a simple or slightly comminuted fracture. It may be a stable or unstable fracture (Greenspan, 1992).

ii. Pedicolaminar fracture-separation (Types I-IV)

The pedicolaminar fracture-separation is a more complex variation of a pillar fracture and is characterized by ipsilateral pedicle and laminar fractures that result in the articular mass (articular pillar) becoming a free-floating body. The mechanism of injury is similar to the pillar fracture, with hyperextension and rotation resulting in a large compressive stress within the pillar. This fracture is classified as a type I, type II, type III, or type IV fracture (Harris and Mirvis, 1996). A type I fracture has minimal or no displacement. The Type II fracture shows a rotation of the free-floating articular mass indicating a loss of zygapophyseal ligament capsule integrity with anterior sliding of the vertebra without disk space narrowing. The type III fracture is similar to the type II fracture with the addition of a narrowing of the intervertebral disk space between the adjacent vertebrae. The type IV fracture involves a rupture of the anterior longitudinal ligament and a comminuted (many pieces) fracture of the articular pillar. In a type IV fracture, the adjacent vertebra above moves anteriorly through the comminuted articular mass along with zygapophyseal joint subluxation or dislocation on the contralateral side (Harris and Mirvis, 1996). (Figure 11.24)

e. Vertical compression fracture
i. Jefferson fracture—C1

The Jefferson burst fracture results from vertical compression of C1 due to an axial load applied to the vertex of the skull (top of the calvarium). There are bilateral fractures of the anterior and posterior arches of C1. The transverse component of the cruciform ligament may remain intact or may be partially or fully disrupted. The fracture is not considered stable (Greenspan, 1992). However, the pieces of bone that fracture will usually not cause damage to the spinal cord because the lateral masses of the atlas will move away from the neural canal. (Figure 11.25)

ii. Burst fracture—C3–C7

The burst fracture in C3–C7 region is a comminuted fracture often times with some retropulsion of vertebral body bony fragments into the neural canal caused by the compressive load. (Figure 11.26) The bony fragments can be displaced in all directions. Since bone is a viscoelastic material, it will absorb more energy and is less likely to fail if loaded quickly. However, if the vertebral body does fail after significant energy has been stored, then a highly comminuted explosive burst fracture will occur in rapid loading, with resulting severe damage to the spinal cord and potential quadriplegia. In similar fashion to the Jefferson fracture, this fracture is produced by an axial load applied to the vertex of the skull. Maintaining a curved column (normal lordosis, i.e., head up) in the cervical spine reduces the probability of this very serious unstable fracture failure.

f. Lateral compression fractures. In cases of lateral flexion, compression fractures can occur on the bent spine concave side, and avulsion (tension) fractures may occur on the convex spine contralateral side. In the upper cervical spine, occipital condyle fractures result from forced lateral flexion that causes an asymmetrical axial load. There is little displacement of these fractures, and

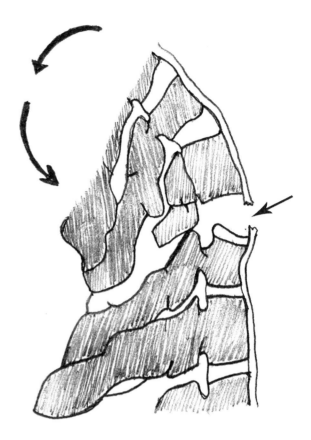

Figure 11.24 *Pedicolaminar fracture–separation (type IV). Note that the anterior longitudinal ligament has ruptured. (Courtesy of Dave Williams M.F.A.)*

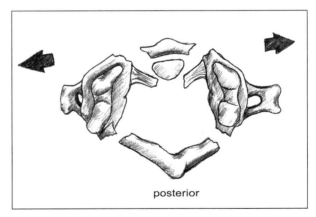

Figure 11.25 *Jefferson fracture–C1. (Courtesy of Dave Williams M.F.A.)*

they are usually vertically oriented. Rarely are neurologic deficits produced (Harris and Mirvis, 1996).

Asymmetric Jefferson fractures of C1 may also result from lateral flexion producing a compression stress on the concave side (pinching of the C1 washer). Ring fractures may occur or a comminuted fracture may occur through the lateral mass of the atlas due to the compression stress (Harris and Mirvis, 1996). Many times only two or three fractures will occur within the C1 ring. However, physicians will still refer to this pathology as a Jefferson fracture.

At lower cervical spine levels, compression of the lateral aspect or a single vertically oriented fracture of the vertebral body may occur in C3–C7. Transverse process fractures may also occur with coincident vertebral arch damage. The uncinate processes of the cervical vertebral body may fracture and may be sheared off from lateral flexion of the cervical spine. These fractures lead to asymmetry of the uncovertebral joint and lateral dislocation of the vertebral body above the uncinate fracture along with disk space disruption (Harris and Mirvis, 1996). These fractures are usually stable (Greenspan, 1992) but may be unstable if the vertebral body or the vertebral arch is significantly displaced. Figure 11.27 illustrates a lateral compression fracture.

g. Occipitoatlantal disassociation and dens fractures. Occipitoatlantal disassociation (OAD) describes any separation of the occipitoatlantal junction. This injury mainly involves the strain or complete failure of the anterior and posterior ligaments, the facet capsules of C1, and the occiput of the skull and ligaments that attach or are in close proximity to the dens of C2 (i.e., alar, longitudinal component of the cruciform and the apical—all of which

probably provide relatively little resistance in a severe occipitoatlantal disassociation). The loading may be the result of loads producing extremes in flexion, hyperextension, lateral flexion, or distraction. When these head and neck motions create loads that exceed the tolerance of these ligaments, there will be disruption and avulsion at C1 and the skull occiput. A partial disassociation (subluxation) is survivable and considered stable (Greenspan, 1992). A complete disassociation will result in immediate death (Harris and Mirvis, 1996). Sometimes OAD is accompanied by atlantoaxial disassociation (tension loading) (Harris and Edeiken-Monroe, 1987).

Odontoid (dens) fractures of the axis may result from significant loads imposed during hyperextension, hyperflexion, lateral flexion, distraction, or any combination of these cervical spine motions. Dens fractures are classified as types I, II, and III. A type I fracture is the avulsion fracture of the tip of the dens (apical ligament tension) and is associated with OAD. The type II fracture is a transverse fracture of the dens near its base but above the axis body and may also be referred to as a high fracture. This fracture is the most common of the three and is limited to the odontoid process without involvement of the accessory ligaments unless the fracture is comminuted. A type II dens fracture is common because a bending load will produce

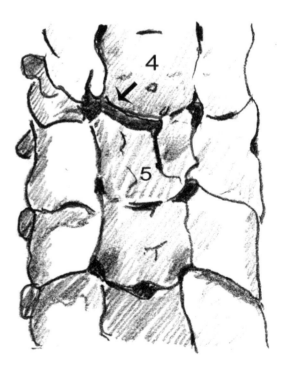

Figure 11.27 Lateral compression fracture. Note the damage of C4 and C5. *(Courtesy of Dave Williams M.F.A.)*

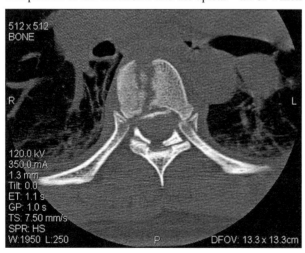

Figure 11.26 Burst fracture. CAT scan of a burst fracture within the thoracic spine. *(Courtesy of Patrick Hannon)*

a fracture at a point on the axis where the area moment of inertia is small and the bending moment arm is large. (See Chapter 4.) The type III fracture (a.k.a. low fracture) is a fracture of the superior portion of the C2 vertebral body and probably also involves a compression stress in addition to a bending load. This type III fracture is more severe and represents an unstable fracture with probable damage to the cervical spinal cord. Figure 11.28 shows the three types of dens fractures.

B. Soft tissues of the cervical spine

1. Ligaments and synovial capsules

A ligament sprain will occur when a joint is forced through an abnormal range of motion and the ligaments of the neck lose some or all integrity. Isolated ligamentous injuries are rare, because muscle elements will fail first and because relatively high loading and joint displacement are required for ligamentous injuries of the cervical spine which usually result in the coincident failure of bony elements.

One notable exception is the failure or loss of integrity of the transverse component of the cruciform ligament, which is responsible for maintaining the position of the dens of C2 within close approximation to the anterior ring of C1. Although a type II dens fracture is still more

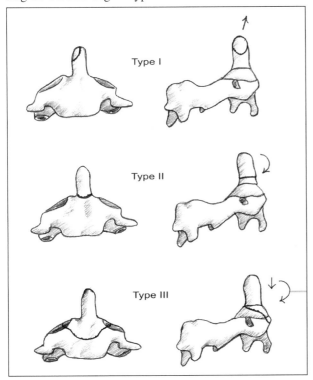

Figure 11.28 *Dens fractures (types I-III). (Courtesy of Dave Williams M.F.A.)*

probable, ligament damage to this cruciform component also may occur due to significant forced neck flexion and is by no means rare in cases of C1–C2 instability. However, these cases must be evaluated carefully due to biological individuality in terms of normal dens translation backward and in terms of competing etiology such as rheumatoid arthritis and Grisel's syndrome (an infectious process). Finally, Down's syndrome children and adults may be predisposed to laxity in the transverse component of the cruciform ligament, and therefore caution must be exercised in activities that require or may lead to forced cervical spine flexion (e.g., sports activities such as a backward roll).

Another site of possible ligament disruption is the zygapophyseal ligament capsule and the associated synovial capsules in addition to the ligament structures that surround the joints between the vertebral bodies of the cervical spine. This trauma is produced in the vast majority of cases through the indirect loading previously described. Without question, indirect loading resulting from *head impact* is higher than is most inertial loading (whiplash mechanism) and is therefore more likely to result in soft tissue injury due to excessive and rapid motion cervical spine excursions in addition to an increased probability of bone fracture failure and joint dislocations (Clark et al., 1974). Pettersson et al. (1997), examined thirty-nine cervical whiplash patients with magnetic resonance imaging (MRI) within fifteen days post motor vehicle collision loading and were not able to document any cases of cervical spine ligament damage.

Panjabi et al. (1998) subjected fresh cadaver cervical spines stripped of muscle elements (preserving osteoligamentous structures) to inertial loading by attaching a biofidelic head to each specimen. Specimens were tested on a sled acceleration apparatus, and the focus of the paper was to propose a new experimental testing model and to measure the dynamic excursion strain of facet capsule ligaments during inertial loading. Although the authors hypothesized ligamentous injury and dynamic (within the elastic zone) strains would be observed during inertial loading, no permanent ligament strain (i.e., injury) was observed on gross examination of the cadaver ligaments. Microscopic examination was not performed. Furthermore, and most importantly, correlations between the sled accelerations (up to 10.5 gs) and ligament strains of the cervical spine were essentially absent in the regression statistical analysis (highest R2 = 0.18) indicating a lack of relationship between loading and ligament strain in the proposed model. Furthermore, in this author's opinion, the model may be further improved by incorporating viscoelastic putty around the cadaver cervical spine physical model to simulate the passive elastic elements of inactivated muscle. This would also serve to further decrease the loading to ligament structures. This Panjabi et al. (1998) physical model may still have some value at much higher levels of inertial whiplash loading where testing of human subjects is necessarily prohibited (Panjabi et al., 1998b). However, at present, this model has not been useful in examining low impact front and rear collisions where experimental test results using live human subjects are available. Such low impact rear and front collision experiments with human volunteers (albeit with experimental limitations) have now resulted in well over 700 low rear and front impact exposures including male children as young as six years of age (Arbogast, et al., 2009). All human subjects in these 700 plus impact exposures are without any reports of cervical spine injury (excepting minority reports of transient cervical spine muscle soreness, i.e., delayed onset muscle soreness, which typically disappears within one week without any medical treatment).

At higher levels of inertial loading Clemens and Burow (1972) indicate that soft tissue injuries may occur to a number of structures including the zygapophyseal joint capsules and the intervertebral disk. These investigators tested fifty-three human cadaver torsos at high levels of inertial loading in front and rear impacts (no head rest). In addition to joint capsule and disk damage, trauma occurred in the form of rupture of muscle elements, the ALL and PLL (ligaments), fractures of vertebral bodies and vertebral arches, the articular process (two times), and the dens of C2 (one time). One cadaver subject test resulted in a complete avulsion of the head due to the extreme inertial whiplash mechanism. The ligament damage in this and similar research efforts is the result of tension and shear stresses applied to the cervical spine as the result of very high levels of frontal collision whiplash and very high levels of rear impact whiplash loading without a headrest (Clemens and Burow, 1972).

More recently, Siegmund et al. (2001) applied shear, compression, and extension loads to the zygapophyseal joints of seven female cadaver subjects (upper cervical spine motion segments). A posterior shear load of 135 Newtons and pre-load compression loads of up to 325 Newtons were imposed to the spinal motion segments which resulted in specimen failures. Only the shear load at a 135 N level, rather than the progressively increasing compression loads, affected the failure-dependent measure (zygapophyseal joint capsule strain and rupture).

Loading of the zygapophyseal joints in compression may also lead to damage of the articular cartilage that lines the facet surfaces even without damage to the bone articular lamina below the joint surface or complete bone failure. (See Chapter 5.) A rationale exists for future articular cartilage degeneration and inflammation due to traumatic osteoarthritis under these circumstances when high compression loads are imposed upon the articular cartilage surfaces (facets) of the zygapophyseal joints. Furthermore, these arthritic changes and the inflammatory process over time lead to pain. In this case, the trauma may lead to facet joint syndrome which occurs primarily in the cervical or lumbar spine. Please note however that this syndrome most commonly results from chronic loading to the zygapophyseal joints rather than acute trauma.

At the other end of the loading continuum, Kaneoka et al. (1999) examined the cervical spine motion during anatomical hyperextension using cineradiography (motion picture x-rays) in low magnitude inertial loading. The study was designed to investigate possible mechanisms of zygapophyseal joint injury in low impact rear collisions without a head rest. Human subjects (face forward) were placed on a sled that glided backwards down an incline and impacted into a stopper at 4 km/hr. The Rouleaux method was applied in determining the instantaneous segment centers (i.e., IAR's) during the cervical hyperextension motion. The most interesting findings in this study were revealed by the identification of a shift upwards in the IAR at the C5–C6 motion unit in the majority of the ten subjects. This produced an open-book motion between the C5 and C6 motion segments in eight subjects. Kaneoka et al. (1999) hypothesized that this cervical spine displacement may result in impingement of synovial folds within the facets of the zygapophyseal joints and may be a source of pain as the superior and inferior facets are pressed together during the hyperextension motion (whiplash associated disorder—WAD) (Kaneoka et al., 1999). Please note that in this research effort (albeit at a low loading level) subjects reported a complete absence of pain symptoms. Other studies detailing zygapophyseal damage in cadaver specimens subjected to inertial loading are discussed in Hartwig et al. (2004), Yang and King (2003), Yoganandan et al. (1998), Yoganandan et. al. (2002) Without detailing the relative merits and limitations of these papers, the reader is referred to these research efforts for further review.

Ligament damage proximate to the joints between the vertebral bodies may occur in high level loading (Clark et al., 1988; Bucholz et al., 1979; Clemens and Burow, 1972; Harris and Mirvis, 1996; Greenspan, 1992) and usually results in fractures or dislocations within the cervical spine. Finally, Steilen et al. (2014), in their review of facet joint ligament laxity, postulate that facet capsular ligament laxity from a single trauma or from repetitive chronic loading (i.e., ligament creep resulting from forward head position posture) may result in disabling pain, vertigo, tinnitus or other concomitant symptoms of cervical instability.

2. The intervertebral disk

a. Childhood and adolescent pathology. The interface of the disk and the vertebral body (osteocartilaginous junction) is more vulnerable during childhood and adolescence. Extensions of the annulus fibrosus (Sharpey's fibers) evaginate the cartilaginous vertebral rim and act as rootlets to anchor the disk (Keller, 1974). Keller found failure in the cervical spine osteocartilaginous interface with forward displacement of the ossified vertebral rim in four adolescent patients subjected to cervical spine trauma. Inertial versus head impact loading was not specified. Two similar cases with disk-bone interface failure in the lumbar spine were also reported (Keller, 1974).

Natarajan et al. (2005) reported a five year old boy with his neck tilted to the left. The boy was unable to produce cervical spine flexion but was able to rotate his head laterally. All blood markers were negative for infection. A CT scan of the neck was normal. However, a subsequent cervical MRI revealed discitis (an infectious condition) of C6–7 disk.

b. Adult pathology. The most common pathology of the intervertebral disk involve a degeneration of the annular fibers and a symmetrical bulge, an asymmetrical protrusion, or a frank herniation of the nucleus pulposus. The leakage of nuclear material outside the disk is often preceded by a bulge or protrusion due to a weakness in the annular wall (i.e., annulus fibrosus; a.k.a. anulus fibrosus). Please note that some physicians refer to all three conditions as a disk herniation.

Causes of disk herniation are still under investigation with possible causes including physical overuse, poor biomechanics, and biological individuality. Intervertebral disks do undergo age-related chemical changes that include an alteration in the types I and II collagen of the annular fibers and a general drying up of the gelatinous nucleus pulposus over time. The result is a disk that is less resistant to compressive, tensile, and shear stresses. Narrowing of the disk space suggests advanced structural deterioration of the disk and may be identified in a simple radiograph.

Clearly, as discussed previously, acute intervertebral cervical disk damage may occur with fractures and dislocations. However, some evidence indicates that disk damage may occur even in the absence of zygapophyseal dislocation (case study) (Yue et al., 2004) or in inertial injury (Pettersson et al., 1997) in the absence of damage

to bony elements. However, one must clearly understand that these studies can only assess an association between disk damage and a trauma event, as post-test only research designs (without a control group) involving MRI imaging do not permit addressing causation. Evidence of pathology (known to also occur with chronic loading) after a specific trauma event cannot be ascribed to that event with any certainty in these research efforts. Pathology may have been present long before the event. Furthermore, intervertebral disk injuries are difficult to diagnose with certainty, as imaging is inconclusive and a large percentage of positive imaging results are asymptomatic in cervical spine standard radiographs or MRI (Gore et al., 1986; Boden et al., 1990). Cervical disk protrusions have been found in approximately 20% of patients four years of age and have been found in 57% of patients over sixty-four years of age who underwent MRI testing of the larynx. These incidental findings were reported in patients who were asymptomatic for cervical spine symptoms. Furthermore, a lower but significant number of these asymptomatic patients were found to have spinal cord impingement or spinal cord impingement with spinal cord compression (Teresi et al., 1987). These positive findings in asymptomatic individuals indicate that disk pathology is much more common in the general population than previously believed and may be completely asymptomatic.

As discogenic problems are more common in the lumbar spine, please refer to Chapter 12 for a more detailed discussion of disk trauma and the etiology of disk pathology.

3. Cervical spine musculature

The most common neck injury is a simple uncomplicated cervical muscle strain. This may result from a sports injury, a motor vehicle accident, or a work injury. Since there are a large number of small muscles in the neck that have different functions, a muscular strain can be very complex.

Injuries to muscle tissue can be a result of contusion, laceration, rupture, ischemia, and denervation. Contusion is often the result of direct blunt trauma to the neck that disrupts the blood flow and nutrition of the muscle, resulting in weakness and inflammation. Penetrating trauma can cause tears and lacerations which secondarily interrupt blood flow, increase the potential for infection, and weaken the muscle unit. A muscle strain is a stretching (tension load) of the muscle in which muscle fibers are either partially or completely ruptured. Active functioning and passive stretching will be painful when a muscle strain occurs. Overuse of muscles or resistance to a load when the muscles are active can result in a muscle spasm.

In respect to inertial loading, Albano and Stanford (1998) report that in the United States Air Force, F-16 high performance aircraft pilots report a one-year prevalence of neck injury of 56.6% and an F-16 career neck injury incidence of 85.4%. The authors estimate that certain positions demanding neck flexion and rotation (e.g., checking 6) demand up to fifteen times more muscular force than when the head is in the neutral position. High loads are placed upon the trapezius and sternocleidomastoid muscles of these fighter pilots, especially during +Gz acceleration loading (vertical loading from the pilot's head through the buttocks). Frontal impacts with the head turned have been investigated recently in volunteers. Same side (e.g., head rotation to the left) trapezius and splenius muscle activity and contralateral sternocleidomastoid muscles were found to be more active when the head was turned based upon electromyographical measurements (Kumar, S. et al., 2005). Similar results are indicated in offset rear impacts applied to human volunteers (Kumar et al., 2004).

Any injury to muscle can lead to ischemia if blood flow is sufficiently impaired. Prolonged ischemia usually involving lacerations will result in necrosis and usually temporary peripheral nerve denervation. (See Chapter 8.) Fortunately, muscle tissue is very well vascularized and has the ability to repair itself through the hypertrophy of surviving muscle fibers. In addition, muscle tissue is perfused with undifferentiated satellite cells that are capable of fusing into entirely new muscle fibers (i.e., cells) to replace those that have been lost due to necrosis. However, this process in skeletal muscle is limited (in contrast to smooth visceral muscle), and therefore a less than complete recovery (muscle strength and extensibility) may result after muscle repair. (See Chapter 7 for a more detailed discussion.)

11.5 Tolerance Limits of Cervical Spine Tissues

A. Bone elements

A principal consideration regarding the tolerance limits of any tissue is the rate at which the tissue is loaded. The rate of loading has a large influence on the type of fracture or injury. For example, when vertebral bodies are rapidly loaded in a flexion bending load and the anterior body is put under a compression stress, a vertebral burst fracture is likely to result. Conversely, slow loading may lead only to a simple wedge fracture of the vertebral body without explosive fragments moving into the neural canal. The faster the rate of loading, the greater the potential for spinal canal occlusion and spinal cord damage if the bony

Table 11.1
Compression and Tension Loads to Failure in
Cervical Vertebrae Bodies
Adapted from Yamada (1970)

Age Group	Compression Failure	Tension Failure
20–39	4180 N / 939 lbs	1140 N / 256 lbs
40–59	3370 N / 757 lbs	910 N / 205 lbs
60–79	1900 N / 427 lbs	

elements fail. This is due to the viscoelastic nature of bone and the large amount of energy that may be stored and released at failure during rapid loading.

The vertebrae of the spine are dependent upon cortical and cancellous bone for strength in resisting compression, tension and shear stresses. Vertebral bodies are covered with a relatively thin bony shell of cortical bone and therefore are primarily dependent upon cancellous bone for their strength. Cancellous bone (many body sites) can vary enormously with density variation of .07 to .97 g/cm³ (Albright, 1987), and biological individuality, age, and activity level all affect the density and strength of vertebral body cancellous bone.

Table 11.1 indicates specific failure level data averages of cervical vertebral bodies for selected age groups. Note that 4.45 newtons equal approximately 1 pound of force.

B. Ligaments and joints

The zygapophyseal joints (diarthrodial joints) with shallow articular surfaces are dependent upon the joint ligament capsule that surrounds the joint and surrounding muscle tissue which when active will stabilize all the joints of the cervical spine when exposed to tension or shear stresses. The joints between the vertebral bodies (amphiarthrodial joints) are stabilized by the intervertebral disk in tension and shear stresses, in conjunction with the stabilization via ligament and muscle elements. (Tables 11.3, 11.4, and 11.5)

Ligament tissue by definition attaches bone to bone (providing joint integrity). If the joint stays within its normal range of motion, then ligament tissue surrounding the cervical spine will not move into its non-elastic zone or fail (ligament injury). Therefore the normal ROM must be exceeded for ligament injury to occur within a specific spinal motion unit and the specific components of that functional unit (e.g., zygapophyseal joint ligament capsules).

Cervical spine ligament tolerance limits must be inferred from relatively little literature involving live human subjects. Ewing and Thomas (1967) tested human volunteers in addition to anthropometric dummies. Three of the human volunteers developed dynamic bending moments in a forward direction of 22.5 ft.-lbs, 33.2 ft.-lbs, and 36.9 ft.-lbs without any neck injury. These data are consistent with Mertz and Patrick (1971) who tested one human volunteer in a dynamic flexion test producing 65 ft.-lbs of moment without injury (some neck pain). Other much less conservative injury data comes from the Mertz and Patrick (1971) cadaver data which indicate that for flexion a resulting bending moment of 140 ft.-lbs was proposed as a lower boundary for an injury tolerance level. No discernible ligamentous damage was produced to the cadaver subject (Mertz and Patrick, 1971).

More recently Yoganandan et al. (1989) conducted a study detailing the dynamic response of human cadaveric cervical spine ligaments to uniaxial tensile failure tests. The tests specifically identified the biomechanical properties of the anterior longitudinal ligament and the ligamentum flavum. Results are summarized in Table 11.2.

In further studies, Yoganandan et al. (2000) indicated that the posterior components (interspinous ligament, joint capsules and ligamentum flavum) collectively exhibited a higher ultimate failure strain than the anterior components (anterior and posterior longitudinal ligaments).

In general, ligaments with little elastin and a high percentage of primarily type I collagen are stronger. However, ligament size in terms of the cross-section area is an important factor in determining the load to the failure. Yoganandan et al. (2000) indicate an overall larger cross-

sectional ligament area in the lower cervical spine, with the ligamentum flavum (high elastin content) being thickest of all structures. The lower cervical spine ligaments exhibit the greatest strength.

Dvorak et al. (1988) investigated the tensile strength of the alar and transverse (component of the cruciform) ligaments in the upper cervical spine. Histologic analysis revealed that these ligaments are mainly type I collagen. The alar ligaments were weaker with an in-vitro ultimate strength of 200 N while the transverse ligament had an in-vitro ultimate strength of 350 N. These results were surprising due to the larger cross-sectional area of the alar ligaments. Dvorak et al. (1988) suggest that the orientation of the alar ligaments is more crucial for cases of cervical spine rotation or side-bending displacement trauma rather than cervical flexion/extension. In addition, the authors emphasize that the suboccipital musculature is a large contributor to atlanto-occipital stability, and they hypothesize that the alar ligaments may be more susceptible to strain injury in cases of unexpected head rotation when the suboccipital muscles may be relaxed. Schofferman, et al. (2007) in a review paper cite epidemiology evidence that the alar and transverse ligaments of the cruciform may be damaged by inertial loading as evidenced from imaging studies (MRI). However, the research findings at present have not addressed a correlating relationship with patient symptoms and the MRI findings of cruciform ligament abnormalities. Finally, ligament injuries to the cruciform ligaments have not been found in low impact whiplash simulation using a cadaver-physical model (Maak et al., 2006).

C. The cervical intervertebral disk

Intervertebral disks throughout the spine are subject to both axial and bending loads. In the cervical spine, the large range of motion in rotation also permits relatively high torsion loads which are sustained by the orientation of the annular fibers of the disk and by the facet capsules of the zygapophyseal joints. While the cervical disk is known to degenerate and weaken over time, acute high magnitude trauma will usually result in a fracture of the bony elements coincident with disk failure. Alternatively, the degree of cervical disk degeneration at the time of impact may also be a significant factor for intervertebral disk injury under significant loading conditions. Tolerance limits for cervical spine intervertebral disks are presented in Tables 11.3, 11.4, and 11.5 (Sonada, 1962).

Fiser (1985) reports similar material testing results of fresh cervical vertebral bodies and disks. This investigator

Table 11.2

Uniaxial Tensile Loading of the Anterior Longitudinal Ligament (ALL) and the Ligamentum Flavum (LF) Adapted from Yoganandan et al. (1989)

Preset Load Rate (mm/sec)	Tensile Force (N)	Distraction (mm)	Stiffness (N/mm)	Energy (J)
8.89 (ALL)	120.58	7.48	14.93	.54
25.0 (ALL)	122.36	5.53	36.2	.46
250.0 (ALL)	166.39	6.40	47.34	.65
2500.0 (ALL)	349.48	6.34	82.71	1.23
8.89 (LF)	130.64	7.55	21.93	.47
25.0 (LF)	118.24	5.65	29.77	.35
250.0 (LF)	181.52	6.29	62.29	.63
2500.0 (LF)	335.07	7.95	92.92	1.32

Table 11.3
Cervical Disk Ultimate Compression Load
Adapted from Sonada (1962)

Cadaver Age Group	Compressive Stress (N)
40–59	3200 (719 lbs)

Table 11.4
Cervical Disk Ultimate Tension Loads from Bending
Adapted from Sonada (1962)

Cadaver Age Group	Tensile Stress (N)
20–39	1050 (236 lbs)
40–79	800 (180 lbs)

Table 11.5
Cervical Disk Torsion Failure in
Newton-centimeters and foot-pounds
Adapted from Sonada (1962)

Cadaver Age Group (degrees)*	Torque Failure (N-cm)	Ultimate Angle of Twist
20–39	560 (4.1 ft.-lbs)	38
40–69	480 (3.5 ft.-lbs)	31

* It is important to note that these angular displacements (rotation-longitudinal axis) are only possible in the presence of complete failure of the zygapophyseal joints, because these magnitudes of angular excursion are not possible in the intact cervical spine.

found that with uniaxial tension, disk failure occurred at 1,000 newtons (225 lbs). However, when cadaver cervical spines were put into extreme flexion with 20 mm of ligament stretch (more than the width of the vertebral body), the cervical disk was brought to failure at 500 newtons (112.5 lbs). Prolapse failure of the intervertebral disk in compression occurred at approximately 2,000 newtons (450 lbs) and occurred at a lower load magnitude than did the vertebral body. Fiser (1985) compared the ultimate compressive stress of the cervical intervertebral disk to that of conifer wood and the vertebral body to nearly that of oak wood.

Limited data would therefore suggest that the tolerance limits of cervical intervertebral disks are similar to but somewhat lower than those of the cervical vertebral bone bodies. This is not the case in the lumbar spine. (See Chapter 12.)

D. Muscle and tendon tissue

1. Muscle tolerance

Muscle may be loaded in a passive or active state by an external load. External loading of human cadaver muscle tissue (dead passive muscle) has only limited value because muscle material properties change post-mortem (Yamada, 1970). Katake (1961) tested seventy-six human cadaver specimens (abdominal musculature) and found that the ultimate tension stress to failure ranged from 19 g/mm^2 (.19 N/mm^2) for young specimens to 9 g/mm^2 (.09 N/mm^2) for aged specimens. Furthermore, Yamada (1970) states that live human muscle tissue is approximately two times stronger than muscle tested immediately after death.

Of greater importance are the material properties of live active muscle. In this regard, there are several other factors that complicate the overall picture of muscle tissue strength. Cross-sectional area, angle of fiber insertion, rate of loading, and the length of the whole muscle when stimulated all contribute to the amount of force a muscle is able to produce or endure before failure. It is therefore difficult to investigate live muscle tolerance limits in a generalized setting. Please refer to Chapter 7 for additional information.

2. Tendon tolerance

Tendon is a highly specialized dense fibrous connective tissue whose primary function is to transmit the forces of muscle elements. Elastin (elastic) fibers comprise less than 3% of the tissue content. Collagen fibers are arranged longitudinally with a wavy appearance when relaxed. As a load is imposed upon a tendon, the wave-like collagen fibers straighten, producing an initial strain with less stress. However once the fibers are straightened, tendon is generally stiff and exhibits little strain in order to efficiently transmit muscle tension. For this reason, tendon stiffness is highly related to the load magnitude; the greater the load, the stiffer the tendon. A stiff reaction results in a more rapid and precise muscle contraction. Tendon cross-sectional area is variable throughout the body, and therefore tendons exhibit different load to failure properties when subjected to tension loads.

A more detailed discussion of the strength properties of skeletal muscle and tendon can be found in Chapter 7.

11.6 Cervical Spine—Sources of Pain

A. Bone tissue and pain

It is clearly understood that bone fractures are a source of pain. Bone is a highly vascularized and innervated tissue. Bone fractures or bone bruises will result in pain which is variable in intensity. Fractures through the invertebral joint will usually result in significant bone pain as the fracture proceeds through the articular lamella. Please note however that the articular cartilage that lines joint surfaces is avascular and is without neural innervation, and therefore is not thought to be a source of pain. The source of pain at the zygapophyseal joints (occiput through C7) in the absence of fractures and the joints between the vertebral bodies may be related to the ligamentous tissue, the synovial tissue surrounding these joints, or the intervertebral disk at these levels (discogenic pain—C3–C7).

B. Joints—ligamentous and capsular pain

In general, ligaments have a poor blood supply in comparison to muscles, which results in slower healing and re-modeling. During the healing process, ligaments may adhere to other tissues, which reduces their normal gliding capabilities in response to tension.

Although ligaments do not have an extensive blood supply, they do have innervation via proprioceptors (mechanoreceptors) that assist the body in postural awareness, joint range of motion, responses to changes in position, and probably pain. In addition, ligamentous injuries do cause inflammation that can ignite nociceptors (pain receptors) in surrounding soft tissues.

Barnsley et al. (1994) state that cervical zygapophyseal joints are a common source of pain following inertial loading (whiplash). Supporting evidence of zygapophyseal joint mediated pain has come from studies including Bogduk et al. (1988) and Aprill and Bogduk (1992). When the zygapophyseal joints were blocked by anesthetizing the joint with local anesthetics or by blocking the medial branches of the dorsal rami exiting spinal cord, a significant percentage of patients experienced relief from neck pain (Aprill and Bogduk, 1992). This research effort resulted in 64% of the patients experiencing complete relief from the anesthetic injections. Barnsley et al. (1995) administered a short and a longer acting anesthetic to the zygapophyseal joint capsules and found that 54% of this patient population experienced complete relief with each of the two anesthetic blocks (study limited by the absence of a control group). In regard to headaches, Slipman et al. (2001) suggest that therapeutic zygapophyseal injections were found to significantly improve headache symptoms after a cervical spine whiplash event (N=18 patients). No control group was available, and therefore findings were preliminary.

A number of recent studies using cadaver specimens have attempted to examine the contribution of the zygapophyseal joint capsules exposed to shear and axial loading as an explanation of whiplash-associated pain. In this regard, the reader is referred to Hartwig et al. (2004), Yang and King (2003), Yoganandan et al. (1998), Yoganandan et al. (2002) and Schofferman et al. (2007).

C. Discogenic pain

The intervertebral disks are hypothesized to be a possible site of pain in both the acute and later phases of cervical injury (Pettersson et al., 1997). Nerve fibers have been found to enter the cervical disk, and such fibers originate from the ventral nerve rami. These fibers run both parallel and perpendicular to the collagen fibers of the intervertebral disk annulus fibrosis. Due to the fact that these fibers are free nerve endings, they may be able to perform a dual function as mechanoreceptors (sensing loading and movement) and nociceptors (sensing pain) (Porterfield and DeRosa, 1995; Schofferman, 2007). Conversely, Mercer (2004) opines an absence of a significant posterior-lateral annulus fibrosus in the cervical disk (dissimilar to the lumbar disk) and therefore only fissures in the anterior portion of the cervical disk should be properly ascribed to discogenic pain (e.g., cervical spine hyperextension loads).

In general, disk degeneration is more often seen in the lower cervical spine (C5–C7). Degeneration is accompanied by a decrease in the hydrophilic properties of the nucleus pulposus, thus lowering the osmotic pressure. The result is an overall loss of water within the disk, which weakens the annular layers, and with time the disk can become displaced, compressed, or fractured, leading to increased mechanical stresses on the structures within the spinal canal (Porterfield and DeRosa, 1995). Intradiscal pressure is also largely related to neck posture. Hattori et al. (1981) documented that cervical intra-vertebral disk pressures are 1.4 times greater in the sitting position than when measured in supine (flat on the back). In addition, as disk degeneration progresses, structural changes in the disk render it incapable of maintaining its prior intradiscal pressure. As intradiscal pressure decreases, more stress is placed on both the annular fibers and the bony elements of the vertebrae (Hattori et al., 1981).

D. Muscle and myofascial pain

Muscle tissue may be injured in voluntary muscle contractions or in trauma incidents that produce forced eccentric movements with muscles under tension (still within the normal ROM). Fortunately, the widespread expectation regarding muscle strains and tears is that muscle will heal in a matter of weeks due to the sufficient blood supply. The healing results in some scar tissue formation in the muscle, but residual effects in most muscle strains are minimal from a functional standpoint. However, continued increases in the incidence of chronic pain syndromes have resulted in much theory and speculation regarding the long-term cause and effect of muscle and myofascial injury. In this regard, Schofferman et al. (2007) state that: "Furthermore, no studies adequately demonstrate that damage to the soft tissues alone is a primary cause of moderate to severe chronic neck pain " (p. 601).

Myofascial pain is consistently referred to as one of the most common sources of persistent neck and upper thoracic pain. Myofascial pain is thought to result from an acute muscle strain or overload that occurs at the time of loading (Teasell, 1993). Significant muscle strains that include a tearing of individual muscle fibers will result in bleeding within the fascial layers of the tissue. Inflammation due to this bleeding may cause swelling, pain, and scar tissue formation if damage is significant. In addition, tearing of muscle fibers will disrupt the sarcolemma membrane, increasing calcium permeability of muscle fibers which in turn may increase contractile activity (Nordhoff et al., 1996). The authors speculate that this sustained muscle contraction causes a decrease in local blood flow, low oxygen tension, and the production of nociceptive by-products. Finally, Nordoff et al. (1996) speculate that calcium re-uptake may be diminished in ruptured muscle fibers, leaving free calcium behind to perpetuate the contraction process. Friction (1993) speculates that this fiber damage may result in a pain-spasm-pain cycle that can be difficult to treat. Conversely, more recent evidence indicates that free calcium within ruptured muscle fibers after injury may serve as a trigger in attracting histamines, prostaglandins and other immune response substances in speeding the healing response of muscle rather than in perpetuating muscle contraction (Coast, 2004). Finally, the invasion of inflammatory cells such as neutrophils after muscle injury may be useful in repair or conversely may produce further muscle injury (Lieber, 2002).

Aside from the acute effects of muscle injury, there is much debate regarding the extent to which torn muscle fibers can repair themselves. Undifferentiated satellite cells (myogenic precursor cells) lie on the periphery of muscle fibers and have the potential for fusing together as myoblasts and becoming whole new muscle cells in times of injury (Lieber, 2002). However, large muscle tears ultimately involve many layers of the interconnected fascia within and surrounding muscle tissue. Fascial tissue is more likely to heal by way of scarring, which is speculated to result in more permanent tissue restrictions. Abnormally healed myofascial tissue may form adhesions that interrupt normal blood flow, contractile shortening, or provide simple mechanical irritation to peripheral nerves (Nordhoff et al., 1996).

The characteristic features of myofascial pain are referred to as a trigger points or hyperirritable locations of point tenderness. Trigger points in cervical trauma are commonly located at the *infraspinatus, supraspinatus, pectoralis major, scalenes,* and *serratus anterior* muscles (Teasell, 1993). The tenderness of a trigger point is hypothesized to be due to the physiological and chemical changes (described previously) in a muscle undergoing sustained contraction. Specific etiology of myofascial pain has not been determined in the present, and research is ongoing. Friction (1993) did show a stimulation of nociceptive nerve endings due to sustained muscle contraction in cats. However, the symptoms associated with myofascial pain may be very similar to underlying systemic, metabolic, or endocrine disorders as well as to drug reactions, allergies, neoplasm, sleep disorders, or connective tissue disease (Nordhoff et al., 1996). The similarities between myofascial pain symptoms and other disorders makes proper diagnosis difficult and often only speculative.

E. Neural structures of the cervical spine

Nerve endings in bone and some nerve endings in soft tissue structures of the neck may act as nociceptors in addition to mechanoreceptors. Ultimately, nerve endings are the link to bone and soft tissue pain as afferent endings transmit signals to the spinal cord through the dorsal roots. (See Chapter 8.) Additionally, trauma that directly produces shear, tension, or compression strains to the spinal cord, nerve roots, or peripheral nerve will produce pain, irritation, and inflammation and possibly result in sensory and motor deficits. Irritation and inflammation of the spinal cord or nerve roots can occur due to both mechanical strains and biochemical changes within the ruptured disk. The posterior longitudinal ligament is widest in the cervical spine, thus most cervical disk protrusions are lateral and can place tension on the cervical nerve roots (Porterfield and DeRosa, 1995).

References

Albano J. and Stanford, J. "Prevention of Minor Neck Injuries in F-16 Pilots." *Aviation, space, and Environmental Medicine*. 69, 12. (1998)

Arbogast, K., Balasubramanian, S., Seacrist, T., Maltese, M., Garcia-Espana, J.F., Hopely, T., Constans, E., Lopez-Valdes, F.J., Kent, R., Tanji, H., and Higuchi, K. (2009) Comparison of kinematic responses of the head and spine for children and adults in low-speed frontal sled tests. *Stapp Car Crash Journal*, v. 53 (Nov.) pp. 329-372.

Albright JA. "Bone: Physical Properties." In *The Scientific Basis of Orthopedics*. Albright JA Brand RA (Eds.). Norwalk, CT: Appleton and Lange. 213–240. (1987)

Aprill C and Bogduk N. "The Prevalence of Cervical Zygapophyseal Joint Pain: A First Approximation." *Spine*. 17:744–747. (1992)

Barnsley L, Lord S, Wallis B et. al., Lack of Effect of Intraarticular Corticosteroids for Chronic Pain in the Cervical Zygapophyseal Joints. *New England Journal of Medicine*. 330:1047–50. (1994)

Barnsley L, Lord SM, Wallis BJ and Bogduk N. "The Prevalence of Chronic Cervical Zygapophyseal Joint Pain after Whiplash." *Spine*. 20(1):20–26. (1995)

Battie, M and Videman et al. (2008) Genetic and environmental effects on disc degeneration by phenotype and spinal level. *Spine* 33(25), pp. 2801-2808.

Brault JR, Wheeler JB, Siegmund GP, Brault EJ, Clinical response of human subjects to rear-end automobile collisions. *Arch Phys Med Rehabil*. Vol 79, January 1998.

Boden SD, McCovin PR, David DO, Dina TS, Mark AS and Wiesel S. "Abnormal Magnetic Scans of the Cervical Spine in Asymptomatic Subjects. A prospective investigation." *J of Bone and Joint Surg {AM}*. 72:1178–84. (1990)

Bogduk N. "Innervation and Pain Patterns in the Cervical Spine." *Clinical Physical Therapy*. 17:1–13. (1988)

Bucholz RW, Burkhead WZ, Graham W, Petty C. "Occult Cervical Spine Injuries in Fatal Traffic Accidents." *J Trauma*. 119:768–771. (1979)

Callaghan, J. and McGill, S. (2001) Intervertebral disc herniation: studies on a porcine model exposed to highly repetitive flexion/extension motion with compressive force. Clinical Biomechanics, 16, pp. 28-37.

Carlsson, A., Siegmund, G. Linder, A. and Svensson, M. (2010) Motion of the head and neck of female and male volunteers in rear impact car-to-car tests at 4 and 8 km/h , Presented and Published IRCOBI Conference, Hanover, Germany September, 2010.

Castro WHM, Schilgen M, Meyer S, Weber M, Peuker C and Wortler K. Do whiplash injuries occur in low speed rear impacts? *European Spine Journal*. 6:366-375. 1997.

Castro, W.H., Meyer S.J., Becke M.E., Nentwig, C.G., Hein, M.F., Ercan B.I., Thomann, S. Wessels, U. Du Cesne, A.E. (2001) "No stress- no whiplash? Prevalence of "whiplash" symptoms following exposure to a placebo rear-end collision. *Journal of Legal Medicine*, 114, pp. 316-322.

Clark CR, Ingram CM, el Khoury GY, Ehara S. "Radiographic Evaluation of Cervical Spine Injuries." *Spine*. 13:742–747. (1988)

Clemens HJ, Burrow K. "Experimental Investigations on Injury Mechanisms of Cervical Spine at Frontal and Rear-Frontal Vehicle Impacts." In *Proceedings of the Sixteenth STAPP Car Crash Conference*. Warrendale, Society of Automotive engineers, 76–104. (1972)

Coast, R. Personal communication on Oct. 7, 2004.

Davis SJ, Teresi LM, Bradley WGJ, et al. Cervical Spine Hyperextension Injuries: MRI Findings. *Radiology*. 180:245–251. (1991)

Dvorak J, Schneider E, Saldinger P and Rahn B. "Biomechanics of the Craniocervical Region: The Alar and Transverse Ligaments. *Journal of Orthopedic Research*. 6:452–461. (1988)

Effendi B, Roy D, Cornish B et al. "Fractures of the Ring of the Axis: a Classification Based on the Analysis of 131 Cases." *Journal of Bone and Joint Surgery {Br.}*. 63:319. (1981)

Fiser, Z. "Report on Research in Strength, Elasticity and Impact Resistance of the Cervical Vertebrae." *Unfallchirurgie ll* (English translation). 3:111–114. (1985)

Foreman SM and Croft AC. *Whiplash Injuries: The Cervical Acceleration/Deceleration Syndrome*. Baltimore, MD: Williams and Wilkins. (1988)

Frank C, Woo S, Andriacchi T, Brand R, Oakes B, Dahners L, DeHaven K, Lewis J and Sabiston P. "Normal Ligament: Structure, Function, and Composition." In *Injury and Repair of the Musculoskeletal Soft Tissues*. Woo and Buckwalter (Eds.). Park Ridge, Ill: American Academy of Orthopaedic Surgeons. (1987)

Friction JR. "Myofascial Pain and Whiplash: Cervical Flexion-Extension/Whiplash Injuries." *Spine: State of the Art Reviews*. 7:3(5):411–415. (1993)

Gore D, Sepic S, Gardner G. "Roentgenographic Findings of the Cervical Spine in Asymptomatic People."

Spine. 11:6:521–524. (1986)

Greenspan, A. *Orthopedic Radiology. A Practical Approach.* New York: Gower Medical Publishing. (1992)

Hannon, P.R. and Knapp, K.L. "Causes of Injury: A Review of the Low-Impact Human-Subject Literature." In *Low-Speed Automobile Accidents*, Third edition. Watts, A.J. (Ed.) Tucson, AZ: Lawyers & Judges Pub. Co. (2003)

Harris JH and Edeiken-Monroe B. *The Radiology of Acute Cervical Spine Trauma*, Second edition. Baltimore, MD: Williams and Wilkins. (1987)

Harris, J and Mirvis, Stuart, *The Radiology of Acute Cervical Trauma*, Third edition. Baltimore, MD: Williams and Wilkins. (1996)

Hartwig, E. Kettler, A., Schultheib, M., Kinzl, L. Claes, L., Wilke, H, "In vitro Low-Speed Side Collisions Cause Injury to the Lower Cervical Spine but do not Damage Alar Ligaments." *European Spine Journal* 13 590–597. (2004)

Hattori S, Oda H and Kawai S. "Cervical Intradiscal Pressure in Movements and Traction of the Cervical Spine." *J Orthop.* 119:568. (1981)

Hayes W. , Ericson, M., and Power E. (2007) Forensic Injury Biomechanics. Annual Review Biomedical Engineering, doi: 10.1146/annurev.bioeng. 9.060906.151946

Hynes, L. and Dickey, J. (2008) The rate of change of acceleration: implications to head kinematics during rear-end impacts, Accident Analysis Prevention, 40 (3), pp. 1063-1068.

Kaneoka, K., Ono K, Inami S et al. Motion Analysis of Cervical Vertebrae during Whiplash Loading". *Spine*. 24(8):763–770. (1999)

Kaneoka K Hayes W. , Ericson, M., and Power E. (2007) Forensic Injury Biomechanics. Annual Review Biomedical Engineering, doi: 10.1146/annurev.bioeng. 9.060906.151946

Keller, RH. "Traumatic Displacement of the Cartilaginous Vertebral Rim: A Sign of Intervertebral Disc prolapse." *Radiology*. 110:21–24. (1974)

Kumar, S. Ferrari, R, and Narayan, Y. "Electromyographic and Kinematic Exploration of Whiplash-type

Rear Impacts: Effect of Left Offset Impact." *Spine Journal*, 4 (6); 656–665. (2004)

Kumar, S. Ferrari, R, and Narayan, Y. "Turning Away from Whiplash. An EMG Study of Head Rotation in Whiplash Impact." *J. of Orthop. Research.* 23 (1) 224–230. (2005)

Lieber, R. *Skeletal Muscle Structure, Function and Plasticity*, Second edition. Lippencott, Williams and Wilkins. Philadelphia. (2002)

Maak, T., Tominaga, Y., Panjabi, M., Ivancic, P., (2006) Alar, transverse, and apical ligament strain due to head-turned rear impact. *Spine*, 31: 632-638.

Malik, H. and Lovell, (2004) M. Soft tissue neck symptoms following high-energy road traffic accidents. *Spine*, August 11; 29 (15).

Mercer SR. "Structure and Function of the Bones and Joints of the Cervical Spine." In *Kinesiology: The Mechanics and Pathomechanics of Human Movement*. Oatis CA (Ed.). Philadelphia, PA: Lippincott Williams and Wilkins. (2004)

Mertz HJ and Patrick LM. "Investigation of the Kinematics and Kinetics of Whiplash." *11th Stapp Car Crash Conference*. Warrendale, PA: Society of Automotive Engineers. 67-0919. (1967)

Mertz HJ and Patrick LM. "Strength and Response of the Human Neck." *15th Stapp Car Crash Conference*. Warrendale, PA: Society of Automotive Engineers. 71-0855. (1971)

Miles, M. and Clarkson, P. (1994) Exercise-induced muscle pain, soreness, and cramps *J. of Sports Medicine and Physical Fitness*, 34 (3) pp. 203-16.

Myers BS, McElhaney JH and Nightingale R. "Cervical Spine Injury Mechanisms." In Levine RS (Ed.) *Head and Neck Injury*. Warrendale, PA: Society of Automotive Engineers. (1994)

Natarajan, A., Yassa, J., Burke, D. and Fernandes, J. (2005) Not all cases of neck pain with/without torticollis are benign: unusual presentations in a paediatric accident emergency department. *Emergency Medicine Journal*, BMJ journals v. 22 (9).

Nordhoff LS, Murphy D, and Underhill M. "Diagnosis of Common Crash Injuries." In *Motor Vehicle Collision Injuries*. Nordhoff LS (Ed.) Gaithersburg, MD: Aspen Publishing Co. (1996)

Nordin M and Frankel VH. *Basic Biomechanics of the Musculoskeletal System*, Third edition. Philadelphia PA: Lippincott Williams and Wilkins. (2001)

Panjabi M, Dvorak J, Crisco J et al. "Flexion, Extension and Lateral Bending of the Upper Cervical Spine in Response to Alar Ligament Transections." *Journal of Spinal Disorders*. 4:157–167. (1991)

Panjabi M, Cholewicki J, Nibu K, Grauer J and Vahldick M. "Capsular Ligament Stretches during In Vitro Whiplash Simulations." *Journal of Spinal Disorders*. 11:3: 227–232. (1998a)

Panjabi M, Cholewicki J, Nibu, K., Babat, L., Dvorak, J. "Simulation of Whiplash Trauma Using Whole Cervical Spine Specimens." *Spine*, 23:1: 17–24. (1998b)

Pettersson K, Hildingsson C, Toolanen G et. al. "Disk pathology after Whiplash Injury: a Prospective Magnetic Resonance Imaging and Clinical Investigation." *Spine*. 22(3):283–288. (1997)

Porterfield JA and DeRosa C. *Mechanical Neck Pain: Perspectives in Functional Anatomy*. Philadelphia, PA: WB Saunders Company. (1995)

Saldinger P, Dvorak J, Rahn BA and Perren SM. "Histology of the Alar and Transverse Ligaments." *Spine*. 4:257–261. (1990)

Schofferman, J., Bogduk, N., Slosar, P. (2007) Chronic whiplash and whiplash-associated disorders: An Evidence based approach. *Journal of the American Academy of Orthopaedic Surgeons*, v. 15, pp. 596-606.

Siegmund GP, King DJ, Lawrence JM, Wheeler JB, Brault JR and Smith TA. *Head/Neck Kinematic Response of Human Subjects and Low Speed Rear-end Collisions*. Warrendale, PA: Society of Automotive Engineers. 97-3341. (1997)

Slipman, C., Lipetz, J., Plastaras, C., Jackson, H., Yang, S. Meyer, A. "Therapeutic Zygapophyseal Joint Injections for Headaches Emanating from the C2-3 Joint." *American Journal of Physical Med. Rehabilitation*. 80 (3); 182–188. (2001)

Sonada T. "Studies on the Strength for Compression, Tension and Torsion of the Human Vertebral Column." *J Kyoto Pref Med Univ*. 71:659–702. (1962)

Tampier, C. and Drake, D. (2007) Progressive disc hernia-

tion. Spine 32 (25), pp. 2869-2874.

Teasell RW. "The Clinical Picture of Whiplash Injuries. Cervical Flexion-Extension/Whiplash Injuries." *SPINE: State of the Art Reviews*. 7(3):373–37. (1993)

Triano JJ., Schultz AB (1990) Cervical Spine Manipulations: Applied loads, motions and myoelectric responses. Advances in Bioengineering 249-250.

Urban, J. and Roberts, S. (2003) Degeneration of the intervertebral disc. Arthritis Research Therapy, 5 (3), pp. 120-130.

Werne S. "The Possibilities of Movement in the Craniovertebral joints." *Acta Orthop Scand*. 28:165–173. (1959)

Whiting WC and Zernicke RF. *Biomechanics of Musculoskeletal Injury*. Champaign, Il: Human Kinetics. (1998)

Yamada H. *Strength of Biological Materials*. Baltimore, MD: Williams and Wilkins. (1970)

Yang, K, and King, A. "Neck Kinematics in Rear-end Impacts." *Pain Research Management*. 8 (2); 79–85. (2003)

Yoganandan N, Kumar S and Pintar FA. "Geometric and Mechanical Properties of Human Cervical Spine Ligaments." *Journal of Biomechanical Engineering*. 122:623–629. (2000)

Yoganandan N, Pintar FA, and Klienberger, M., "Cervical Spine Vertebral and Facet Joint Kinematics under Whiplash." *Journal of Biomechanical Engineering*. 120; 305–307. (1998)

Yoganandan N, Pintar FA, Butler J, Reinartz J, Sances A Jr. and Larson SJ. "Dynamic Response of Human Cervical Ligaments." *Spine*. 14(10):1102–1110. (1989)

Yoganandan N, Pintar FA, Cusick, J. "Biomechanical Analyses of Whiplash Injuries Using an Experimental Model." *Accident Analysis and Prevention* 34; 663–671. (2002)

Yue JJ, Lawrence BD, Sutton KM, Strugar JJ and Haims AH. "Complete Cervical Intervertebral Disc Extrusion with Spinal Cord Injury in the Absence of Facet Dislocation: a Case Report." *Spine*. 29:E181-18. (2004)

Recommended Reading

Abel MS. "Moderately Severe Whiplash Injuries of the Cervical Spine and Their Roentgenologic Diagnosis." *Clin Orthop* 12:189–208. (1958)

Abel MS. "Occult Traumatic lesions of the Cervical Vertebrae." *Crit Rev Clin Radiol Nucl Med.* 6:469–553. (1975)

Abel MS. "The Radiology of the Chronic Neck Pain: Sequelae of Occult Traumatic Lesions. *Crit Rev Diagn Imaging* 20:27–78. (1982)

Barnsley L, Lord S and Bogduk N. "The Pathophysiology of Whiplash: Cervical Flexion-Extension/Whiplash Injuries," *Spine: State of the Art Reviews.* 7(3,1):329–341. (1993)

Barnsley L, Lord S et. al. "The Pathophysiology of Whiplash and Cervical Zygapophyseal Joint Pain in Whiplash." *Spine.* 7(3):329–372. (1993)

Biemond A, de Jong. JMBV: "On Cervical Nystagmus and Related Disorders." *Brain.* 92:437–458. (1969)

Billig HE Jr. "The Mechanism of Whiplash Injuries." *Int Rec Med.* 69:3–7. (1956)

Binet EF, Moro JJ, Marangola JP, Hodge CJ. "Cervical Spine Tomography in Trauma." *Spine.* 2:163–172. (1977)

Buonocore E, Hartman Jt, Nelson CL. "Cineradiograms of the Cervical Spine in Diagnosis of Soft Tissue Injuries." *JAMA* 198:143–147. (1966)

Burnstein, A and Wright, T. (1994) *Fundamentals of Orthopaedic Biomechanics* Williams and Wilkins, Baltimore.

Cammack KV. "Whiplash Injuries to the Neck." *Am J Surg.* 93:663–666. (1957)

Carragee EJ, Paragioudakis SJ and Khurana S. "2000 Volvo Award Winner in Clinical Studies: Lumbar High-intensity Zone and Discography in Subjects without Low Back Problems." *Spine.* 25(23):2987–92. (2000)

Craig JB, Hodgson BF. Superior Facet Fractures of the Axis Vertebrae. *Spine.* 16:875–877. (1991)

Ewing C and Thomas D. "Human Head and Neck Response to Impact Acceleration." *NAMRL Monograph 21 Army-Navy Joint Report* (Naval Aerospace Medical Research Laboratory and the U.S. Army Aeromedical Research Laboratory). (1972)

Ewing C and Thomas D. *Torque Versus Angular Displacement Response of Human Head to - Gx Impact Acceleration.* (1973)

Giegl BC, Steffan H, Leinzinger P et al. "The Movement of the Head in Cervical Spine during Rear-end Impact." *International Conference on Biomechanics of Impacts.* (1994)

Hamer AJ, Gargan MF, Banister GC, et. al. "Whiplash Injury and Surgically Treated Cervical Disk Disease." *Injury.* 24(8):549–550. (1993)

Harden J and Halla J. "Cervical Spine and Radicular Pain Syndromes." *Current Opinion in Rheumatology.* 7:136–140. (1995)

Howcroft AJ, Jenkins DH. "Potentially Fatal Asphyxia Following a Minor Injury of the Cervical Spine." *J Bone Joint Surg.* 59B:93–94. (1977)

Janes JM, Hooshmand H. "Severe Extension-flexion Injuries of the Cervical Spine. *Mayo Clin Proc.* 40:353–368 (1965)

Jarvik JJ, Hollingworth W, Heagerty P, Haynor DR and Deyo RA. "The Longitudinal Assessment of Imaging and Disability of the Back (LAIDBack) Study: Baseline Data" *Spine.* 26(10):1158–66 (2001)

Jensen MC, Brant-Zawadzki MN, Obuchowski N, Modic MT, Malkasian D and Ross JS. "Magnetic Resonance Imaging of the Lumbar Spine in People without Back Pain." *New England Journal of Medicine.* 331(2). (1994)

Jonsson H Jr, Bring G, Rauschning W, Sahlstedt B. "Hidden Cervical Spine Injuries in Traffic Accidents Victims with Skull Fractures." *J Spinal Disorders.* 4:251–263. (1991)

Kaneoka K, Ono K. "Human Volunteer Studies on Whiplash Injury Mechanisms." In *Frontiers in human head and neck trauma.* Yoganandan N, Pintar F, Larson SJ, Sances A (Eds.). Amsterdam: IOS Press. 313–325. (1998)

King A. "Injury to the Thoraco-Lumbar Spine and Pelvis," in *Accidental Injury.* Nahum AM and Melvin JW, (Eds.). New York: Springer-Verlag. (1993)

Knibestol M, Hildingsson C, and Toolanen G. "Trigeminal Sensory Impairment after Soft Tissue Injury of the Cervical Spine: a Quantitative Evaluation of Cutaneous Thresholds for Vibration and Temperature." *Acta Neurol Scand.* 82:271–276. (1990)

Macnab I. "Whiplash Injuries of the Neck." *Manit Med Rev.* 46:172–174. (1966)

Marieb, EN. *Human Anatomy and Physiology*, Fourth Edition. Menlo Park, CA: Benjamin/Cummings Science Publishing. 725–735. (1998)

Martino F, Ettore GC, Cafaro E, et al. "Lecographia Musclo-tendinea nei Traumi Distorvi Acuti del Collo." *Radio Med Torino.* 83:211–215. (1992)

Matshushita T, Sato TB, Hirabayashi K, et. al. "X-ray Study of the Human Neck Motion Due to Head Inertia Loading." *Proceeding of the 38th Stapp Car Crash Conference.* Warrendale, PA: Society of Automotive Engineers. 94-2208. (1994)

McConnell W, Howard R, Guzman H, Bomar J, Raddin J, Benedict J, Smith H, and Hatsell C. *Analysis of Human Test Subject Kinematic Responses to Low Velocity Rear End Impacts.* Warrendale, PA: Society of Automotive Engineers. 93-0889. (1993)

McConnell WE, Howard RP, Van Poppel J, Krause R, Guzman HM, Bomar JB, Raddin JH, Benedict JV, and Hatsell CP. *Human Head and Neck Kinematics after Low Velocity Rear-end Impacts - Understanding Whiplash.* Warrendale, PA: Society of Automotive Engineers. 95-2724. (1995)

McMillan BS, Silver JR. "Extension Injuries of the Cervical Spine Resulting in Tetraplegia." *Injury.* 18:224–233. (1987)

Meyer S, Weber M, Castro W, Schilgen M, Peuker C. "The Minimal Collision Velocity for Whiplash." *Proceedings of the IROCBI*, Fall 1997. (1997)

Muzzy W and Lustick L. "Comparison of Kinematic Parameters Between Hybrid II Head and Neck System with Human Volunteers for -Gx Acceleration Profiles," *20TH Stapp Car Crash Conference.* Warrendale, PA: Society of Automotive Engineers. (1976)

Nachemson A. *Intravital Dynamic Pressure Measurement in Lumbar Disks.* Stockholm: Almquist & Wiksell. (1970)

Nachemson A. "The Load on Lumbar Disks in Different Positions of the Body." *Clin Orthop.* 45:107–122. (1966)

Nahum A and Melvin. *The Biomechanics of Trauma.* Norwalk, CT: Appleton-Century Crofts. (1985)

Nielsen GP, Gough DM, Little DM, West DH, and Baker VT. "Low Speed Rear Impact Test Summary - Human Test Subjects." *The Accident Reconstruction Journal.* 8(5). (1996)

Nielsen GP, Gough DM, Little DM, West DH, and Baker VT. "Repeated Low Speed Impacts with Utility Vehicles and Humans." *The Accident Reconstruction Journal.* 8(5). (1996)

Ono K and Kanno M. "Influences of the Physical Parameters on the Risk to Neck Injuries and Low Impact Speed Rear-end Collisions." *Accident Analysis and Prevention.* 28:493–499. (1996)

Ortengren T Hansson HA et al. "Membrane Leakage in Spinal Ganglion Nerve Cells Induced by Experimental Whiplash Extension Motion: a Study in Pigs." *Journal of Neurotrauma.* 13:3:171–180 (1996)

Penning L. "Comment on the Paper of Nibu K. et. al (1997). Dynamic Elongation of the Vertebral Artery During an In Vitro Whiplash Simulation." *European Spine Journal.* 7:263–264 (1998)

Porterfield JA and DeRosa C. *Mechanical Low Back Pain: Perspectives in Functional Anatomy*, Second edition. Philadelphia, PA: WB Saunders Company (1998)

"Proceedings of the 17th Stapp Car Crash Conference" *Society of Automotive Engineers* 73–0976.

Prose U and Morgan DL. "Tendon Stiffness: Methods of Measurement and Significance for Control of Movement." *Journal of Biomechanics.* 20:75–82. (1987)

Rauschning W. "Anatomy of the Normal and Traumatized Spine." In *Mechanisms of Head and Spine Trauma.* Sances A et al. (Eds.) New York: Alary. 531–563 (1986)

Sances A, Yoganandan N, Milepost JB. "Biomechanics and Accident Investigation." In *Handbook of Biomedical Engineering.* Milwaukee, WI: Academic Press Inc. (1988)

Sever DM, Matheson JH, and Bechtol CO. "Controlled Automobile Rear-end Collision, an Investigation of Related Engineering and Medical Phenomena". *Canadian Service Medical Journal.* 11:727–759. (1955)

Siegmund GP, Myers MB, Bohnet HF and Winkelstein BA. "Mechanical Evidence of Cervical Facet Capsule Injury During Whiplash: a Cadaveric Study Using Combined Shear, Compression, and Extension Loading." *Spine*. 26(1):2063–2064. (2001)

Signoret F, Feron JM, Bonfait H and Patel A. "Fractured Odontoid with Fractured Superior Articular Process of the Axis." *J Bone Joint Surg*. 68B:182–184. (1986)

Sleets E. "Trauma and the Cervical Portion of the Spine." *J Int Coll Surg*. 40:47–62. (1963)

Sleets E. "Whiplash Injuries: Neuro Physiological Basis for Pain and Methods Used for Rehabilitation." *JAMA*. 168:1750–1755. (1958)

Smith GR, Beckly DE and Abel MS. "Articular Mass Fracture: A Neglected Cause of Post Traumatic Neck Pain?" *Clin Radiol*. 27:335–340. (1976)

Soloman, S. "Chronic Post-Traumatic Neck and Head Pain." *Headache* 45, 1, 53–67. (2005)

Stadnik RW, Lee RR, Caen HL, Neirynck EC, Buisseret TS and Osteaux MJ. "Annular Tears and Disk Herniation: Prevalence and Contrast Enhancement on MR Images in the Absence of Low Back Pain or Sciatica." *Radiology*. 206(1):49–55. (1998)

Steilen, D., Hauser, R.,Woldin, B., and Sawyer, S., (2014) "Chronic neck pain: Making the connection between capsular ligament laxity and cervical instability." *The Open Orthopaedics Journal*, v. 8, pp. 326-345.

Strother and James. *Evaluation of Seat Back Strength and Seat Belt Effectiveness in Rear-End Impacts*. Warrendale, PA: Society of Automotive Engineers. 87-2214. (1987)

Symeli G and Harold ZH. "Prevertebral Shadow in Cervical Trauma". *Isr. J Med Sci*. 16:698–700. (1980)

Szabo T, Welcher J, Anderson R, Rice R, Ward J, Paulo L and Carpenter N. Human *Occupant Kinematic Response to Low Speed Rear-end Impacts*. Warrendale, PA: Society of Automotive Engineers. 94-0532. (1994)

Szabo T and Welcher J. *Human Subject Kinematics and Electromyographic Activity During Low Speed Rear Impacts*. Warrendale, PA: Society of Automotive Engineers. 96-2432. (1996)

Teresi, LM, Lufkin R. Reicher, M, et al. Asymptomatic degenerative disk disease and spondylosis of the cervical spine: MR imaging. *Radiology*. 164: 83-88. (1987)

Triano JJ and Schultz AB. "Cervical Spine Manipulations: Applied loads, Motions and Myoelectric Responses. î*Advances in Bioengineering*. 249–250. (1990)

Waxman S and Rizzo M. "The Whiplash Hyperextension-Flexion Syndrome: A Disorder of Dorsal Root Ganglion Neurons?" *Journal of Neurotrauma*. 13(12):735–739. (1996)

West D, Gough J and Harper G. "Low Speed Rear-end Collision Testing Using Human Subjects." *The Accident Reconstruction Journal*. 5(3). (1993)

White AA and Panjabi MM. *Clinical Biomechanics of the Spine*, Second edition. Philadelphia, PA: JB Lippincott. (1990)

White ML. MR "Imaging Techniques and Anatomy." *The Cervical Spine*. 8(3):455–456. (2000)

Wickstrom J, Martinez JL, Johnston D and Tappen NC. "Acceleration-Deceleration Injuries of the Cervical Spine in Animals," In *Proceedings of the 7th STAPP Car Crash Conference*. Severy DM (Ed.). Springfield, IL: Charles C. Thomas. 284–301. (1965)

Wickstrom J, Martinez J and Rodriguez R Jr. "The Cervical Sprain Syndrome: Experimental Acceleration Injuries to the Head and Neck." In *The Prevention of Highway Injury*. Selzer ML, Gikas PW and Huelke DF (Eds.). Ann Arbor, MI: Highway Safety Research Institute. 182–187. (1967)

Yoganandan N, Sances A, Pintar F, Maiman DJ, Reinartz J, Cusick JF and Larson SJ. "Injury Biomechanics of the Human Cervical Column." *Spine*. 15(10):1031–1039.s. (1990)

Chapter 12

Lumbar Spine

Patrick Hannon

12.1 Introduction

In its entirety, the spine is responsible for both transferring loads throughout the body and protecting the delicate structures of the central nervous system. While the structure of the cervical spine (as discussed in Chapter 11) is ideal for a wide range of functional mobility, the lumbar spine is specifically designed for maintaining overall torso stability. The lumbar spine consists of the five non-fused caudal vertebrae, L1–L5. The lumbar spine is complex in that it permits multidirectional motion while at the same time working in concert with surrounding connective tissues and musculature to provide the primary structural support of the skeleton. Although the vertebrae and functional motion segments in the lumbar spine are similar in appearance to the cervical spine, there are fundamental differences in the shape, joint surface orientation, and overall dimensions that allow enormous loads to be properly distributed. Injuries to the lumbar spine are both extremely common and puzzlingly complex. Despite the fact that "low back pain" is the most frequent patient-client complaint, the structural source of the majority of lumbar disorders and injuries cannot be determined. In many cases, injuries are further complicated by degenerative problems that existed long before the appearance of any symptoms. Litigation therefore involves a thorough knowledge of the anatomy, tolerance limits, and potential sources of trauma and pain in the lumbar spine.

12.2 Structural and Functional Anatomy of the Lumbar Spine

Similar to the C-spine, the lumbar spine has an anteriorly convex (lordotic) curve due to the wedge shape of the intervertebral disks and vertebrae. This lordosis functions to dissipate compressive loads through a subtle give in movement along the curve. The smallest unit of the spine that contains all the elements for movement is called the motion segment or functional unit. Each motion segment consists of two adjacent bony vertebrae, their connecting intervertebral disk, and the surrounding ligaments holding the unit together. Each motion segment in the lumbar spine is sufficiently comparable in function so that they may be discussed as a group. Figure 12.1 illustrates the lumbar spine.

A. Bony elements

The major bony components of each lumbar vertebra are the body, two pedicles, two laminae, two transverse processes, and a spinous process. In addition, each vertebra has two superior articulating processes and two inferior articulating processes, forming the lateral articular pillars of the zygapophyseal joints, discussed in the following section. The vertebral body has an approximate cylindrical shape, with a thin outer layer of cortical bone encom-

ОтображAPPER

стат

passing a cancellous bone core. The cylinder walls are concave, narrow in the center and flare out superiorly and inferiorly. The lumbar bodies are much larger and thicker than the cervical bodies, with short, thick pedicles protruding from the posterolateral sides. The pedicles connect to the laminae at the site of the articular pillars and transverse processes, forming the ring of the spinal canal. The lumbar spinous processes form the posterior connection of the two laminae. They are shorter than in the C-spine and are not forked yet can still be easily palpated with some experience and anatomical knowledge. The intervertebral foramina are created by the connection of two adjacent vertebrae. The borders of the intervertebral foramina are the zygapophyseal joints posteriorly and the intervertebral disks anteriorly.

B. Intervertebral joints

There are two sets of joints that make up the motion segments of the spine: the zygapophyseal joints (a.k.a. apophyseal joints or facet joints) and the joints between the vertebral bodies. There are two lateral zygapophyseal joints and one vertebral body joint in each motion segment. Together the three joints control movement and provide stability for the interaction of consecutive vertebrae. Figure 12.2 illustrates this weight-bearing distribution. The bone-disk-bone interface of the joint between the vertebral bodies sustains roughly 80 to 85% of the total compressive forces, while the zygapophyseal joints withstand the remaining 15 to 20% (Porterfield and DeRosa, 1998). Any disruption of these three loads will in turn affect the efficiency of the entire motion segment. However, it is important to note that this weight distribution changes during movements of the lumbar spine, including flexion, extension, side-bending, and rotation.

1. Zygapophyseal joints

Each vertebral body interacts with both the body above and below via two lateral zygapophyseal joints. They are synovial joints, with a fluid-filled capsule, ligamentous surroundings, and joint surfaces that are lined with articular cartilage. The posterior portion of the lumbar spine zygapophyseal joints is in predominant alignment with the sagittal plane. The superior articulating processes are concave and sit laterally around the convex inferior articulating processes lying medially. (Figure 12.3)

This joint orientation is ideal for flexion and extension in the sagittal plane. Lateral flexion is also allowed, but rotation is minimal at all levels of the lumbar spine. Figure 12.4 shows the permitted range of motion in each spinal segment.

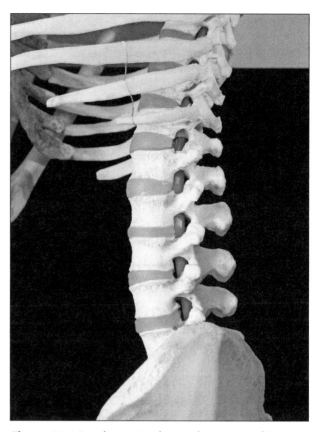

Figure 12.1 Lumbar spine bony elements and intervertebral disks. Approximately 85% of the weight load is born by the vertebral body and the intervertebral discs, and approximately 15% of the load is born by the interface of the zygapophyseal joints. (Courtesy of Patrick Hannon)

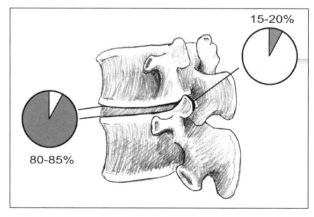

Figure 12.2 Force (load) distribution in intervertebral joints (adapted from Porterfield and DeRosa, 1998). (Courtesy of Dave Williams, M.F.A.)

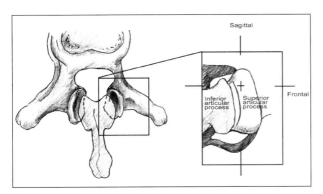

Figure 12.3 *Lumbar zygapophyseal joint orientation. (Courtesy of Dave Williams, M.F.A.)*

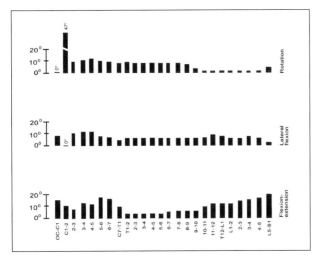

Figure 12.4 *Range of motion in flexion/extension, lateral bending, and rotation for each spinal segment. (Adapted from White and Panjabi, 1978)*

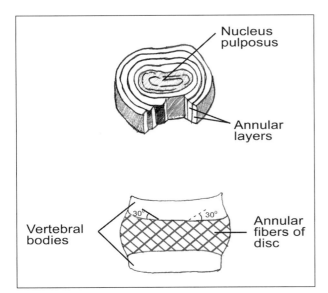

Figure 12.5 *Alternating organization of collagen fibers in successive rings of the annulus fibrosus. (Courtesy of Dave Williams, M.F.A.)*

2. Joints between the bodies

In addition to the zygapophyseal joints, each vertebral body is connected by yet another articulation. The joints between the vertebral bodies are amphiarthrodial, with only slightly movable articulations. The intervertebral disks between vertebral bodies effectively limit the multi-axial range of motion of the functional spinal units. The following section contains a more detailed discussion of the intervertebral disks.

C. The lumbar intervertebral disk

The intervertebral disks are essential for decreasing and distributing loads across the vertebral bodies. These disk structures create a stable bone-disk-bone interface that is able most effectively to resist both compressive and tensile stresses on the spine during movement. At the same time, the presence of a deformable disk between the bony elements of the spine permits a level of mobility and flexibility that would otherwise be impossible. The intervertebral disks are largely avascular, depending mostly on passive diffusion through the vertebral bodies for nutrition and waste removal. For this reason, disk repair after injury is minimal at best. The major components of the intervertebral disk are the nucleus pulposus, the annulus fibrosus (a.k.a. anulus fibrosus), and the cartilaginous end plates. These components are mainly composed of proteoglycans, fibrocartilage, dense collagenous fibrous tissue, and hyaline cartilage.

The nucleus pulposus is located centrally in the lumbar spine intervertebral disks. It is a gel-like substance consisting of predominantly type II collagen and proteoglycans such as hyaluronic acid and sulfated glycosaminoglycans (White, 2000). The proteoglycans within the nucleus are very hydrophilic, providing a negative net charge necessary for water retention in the disk. The fluid volume support of the nucleus pulposus acts as a pressurized cylinder that pushes outward against the annulus fibrosus and the cartilaginous end plates. The nucleus is effectively contained within the center of the healthy disk by the annulus fibrosus laterally and by the cartilaginous end plates both superiorly and inferiorly. Proper disk function depends on this internal pressure for maintaining disk height, capsular tension, and movement dynamics, as well as zygapophyseal alignment (Porterfield and DeRosa, 1998).

The annulus fibrosus is a series of ten to twenty concentric fibro-cartilaginous layers (a.k.a. annular rings or lamellae) surrounding the nucleus pulposus. The collagen in the annulus is arranged in a unique orientation that differs from the disks of the cervical spine. Each successive ring has an alternating diagonal fiber alignment that collectively resists multi-directional tensile and torsion loads.

The annulus has three major functions: to encase the nucleus and maintain a pressurized fluid volume, to absorb compression loads via the bulk of the rings, and to restrict and regulate movement. The outer rings insert onto the ring apophysis of the adjacent vertebrae and the adjacent cartilaginous endplates. The type of collagen present changes across the radius of the annulus. At the outer rings of the annulus, the collagen is in higher concentration and is mainly type I, progressing to type II as the annulus transitions inward to the nucleus pulposus (White, 2000). There is often no distinct demarcation between the annulus and the nucleus, rather there is a subtle transition from fibrous rings to a gelatinous interior (nucleus pulposus). Therefore, the analogy of the jelly filled pastry in describing the intevertebral disk is not a good one. The annulus fibrosus is somewhat thicker in the posterior disk in order to resist lumbar spine tension loading during lumbar spine flexion. However, in accord with normal lumbar spine lordosis, the anterior portion of the disk has a greater absolute height than does the posterior disk. In addition, the thick anterior longitudinal ligament (ALL) helps the disks provide support to the spine in extension.

The cartilaginous endplates effectively contain the nucleus within the center of the disk while at the same time allowing nutrients to diffuse passively from the vertebra to the disk. The collagen fibers of the endplates are aligned horizontally, resisting tensile forces due to the nucleus pushing outward, thus maintaining hydrostatic pressure in all directions (i.e., Pascal's Law) (Porterfield and DeRosa, 1998). Figure 12.6 shows the organization and interaction among the nucleus, the annulus, and the

cartilaginous endplate. Note however, that Figure 12.6 does not imply a sharp demarcation between the nucleus pulposus and annulus fibrosus.

Within the intervertebral disk, the proteoglycan content varies inversely with the collagen content: with the least amount of proteoglycan content in the outer aspect of the annulus and the greatest amount found within the nucleus pulposus.

The chemical makeup of the intervertebral disk changes from infancy to adulthood. In children and young adults, the nucleus pulposus is a semi-fluid gel with a water content of 80% or more. The nuclear water content naturally decreases with age due to a loss of the hydrophilic proteoglycans, and disks will thin with a concomitant decrease in hydrostatic pressure. This decrease in water content is less in the lumbar disks compared to the thoracic and cervical disks. With aging there is also a change in the collagen fiber content, making the annular layers more brittle, dry, and less elastic (White, 2000). This can cause cracks or fissures in the rings which may allow migration of the nucleus pulposus (a.k.a. annular streamers) into the outer layers or even posterior protrusion into the spinal canal. Herniations and other disk pathologies are discussed in more detail in the section on trauma.

D. Ligaments of the lumbar spine

Ligaments provide a significant contribution to the intrinsic stability of the lumbar spine both at rest and in motion. They are highly organized and strong connective tissue elements consisting of mostly type I collagen. They are the primary restriction of excessive movements beyond the normal physiological range of motion. The three most important ligaments of the lumbar spine include the ligamentum flavum (LF), the anterior longitudinal ligament (ALL), and the posterior longitudinal ligament (PLL). Smaller ligaments include the supraspinous ligaments, interspinous ligaments, intertransverse ligaments, and the iliolumbar ligaments. (Figure 12.7)

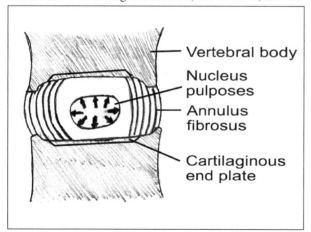

Figure 12.6 The intervertebral disk major components: the nucleus pulposus, the annulus fibrosus, and the cartilaginous endplates. (Courtesy of Dave Williams, M.F.A.)

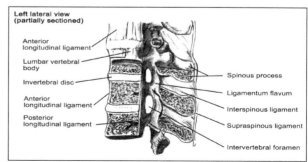

Figure 12.7 Lumbar spine ligaments—Sagittal plane view. (Courtesy of Dave Williams, M.F.A.)

The ligamentum flavum (LF) forms a cover over the posterior dura mater and connects under the zygapophyseal joints to create a small curtain over the posterior openings between two adjacent vertebral arches. Frequently referred to as the yellow ligament, the LF is unique in that it contains the highest percentage of elastin fibers of any ligament in the body, giving it a yellowish color. The elasticity allows it to elongate during flexion and relax without buckling during spine extension. This flexibility is essential due to the LF's close proximity to and potential impingement of the spinal cord or, in the lumbar spine, the cauda equina. Ligamentum flavum is under tension even with the spine in a neutral position, and the constant tension acts as a pre-stressor to the spinal column, maintaining a healthy intradiscal pressure as well as providing intrinsic spine support.

The anterior longitudinal ligament (ALL) attaches to the front of each vertebra and runs along the length of the spine from the axis vertebra to the sacrum. Its primary functions are to limit spine extension, reinforce the front of the annulus fibrosis, and resist anterior shear in the lower lumbar spine. It is the only ligament on the anterior aspect of the spinal column and is the strongest single ligament of the entire spine. The ALL is thinner in the cervical region and becomes progressively thicker as it travels inferiorly. The thickness of the ALL in the lumbar region provides effective resistance to the anterior shear of the lordotic vertebrae due to the gravitational vector and muscle action (primarily psoas major muscle).

The posterior longitudinal ligament (PLL) also runs the length of the spine from the axis to the sacrum. It lies inside the spinal canal along the posterior aspect of the vertebral bodies. The PLL limits flexion, reinforces the posterior disk annulus fibrosus, resists anterior shear loads, and protects the cauda equina from injury. In addition, the PLL is thickest in its central portion, making central posterior frank extrusions of the intervertebral disk less common than extrusions that migrate somewhat laterally to the left or right side.

The supraspinous ligament extends from C7 to the sacrum, interconnecting the tips of each spinous process. Its primary function is to stabilize the spine in flexion. The interspinous ligaments can be found throughout the spine as thin membranes located between adjacent spinous processes and help to provide stability to the lumbar spine during flexion. The intertransverse ligaments connect adjacent transverse processes and resist excessive lateral flexion. The iliolumbar ligament is actually a medial extension of the *quadratus lumborum* muscle. This ligament runs from the left and right iliac crests of the pelvis to the

left and right fifth lumbar transverse processes. The steep lordotic angle (i.e., accelerated curve) of the L4–L5–S1 interfaces makes these joints most susceptible to spondylolisthesis, and the iliolumbar ligament provides some additional support to protect L5 and potentially L4 from sliding anteriorly on the sacrum (i.e., spondylolisthesis).

E. Neurovascular structures of the lumbar region

1. Cauda equina and nerve roots

At roughly the level of T12–L1–L2, the spinal cord ends. Here, the lumbar and sacral nerve root plexi are formed and travel inferiorly in elongated strands called the cauda equina. There are five pairs of lumbar spinal nerves, each exiting out their respective intervertebral foramina to provide sensory, motor and autonomic innervation to the trunk and lower extremities as well as the abdominal organs. (Figure 12.8)

2. Arteries

Arterial blood supply to the lumbar spine is provided by several branches of the abdominal aorta. The abdominal aorta is a direct extension of the thoracic aorta as it passes through the abdominal diaphragm and runs longitudinally adjacent to the vertebral column. Prevertebral

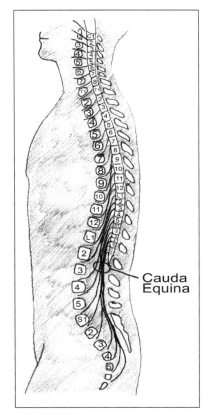

Figure 12.8
Spinal nerves and the cauda equina. (Courtesy of Dave Williams, M.F.A.)

Cauda Equina

and paravertebral anastomoses supply the vertebrae, with smaller blood vessel branches reaching the dura mater and vertebral bodies. These smaller branches include the anterior and posterior radicular arteries traveling along the nerves and nerve roots, as well as the anterior spinal artery which runs along the anterior aspect of the spinal cord. At the lower lumbar levels, where the spinal cord gives way to the cauda equina, lumbar arteries branch off the abdominal aorta and become the major supplier of arterial blood. In the area of the lumbosacral junction, the abdominal aorta splits into the left and right common iliac arteries which supply the pelvic organs and the lower extremities. Three additional branches that supply the lumbosacral region include the middle sacral, iliolumbar, and internal iliac arteries.

3. Veins

Venous drainage of the lumbar spine is collectively accomplished by several intricate venous plexi. In the lumbosacral region, middle and lateral sacral veins drain to the internal iliac vein and up to the inferior vena cava. Within the spinal canal, the anterior and posterior internal venous plexi, the anterior and posterior spinal veins, and the basivertebral vein remove the blood from the spinal cord, cauda equina, and inner vertebral bodies. These veins join together in the intervertebral foramina to become the intervertebral veins, which filter out to the left and right lumbar veins and finally empty into the inferior vena cava. The anterior and posterior external venous plexi surround the spinal column, collecting the blood from the outer aspects of the vertebrae before joining with the lumbar veins. The azygous and hemizygous veins course upward along the thoracic spine just anterior to the vertebrae, piercing the abdominal diaphragm and providing an alternate route for venous return of the lumbar veins other than the inferior vena cava.

F. Lumbar spine musculature

The musculature of the lumbar region is best explained by the networks of organized fascial systems surrounding the trunk: the thoracolumbar fascia and the abdominal fascia. All major muscles that have a direct influence on the lumbar spine are either encased in or attached to one of these fascial networks. As a whole, the fascial systems act in concert to coordinate movement and provide crucial dynamic stability to the lumbar spine. Barker et al. (2004) found that tension applied to the abdominal and posterior musculature of unembalmed cadavers is efficiently transmitted to the thoracolumbar fascia. When viewed in cross-section, the enveloping and protective nature of the surrounding musculature is apparent.

In general, fascia is an organized dense connective tissue that surrounds and contains muscle tissue. Fascia wraps throughout muscle in multiple layers, starting with each individual muscle fiber and finally creating a sheath around the entire muscle (epimysium). The fascia forms tendons that in turn usually connect to a bony element. Each fascial layer is interconnected and is able to effectively transmit the force of a muscle contraction to the skeleton for movement. (See Chapter 7.) In several places on the body, outer fascial layers thicken into large sheets connecting multiple muscles. With this architecture, the actions of several muscles influence a larger single network, creating a taut protective tissue that effectively stabilizes the thoracolumbar spine.

In the case of the lumbar spine, the systems of fascia connect to each other, providing a complex unit that both moves and stabilizes through muscle action. Muscles that are encased in the fascia will exert a push on the fascial sheet, while muscle attached to the outside of the fascial sheet will pull on the system (Porterfield and DeRosa, 1998). If any one of these fascial networks is injured, disrupted (e.g., surgery), or generally weak, the stability of the lumbar spine may be significantly compromised. Patwardhan et al. (2003) found that the ex-vivo human spine will collapse under just 120 N (27 lbs) of vertical compressive load in the absence of surrounding musculature. It is important to note that this in-vitro buckling is not a failure of the bone or disk segments, but a collapse of the spinal column. Mathematical modeling of simulated compressive loads on the lumbar spine with surrounding trunk musculature reveals that anterior and posterior muscle elements are successful in increasing the load carrying capacity of the spine (Patwardhan et al., 2003). In addition, due to the multidirectional attachments that entirely surround the spine, active muscle elements create a net internal resultant force (due to muscle co-contraction)

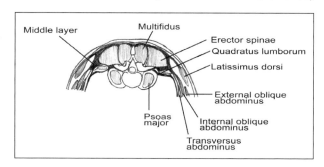

Figure 12.9 *Cross sectional view of the lumbar region, its surrounding musculature and the anterior, middle and posterior thoracolumbar fascia. (Courtesy of Dave Williams, M.F.A.)*

that minimizes both shear loads and bending moments on spinal structures and therefore stabilizes the spine (Patwardhan et al., 2001). Investigating the concept of trunk muscle co-contraction further, McGill (2004) has suggested that the patterns of muscle contraction may vary either to increase or decrease stability. A unified coordination of muscle contraction is essential for a bracing and stabilizing effect, but an imbalance of that muscle action can in fact impose large joint loads. Thus, the ultimate stability generated by the musculature is exclusively dependent on each individual's strategy of coordinated muscle co-contraction (i.e., neural control) (McGill, 2004).

1. Spinal extensors—(thoracolumbar fascia)

The thoracolumbar fascia is the posterior muscular system of the lumbar region. The fascial sheet originates superficially on the tips of the spinous processes of the thoracic and lumbar vertebrae, as well as the surface of the sacrum and ilium. This superficial layer widens laterally before wrapping back around to create a second, deep layer attaching to the transverse processes of the thoracic and lumbar vertebrae. There are nine muscles that interact with the thoracolumbar fascia. Muscles attached to the superficial layer include the *latissimus dorsi* and the *gluteus maximus*. Muscles attaching to the lateral portion of the fascia (a.k.a. lateral raphe) are the *transversus abdominis* and the internal abdominal obliques. Muscles encased within the fascia are the posteriorly positioned superficial erector spinae, the deep erector spinae and the multifidus group. Finally, the muscles that lie deep to the thoracolumbar fascia are *quadratus lumborum* and *psoas major*. (Figure 12.10) Two additional groups of tiny muscles that lie deeper between individual vertebrae do not have significant attachments to the thoracolumbar fascia. The interspinales muscles connect each spinous process, and the lateral intertransversi muscles attach each transverse process. These muscles are too small to contribute much to overall movement but do provide some additional intrinsic support to the spine.

The *latissimus dorsi* muscles are large, flat muscles that traverse most of the lower back on both sides. Muscle actions include shoulder adduction, internal rotation, and extension. While the primary actions of the *latissimus dorsi* are on the upper arms, the attachments to the fascia play a crucial role in pulling the fascia taut and creating lumbar spine stability when working with the *gluteus maximus* of the buttocks.

The *gluteus maximus* muscles attach to the inferior aspect of the thoracolumbar fascia along the iliac crest of the pelvis and apex of the sacrum. The inferior attach-

ments are the fascia lata and the femur bone, allowing the gluteus maximus to extend the hip joint. A shortening contraction of the *gluteus maximus* muscle also causes a posterior pelvic tilt (pelvis tucked under position) and an inferior tightening of the thoracolumbar fascia. Together, the *latissimus dorsi* and *gluteus maximus* muscles create opposite pulling tension on the fascia, creating an X pull pattern of stability, as shown in Figure 12.10. It is important to note here how the inferior attachments of the *gluteus maximus* to the fascia lata of the thigh tie the entire lower extremity to the function of the lumbar region. Other muscles of the lower extremity, such as the hamstrings and the quadriceps, have attachments to the pelvis that can also significantly place loads on or provide stability to the lumbar spine. The muscular linkage between different anatomical regions is essential when investigating accidents and injury.

The *transversus abdominis* and internal abdominal oblique muscles attach to the lateral portion of the thoracolumbar fascia (a.k.a. lateral raphe) and tighten the fascia laterally upon contraction. These muscles provide the link between the thoracolumbar and abdominal fascial systems. Since they are more intimately involved in the abdominal fascia, they are discussed in more detail in the following section.

The three muscle groups encased in the thoracolumbar fascia run in longitudinal columns along the sides of the spine. As a whole, they provide an internal stabilizing bulk to the fascia. The superficial erector spinae are a large and strong muscle group that originates on the dorsal sacrum as a broad tendon called the erector spinae aponeurosis. This muscle group then travels superior to insert on all the ribs just lateral to the thoracic vertebrae. There are three divisions of the superficial erector spinae within the lumbar spine. From lateral to medial this muscle group

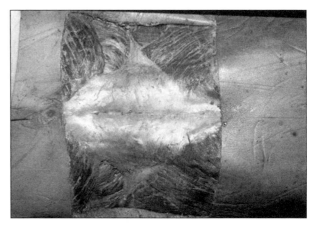

Figure 12.10 *Thoracolumbar fascia and its attached musculature. (Courtesy of Carl DeRosa)*

consists of the *iliocostalis lumborum, longissimus thoracis*, and *spinalis thoracis*. The superficial erector spinae extend the thorocolumbar spine and serve an important role in eccentric (lengthening) control of spinal flexion of the spine.

The deep erector spinae lie below, attaching on the ilium and inserting on the lumbar and thoracic spinous or transverse processes. The specific muscles comprising the deep erector spinae in the lumbar spine are the *spinalis thoracis* and the *longissimus thoracis* muscles. Primary actions of the deep erector spinae include lumbar compression and stabilization. Due to the attachments on the transverse processes, the *longissimus thoracis* muscles on both sides do not exert a large extensor moment on the lumbar spine. Unilaterally, the deep erector spinae will produce lateral flexion.

The multifidus muscles are the deepest of the three muscle groups encased within the thoracolumbar fascia, attaching along the sacrum and up to the lumbar spinous processes. This is the primary lumbar spine extensor muscle group, due to the long lever (moment) arm created by the attachments to the spinous processes. In addition, multifidi contribute to lumbar stability by providing joint compression and capsular tension. Figure 12.11 shows the muscles encased within the thoracolumbar fascia.

The two muscles lying deep to the fascia are the *quadratus lumborum* and the *psoas major*. (Figure 12.9) The *quadratus lumborum* runs from the iliac crest of the pelvis to the lumbar transverse processes, serving as a stabilizing muscle that helps control lateral bending. The *psoas major* muscle also attaches to the lumbar transverse processes above and the femur below. The primary actions of the *psoas* are hip flexion and anterior pelvic tilt (lower pelvis pushed backward) in conjunction with the *iliacus* muscle. However, with regard to lumbar spine movements, contraction of the *psoas* pulls the transverse processes of the vertebrae inferior and anterior, imposing strong compression and anterior shear loads upon the lumbar spine.

2. Spinal flexors (abdominal fascia)

The importance of the abdominal wall for lumbar stability is often underestimated due to its anterior location. There are four major muscles that interact with the abdominal fascia: the external and internal abdominal obliques, the *transversus abdominis*, and the *rectus abdominis*. The *rectus abdominis* is the only muscle that is encased by the abdominal fascia. Each of these muscles has a different fiber direction orientation that creates multidirectional tension on the abdominal fascia. (Figures 12.12a and 12.12b) In addition to these primary muscles,

Figure 12.11 *Superficial and deep erector spinae and the multifidus muscles. (Courtesy of Carl DeRosa)*

the abdominal fascia is linked to the upper extremity via superior attachments to the *pectoralis* major and the *serratus anterior* muscles.

The *rectus abdominis* lies within the fascial layers, running longitudinally from the lower sternum and ribs to the pelvis. The length of the muscle is broken into sections by roughly four or five tendons. This divides the muscle into shorter, more powerful contractile units in series that make it the most effective trunk flexor of all the abdominal muscles. (Figure 12.12c)

The external oblique muscles have fibers that run diagonally lateral to medial and superior to inferior from the ribs to the iliac crest of the pelvis and the abdominal fascia. Bilaterally, the muscles flex the thoracolumbar spine, create a posterior pelvic tilt and provide tension to the abdominal fascia, forming a "V" shape. Unilaterally, the external obliques provide contralateral rotation of the thorax and ipsilateral side bending. The internal oblique muscles lie just deep to the external obliques and have an opposite fiber orientation like a mountain peak. The internal obliques originate at the medial lower ribs and abdominal fascia and travel laterally to attach at the lateral raphe of the

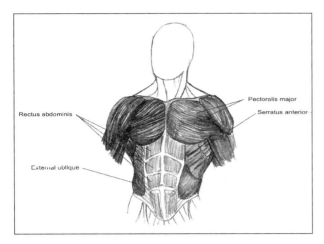

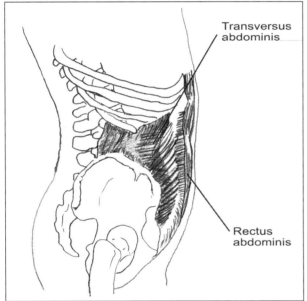

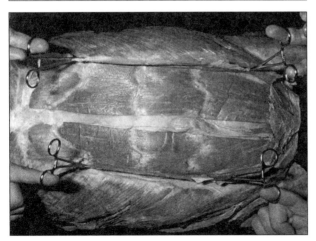

Figure 12.12a (top) Muscles of the abdominal wall. *(Courtesy of Dave Williams, M.F.A.)*

Figure 12.12b (middle) Muscles of the abdominal wall. *(Courtesy of Dave Williams, M.F.A.)*

Figure 12.12c (bottom) The rectus abdominis is an effective thorocolumber flexor. *(Courtesy of Carl De Rosa.)*

thoracolumbar fascia as well as the iliac crest of the pelvis. Bilateral muscle actions are similar: fascial tightening (both abdominal and thoracolumbar fascias), spine flexion, and posterior pelvic tilt. Unilaterally, the internal obliques contribute to lateral flexion (side bending) and ipsilateral rotation.

The *transversus abdominis* muscle lies one layer deeper than the obliques, running from the abdominal fascia and medial pelvis to the thoracolumbar fascia and ribs with a horizontal fiber orientation (coincident with a horizontal body plane). The function of this muscle is to place both fascial systems under tension and to maintain compression of abdominal organ contents. This muscle is often weak and can contribute significantly to lumbar spine instability.

Together, these four muscles work in concert with the pelvic floor, abdominal diaphragm, and the spinal extensors to create a pressurized abdominal cylinder that is the strongest and most protective unit for the spine and abdominal organs (Porterfield and DeRosa, 1998). Furthermore, Hodges et al. (2001) used a nasalgastric pressure probe on awake human subjects to measure the effect of intra-abdominal pressure (IAP) on the thoracolumbar spine. They found that a 15% increase in IAP caused an extensor moment on the thoracolumbar spine of six newton-meters, indicating that there is an intimate positive connection between the role of active abdominal muscles and increased spinal stability.

12.3 Loading to the Lumbar Spine Elements

The lumbar spine is the primary load bearing structure of the human skeleton. Internal loads are imposed due to body weight, muscle activity, and prestress from surrounding ligaments. External loading in lifting activity is also centralized to the lumbar spine. The vertebral bodies and intervertebral disks are largest in the lumbar spine to accommodate these additional load bearing requirements. Flexion, extension, and lateral bending produce tensile and compressive stresses upon lumbar spine elements. Torsion loads acting at the lumbar spine produce minimal rotation because of limits imposed by the zygapophyseal joints. Torsion loads imposed upon the lumbar spine instead result in compression stresses on one side (zygapophyseal joints), with tension stresses on the other side zygapophyseal joints.

A. Direct loading

Direct loading to the lumbar spine is more frequent than in the cervical spine but is still relatively uncommon. Penetrating traumas such as stabbings or gunshot wounds are among the most frequent. Blunt trauma is rare but is possible in the form of a fall to a flat back or a sports impact injury. Denis (1983) describes four cases of lumberjacks who were struck mid-back by falling trees, resulting in fracture dislocation of the thoracolumbar spine. Lacerations can occur as well, an example being bomb shrapnel from explosions. Direct loading in the lumbar region can result in bone fracture, musculo-tendinous rupture, vascular disruption, or neurological trauma.

B. Indirect loading

1. Indirect impact loads

Impact to body regions such as the thorax, buttocks, and upper or lower extremities can result in indirect loads to the lumbar region. Falls are perhaps the most common injury of this nature. A fall to the posterior upper torso can exert a bending flexion load on the lumbar spine and may occur in such sports as football or ice hockey. Bending loads can rupture soft tissues, tear ligaments, or cause bony subluxation or fracture. In severe cases, neural structures can be involved.

Vertical compression loading of the spinal column can result in injury. For example, falls that result in a direct landing upon the feet or buttocks can transmit sufficient energy to vertically compress and injure structures of the lumbar spine, and this author has examined several such civil cases involving such trauma. The most common structures to be injured in these cases are the bony elements. In severe cases, bone fracture fragments may enter the spinal canal, causing damage to neurological structures.

Injury can also occur due to a combination of rotation and either extreme flexion or extreme extension. Extreme flexion with rotation (longitudinal axis) causes a zygapophyseal joint distraction (tension) on one side, and the zygapophyseal joints opposite the direction of rotation may become dislocated, or fracture failure of bony elements may occur due to shear or compression stresses. Simultaneous extreme extension and rotation will create large compressive and shear loads upon the vertebral arch portion of the posterior vertebral elements, resulting in possible fracture failure.

Manoogian et al. (2010) addressed human tolerance limits during exposure to indirect loading to the lumbar and upper thoracic spine. Volunteer male and female subjects (N= 20) age 26-58 years old participated in aggressive seat plops to a chair, suspended seat drops, chair tips, and jumps to a force plate on the floor below at three prescribed heights (feet first landing). Prior to experimental testing, subjects were standard x-ray screened for degrees of osteoporosis, intervertebral disk height, end plate sclerosis (vertebral body), zygapophyseal joint arthrosis and osteophytosis. None of the subjects had evidence of any osteoporosis. However, several subjects had abnormalities of moderate disk pathology and zygapophyseal joint degenerative changes and were still able to participate in this study.

The subjects were instrumented with triaxial accelerometers attached securely to the upper thoracic and lumbar spine areas and additionally, force plate data was collected for some of the tests. The most interesting findings included a vertical average peak lumbar acceleration in the seat plop of a -3.3 g (SD +- 2.2g). The test protocol instructed the subjects to simply aggressively plop into the wooden chair. Additionally, the suspended seat drop from a 100 mm height (approximately four inches) to the buttocks landing upon a force plate resulted in average peak accelerations of the lumbar spine just under 8 g. In the feet first jumps to the force plate below, the 900 mm drop (three feet) resulted in an average peak vertical acceleration of -13.2 g (SD +-5.3g). The average peak force plate value for the participating subjects in this three foot jump downwards was 8,493 Newtons (1,909 lbs) with one subject producing a vertical peak force of 14,000 newtons (3,147 lbs) at floor landing. Subjects did damp their impact loading by bending lower extremity joints. In all, 181 experimental tests were run on the volunteer subjects. All subjects were given a medical examination post testing and only complaints of soreness and discomfort were reported with all complaints disappearing within two days. This research effort helps to put into perspective the loading that may be safely applied to the lumbar and upper thoracic spinal column during activities which in many cases considerably exceeded normal everyday loading activity.

2. Inertial loads

Inertial loading to the lumbar spine is most easily illustrated by a hyperflexion injury during a frontal motor vehicle accident with only a lap belt. While there may be no direct impact to the body, rapid deceleration of a vehicle may result in forward motion of the torso (Newton's first law), which results in a bending load imposed upon the thoracolumbar spine due to the lap belt only restraint. As the vehicle rapidly changes velocity, the seat belt brings the lumbar region to a halt while the upper and lower portions of the body continue in their forward trajectory, resulting in forced flexion of the lumbar spine and simultaneous distraction of the posterior spinal columns (posterior elements) and compression of the anterior spinal columns. Trauma may occur in bony elements as well as within soft tissue, and the extent of injury due to these displacements is directly dependent upon the acceleration level, the loading duration, and the displacement magnitude of the torso.

The anterior structures resisting flexion are the intervertebral disks and vertebral bodies, whereas the posterior structures stretched in hyperflexion are the zygapophyseal joint capsules, articular pillars, posterior ligaments, and the posterior torso muscles. Anterior subluxation resulting from hyperflexion may produce disruption of the posterior ligament complex and the zygapophyseal joint capsules. A rationale exists for the posterior portion of the annulus fibrosus of the intervertebral disk to be disrupted during high flexion loads due to significant tension stresses. However, in most cases the disk and the posterior longitudinal ligament will only experience manageable levels of loading. These structures and additionally ligamentum flavum have been termed the middle column of the lumbar spine, and failure of this column during flexion loads results in an unstable spine (Denis, 1983), allowing the vertebra above the injury site to rotate or slide anteriorly over the subjacent vertebra.

In cases of forced lumbar hyperextension, the anterior structures experience tension loads: the ALL, the anterior abdominal muscles, the anterior disk, and the anterior vertebral body.

3. Loads imposed by lifting

Injuries that occur due to a lifting load are common, and frequently occur in cases of litigation. However, evidence suggests that the most common injury etiology is due to thoracolumbar muscle element failure (muscle strain). The mechanism of a lifting injury is a loading through voluntary muscle contraction. Not only is muscle tissue the most susceptible to injury, but cases of lifting always involve an active muscle tension. Muscular elements will usually be the first to fail, and usually the loads will not exceed the tolerance limits required to damage other structures. In addition, injuries to muscle and soft tissues usually heal quite well, with few or lasting effects. Discogenic episodes and neural compromise are common claims with lifting injuries, yet rupture of a healthy lumbar intervertebral disk is extremely improbable in an acute event, and the disk injury most likely involves an ongoing history of degenerative changes. Lifting injuries can be further complicated by factors such as fatigue, weakness, prior injury, surgical history, and posture. In chronic cases of severe lumbar spine degeneration and arthritis, spinal elements may be sufficiently weakened so as to fail below normal tolerance limits. These long-term changes must be considered in cases of acute injury. I have been

involved in one such case where two industrial workers were injured seriously during a test designed to measure their lifting ability from the ground surface. One middle aged man suffered a significant axial compression lumbar spine fracture that approached 50% of the lumbar body's height. In that subject case, bony elements were not retropulsed into the neural canal of the lumbar spine and although there was significant pain, no neurological injury resulted from the incident.

12.4 Lumbar Spine Trauma

Acute trauma to the lumbar spine generally requires a very large or rapid transfer of energy due to lumbar spine strength and the supportive nature of the surrounding muscles and ligaments. However, the lumbar spine is subject to constant weight bearing and loading within physiologic limits. Almost all dynamic motion in the body increases the load on the lumbar spine. Over time, these repetitive small and moderate loads may develop into degenerative disorders that compromise the integrity of the system in times of acute injury. For this reason, it is sometimes difficult to identify the absolute source of injury in the lumbar spine region. Injury is dependent on age, health, posture, prior injury, degeneration, and even muscular tension. However, the biomechanist is frequently able to exclude injury mechanisms based upon bone fracture patterns, other element failures, or the physiological range of motion of the lumbar spine. Vertebral fractures or muscle tissue damage are common acute lumbar injuries. In general, intervertebral disk pathologies tend to be more related to long-term loading and degenerative processes.

In general, low back pain is the most common injury complaint in this nation's adult population. Pain can range from dull, constant, and aching to sharp and radiating to the lower extremities. Some symptoms can be caused by simple delayed onset muscle soreness (DOMS). Nonetheless, it is possible to have appreciable muscle injury with resulting swelling and hemorrhage that requires treatment. With regard to soft tissue injuries, muscle strain may occur within the physiologic limits of motion, while ligamentous injuries occur only when the normal range of motion of a joint is exceeded.

The area of the lumbar spine that is most susceptible to injury are the L4–L5–S1 motion segments. This occurs because the segment bears more weight than any other vertebral joint. In addition, the angle downward between L4–L5 and L5–S1 is greater than motion units, which allows for an increased shear load being applied (Porterfield and DeRosa, 1998). This is also termed an accelerated curve. Axial compression and extreme flexion injuries are the most common cause of lumbar spine fractures, although lateral compression, rotation, shear, extension, and distraction loads may also contribute to bone element fracture failure.

A. Bony elements (fracture failure) and the intervertebral joints

Failure or fracture in the lumbar spine is typically due to a high velocity dynamic loading but can also occur at lower loading due to a weakened bony structure (e.g., osteoporosis). There are several types of fracture patterns that are dependent primarily on the rate and the direction of loading. Fractures may also occur in both single or combined loading modes. Bone fracture patterns and the displacement magnitude and direction of bone fragments lodged within soft tissue are also important in a biomechanical analysis of the injury mechanism.

Fractures to the spinal column account for between 3% and 6% of all musculoskeletal injuries (Greenspan, 1992). These fractures are of particular concern given the fragile neural structures that may be damaged following bony failure. Most of these fractures occur in young men involved in high-speed motor vehicle accidents, falls, sporting accidents, and violent criminal assaults.

1. Classification of fractures in the lumbar spine
a. Hyperflexion fractures
i. Wedge compression fractures

Anterior wedge compression fractures in the lower back typically target the segments between T10 and L2. Nonetheless, these injuries occur at all levels of the thoracolumbar spine and are common in both aircraft and automotive accidents, particularly those involving frontal impacts or vertical loading (e.g., aircraft crash landing) (King, 2002). Anterior wedge compression fractures can also be a result of falling from a height onto the buttocks resulting from lumbar spine flexion and axial compression. Begeman et al. (1973) found that cadaver subjects restrained by a lap belt and an upper torso belt developed high spinal loads during frontal loading that can cause wedge fractures similar to high performance fighter aircraft ejection seat injuries. Wedge fractures can be either stable or unstable, depending upon the degree of bone fragment displacement and the integrity of supporting soft tissue structures.

A relatively stable wedge fracture represents an isolated failure in compression of the anterior column. (Figure 12.13a) Axial loading combined with lumbar flexion causes both compression to the anterior vertebral body and tension to the posterior ligamentous complex. The

posterior walls remain intact; however, the spinal column may be unstable with sufficient anterior body compression. A stable wedge compression fracture can be effectively treated non-operatively. A common guideline is that when the anterior vertebral body is compressed beyond 50%, posterior ligamentous stability is lost and surgical intervention may be necessary.

The unstable anterior wedge compression fracture is the result of extreme flexion with a lesser element of axial compression through the vertebral body. Fracture failure includes the anterior and posterior portions of the vertebral body and may involve retropulsion of bone fragments into the spinal canal as well as variable posterior ligament disruption. The pedicles remain intact and in continuity with the body.

b. Axial compression fractures
i. Burst fractures

Burst fractures are due to high levels of axial loading, where the vertebral body is compressed and fractured into two or more pieces. These lumbar spine fractures typi-

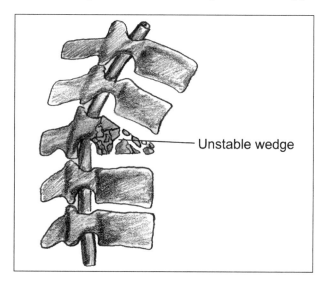

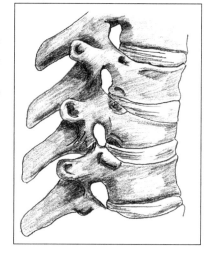

Figure 12.13a and 12.13b Stable and unstable anterior wedge fractures. (Courtesy of Dave Williams, M.F.A.)

cally occur from severe axial compression trauma, such as a fall from a height to the lower extremities (feet) or buttocks where the natural lordosis of the lumbar spine is straightened at ground impact. Depending on the extent of the load, a vertebra body may be crushed and move outward in all directions. Severely displaced burst fractures are extremely unstable. Neurological involvement is common if there is movement of the bone fragments posteriorly into the spinal canal, with injury to the spinal cord or cauda equina. Furthermore, because the axial load is also imposed upon the posterior bone elements, these structures may also fail. Neurologic deficits can range from minor sensory and motor impairment to complete paralysis. Denis (1983) has divided burst fractures into five different subgroups: type A involves both vertebral endplates; type B involves the superior endplate; type C only involves the inferior endplate; type D has a fracture of both endplates with some rotational mal-alignment; and type E can have any pattern of endplate involvement with asymmetric lateral compression. Compression fractures subtle in nature and resulting from lower levels of compression loading are best identified by MR imaging of bone marrow edema after traumatic injury (Brinckman et al. 2015).

Recently, Ivancic (2013) has developed a hybrid cadaveric/surrogate lumbar spine test model involving a mechanical model dummy and an inserted cadaveric lumbar specimen comprised of L3–L4–L5 vertebrae for examination of simulated falls to the buttocks which involved both axial compression and subsequent forward spine flexion bending. At ground impact, a single test iteration found an axial compression load of 44.7 kN (10,049 lbs) at buttocks ground impact, 9.1 kN (2,046 lbs) at the pelvis, and 4.5 kN (1,012 lbs) at the lumbar spine of the 74 year old

female cadaver spine. This testing also illustrates how buttocks damping (simulated by the physical model in this example) can reduce the loading at the lumbar spine level. Note that this single test did result in a comminuted burst fracture of the L4 vertebra (Ivancic, 2013).

c. Fractures associated with seat-belt injuries. The predominate mode of failure in seat-belt injuries is extreme flexion. This can occur when the shoulder belt is not used properly or if only a lap belt is available, resulting in distraction of the posterior elements. In order to describe lap belt injuries, Denis (1983) divides the thoracolumbar spine into anterior, middle, and posterior columns. The anterior column consists of the anterior longitudinal ligament, anterior vertebral body, and the anterior annulus of the disk. The middle column is composed of the posterior body, posterior disk annulus, and the posterior longitudinal ligament along with the neural elements. Finally, the posterior column comprises the neural arch and the posterior osteoligamentous complex.

i. Flexio distraction fractures

The primary feature of flexion distraction fractures is a disruption and separation of the posterior elements, either ligamentous or osseous. Failure occurs at the middle and posterior columns. Wedging of the anterior vertebral body and slight anterior or lateral displacement are not as common but can occur. These injuries can occur through one or more vertebral levels and can vary in severity according to the amount of soft tissue injury, primarily ligament or disk (Greenspan, 1992). (Figure 12.16) Other common complications are posterior tenderness, hematoma, interspinous widening, and intra-abdominal injuries. The first three vertebrae (L1–L2–L3) are the most commonly involved segments.

ii. Chance fractures

Chance fractures result from the tensile failure of all

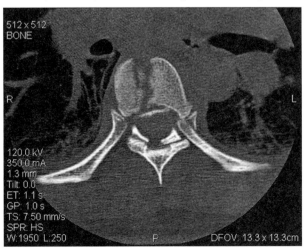

Figure 12.14 Burst fracture within the lower thoracic spine. (Courtesy of Patrick Hannon)

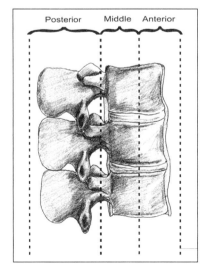

Figure 12.15 *Anterior, middle and posterior columns of the thoracolumbar spine (Denis, 1983). (Courtesy of Dave Williams, M.F.A.)*

three column divisions of the spine. Chance (1948) first identified this extreme flexion injury in frontal collisions where the lap belt allows forward torso motion. The fracture consists of a complete splitting of a lumbar vertebra in the approximate horizontal plane, from the spinous process through the anterior body (Figure 12.17a and 12.17b) and may even result in a splitting of the transverse processes (Greenspan, 1992). The lap belt rides over the iliac wings of the pelvis and acts as a fulcrum at the lumbar spine to permit a large forward torso moment. The result is a marked separation of the posterior elements without any evidence of wedging (Steckler et al., 1969; King, 1993). The anterior column remains intact, acting as a secondary fulcrum hinge. In trauma related cases, intra-abdominal injuries may also occur due to lap belt compression. This injury is prevented largely by the use of a properly functioning shoulder strap (three-point restraint) and more recently by the widespread adoption of pretensioning three point restraints in new vehicles which deploy during frontal collisions and rollovers.

d. Dislocations and fracture-dislocations. In general, dislocations and fracture-dislocations are flexion injuries accompanied by rotation and posteroanterior shear. The forces required for lumbar dislocation are extremely high.

i. Dislocations

Dislocations, unlike fracture-dislocations, do not involve bony deformities. Unilateral dislocations require an axial rotational component, while bilateral dislocations can be due solely to flexion (King, 1993). The degree of the dislocation may vary, and the inferior facets can be simply moved upward relative to the superior facets, or the facets can be perched on top of each other (zygapophyseal joints). Bilateral facet dislocation results from significant flexion applied to the spine along with an element of distraction. These injuries are highly unstable, with extensive ligamentous injury. There is often a complete disruption of the posterior ligamentous complex with concomitant neural trauma. The posterior wall of the vertebral bodies remains intact.

ii. Fracture dislocations

Fracture of the facets or neural arch results in an instability that can also lead to dislocation. Considering the high shearing and stretching forces needed for a fracture-dislocation, there is a high probability of neurologic damage. The majority of fracture-dislocations result in neurological compromise, often with complete neurologic deficits and paraplegia (Denis, 1983). An isolated fracture-dislocation of the lumbar spine can be a result of trauma and has been seen in cases of child abuse. Denis

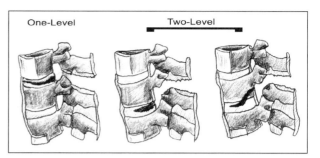

Figure 12.16 *Flexion-distraction fractures. One and two level fractures. (Courtesy of Dave Williams, M.F.A.)*

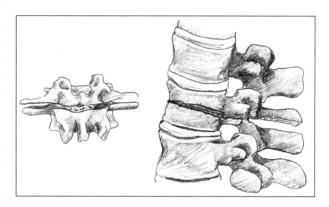

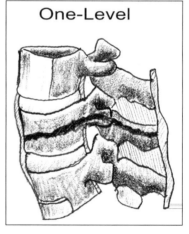

Figure 12.17a and **12.17b** *Chance fracture in the lumbar spine. One level. (Courtesy of Dave Williams, M.F.A.)*

(1983) has subdivided this injury by the mechanism or injury. Type A is a flexion-rotation injury; type B results from a shearing force that is perpendicular to the long axis of the spine; and type C is a flexion-distraction injury with bilateral facet dislocations. Fracture dislocation from flexion-distraction may also result in a split through the intervertebral disk and is sometimes seen in the absence of breaks through bone elements (Greenspan, 1992).

e. Rotation fractures
i. Lateral wedge fractures

Lateral wedge fractures are the result of a torsion load around the longitudinal axis. This axial twisting can result in a fracture of the vertebral body or the facet joint sur-

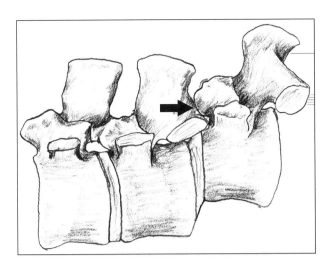

Figure 12.18 *Lumbar spine dislocation. Note that the facets are displaced. (Courtesy of Dave Williams, M.F.A.)*

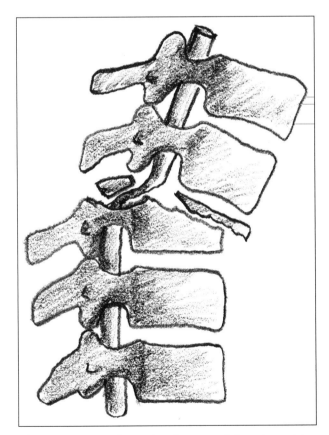

Figure 12.19 *Lumbar spine fracture-dislocation with resulting shear loading and damage to the spinal cord or cauda equina (depending upon the level of injury). (Courtesy of Dave Williams, M.F.A.)*

faces. The concave facet of the superior articulating process is more susceptible to fracture as it sits lateral to the convex inferior facet of the vertebra above and thus has a longer moment arm in rotation (greater imposed torque). These fractures may occur in the lumbar spine but are more typical in the thoracic spine, particularly T2–T6 or T7–T10.

f. Other fractures

There are some other minor fractures that occur in the lumbar spine. Isolated fractures to the transverse processes, spinous processes, or the articular processes generally result from a direct blow or a violent muscular contracture. They are typically stable injuries (with some exceptions) that require only non-operative treatment. Again, lumbar spine muscle forces during heavy lifting or tonic-clonic (a.k.a. grand mal) seizures may also result in spinous process and transverse process fractures.

i. Transverse process fractures

Lumbar transverse process fractures can be unilateral or bilateral and typically occur in conjunction with other bony fractures involving vertebral bodies or the rib cage (Kazarian, 1980). There can also be considerable displacement of the separated transverse process fragments. These fractures are caused by sudden muscular arrest and imposed strong tension loads to the bone to which they are attached. They may occur following relatively minor blunt trauma and may be missed by the clinician. The fracture line usually occurs at the point of muscle insertion (Kazarian, 1980) or at the base of the long process (i.e., long moment arm; F x fma). Purohit et al., (2015) found that these fractures are the most commonly found in a hospital radiology department (32.5% all spinal fractures).

ii. Extension distraction fractures

Extension distraction fractures are very rare in the lumbar spine. Hyperextension force tears the ALL and may lead to the separation of the disk. It is an unstable injury that requires fixation. The injury occurs due to a component of posterior compression that leads to the fracture of the posterior elements (direct impact injury).

iii. Pars interarticularis fracture (Spondylolysis)

The pars interarticularis is the bony mass between the superior and inferior articulating processes of the vertebrae. Sufficient torsion loading to the lumbar spine can fracture this mass, resulting in an unstable motion segment that is unable to resist anterior shear. (Figure 12.20) This fracture is also referred to as the "Scotty Dog" fracture due to the fracture line creating a shape that resembles the head of a dog in lateral radiographs. This acute trauma may result in traumatic spondylolisthesis and a disruption of the disk-end plate interface with forward slipping motion of one vertebral body on top of the other. Rarely is a pars interarticularis separation at the isthmus due to a congenital defect but is more commonly acquired as the result of chronic shear loading (rather than acute trauma or congenital defect) (Greenspan, 1992).

iv. Pathological fractures

Pathological fractures of the vertebrae are the result of loading in the presence of pathology (e.g., osteoporosis or a bone tumor). These fractures of the lumbar spinal vertebrae may be classified in terms of the mechanism of injury (Parizel et al., 2010). The important point is that the vertebrae are much weaker because of the presence of disease. One type is a wedge fracture due to a compression and flexion, lateral flexion or extension load. Most common among pathological wedge fractures is a compression of the anterior portion of the vertebral body. A second type is a concave or biconcave fracture which involves the central portion of the vertebral body. The external walls of the vertebral body may be intact or show less comparative decrease in height. Axial compression in the presence of disease pathology is responsible for this type of fracture. The third type is a crush fracture involving comminuted fragments and affecting all three columns of a vertebra (i.e., posterior, anterior and central elements) (Parizel et al., 2010). This fracture may have involved a high energy event.

Within each category, these pathological fractures may be classified in terms of the vertebral height remaining:

Grade I: vertebral height is > 75% of normal value
Grade II: vertebral height is between 50 and 75% of normal value
Grade III: vertebral height is < 50% of normal value
(Parizel et al., 2010)

v. Projectile trauma to the thorocolumbar spine

Fractures from gunshot wounds are becoming increasingly more common. These are mostly unstable injuries that cause retropulsion of bony, bullet, and disk fragments into the neural canal, resulting in laceration,

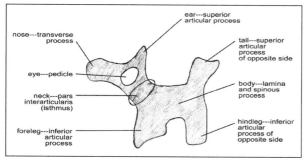

Figure 12.20 *Spondylolysis. This defect is located a the neck of the scotty dog (isthmus). (Courtesy of Dave Williams, M.F.A.)*

compression, and implosion. Sometimes these fragments are removed surgically. At other times, bullet fragments and comminuted bone are not removed surgically due to the close proximity of the neural canal. I have been involved in two such cases. Infection is also a major concern with these penetrating injuries, and bony fracture is almost always associated with substantial internal injuries to the abdominal organs or surrounding tissues. Recall that bone is a viscoelastic material and that the absorption of energy is dependent upon the rate of loading. Gunshot projectiles load very rapidly, allowing bone to absorb a large amount of energy, and when the bone is brought to failure, an explosive fracture pattern results. Alternatively, small caliper bullets in proximity to the spine column may not result in explosive, highly comminuted fractures.

B. Soft tissues of the lumbar spine

1. Ligament and synovial capsules

A ligament sprain will occur when a joint is forced through an abnormal range of motion, and the ligaments of the back may lose some or all integrity. Isolated ligamentous injuries are rare in the lumbar spine, because muscle elements will fail first and because relatively high loading and joint displacement are required for ligamentous injuries of the lumbar or thoracic spine which usually result in failure of bony elements first.

Trauma to the zygapophyseal ligament capsule, associated synovial capsules, and the ligament structures that surround the joints between the bodies of the lumbar spine is produced in the vast majority of cases through the indirect loading previously described. These ligament structures are most vulnerable to hyperflexion loads which put tension on posterior elements, including ligaments, resulting in ligament strain and sometimes facet dislocation. Hyperflexion ligament injuries of the lumbar spine may result from inertial loading (e.g., lap-belt related injuries). However, this mechanism of injury is currently not seen as frequently due to an increase in three-point restraint seat belts (usually with pretensioners) in both the front and rear seat passengers in newer vehicles.

Loading of the zygapophyseal joints (posterior to the vertebral bodies) in compression during lumbar spine hyperextension may also lead to damage of the articular cartilage that lines the zygapophyseal facet surfaces even without damage to the bone articular lamina below the joint surface or complete bone failure. (See Chapter 5.) High compression loading (acute trauma) presents a rationale for future articular cartilage degeneration, inflammation, and osteoarthritis under these circumstances.

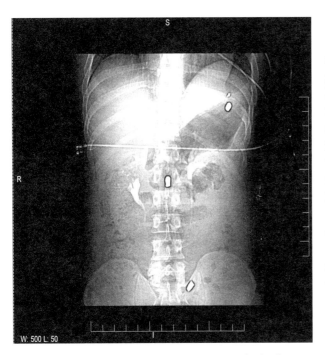

Figure 12.21 *Three distinct bullets; two of which are near the lumbosacral spine. This projectile trauma was from an assault. (Courtesy of Patrick Hannon)*

Furthermore, with chronic loading to the zygapophyseal joints, these arthritic changes and the inflammatory process over time lead to pain (i.e., facet joint syndrome in the cervical or lumbar spine).

The zygapophyseal joints of the lumbar spine do contain what most probably are mechanoreceptors and nociceptive receptor fibers of the autonomic nervous system. The sympathetic and parasympathetic ganglia of the autonomic nervous system receive this input when the receptor endings are exposed to compressive pressure or stretch of the ligament capsule surrounding the zygapophyseal joint. Malanga et al. (2013) state that nociceptive type IV unmyelinated nerve fibers have been found in the fibrous ligament capsule of the zygapophyseal joints and represent a nerve plexus of unmyelinated nerve fibers which also contain type I and II mechanoreceptor nerve fibers with a proprioceptive function. Malanga et al. (2013) further state that "the Z-joints [zygapophyseal joints] have been found to undergo [pain] sensitization of neurons by naturally occurring inflammatory mediators such as substance P and phospholipase A2. Peripheral nerve endings release chemical mediators such as bradykinin, serotonin, histamine, and prostaglandins which are noxious and can cause pain" (p. 7). The release of these substances then sets up inflammation surrounding the zygapophyseal joints and prolonged nociceptive excitation of peripheral nerve fibers leading to one source of lumbar spine pain.

2. Intervertebral disk

a. Childhood and adolescent pathology. The interface of the disk and the vertebral body (osteocartilaginous junction) is more vulnerable during childhood and adolescence. Extensions of the annulus fibrosis (Sharpey's fibers) invaginate the cartilaginous vertebral rim and act as rootlets to anchor the disk (Keller, 1974). Keller found failure in the lumbar spine osteocartilaginous interface with forward displacement of the ossified vertebral rim in two adolescent patients subjected to lumbar spine trauma. Inertial versus impact loading was not specified.

b. Adult pathology. Narrowing of the disk space (i.e., loss of disk height), which can be identified in a simple radiograph, suggests advanced structural deterioration of the disk. The result is a disk that is less resistant to compressive, tensile, and shear stresses. However, this measurement of the disk height or volume is affected by normal diurnal fluctuations. Martin et al. (2018) found that there was an 8% and 9% decrease in the disk height and volume respectively of the L5–S1 disk with repeated MRI scans over the course of an eight hour workday in healthy young men.

The most common pathology of the intervertebral disk involves a degeneration of the annular fibers with either a symmetrical bulge, an asymmetrical protrusion of the disk or a frank herniation of the nucleus pulposus external to the disk. Please note that some physicians refer to all three conditions as a disk herniation. Disk herniations are quite prevalent in the lumbar spine and are a large subject of controversy due to pathologic findings in both symptomatic and asymptomatic people.

Herniated discs are most often found in middle-aged adults (ages forty to fifty-five). This is due to the fact that age-related changes of the disk include a drying out of the nucleus pulposus, causing material stiffening (i.e., loss of flexibility). In addition, as the annulus fibrosus ages it will undergo changes in the collagen fibers, becoming weaker and more likely to tear. This annulus fibrosus degeneration may be an unavoidable process that simply advances at different rates for different people. In the middle-aged person, the nucleus is still viable and gelatinous, allowing it to seep through torn annular layers. However, in the elderly person, a decreased fluid nucleus has lost its ability to migrate into the spinal canal through annular tears, and therefore new disk herniations are less prevalent. A larger concern for the geriatric population is the inability of the disk to absorb spinal loads or allow for proper lumbar spine motion. A large disparity exists between the intervertebral disk failure point and the failure point of the lumbar vertebral body (lumbar bodies are the weak link). Furthermore, this effect in the elderly is due to the increased porosity in vertebral body cancellous bone. This is especially true in elderly women who may suffer from osteopenia or osteoporosis, and in some cases a gradual collapse of the lumbar vertebral bodies over time may occur (i.e., a pathological fracture failure).

A herniated disk (frank herniation) occurs when the nucleus pulposus ruptures through a tear in the wall of the annulus fibrosus. The leakage of nuclear material outside the disk is often preceded by a bulge or protrusion due to a weakness in the annular wall. Streamers may develop gradually as fluid pressure allows the nucleus pulposus to push through the degenerated annulus.

Typically, this is a gradual process that occurs as a result of chronic loading. Frequently, repetitive traumas or aging may result in partial disruption of the annular layers without immediate prolapse of the nucleus (Gordon et al., 1990). The nucleus pulposus then seeps slowly through with small impurities into the annular fibers. These advancing streamers of nucleus pulposus can accelerate the degeneration of annular integrity as the disk becomes a less effective load bearing structure. The disk contents may discharge through the annulus but may be contained by the PLL (posterior longitudinal ligament). A frank herniation with extruded nucleus pulposus may result in pain perceived in the lower back, or it may radiate down through the lower extremities. Numbness and decreased motor output (measured by muscle strength) may also result. These symptoms resulting from lumbar spine disk herniation are due to compression stress upon the spinal cord or the intervertebral spinal nerve roots with coincident inflammation. (See Chapter 8.)

Underlying causes of disk herniation are still under investigation, with possible causes including physical overuse, poor biomechanics, and biological individuality. The age-related chemical changes are also a significant factor in the health of the intervertebral disk. Unfortunately, these age-related changes are ultimately inevitable but do seem to occur at different rates for each individual. Furthermore, Buckwalter (1995) suggests that identification and elimination of some factors that predispose the disk to degeneration can actually help to regenerate disk tissue (e.g., poor posture or excess weight). Wilder et al. (1988) tested twenty male and female cadaver subjects. Motion segments involved in the testing included twenty L3–L4 segments and twenty L4–L5 segments tested under loading which allowed for six degree motion. The authors imposed a simulated sitting load to the motion unit for one hour in one set of experiments and found that significant changes occurred in the mechanical properties of the intervertebral disk within the motion unit. In this

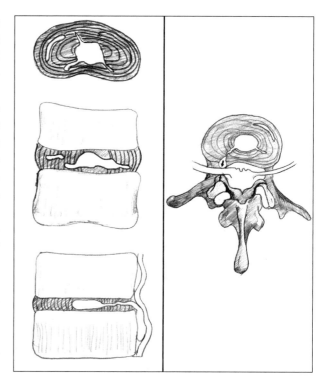

Figure 12.22a and **12.22b** Fluid streamers have developed and have proceeded through the cross-section layers of the annulus fibrosus of the disk. (Courtesy of Dave Williams, M.F.A.)

testing, following the one hour sitting simulation, an axial load was applied with a concomitant flexion or lateral flexion load applied and tension failure occurred in some disk specimens in the posterior disk region. Furthermore, a combined load of lateral flexion, flexion, and axial rotation vibration caused tracking tears emanating from the center nucleus pulposus to the outer annulus again in the posterior region of the intervertebral disk (Wilder et al., 1988).

In vivo animal models provide one line of evidence regarding the degeneration and age-related remodeling that occurs in intervertebral disks. Walsh and Lotz (2004) utilized a mouse model to examine cellular changes that occurred to the disk in response to various dynamic loading conditions. Application of cyclic compressive loads attempted to simulate human lumbar stresses during repetitive lifting. Results revealed a cellular disruption and an increase in cell death (apoptosis) even without sufficient loading to produce gross injury to the annulus fibrosus. Apoptosis (programmed cell death) may occur during repetitive excessive loading to stimulate healing and remodeling of tissues by initiating an inflammatory response. Previous studies have linked apoptosis to the advancement of disk degenerative processes (Gruber and Hanley, 1998; Lotz and Chin, 2000). Furthermore, genetic influences appear to play a part in lumbar intervertebral disk degeneration (DDD). Battie et al. (2008) administered lumbar spine MRIs with quantitative and qualitative assessments of the disk signal, disk bulging and the inter-space between human lumbar vertebral bodies. Research subjects consisted of 152 male monozygotic and 148 male dizygotic twins between 35 and 70 years old. Subjects were transported to a central location in Finland and given an extensive personal interview which included an assessment of environmental influences such as subject's occupation and the level of physical leisure activity. The medical history was taken and all subjects were administered a lumbar spine MRI. Genetic influences (a.k.a. heritability estimates) ranged between 29% and 54% depending upon the pathology measure and the vertebral level (lumbar functional unit 1 through 5). Battie et al. (2008) concluded that both environment and heritability influence DDD. However, the authors opine a cautionary note that specific environmental influences remain elusive with the level of the work loading or recreational loading (high or low) to the lumbar spine, explaining little of the inter-individual variation (multivariate analysis) seen in DDD.

Disk degeneration has a large effect upon the material properties of the disk. Gu et al. (1999) found that degenerative changes are evident and measurable due to changes in disk material properties and include a decreased fixed charge density, changes in hydraulic permeability (with respect to direction), decreased disk tissue hydration, and an increase in disk stiffness. This increase in disk stiffness decreases the energy-absorbing qualities of the disk. These research efforts suggest that disk degeneration is initiated by a cellular response to long-term stresses rather than the mechanical tearing of the structures due to acute trauma (Walsh and Lotz, 2004).

Some other chemical changes have also been noted in the degenerated intervertebral disk. Saal (1995) found high levels of phospholipase A2 in surgically excised herniated lumbar disks of patients (approximately forty disk samples). This enzyme is associated with inflammation and Saal (1995) hypothesized that this chemical factor may stimulate nociceptive (pain) receptors within the intervertebral disk or surrounding neural tissue.

It is clear that acute intervertebral disk damage may occur with fractures and dislocations. Furthermore, some evidence indicates that acute disk damage may occur even in the absence of zygapophyseal joint dislocation or damage to bony elements (Yue et al., 2004). However, it is important to appreciate that case studies such as Yue et al. (2004) can only assess an association between disk damage and a trauma event, as post-test only research designs (without a control group) involving MRI imaging do not permit addressing causation. Evidence of pathology (known to also occur with chronic loading) after a specific trauma event cannot be ascribed to that event with any assurance. Pathology may have been present long before the event. Furthermore, intervertebral disk injuries are difficult to diagnose with certainty, as many MRI results are inconclusive and a large percentage of positive MRI results are asymptomatic in lumbar spines of research subjects (Jensen et al., 1994; Javik et al., 2001; Carragee et al., 2000; Healy et al., 1996 and Stadnik et al., 1998). Healy et al. (1996) found that in very active lifelong male athletes with an age range of 41-69 years, there were asymptomatic degenerative changes of the cervical and lumbar spine including disk protrusion and herniation, spinal spondylosis/stenosis with an increased prevalence with age. Upon questioning of these nineteen subjects, these symptomatic findings did not limit the athletic activity of these men (Healy et al., 1996). These pathological findings in asymptomatic individuals indicate that disk pathology is much more common in the general population than previously believed. Positive disk pathology in asymptomatic people is discussed in more detail later in this chapter.

3. Lumbar spine musculature

The most common cause of low back pain is a simple uncomplicated lumbar muscle strain. This may result from either direct or indirect injuries: a sports injury, a motor vehicle accident, a lifting injury, or a work injury. In the lumbar spine, muscles play an essential role of stability that is more crucial than any other part of the body. The networks of interconnected fascia discussed earlier in this chapter create a column of tissue that stabilizes with active muscle contraction and with an increase in intra-abdominal pressure. Cholewicki et al. (2000) and Stokes and Gardner-Morse (2003) found that spinal stability significantly improved with increased loads to the trunk as a result of heightened muscle activation. A disruption of these muscle elements anywhere in the tissue column may significantly affect the stiffness of the system as a whole (Gardner-Morse and Stokes, 2004). Trauma to the musculature of the lumbar spine has been hypothesized to force other structures of the lumbar spine to bear abnormal loads, which in turn may result in additional and more severe injury.

Fatigue is a large concern regarding trauma to muscle tissue, particularly in cases of lifting weight loads. The compressive loading and bending moments imposed on the lumbar spine during lifting are largely balanced by the musculature. Adams and Dolan (1995) have suggested that mechanical muscle fatigue may be the underlying source of low back pain and may initiate biological changes leading to disk degeneration and other disk pathology. Fatigue and/or muscle weakness due to repetitive lifting or due to a detrained muscle fitness level can significantly increase these bending moments due to poor body mechanics, putting the lumbar spine at a higher risk for injury (Dolan and Adams, 1998). Please refer to Chapter 7 for a more detailed discussion on muscle trauma.

4. Multiple tissue trauma

a. Spondylolisthesis. Spondylolisthesis is a forward slipping of one vertebral body upon another, commonly termed a slipped vertebra. It may occur at any level of the spine but most commonly occurs in the lower lumbar spine, specifically at the L4–L5 and L5–S1 levels, most likely due to the increased lordotic curve (accelerated curve) and an increased anterior shear load due to the gravity vector. This condition is also affected by a presence of segmental instability or weakening of the mechanical support between the vertebral bodies. Spondylolisthesis may produce back pain as well as nerve root and peripheral nerve-related pain, which is often referred to as sciatica (sciatic nerve irritation). The nerve pain may be caused by the narrowing of the spinal canal as the superior vertebral body slides anteriorly, possibly pinching or even applying tension to the structures contained within. Nerve and nerve root impingement cause specific radicular pain patterns that travel distally throughout the length of the affected peripheral nerve. (See Chapter 8.)

There are three forms of spondylolisthesis: (1) isthmic, (2) degenerative, and (3) traumatic. Isthmic spondylolisthesis occurs due to a congenital defect in the bony architecture of the vertebrae, typically in the ring of the neural arch. Continued loading over time leads to a weakening that can allow the vertebral body above to slip forward. This is a fairly common condition that may affect up to 5 to 6% of males and 2 to 3% of females (Greenspan, 1992). It is common for isthmic spondylolisthesis to remain asymptomatic during young age and adolescent growth. Typical onset of symptoms is between the ages of twenty to forty years. The most common symptoms include pain and sciatica, which predominantly occur as a result of mechanical instability.

Degenerative spondylolisthesis occurs as the result of age-related changes to tissues such as muscle detraining, ligament instability, loss of disk support, and joint wear and tear. The combination of weakened spinal support

structures, degeneration of the intervertebral disks, and arthrosis of the zygapophyseal joints renders the affected segment(s) unstable.

The third type of spondylolisthesis, traumatic spondylolisthesis, is an instability related to a specific acute injury to the bone (fracture) or ligaments. Spondylolysis (a pars interarticularis failure) is the most common site of bone failure that can induce a traumatic spondylolisthesis. (Figure 12.23) However, a failure of any other bony posterior spinal elements (i.e., pedicle, lamina, or facets) can also contribute to a traumatic spondylolisthesis.

The lumbar spine is responsible for tolerating the resultant forces of both gravity and movement. Disruption of the bony elements or supporting ligaments creates an instability that renders the lumbar spine unable to resist normal anterior shear loads, making spondylolisthesis inevitable without external support.

There are four grades of severity in spondylolisthesis, based on the percentage of forward slippage that has occurred. (Figure 12.23) Grade I is defined as 0 to 25% of anterior slippage; grade II indicates 25 to 50% of displacement; grade III is between 50 and 75%; and grade IV is complete anterior separation of the superior vertebra (rare). Grades III and IV cannot occur without rupture of ligamentous structures and a spondylolysis (Greenspan, 1992).

b. Lumbar spine stenosis. Lumbar spine stenosis most commonly affects the middle-aged and an elderly population. Central stenosis is characterized by a narrowing of the spinal canal with compression of the cauda equina and nerve roots. Lateral stenosis is a compromise of the intervertebral foramen space that impinges the nerve root as it exits the spinal canal. Symptoms of central stenosis can present bilaterally, while lateral stenosis usually affects only unilateral regions. This lateral narrowing can be caused by thickened posterior vertebral elements, arthrosis of zygapophyseal joints, marginal osteophytes (bone spurs), or inflamed soft tissue structures in close approximation to the intervertebral foramen. Acute trauma can also cause impingement of the spinal canal or the intervertebral foramina. Entrapment of the cauda equina roots by enlargement of the osseous and soft tissue structures surrounding the lumbar spinal canal is often associated with disabling pain in the back and lower extremities. Frequently, the cause of pain is due to a vascular claudication of the blood vessels in the spinal canal due to stenosis which prevents adequate blood flow from reaching the cauda equina, causing ischemia and hypoxia of the neural tissues (Porter, 1995). In turn, the ischemia inhibits neural impulse transmission throughout the length of the affected nerve root(s), and peripheral symptoms are reported. Ra-

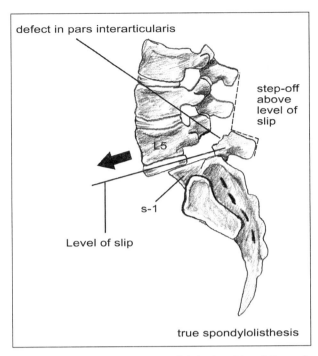

Figure 12.23 *Traumatic spondylolysis with a bilateral pars interarticularis failure. (Courtesy of Dave Williams, M.F.A.)*

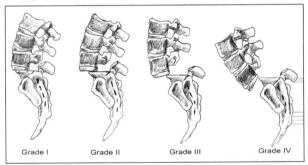

Figure 12.24 *The four grades of spondylolisthesis. (Courtesy of Dave Williams, M.F.A.)*

dicular symptoms (symptoms of nerve root compression) often include specific patterns of radiating leg pain that is much more severe than the back pain. Due to the increasing ischemia with activity, pain typically increases with walking or standing and decreases with sitting or spinal flexion (Porter, 1995).

i. Diagnosis

Lumbar spinal stenosis can be difficult to diagnose due to both a slow onset and symptoms that resemble other disorders. Pain patterns can be similar to those seen in spondylolisthesis and may manifest as difficulty in walking, leg paresthesia (decreased sensations), muscle weakness, and in severe cases, bowel or bladder disturbances (Alvarez and Hardy, 1998). Arterial intermittent claudication is another condition that is often confused with lumbar stenosis. While the symptoms are similar, this type of

claudication has a cardiopulmonary source: reduced arterial blood flow in the periphery associated with coronary artery disease or atherosclerosis. A cardiopulmonary assessment is required for diagnosis distinction.

ii. Etiology

In this text, lumbar spine stenoses can be divided into congenital or acquired forms. Although less common, congenital lumbar stenosis may result from several anatomical defects during development. Congenitally short pedicles, thickened lamina and facets, or an excessive lordotic curve of the lumbar spine are a few examples. It should be noted as well that many people with congenitally small lumbar canals remain asymptomatic until age-related changes develop into an acquired stenosis.

In most cases, stenosis of the lumbar canal may be attributed to acquired degenerative or arthritic changes of the intervertebral disks, ligaments, and zygapophyseal joints surrounding the lumbar canal (Alvarez and Hardy, 1998). Hypertrophy of the articulations surrounding the canal, intervertebral disk bulges, or frank herniations, hypertrophy of the ligamentum flavum, and osteophyte (bone) formation are all arthritic changes that may occur and exacerbate lumbar spine stenosis.

Other possible contributions to a narrowing of the spinal canal include various cysts or tumors that may develop on the spinal cord itself.

12.5 Lumbar Spine Tolerance Limits

Modeling of the lumbar spine for tolerance limits is complex due to the significant contribution of the surrounding musculature. Accurate spinal computer models must incorporate the muscle elements and other osteoligamentous structures that create the biomechanical balance of the whole system (Reeves and Cholewicki, 2003). In this regard, the engineer is referred to Yamaguchi (2001) for a general review of models of the musculoskeletal system. Tolerance limits are presented here by isolating each of the lumbar structures. It is essential for the attorney to appreciate that each of these components contributes to the ultimate integrity of the lumbar spine and that many factors may play a role in lumbar spine injury or pathology.

A. Bony elements

A principal consideration regarding the tolerance limits of any tissue is the rate at which the tissue is loaded. The rate of loading has a large influence on the type of fracture or injury. For example, when vertebral bodies are rapidly loaded in a flexion bending load and the anterior body is subjected to a compression stress, a vertebral body burst fracture is likely to result. Conversely, slow loading may lead only to a simple wedge fracture of the vertebral body without explosive fragments moving into the neural canal. The faster the rate of loading, the greater the potential for spinal canal occlusion and spinal cord damage if the bony elements fail.

The vertebrae of the spine are dependent upon cortical and cancellous bone for strength in resisting compression, tension, and shear stresses. However, vertebral bodies are covered with a relatively thin bony shell of cortical bone and therefore are primarily dependent upon cancellous bone for their strength. Cancellous bone (many body sites) can vary enormously, with density variation of .07 to .97 g/cm³ (Albright, 1987), and biological individuality, age, and activity level all affect the density and strength of vertebrae. The vertebrae of the lumbar spine are required to withstand the largest loads in compression and are much larger and stronger than the cervical vertebrae. Table 12.1 indicates specific failure level data averages of lumbar vertebral bodies for selected age groups.

However, it should be appreciated that these data are the result of testing single lumbar spine functional units (two bony vertebra and the lumbar intervertebral disk in-between the two bone bodies). More recent testing (Duma et al., 2006) involved axial compression testing of lumbar functional units from four cadaver subjects exposed to axial loads resulted in higher ultimate failure points compared to the Sonada 1962 data falling between 11,203 Newtons and 13,065 Newtons (2,519 to 2,937 pounds).

Furthermore, Duma et al. (2006) found that when whole lumbar spine units (N= 2) were tested (T12 vertebra included), the axial compression ultimate failure point reduced to 5,009 and 5,911 Newtons (1,126 and 1,329 pounds) for these older subjects (ages 66 and 61 respectively). These latter results appear to be the result of buckling of the entire lumbar spine unit and therefore the axial compression load resulted in a bending load also being imposed under this test protocol. Duma et al. (2006) state that "these failures occurred as the spine behaved in first order buckling which resulted in concentrated loading and bending of the anterior aspects of the vertebral

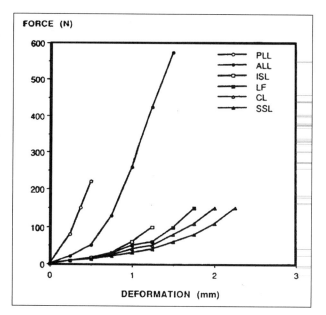

Figure 12.25 Various lumbar spinal ligament deformation responses to tensile stress. (Adapted from Panjabi et al., 1984)

bodies" (p. 480). In these whole spine cadaver tests, failure occurred with a compression fracture of the vertebral body in both cadaver subjects at the T12 vertebra level (Duma et al. 2006).

B. Ligaments and joints

The zygapophyseal joints (diarthrodial joints) with shallow articular surfaces are dependent upon the joint ligament capsule that surrounds the joint and upon surrounding muscle tissue which when active will stabilize all the joints of the lumbar spine when exposed to tension or shear stresses. The joints between the vertebral bodies (amphiarthrodial joints) are stabilized by the intervertebral disk in tension and shear stresses, in conjunction with the stabilization via ligament and muscle elements. The intervertebral disks occupying the space between the bodies are also able to resist compression stresses. (Tables 12.2, 12.3, 12.4)

Ligament tissue by definition attaches bone to bone (providing joint integrity). Ligaments, unlike muscle tissue, must be taken beyond the ROM (a.k.a. physiological range) in order to result in ligament trauma, including micro-trauma of ligaments (entering into P point on the stress-strain graph (i.e., P = proportionality limit point); (Nordin et al., in Nordin and Frankel, 2001, pp. 112-113 and chapter 3 of this present text. If the joint stays within its normal range of motion, then ligament tissue surrounding the lumbar spine will not move into its non-elastic zone or fail. Therefore the normal ROM must be exceeded for

Table 12.1
Compression and Tension Loads to Failure in Lumbar Vertebrae. Note that 4.45 newtons equal approximately 1 pound of force.
Adapted from Sonada (1962)

Age Group	Tension Failure	Compression Failure
20–39	7300 N / 1640 lbs	4640 N / 1043 lbs
40–59	4770 N / 1072 lbs	3820 N / 858 lbs
60–79	3080 N / 692 lbs	

ligament injury to occur within a specific motion unit of the spinal column.

One of the primary concerns when evaluating the tolerance limits of ligament is that various ligaments will have different responses to tensile loading due to their distinct make-up. Panjabi et al. (1984) have illustrated the diversity of lumbar ligament tensile responses related to collagen and elastin content. Here it is obvious that ligaments high in collagen (anterior and posterior longitudinal ligaments) have a much lower deformation under loading, while ligaments higher in elastin (ligamentum flavum) will deform easily under a smaller load. Further studies have confirmed these tests. Yoganandan et al. (2000) indicated that the posterior components (interspinous ligaments, joint capsules, and ligamentum flavum) exhibited a higher ultimate failure strain than the anterior components (anterior and posterior longitudinal ligaments). The

Table 12.2
Lumbar Disk Ultimate Compression Stress from
Bending Loads in Newtons and Pounds.
Adapted from Sonada (1962)

Cadaver Age Group	Compressive Stress
40–59	15000 (N) (3371 lbs)

Table 12.3
Lumbar Disk Ultimate Tension Stress from Bending
Loads in Newtons and Pounds.
Adapted from Sonada (1962)

Cadaver Age Group	Tensile Stress
20–39	3940 (N) (885 lbs)
40–79	2900 (N) (652 lbs)

Table 12.4
Lumbar Disk Torque Failure in
Newton-centimeters and foot-pounds.
Adapted from Sonada (1962)

Cadaver Age Group	Torque Failure (N-cm)	Ultimate Angle of Twist (degrees)*
20–39	4630 (34.3 ft.-lbs)	15
40–69	4250 (31.45 ft.-lbs)	13

* It is important to note that these angular displacements (rotation-longitudinal axis) are only possible in the presence of complete failure of the zygapophyseal joints, because these magnitudes of angular excursion are not possible in the intact lumbar spine.

reader is referred to Chapter 7 for a more detailed discussion of the material properties of ligament tissues.

C. The intervertebral disk

Intervertebral disks throughout the spine are subject to both axial and bending loads. The lumbar disks are subjected to much higher compressive loads than the cervical spine due to the large weight-bearing requirements and muscular attachments to the lumbar segments. In torsion load applications, the lumbar vertebral motion units have very little range of motion due in part to the orientation of the zygapophyseal joints, making the ultimate angle of twist much smaller (2 to 5°).

In acute single event rapid loading, it is the lumbar vertebral body that fails rather than the lumbar intervertebral disk. In other words, it is the vertebral body and the zygapophyseal joints that present the weak links rather than the intervertebral disk when loading is significant and rapid in the lumbar spine. The experimental evidence is clear in this regard. King (1993) states the following:

> With regard to the relationship between disc rupture and impact loading on the spine, it can be safely said that disc ruptures do not occur as the result of a single loading event, unless there are associated massive bony injuries to the spine.

This statement is based on a review of the literature on spinal response by Henzel et al. (1968), who indicated that early researchers such as Roaf (1960) observed that the vertebral body always broke before the adjacent disc incurred visible damage. Moreover, Brinckmann (1986) has shown that a severely weakened lumbar disc, with the posterior elements removed, could not be ruptured and hardly even bulged when loaded in compression to 1 kN (225 lbs). Additional loads causing fracture of the vertebral body did not result in herniation or excessive bulging of the disk.

Sonoda (1962) indicates that the compressive force necessary to rupture the intervertebral disk in the lumbar spine in people age forty to fifty-nine years is an average of 15,000 newtons (approximately 3,371 lbs). Furthermore, Sonoda found that tension loads which may occur during spine bending moments (e.g., flexion) produce failure of the lumbar spine intervertebral disk at approximately 2,900 newtons (648 lbs) for humans in this same age range. In terms of torsion (twisting loads), intervertebral disks in the lumbar spine in eleven specimens failed at averages of 4,630 newton-centimeters (20 to 39 years age range) and 4,250 newton-centimeters (40 to 69 age range) (Sonoda, 1962). However, it should be appreciated that these torsion failures only occurred in the laboratory setting when the lumbar spine disks could be taken to an average 13 to 15° of rotation. This rotation excursion in vivo lumbar spine would always produce zygapophyseal joint subluxation, dislocation or complete failure of the posterior bony elements of the vertebrae and therefore, in the absence of these bone fractures, this mechanism of disk injury is unrealistic. The intact lumbar spine is also protected and limited in axial rotation due to the orientation of the zygapophyseal joints as previously stated. In the absence of severe disruption of the these joints, rupture of the intervertebral disks would not occur consistent with the Sonoda 1962 data.

Farfan et al. (1970) achieved similar results when testing cadaver lumbar spine motion segments (two vertebral bodies and one intervertebral disk between the two bodies), with failure occurring at 22.9° of rotation for normal lumbar disks and failure at 15.2° of rotation for abnormal lumbar disks. Farfan also found that the facet ligament capsules failed at an earlier rotation displacement (14° for normal lumbar disks and 12° for abnormal lumbar disks). In other words, if the facets were allowed to slide completely over one another or they were allowed to fracture (facet bony elements), then rupture of the intervertebral disk could occur (King, 1993).

Finally, Adams and Hutton (1982) were able to bring lumbar intervertebral disks to failure if they brought the vertebral motion unit to a position beyond full physiological flexion (average of 12.9°) during coincident application of a large axial compression load.

King (1993) comments on these two research efforts in reference to lumbar spine disks:

This situation is again not representative of a realistic loading condition as it is extremely rare that a large compressive force would be applied to a spine that is virtually doubled over. Moreover, the herniation occurred between the disk (a.k.a. disc) and the end plate due to extreme tension on the posterior aspect of the disk. There was no rupture of the annulus (Adams and Hutton, 1982). In fact, both of these reports (Farfan et al., 1970 and Adams and Hutton, 1982) tend to reinforce the point of view that a single loading event is unable to cause disk rupture.

It must be appreciated that there is strong evidence that small repeated loads (thousands of cycles) can result in intervertebral disk bulging and failure most probably in the cervical or the lumbar spine. Any time the neck or torso is bent forward, backwards or sideways, it results in neck and torso moments with consequent stresses being applied to the intervertebral disks. When weight is added, the loads can increase dramatically in the lumbar spine due to the relatively long lever arm (Nordin and Frankel, 2001).

Experimental results of Nachemson (1966 and 1970) and Wilke (1999) during actual human in-vivo measurements of lumbar spine disks during selected body positions verify the high lumbar disk loading during forward bending body positions. Lifting with straight knees further increases the lumbar spine loading. Furthermore, these moments and forces are usually applied many times each day in moderately active people. In lumbar spine, Yang et al. (1988) were able to produce human cadaver lumbar disk herniation with extrusion of nucleus pulposus outside the lumbar disk with the application of repetitive combined loads of torsion, compression, and flexion. Failure occurred in the cadaver specimens after approximately 20,000 loading cycles (King, 1993). Gordon et al. (1991) were able to produce extrusion of the nucleus pulposus in only 4 of 14 motion units subjected to axial loads while the vertebral unit was also flexed and rotated (torsion). Ten disks failed via annular protrusion. Failure occurred at an average of 36,750 loading cycles (Gordon et al., 1991). It is clear that moderate loads that are normally imposed on the lumbar or cervical spine on a daily basis and over time can result in a bulge, protrusion and subsequent rupture of intervertebral disks in the degenerated spine.

Therefore, while the intervertebral disk is known to degenerate and weaken over time, acute high velocity trauma will usually result in a fracture of the bony elements before or coincident with disk failure. Certainly, this statement strongly applies to the lumbar spine. Alternatively, the level of disk degeneration at the time of impact may also be a factor in lumbar or in cervical intervertebral disk injury in significant loading. Each personal injury claim must be carefully examined by the biomechanist, and one analysis does not fit all.

Tolerance limits for lumbar spine intervertebral disks are presented in Tables 12.2, 12.3, and 12.4.

Another consideration with regard to torsion strength and degrees of twist (angular displacement) is possible pre-existing tears in the annulus fibrosus. Haughton et al. (2000) found that transverse and radial tears in the annular layers increase the flexibility of the lumbar spine when loaded in axial rotation. In normal disks, a torque of 570 N-cm resulted in 1.2° of rotation. In disks with transverse and radial tears of the annulus fibrosus, this same torque magnitude resulted in 2.5 and 2.6° of rotation, respectively. If these research results can be repeated with a larger group of cadaver specimens, then this is an interesting academic point. However, because normal and abnormal lumbar disks do not approach their failure point above and beyond ten degrees of rotation, this research effort does not imply an increased risk of injury under torsion loads in disks with annular tears.

D. Muscle and tendon tissue

1. Muscle tolerance

Muscles help to balance the external forces, moments, and torques applied to the lumbar spine in an attempt to maintain stability and minimize injury-producing internal forces transmitted to the spinal column. Unfortunately, muscle tissue is susceptible to injury, atrophy due to disuse, and fatigue due to overuse. The tolerance limits of the lumbar musculature are particularly important because of their crucial role in spinal stabilization. In addition, Shirazi-Adl et al. (2002) identified the importance of postural changes such as the degree of lumbar lordosis (convex forward lumbar spine), forward pelvic tilt, and the active and passive load distribution imposed upon the various spinal elements. Specific tolerance limits for human lumbar spine musculature have not been established. Please refer to Chapter 7 for a general discussion of muscle and Chapter 11 for additional information on spinal muscle elements.

2. Tendon tolerance

Tendon is a highly specialized dense fibrous connective tissue whose primary function is to transmit the forces of muscle elements. Elastin fibers comprise less than 3% of the tissue content. Collagen fibers are arranged longitudinally with a wavy appearance when relaxed. As a tension load is imposed upon a tendon, the wave-like collagen fibers straighten, producing an initial strain with a lower stress magnitude. However, once the fibers are straightened, tendon is generally stiff and exhibits little strain in order to transmit muscle tension effectively. For this reason, tendon stiffness is highly related to the load magnitude: the greater the load, the stiffer the tendon. A stiff reaction results in a more rapid and precise muscle contraction. However, Proske and Morgan (1987) state that initial tendon stretch (albeit small) helps to protect contracting muscle fibers by storing elastic energy. Tendon size is also variable throughout the body, exhibiting different ultimate tension failure points when tested (cross-sectional area being the determinant factor in tendons). A more detailed discussion of the strength properties of tendon can be found in Chapter 7.

E. Neural structures

With regards to nerve root tolerance limits, it is important to note that the ultimate strength of neural tissue alone is extremely low. Neural tissue is delicate and very susceptible to injury. In vivo, however, the central nervous system is protected by the thick dural sheath that extends as far as the nerve roots. The dural covering shields the nerve roots as they pass through the intervertebral foramina, then funnels as the roots become peripheral nerves. The protection at this junction is crucial in that the nerve root is subjected to significant tension and shear stresses during movement of the spinal column and extremities. See Chapter 8 for a more detailed discussion of neural tissue tolerance limits.

12.6 Lumbar Spine Sources of Pain

It is estimated that back disorders and low back pain are responsible for a quarter of the total lost workdays in the United States, with billions of dollars being spent annually for compensation costs (Waters et al., 1998). In general, pain is a subjective phenomenon that is impossible to measure objectively. While science can measure stimulation of nociceptive systems, the perception of pain has a different threshold and tolerance level for everyone. It is essential to recognize that pain can be caused not only by mechanical deformation but by biochemical irritation as well. The lumbar spine is particularly vulnerable to biochemical irritation induced pain due to the close proximity of neural tissue and intervertebral disk materials. Studies have shown a significant increase in inflammatory enzymes to be present in lumbar herniated and degenerated disks (Saal, 1995). The neurotoxic effects of the nucleus pulposus upon neural tissue may cause a cascade of inflammatory and immunochemical reactions and may play a large role in some patients with lumbar spine pain.

Understanding the sources of potential pain in the lumbar region is particularly important due to both the frequency of low back pain and the difficulty in isolating the etiology. Deyo (1998) indicates that bony elements, musculature, ligaments, intervertebral disks, neural tissues, and blood vessels all have the potential to be an underlying cause lumbar spine pain. One final passageway is the nerve afferent nociceptor (pain neuron) in the spine (sacral, lumbar, thoracic and cervical) which transmits impulses with what is sometimes termed a bifurcated axon to an afferent neuron cell body located in the dorsal root ganglion. Some of these nociceptive neurons also have a somatosensory function as well as being able to sense pain. This electrical signal is then transmitted away from the cell body in the dorsal root ganglion to the dorsal horn of the spinal cord to a second order neuron which then relays and transmits the impulses to the higher centers of the central nervous system by means of afferent ascending nerve tracts to the thalamus (diencephalon) and/or mid-brain (mesencephalon) of the upper central nervous system. In turn, third order neurons send signals to the somatosensory cerebral cortex and cingulate cortex (telencephalon structures) for somatosensory function (e.g., joint position or muscle length monitoring; see chapter 19) and pain (nociceptive) discrimination/perception (Allegri et al., 2016). At the spinal level, Allegri et al. (2016) indicate that within the dorsal horn of the spinal cord, the integration of second order neuron activity is inhibited or facilitated by several interneuron populations forming descending pathways which are able to modulate the nocicepitive (pain) signals.

A second pathway has now been clarified and is a non-segmental pathway ascending through the paravertebral sympathetic chain (part of the autonomic nervous system) with re-entry through the thoracolumbar white rami communicantes (Edgar, 2007). Ohtori et al. (2015) also report that although the presence and nature of intervertebral disk nerve innervation still presents some controversy, many investigators have reported that in the lumbar spine, innervation of the sinuvertebral nerves consisting of sensory and postganglionic sympathetic fibers is present. In terms of pain originating within the intervertebral disk, several studies have reported nerve innervation of free nerve endings and complex nerve endings, primarily in the outer layers of the annulus fibrosus which most probably serve as sensory proprioceptors as well as nociceptive (pain) receptors. Furthermore, some evidence indicates that sensory nerve endings in the degenerative disk penetrate deep into the disrupted nucleus pulposus and become sensitive to pain stimuli leading to one source of chronic lower back pain (Edgar, 2007). Ohtori et al. (2015) indicate the immunohistochemical studies have revealed molecular substances of these nerve fibers innervating the intervertebral disk. These molecular substances within human intervertebral disks include: "protein-gene-related product 9.5, substance P (i.e., SP), calcitonin, gene-related peptide (CGRP), dopamine Beta-hydroxylase, neuropeptide Y, and tyrosine hydroxylase" (Ohtori et al. 2015, p 1348). If these neurtoxic substances persist within the lumbar spine region, peripheral and central nervous system sensitization may occur. This sensitization may convert lower back pain from acute to chronic and central sensitization (spinal cord level) is thought to be due to increased excitability of nociceptive second order neurons wherein normal sensory inputs from the body peripheral inputs result in abnormal nociceptive responses (Allegri et al. 2016).

Furthermore, Binch et al. (2014) discuss the release of cytokine IL-1Beta during intervertebral disk degeneration which may induce significant increases in neural growth factor and vascular endothelial growth factor which could promote neuronal and vascular ingrowth within the disk. Therefore cytokine IL-1Beta appears to be a key regulatory cytokine which results in the upregulation of innervation and vascularisation of tissue such as the intervertebral disk (Binch, et al., 2014). An increase in innervation at the very least indicates a rationale for an increased or prolonged (chronic) pain response.

A. Bony structures

It is clearly understood that bone fractures are a source of pain. Bone is a highly vascularized and innervated tissue. Bone fractures or bone bruises will result in pain which may be variable in intensity. Fractures through the joint will usually result in significant bone pain as the fracture proceeds through the articular lamella. Please note however that the articular cartilage that lines joint surfaces is avascular and without neural innervation and therefore is not thought to be a source of pain. The source of pain at the zygapophyseal joints of the lumbar spine in the absence of fractures and the joints between the vertebral bodies may be related to the inflammation of ligamentous tissue or synovial tissue. Other sources of lower back pain include discogenic pain and stenosis of the spinal cord/ cauda equina or of compression or tension loads applied to nerve roots at the intervertebral foramina. See chapter 8 for additional information.

B. Joints—ligamentous and capsular pain

In general, ligaments have a poor blood supply in comparison to muscles, which results in slower healing and remodeling of tissues, which reduces their normal gliding capabilities in response to tension.

Although ligaments do not have an extensive blood supply, they do have innervation via proprioceptors (mechanoreceptors) that assist the body in postural awareness, joint range of motion, responses to changes in position and pain. In addition, ligamentous injuries do cause inflammation that can ignite nociceptors in surrounding soft tissues.

C. The intervertebral disk

The lumbar spine, in particular L4–L5 and L5–S1, is the most common site of disk degeneration. Degeneration is accompanied by a decrease in the hydrophilic properties of the nucleus pulposus, thus lowering the osmotic pressure. An overall loss of water within the disk weakens the annular layers, and with time the disk can become displaced, compressed, or fractured, leading to increased mechanical stresses upon the structures within the spinal canal (Porterfield and DeRosa, 1998).

Intradiscal pressure is also largely related to posture. Wilke (1999) used intradiscal pressure probes (L4–L5) in-vivo to investigate postures and disk pressures in human subjects. He found that a standing forward stooped posture, for example, can more than double the intradiscal pressure compared to normal upright standing. In addition, as disk degeneration progresses, changes in the disk render it incapable of maintaining its prior intradiscal pressure.

D. The lumbar intervertebral disk in asymptomatic people

Many studies have correlated lumbar disk herniations as a significant source of pain that can be identified through imaging techniques. However, recent findings indicate similar pathologic MRI and radiographic findings in control groups of asymptomatic people.

Jensen et al. (1994) evaluated the lumbar spine magnetic resonance (MR) imaging results of ninety-eight volunteer subjects (ages twenty to eighty years) without symptoms of low back pain and without any past history of low back pain lasting more than forty-eight hours. Findings revealed that 52% of the participants were positive for an intervertebral disk bulge at one or more levels within the lumbar spine; 27% showed disk protrusion; and 1% had actual extrusion of nucleus pulposus (i.e., frank herniation). Fourteen percent of the disks showed annular defects, and 38% of the subjects had a bulge or protrusion in more than one lumbar disk. In addition, several abnormalities were identified that were not related to the intervertebral disk. Nineteen percent of the subjects presented with Schmorl's nodes, and 8% had significant facet arthropathy. All subjects were completely asymptomatic.

Weishaupt et al. (1998) examined the lumbar MR images of sixty asymptomatic people between the ages of twenty and fifty years. Results found disk bulging in 62% of the patients and disk protrusion in 67% of the patients. Interestingly, some 18% of the subjects had frank disk extrusions, and one patient presented with apparent nerve root compression.

Stadnik et al. (1998) performed lumbar MR imaging of 36 asymptomatic volunteers. Eighty-one percent of the subjects had obvious disk bulges, 33% with focal disk protrusions. Annular tears were also present in 56% of the subjects, with 27 annular tears showing contrast enhancement.

Jarvik et al. (2001) evaluated the lumbar MR images of 148 asymptomatic participants. Roughly half of the group (46%) had never suffered from low back pain and the remainder of subjects had been pain free for at least four months. Moderate to severe disk desiccation (altered magnetic signal due to dehydration) was seen in 123 of the subjects (83%). In addition, bulging disk(s) were seen in ninety-five (64%) subjects, and eighty-three (56%) subjects showed a loss in disk height (Jarvik et al., 2001). Further progression of disk degeneration was observed, with 32% of the subjects showing at least one disk protrusion, 6% with greater than one protrusion, and 3% of the subjects showing herniations large enough to be associated with neural compromise (Jarvik et al., 2001).

Carragee et al. (2000) compared MRI results with discography to observe the relationship between magnetic high intensity zones and disk pathology. This research effort evaluated a low back pain symptomatic group and an asymptomatic group (but known to have disk degeneration risk factors). Previous studies have argued that the presence of a high intensity zone on MR images is strongly suggestive of a positive discography due to annular tears (Aprill and Bogduk, 1992). Carragee et al. (2000) found that 59% of the symptomatic group and 24% of the asymptomatic group revealed areas of lumbar disk high intensity on MR imaging. However, only 72.7% (symptomatic) and 69.2% (asymptomatic) of patients with these lumbar disk high intensity zones had a positive discography finding with follow-up testing. In addition, discography testing showed positive results for patients without high intensity zones: 38.2% in the symptomatic group and 10% in the asymptomatic group. Carragee et al. (2000) state that these results indicate no clinically meaningful relationship between high intensity MRI findings and symptomatic disk pathology. Therefore, the frequent positive lumbar spine disk MRIs of asymptomatic people are problematic for use of high intensity zones as a diagnostic tool for symptomatic internal disk disruption (Carragee et al., 2000).

As positive lumbar disk imaging results are seen in multiple studies involving the asymptomatic adult population, one has to question a cause and effect relationship between acute trauma and disk bulges, protrusions, and frank herniations. Although the presence of frank extrusions and severe herniations are less common in asymptomatic people, they can and do occur. Furthermore, positive imaging on patients complaining of low back pain may be merely coincidental. More recently, CT scan methodology and/or live fluoroscopy with contrast is being used in provocation testing of the intervertebral disk to look at abnormality of the intervertebral disk with additional detail. However, provocative discography has been criticized for its diagnostic accuracy and specificity and it has been demonstrated that the needle puncture of the tested disk may lead to an acceleration of DDD. It is hypothesized that this iatrogenic damage may be due to needle puncture entry, pressurization, and toxicity of the contrast media (Allegri et al., 2016).

E. Muscle tissue

Due to the complex fascial networks encompassing the lumbar spine, many complaints of pain are attributed to a myofascial source. Myofascial pain is thought to result from an acute muscle strain or muscle overload that occurs at the time of loading (Teasell, 1993). Muscle strains that include a tearing of individual muscle fibers will result in bleeding within the fascial layers of the tissue. Inflammation due to this bleeding can cause swelling, pain, and scar tissue formation if damage is significant. In addition, tearing of muscle fibers will disrupt the sarcolemma membrane, increasing calcium permeability of muscle fibers which in turn may increase contractile activity (Nordhoff et al., 1996). The authors speculate that this sustained muscle contraction causes a decrease in local blood flow, low oxygen tension, and the production of nociceptive by-products. Finally, Nordhoff et al. (1996) speculate that calcium re-uptake may be diminished in ruptured muscle fibers, leaving free calcium behind to perpetuate the contraction process. Friction (1993) speculates that this fiber damage may result in a pain-spasm-pain cycle that can be difficult to treat. Conversely, more recent evidence indicates that free calcium within ruptured muscle fibers after injury may serve as a trigger in attracting histamines, prostaglandins, and other immune response substances in speeding the healing response of muscle rather than in perpetuating muscle contraction (Coast, 2004). Finally, the invasion of inflammatory cells such as neutrophils after muscle injury may be useful in repair or conversely may produce further muscle injury (Lieber, 2002).

Aside from the acute effects of muscle injury, there is much debate regarding the extent to which torn muscle fibers can repair themselves. Undifferentiated satellite cells (myogenic precursor cells) lie on the periphery of muscle fibers and have the potential for fusing together as myoblasts and becoming whole new muscle cells in times of injury (Lieber, 2002). However, large muscle tears ultimately involve many layers of the interconnected fascia within and surrounding muscle tissue. Fascial tissue is more likely to heal by way of scarring, which is speculated to result in more permanent tissue restrictions.

Abnormally healed myofascial tissue may form adhesions that interrupt normal blood flow, contractile shortening, or provide simple mechanical irritation to peripheral nerves (Nordhoff et al., 1996). Biological individuality most probably plays an important role in the formation of abnormally formed myofascial tissue after muscle injury.

The characteristic features of myofascial pain are referred to as trigger points or hyperirritable locations of point tenderness. The tenderness of a trigger point is hypothesized to be due to the physiological and chemical changes (described previously) in a muscle undergoing sustained contraction. Specific etiology of myofascial pain has not been determined in the present, and research is ongoing. Friction (1993) did show a stimulation of nociceptive nerve endings due to sustained muscle contraction in cats. However, the symptoms associated with myofascial pain may be very similar to underlying systemic, metabolic, or endocrine disorders, as well as to drug reactions, allergies, neoplasm, sleep disorders, or connective tissue disease (Nordhoff et al., 1996). The similarities between myofascial pain symptoms and other disorders makes proper diagnosis difficult and oftentimes only speculative.

F. Neural structures

Nerve Nerve endings in bone and some nerve endings in soft tissue structures surrounding the lumbar spine act as nociceptors in addition to mechanoreceptors. Ultimately, these are the link to bone and soft tissue pain as afferent endings transmit signals to the spinal cord through the dorsal roots to the spinal cord and upper central nervous system (See Chapter 8 and 9). Additionally, trauma that directly produces shear, tension, or compression strains to the spinal cord, nerve roots, or peripheral nerves will produce pain, irritation, and inflammation as well as possibly result in sensory and motor deficits. Irritation and inflammation of the spinal cord or nerve roots can occur due to both mechanical strains and biochemical changes within the ruptured disk. Posterior herniations are more common in the lumbar spine due to the lack of protection of the thin posterior longitudinal ligament, larger amounts of nucleus pulposus within the lumbar disk in comparison to the cervical spine disk, and the increased lordotic curve in the lower lumbar spine (Porterfield and DeRosa, 1998).

References

Adams MA and Dolan P. "Recent Advances in Lumbar Spine Mechanics and their Clinical Significance." *Clinical Biomechanics*. 10(1):3–19. (1995)

Adams MA and Hutton WC. "Prolapsed Intervertebral Disc. A Hyperflexion Injury." *Spine.* 7(3):184–191. (1982)

Albright JA. "Bone: Physical Properties." *The Scientific Basis of Orthopedics.* Albright JA Brand RA (Eds.). Norwalk, CT: Appleton and Lange. 213–240. (1987)

Allegri, M., Montella, S., Salici, F. Valente, A., Marchesini, M., Compagnone, C., Baciarello, M., Manferdini, M. and Fanelli, G. (2016) Mechanisms of low back pain: a guide for diagnosis and therapy. Version 2. F1000Res. v. 5: F1000 Faculty Rev-1530. October. doi: 10.12688/f1000research.8105.2

Alvarez JA and Hardy RH. "Lumbar Spine Stenosis: a Common Cause of Back and Leg Pain." *American Family Physician.* 1–12. (1998)

Barker PJ, Briggs CA and Bogeski G. "Tensile Transmission Across the Lumbar Fascia in Unembalmed Cadavers." *Spine.* 29(2):129–138. (2004)

Battie, M., Videman, T., Levalahti, E., Gill, K. Kaprio, J. (2008) Genetic and environmental effects of disc degeneration by phenotype and spinal level: A multivariate twin study. Spine, V. 33(25), pp. 2801-2808.

Begeman PC, King AI and Prasad P. "Spinal Loads Resulting From -Gx Acceleration." *Proceedings from the 17th Stapp Car Crash Conference.* Warrendale, PA: Society of Automotive Engineers. 73-0977. (1973)

Binch, A., Cole, A., Breakwell, L., Michael, A., Chiverton, N., Cross, A., Le Maitre, C. (2014) Expression and regulation of neurotrophic and angiogenic factors during human intervertebral disk degeneration. Arthritis Research and Therapy v. 16(5) 416. 10.1186/s13075-014-0416-1

Brinckman, M., Chau, C. and Ross, J. (2015) Marrow edema variability in acute spine fractures. The Spine Journal v. 15, pp. 454-460.

Buckwalter JA. "Aging and Degeneration of the Human Intervertebral Disk." *Spine.* 20(11):1307–1314. (1995)

Carragee EJ, Paragioudakis SJ and Khurana S. "2000 Volvo Award Winner in Clinical Studies: Lumbar High-intensity Zone and Discography in Subjects without Low Back Problems." *Spine.* 25(23):2987–92. (2000)

Chance GO. "Note of a Type of Flexion Fracture of the Spine." *British Journal of Radiology.* 21:452–453. (1948)

Cholewicki J, Simons APD and Radebold A. "Effects of External Trunk Loads on Lumbar Spine Stability." *Journal of Biomechanics.* 33(11):1377–1385. (2000)

Coast, R. Personal communication on Oct. 7, 2004.

Denis F. "The Three Column Spine and its Significance in the Classification of Acute Thoracolumbar Spine Injuries." *Spine.* 8(8):817–31. (1983)

Deyo R. "Low Back Pain." *Scientific American.* 279(2):48–53. (1998)

Dolan P and Adams MA. "Repetitive Lifting Tasks Fatigue the Back Muscles and Increase the Bending Moment Acting on the Spine." *Journal of Biomechanics.* 31:713–721. (1998)

Duma, S., Kemper, A., McNeely, D., Brolinson, G., and Matsuoka, F. (2006) Biomechanical response of the lumbar spine in dynamic compression. Presentation at the Rocky Mountain Bioengineering Symposium & International ISA Biomedical Sciences Instrumentation Symposium, April 7-9, 2006, Terre Haute, Indiana.

Edgar, M. (2007) The nerve supply of the lumbar intervertebral disc. British Journal of Bone and Joint Surgery. v. 89(9). pp. 1135-1139.h

Farfan HF, Cossette JW, Robertson GH, Wells RV, Kraus H. "The Effects of Torsion on the Lumbar Intervertebral Joints: the Role of Torsion in the Production of Disc Degeneration." *J. of Bone and Joint Surgery* 52A:468–497. (1970)

Gardner-Morse M and Stokes IA. "Structural Behavior of Human Lumbar Ligaments." *Journal of Biomechanics.* 37(2):205–212. (2004)

Gibson, L. and Ashby, M. (1988) Cellular Solids Structure and Properties, Pergamon Press, Oxford.

Gordon SJ, Yang KH, Mayer PJ, Mace AH, Kish VL and Radin EL. "Mechanism of Disk Rupture: a Preliminary Report." *Spine.* 16(4):450–456. (1991)

Greenspan, A. *Orthopedic Radiology. A Practical Approach.* New York: Gower Medical Publishing.(1992)

Gruber HE and Hanley EN. "Human Disc Cells in Mono-layer vs 3d Culture: Cell Shape and Matrix Formation." *BMC Musculoskeletal Disorders.* 1:1 (2000).

Gu WY, Rawlins BA, Iatridis JC, Foster RJ, Sun DN, Weidenbaum M and Mow VC. "Streaming Potential of Human Lumbar Annulus Fibrosus is Anisotropic and Affected by Disk Degeneration." *Journal of Biomechanics.* 32:1177–1182.(1999)

Haughton VM, Schmidt TA, Keele K, An HS and Lim T. "Flexibility of Lumbar Spinal Motion Segments Correlated to Type of Tears in the Annulus Fibrosus." *Journal of Neurosurgery.* 92:81-6. (2000)

Healy, J., Healy, B., Wong, S., and Olson, E. (1996) Cervical and lumbar MRI in symptomatic older male lifelong athletes: Frequency of degenerative findings. Journal of Computer Assisted Tomography v. 20(1), pp. 107-112.

Hodges PW, Cresswell AG, Daggfeldt K and Thorstensson A. (2001) *Journal of Biomechanics.* 34:347–353.

Ivancic, P. (2013) Hybrid cadaveric/surrogate model of thoracolumbar spine injury due to simulated fall from height. Accident Analysis and Prevention. v. 59, pp. 185-191.

Jarvik JJ, Hollingworth W, Heagerty P, Haynor DR and Deyo RA. "The Longitudinal Assessment of Imaging and Disability of the Back (LAIDBack) Study:" Baseline data. *Spine.* 26(10):1158–66. (2001)

Jensen MC, Brant-Zawadzki MN, Obuchowski N, Modic MT, Malkasian D and Ross JS. "Magnetic Resonance Imaging of the Lumbar Spine in People without Back Pain." *New England Journal of Medicine.* 331(2). (1994)

Kazarian LE. "Injuries to the Human Spinal Column: Biomechanics and Injury Classification." *Exercise and Sports Science Review.* 9:297–352. (1982)

Keller, RH. "Traumatic Displacement of the Cartilaginous Vertebral Rim: A Sign of Intervertebral Disc Prolapse." *Radiology.* 110:21–24. (1974)

King AI. "Injury to the Thoraco-Lumbar Spine and Pelvis" *Accidental Injury.* Nahum AM and Melvin JW,(Eds.). New York: Springer-Verlag. (1993)

King AI. "Injury to the Thoraco-Lumbar Spine and Pelvis," *Accidental Injury,* Second edition. Nahum AM and Melvin JW,(Eds.). New York: Springer-Verlag. (2002)

Lieber, R. *Skeletal Muscle Structure, Function and Plasticity, Second ed.* Lippencott, Williams and Wilkins. Philadelphia. (2002)

Lotz JC and Chin JR. "Intervertebral Disc Cell Death is Dependent on the Magnitude and Duration of Spinal Loading." *Spine.* 15(25):1477–83. (2000)

Malanga, G., Young, C., Memmo, P., Chimes, G., Talavera, F., and Perron, A. (2013) Lumbosacral facet syndrome. Medscape, 9/13/2015 update. http://emedicine.medscapte.com/article/94871-overview

Manoogian, S., Funk, J., Cormier, J., Bain, C., Guzman, H., and Bonugli, E. (2010) Evaluation of thoracic and lumbar accelerations of volunteers in vertical and horizontal loading scenarios. SAE Publication (2010-01-0146)

Martin, J., Oldweiler, A., Spritzer, C., Soher, B., Erickson, M., Goode, A., and DeFrate, L. (2018) A magnetic resonance imaging framework for quantifying intervertebral disc deformation in vivo: Reliability and application to diurnal variations in lumbar disc shape, Journal of Biomechanics, v. 71,pp. 291-295.

McGill SM. "Linking Latest Knowledge of Injury Mechanisms and Spine Function to the Prevention of Low Back Disorders."*Journal of Electromyology and Kinesiology.* 14(1):43–47. (2004)

Nachemson A. *Intravital Dynamic Pressure Measurement in Lumbar Disks.* Stockholm: Almquist & Wiksell. (1970)

Nachemson A. "The Load on Lumbar Disks in Different Positions of the Body." *Clin Orthop.* 45:107–122 (1966)

Nordhoff LS, Murphy D, and Underhill M. "Diagnosis of Common Crash Injuries." *Motor Vehicle Collision Injuries.* Nordhoff LS (Ed.) Gaithersburg, MD: Aspen Publishing Co. (1996)

Nordin M and Frankel VH. *Basic Biomechanics of the Musculoskeletal System,* Third edition. Philadelphia PA: Lippincott Williams and Wilkins. (2001)

Panjabi M, Jorneus L and Greenskin G. "Physical Properties of Lumbar Spine Ligaments." *Trans Orthopedic Res Soc.* 9:112. (1984)

Parizel, P., van der Zijden, T., Gaudino, S., Spaepen, M., Voormolen, M., Venstermans, C., De Belder, F. van den Hauwe, L. and Van Goethem, J. (2010) Trauma of the spine and spinal cord: imaging strategies. European Spine Journal, v. 19(1), pp. 8-17.

Patwardhan AG, Havey RM, Carandang G, Simonds J, Voronov LI, Ghanayem AJ, Meade KP, Gavin TM and Paxinos O. "Effect of Compressive Follower Preload on the Flexion-extension Response of the Human Lumbar Spine." *Journal of Biomechanics.* 21:540–546. (2003)

Patwardhan AG, Meade KP and Lee B. "A Frontal Plane Model of the Lumbar Spine Subjected to a Follower Preload: Implications for the Roles of Muscles.*" Journal of Biomechanical Engineering.* 123:212–217. (2001)

Porter RW. "The Pathophysiology of Neurogenic Claudication." *Lumbar Spine Disorders: Current Concepts.* Aspden RM and Porter RW (Eds.). Singapore: World Scientific Publishing Co.s (1995)

Porterfield JA and DeRosa C. *Mechanical Low Back Pain: Perspectives in Functional Anatomy,* Second edition. Philadelphia, PA: WB Saunders Company. (1998)

Porterfield JA and DeRosa C. *Mechanical Neck Pain: Perspectives in Functional Anatomy.* Philadelphia, PA: WB Saunders Company. (1995)

Proske U and Morgan DL. "Tendon Stiffness: Methods of Measurement and Significance for Control of Movement." *Journal of Biomechanics.* 20:75–82. (1987)

Purohit, N., Skiadas, V. and Sampson, M. (2015) Imaging features of spinal trauma: what the radiologist needs to know. Clinical Radiology. v. 70, pp. 544-554.

Reeves NP and Cholewicki J. "Modeling the Human Lumbar Spine for Assessing Loads, Stability and Risk of Injury." *Critical Reviews in Biomechanical Engineering.* 31(1):73–139. (2003)

Saal JS. "The Role of Inflammation in Lumbar Pain." *Spine.* 20(16):1821–1827. (1995)

Shirazi-Adi A, Sadouk S, Parnianpour M, Pop D and El-Rich M. "Muscle Force Evaluation and the Role of Posture in Human Lumbar Spine under Compression." *European Spine Journal.* 11:519–526. (2002)

Sonada T. "Studies on the Strength for Compression, Ten-

sion and Torsion of the Human Vertebral Column." *J Kyoto Pref Med Univ.* 71:659–7023. (1962)

Stadnik RW, Lee RR, Caen HL, Neirynck EC, Buisseret TS and Osteaux MJ. "Annular Tears and Disk Herniation: Prevalence and Contrast Enhancement on MR Images in the Absence of Low Back Pain or Sciatica." *Radiology.* 206(1):49–55. (1998)

Steckler RM, Epstein JA and Epstein BS. 'Seatbelt Trauma to the Lumbar Spine." *Journal of Trauma.* 9:508–513. (1969)

Stokes IA and Gardner-Morse M. *Journal of Electromyography and Kinesiology.* 13(4):397–402. (2003)

Teasell RW. "The Clinical Picture of Whiplash Injuries. Cervical Flexion-Extension/Whiplash Injuries." *SPINE: State of the Art Reviews.* 7(3):373–37. (1993)

Walsh JL and Lotz JC. "Biological Response of the Intervertebral Disk to Dynamic Loading." *Journal of Biomechanics.* 37:329–337. (2004)

Waters TR, Baron SL, Piacitelli LA, Anderson VP, Skov T, Haring-Sweeney M, Wall DK and Fine LJ. "Evaluation of the Revised NIOSH Lifting Equation: a Cross-sectional Epidemiologic Study." *Spine.* 24(4):386–395. (1999)

Weishaupt D, Zanetti M, Hodler J and Boos N. "MR Imaging of the Lumbar Spine: Prevalence of Intervertebral Disk Extrusion and Sequestration, Nerve Root Compression, End Plate Abnormalities and Osteoarthritis of the Facet Joints in Asymptomatic Volunteers." *Radiology.* 209(3):661–666. (1998)

White AA and Panjabi, M., *Clinical Biomechanics of the Spine.* Lippincott, Philadelphia. (1978)

White AA and Panjabi MM. *Clinical Biomechanics of the Spine,* Second edition. Philiadelphia, PA: JB Lippincott. (1990)

White ML. "MR Imaging Techniques and Anatomy.*"The Cervical Spine.* 8(3):455–456. (2000)

Wilke HJ, Neef P, Caimi M, et al. "New in Vivo Measurements of Pressures in the Intervertebral Disc in Daily Life." *Spine.* 24:755. (1999)

Yamada H. *Strength of Biological Materials.* Baltimore, MD: Williams and Wilkins. (1970)

Yamaguchi G. *Dynamic Modeling of Musculoskeletal Motion: A Vectorized Approach for Biomechanical Analysis in Three Dimensions.* Boston, MA: Kluwer Academic Publishers. (2001)

Yoganandan N, Kumaresan S and Pintar FA. "Geometric and Mechanical Properties of Human Cervical Spine Ligaments." *Journal of Biomechanical Engineering.* 122:623–629. (2000)

Yue JJ, Lawrence BD, Sutton KM, Strugar JJ and Haims AH. "Complete Cervical intervertebral Disc Extrusion with Spinal Cord Injury in the Absence of Facet Dislocation: a Case Report." *Spine.* 29:E181-184. (2004)

Recommended Reading

Adams MA and Hutton WC. "The Mechanical Functions of the Lumbar Apophyseal Joints." *Spine.* 8:327. (1983)

Aprill C and Bogduk N. "The Prevalence of Cervical Zygapophyseal Joint Pain: A first Approximation." *Spine.* 17:744–747. (1992)

Atlas OK, Dodds S and Panjabi MM. "Single and Incremental Trauma Models: a Biomechanical Assessment of Spinal Instability." *European Spine Journal.* 12:205–210.s (2003)

Barnsley L, Lord S, Wallis B et. al. "Lack of Effect of Intraarticular Corticosteroids for Chronic Pain in the Cervial Zygoapophyseal joints." *New England Journal of Medicine.* 330:1047–50. (1994)

Delp SL, Suryanarayanan S, Murray WM, Uhlir J and Triolo RJ. "Architechture of the Rectus Abdominis, Quadratus Lumborum and Erector Spinae. *Journal of Biomechanics.* 34:371–375. (2001)

Frank C, Woo S, Andriacchi T, Brand R, Oakes B, Dahners L, DeHaven K, Lewis J and Sabiston P. "Normal Ligament: Structure, Function, and Composition." *Injury and Repair of the Musculoskeletal Soft Tissues.* Woo and Buckwalter (Eds.). Park Ridge, Ill: American Academy of Orthopaedic Surgeons.

Gore D, Sepic S, Gardner G. "Roentgenographic Findings of the Cervical Spine in Asymptomatic People.' *Spine.* 11:6:521–524. (1986)

Hannon, P.R. and Knapp, K.L. "Causes of Injury: A Review of the Low-Impact Human-Subject Literature." *Low-Speed Automobile Accidents,* Third edition.

Watts, A.J. (Ed.) Tucson, AZ: Lawyers & Judges Pub. Co. (2003)

Magee DJ. *Orthopedic Physical Assessment,* Fourth edition Philiadelphia, PA: WB Saunders Co. (2002)

Marieb, EN. *Human Anatomy and Physiology, Fourth Edition.* Menlo Park, CA: Benjamin/Cummings Science Publishing. 725–735. (1998)

Nahum AM and Melvin JW. *The Biomechanics of Trauma.* Norwalk, CT: Appleton-Century Crofts. (1985)

Nahum AM and Melvin JW. *Accidental Injury: Biomechanics and Prevention.* New York , NY: Springer-Verlag. (2002)

Rauschning W. "Anatomy of the Normal and Traumatized Spine." *Mechanisms of Head and Spine Trauma.* Sances A et al. (Eds.) New York: Alory. 531–563. (1986)

Riches PE, Dhillon N, Lotz J, Woods AW and McNally DS. "The Internal Mechanics of the Intervertebral Disk under Cyclic Loading." *Journal of Biomechanics.* 35:1263–1271. (2002)

Saal JA. "Natural History and Nonoperative treatment of Lumbar Disk Herniation." *Spine.* 21(24S):2S-9S. (1996)

Sances A, Yoganandan N, Myklebust JB. "Biomechanics and Accident Investigation." *Handbook of Biomedical Engineering.* Milwaukee, WI: Academic Press Inc. (1988)

Strother and James. *Evaluation of Seat Back Strength and Seat Belt Effectiveness in Rear-end Impacts.* Warrendale, PA: Society of Automotive Engineers. 87-2214. (1987)

Szabo T, Welcher J, Anderson R, Rice R, Ward J, Paulo L, Carpenter N. *Human Occupant Kinematic Response to Low Speed Rear-end Impacts.* Warrendale, PA: Society of Automotive Engineers. 94-0532 (1994)

Szabo T and Welcher J. *Human Subject Kinematics and Electromyographic Activity During Low Speed Rear Impacts.* Warrendale, PA: Society of Automotive Engineers. 96-2432 (1996)

Whiting WC and Zernicke RF. *Biomechanics of Musculoskeletal Injury.* Champaign, Il: Human Kinetics. (1998)

Wilder, C., Pope, M., Frymoyer, J. (1988) The biomechanics of lumbar disc herniation and the effect of
overload and instabilty. Journal of Spinal Disorders,
v. 1 (1) pp. 16-32.

Yang KH, Byrd III, AJ, Kish, VL, Radin , EL . *Annulus
Fibrosus Tears-an Experimental Model.* Orthop Trans
12:86–87. (1988)

The Human Upper Extremity

Mark W. Cornwall

(See CD-Rom Upper Extremity Anatomy)

The human upper extremity is very well adapted to maximize the functional capacity of the hand. Without its unique structure, humans would not be able to position their hand through a very wide range of motion. Further, it plays an important role in being able to lift, move and position objects. In addition, when both extremities are combined, this ability to move and position objects is significantly increased. This increased mobility and functionality, however, come at a cost. The joints of the up-

per extremity often sacrifice structural stability in order to provide the increased mobility.

The next three chapters will examine the three major regions of the upper extremity: the shoulder complex, the elbow and the wrist and hand. Common injuries or diseases seen in each of these regions will also be presented. In addition to the content in these chapters, the anatomical structures of the upper extremity are further illustrated on the accompanying CD.

Chapter 13

The Shoulder

Mark W. Cornwall

13.1 Introduction

The shoulder joint complex is extremely important for the many things that we either need to do or like to do. Without a strong, functioning shoulder complex, we would have difficulty doing a very large array of activities that are essential to daily life. Unfortunately, we often take these for granted; such things as "activities of daily living," which includes combing our hair, brushing our teeth, bringing food to our mouth and getting dressed. In addition, we need the shoulder to lift, reach and manipulate objects either around our home or at our place of employment. The anatomical structures and their organization allow for such important activities. Unfortunately, the versatility and capability of the shoulder joint complex means that it is susceptible to injury, especially as we age. This chapter will describe the basic anatomy of the shoulder joint complex, the motions that are available and the actions of the surrounding musculature that produce those movements. We will then discuss some of the more common injuries or disorders that are found in the shoulder.

13.2 Anatomy of the Shoulder

A. Bones and joints of the shoulder

The shoulder joint complex is composed of four different bones. These bones are the sternum ("breast bone"), the clavicle ("collar bone"), the scapula ("shoulder blade") and the humerus (arm). (Figure 13.1) These bones then form three joints, the sternoclavicular joint, the acromio-clavicular joint and the glenohumeral joint. The gleno-humeral joint is the one that people typically think of as the shoulder joint. The shoulder joint is composed of the humerus articulating with the scapula and is classified as a "ball" and "socket" joint. The humerus being the "ball" and the glenoid fossa of the scapula being the "socket". (Figure 13.2) This "socket" is fairly shallow, but is made

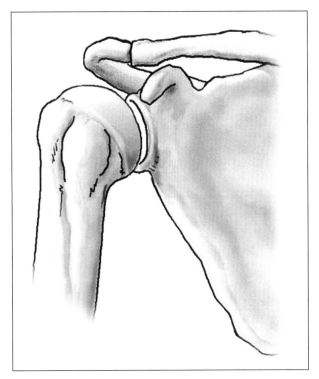

Figure 13.1 *Glenohumeral joint. (Courtesy of Robert Perry)*

263

slightly deeper by a fibrocartilaginous ring called the glenoid labrum that is on the outer edge of the glenoid. The shoulder joint's large range of motion is made possible by the interplay of the sternoclavicular joint, acromioclavicular joint, and the scapulothoracic articulation with the glenohumeral joint. It has been estimated that the sternoclavicular and acromioclavicular joints contribute approximately 2/3 of the total motion of the shoulder (Inman, Saunders, & Abbott, 1996).

From the top, the clavicle looks something like a "French Curve" and extends laterally from the sternum to the acromial end of the scapula. Its lateral end is flattened in shape and articulates with the medial side of the acromion process of the scapula forming the acromioclavicular joint. Its medial, or sternal, end is enlarged and articulates with the clavicular notch of the sternum creating the sternoclavicular joint. (Figure 13.2)

The scapula forms the posterior portion of the shoulder complex. The scapula is a large flattened, triangular bone laying on the posterior and lateral aspect of the thorax. The scapula, whose most lateral aspect is the shallow cup or glenoid fossa articulates with the humerus. As mentioned previously, the lateral end of the clavicle is connected to the acromial process of the scapula, forming the acromioclavicular joint. (Figure 13.2)

The sternoclavicular joint, formed by the articulation of the medial end of the clavicle and the sternum is a synovial joint with its articular surfaces covered by thick fibrocartilage. The joint is saddle-like in shape with an

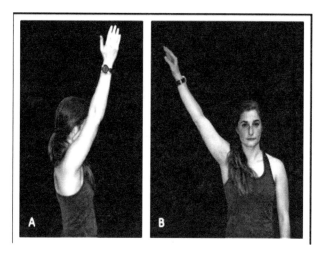

Figure 13.3 Illustration of shoulder flexion (A) and abduction (B).

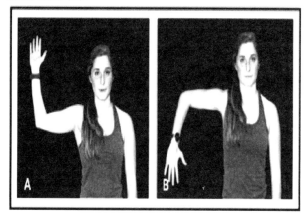

Figure 13.4 Illustration of shoulder external (A) and internal rotation (B).

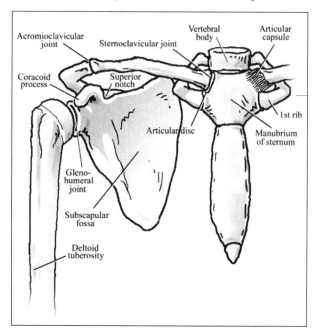

Figure 13.2 Bones and joints of the shoulder. (Courtesy of Robert Perry)

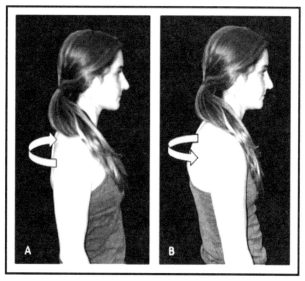

Figure 13.5 Illustration of shoulder retraction (A) and protraction (B).

intra-articular disc. This disc helps absorb compressive forces to the upper extremity. The sternoclavicular joint, by its structural nature (shallow), is inherently unstable and as such, relies upon ligaments for the majority of is strength and support. The sternoclavicular joint provides the only bone-to-bone articulation of the upper extremity with the trunk.

B. Major ligaments of the shoulder

Because the cup ("socket") of the glenoid fossa on the scapula is not very deep, stability of the joint must be provided by the fibrous capsule that surrounds the joint and a number of ligaments which reinforce it. The glenohumeral joint has a large, fairly loose capsule in order to allow for the large range of motion that the joint is able to perform. This capsule is then reinforced by four ligaments, the "coracoacromial" ligament, and the superior, middle and inferior "glenohumeral" ligaments. The majority of these ligaments are oriented such that they reinforce the front of the capsule more than the posterior or lateral sides of the capsule. Together, these ligaments stabilize the shoulder during motion. Following injury of these ligaments or capsule, the stability of the shoulder joint may be compromised, leading to dysfunction and pain.

The clavicle is secured to the sternum (sternoclavicular joint) by a ligament in the front and another in the back called the anterior and posterior sternoclavicular ligaments. The clavicle is further stabilized by the costoclavicular ligament that binds it to the first rib. This ligament is composed of two laminae binding the inferior surface of the clavicle to the superior surface of the first costal cartilage and the first rib. This means that as the arm is raised overhead, the clavicle must also elevate along with the first rib. This ligament is a major stabilizer of the sternoclavicular joint.

The Acromioclavicular joint is stabilized by a superior and inferior acromioclavicular ligament as well as two stronger ligaments, called the "conoid" and "trapezoid" ligaments. These later two ligaments are often referred to as a single ligament called the coracoclavicular ligament. They play an important role in stabilizing the clavicle to the scapula.

C. Muscles and available movements of the shoulder

From a boney perspective, the glenohumeral joint is less stable compared to the hip, but it is significantly more mobile than the hip, with a much greater range of motion. The motions available at the shoulder include flexion/extension, (Figure 13.3a) internal/external rotation, (Figure 13.4) and abduction/adduction (Figure 13.3b). In addition, these motions may be combined to produce "circumduction" which the ability to move the arm in circles. To accomplish all of these movements requires a delicate coordination between each of the three previously mentioned joints. Of particular importance is the ability of the scapula to move such that it essentially follows what the humerus is doing so that as much stability as possible is maintained. This movement of the scapula is the direct result of movement at both the sternoclavicular and acromioclavicular joints discussed above. The lack of osseous connection to the axial skeleton of the trunk allows for movement in several directions simultaneously. These movements of the scapula are referred to as protraction, which is when you round your shoulders forward, retraction, which is pinching your shoulder blades together, elevation, which is shrugging your shoulders, and depression, which is moving your shoulders down. (See Figure 13.5)

As would be expected, there is a fairly large number of muscles in the shoulder. These many muscles produce and control the motions available at the shoulder joint complex. There are muscles designated to specifically control the scapula, like the *trapezius*, *rhomboids*, and *serratus anterior*. There are other muscles that primarily control the glenohumeral joint such as the deltoid, the *pectoralis major, teres major, latissimus dorsi* and what is generally referred to as the 'rotator cuff' muscles. The rotator cuff muscles include the *supraspinatus, infraspinatus, teres minor* and *subscapularis*. (Figure 13.6) Together, these muscles are able to flex, abduct, adduct, and internally and externally rotate the shoulder. These muscles play an important role in not just lifting the arm overhead, but in making sure that there is no "pinching" of the soft tissues covering the superior aspect of the humerus as it moves under the acromion process during overhead motions.

D. Nerves and arteries of the shoulder

An important anatomical structure of the shoulder is the brachial plexus. (Figures 13.7) The brachial plexus is divided into four different regions, labeled "roots", "trunks," "cords," and "branches." The ventral and dorsal nerve roots emerge from the spinal cord in the neck and combine at the intervertebral foramen of the spine to form individual spinal nerves. Behind the anterior scalene muscle in the neck from the 5th to the 6th cervical vertebrae, nerve roots merge to form the upper trunk of the brachial plexus. The 7th cervical nerve roots form the middle trunk and the 8th cervical and 1st thoracic nerve roots merge to form the lower trunk of the brachial plexus. The trunks

Rotator Cuff Muscles

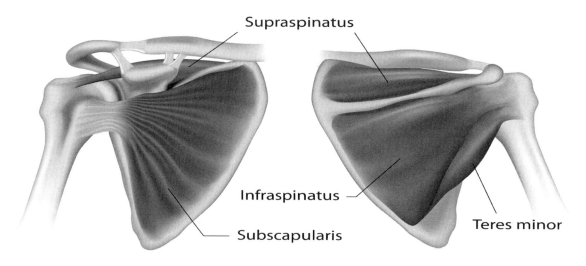

Figure 13.6 *Anterior and posterior muscles of the shoulder joint. Shutterstock.com*

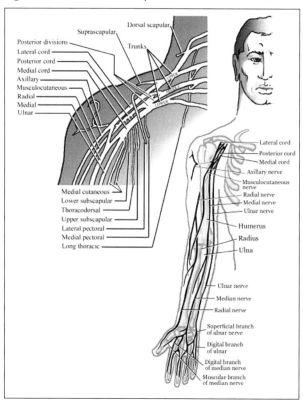

Figure 13.7 *Brachial plexus. (Courtesy of Robert Perry)*

run laterally where they lie deep to the skin and fascia, just above the clavicle. Posterior to the clavicle, the trunks divide into anterior and posterior divisions as they enter the axilla (arm pit). Finally, in the area of the axilla, all of the major nerves going to the muscles and skin of the upper extremity form. These include the axillary nerve, the musculocutaneous, the median nerve, the radial nerve and the ulnar nerve.

A very large important artery is found in the shoulder area which provides the needed blood supply to the joints and muscles of the upper extremity. The large subclavian artery which is derived from the aorta passes beneath the clavicle and becomes the axillary artery. This artery provides numerous branches supplying the superior chest and upper back as well as the muscles (e.g. pectoralis major and minor, rhomboids, and deltoid) and joints of the shoulder (e.g. acromioclavicular joint, glenohumeral joint. In the axilla, the axillary artery changes its name to that of the brachial artery. During the brachial artery's course to the elbow, it provides blood to the muscles of the upper arm (i.e. biceps, brachialis and triceps).

13.3 Shoulder Injuries

As we will see below, disease and injury to the shoulder frequently occur among the very young and the elderly.

A. Peripheral nerve injuries

See CD–Folder: Trunk/Scapulo–Thoracic, Movie: Thoracic Outlet Syndrome

The term thoracic outlet syndrome (TOS) refers to a group of neuro-vascular disorders in the upper extremities arising from compression of the (1) brachial plexus fibers; (2) subclavian/axillary artery and vein (neurovascular bundle); or (3) the distal cervical roots within the thoracic outlet. Thoracic outlet syndrome may be produced by bone malformation (morphologic variations), fibromuscular anomalies (structural modification due to conditioning, or postural defects), or neck and shoulder injury which produce scarring subsequent to single event trauma based on the structural elements producing symptoms. Thoracic outlet syndrome is generally subdivided into four distinct groups: arterial vascular, venous vascular, true neurologic, and disputed neurologic. The first three types have distinctive, objective characteristic symptoms which are supported by objective clinical findings, can be confirmed by laboratory tests, present with a long history, and are of low incidence (Wilborne, 1990). In contrast, disputed neurologic thoracic outlet syndrome has widely variable symptomatology including pain in the lower trunk, migraines, memory loss and ear pain, none of which is associated with compression of the brachial plexus.

B. Shoulder impingement

Other than irritations of the many bursa surrounding the shoulder complex like that of subdeltoid bursitis, the single most common overuse injury is "shoulder impingement". Shoulder impingement syndrome may result from a variety of conditions and involves the soft tissues of the shoulder in the subacromial space between the humeral head and the acromial arch. (Figure 13.8) Over time, such impingement can produce progressive degenerative changes. The space between the undersurface of the acromion and the superior portion of the humeral head is structurally limited, and when the arm is abducted (lifted away from the trunk), this space becomes even more restricted. Conditions that further narrow the subacromial space often result in pain and dysfunction. The pinching of the humeral head against the acromion may be caused by a number of different situations. This impingement may be the result of structural abnormalities of the acromion, thickening or calcification of the coracoacromial ligament, weakening of the external rotators (supraspinatus, infraspinatus and teres minor), or even thickening of the subacromial bursa. The cause of the impingement generally dictates whether surgical or conservative intervention is warranted. A recent study, however, indicates that although subacromial decompression surgery is common, it provides no significant benefit when compared with placebo surgery or exercise therapy (Lähdeoja et al., 2019). In fact, the authors further conclude that it probably carries a small risk of serious harm.

C. Rotator cuff tear

The rotator cuff is a common tendon of insertion for the muscles of the shoulder that are primarily responsible for external rotation. These muscles include the supraspinatus, the infraspinatus and the teres minor. Although the subscapularis muscle does not share the same tendon and is an internal rather than external rotator, it is generally included as a part of the 'rotator cuff'. A rotator cuff tear then is an injury of one or more of these rotator cuff tendons or muscles. The tendon of the supraspinatus muscle is the most commonly affected muscle. These tears may occur as the result of direct trauma as with a fall or motor vehicle accident, but they also develop gradually over time from repeated use. The symptoms of a rotator cuff tear often include pain that worsens with movement, weakness and the loss of the ability to perform certain movements with the shoulder such as brushing your hair or getting dressed. Risk factors include repetitive activities such as throwing a ball or painting, smoking, as well as a family history of the condition (Craig, Holt, & Rees, 2017). Radiographs are of limited value in making a diagnosis of a rotator cuff tear. MRI is the preferred imaging technique since it is able to demonstrate tears in soft tissue as well as swelling from inflammation. (Figure 13.9)

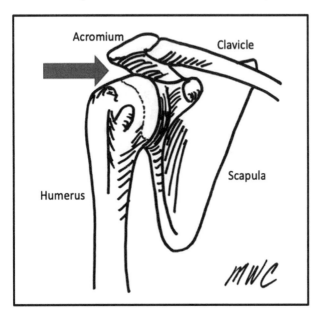

Figure 13.8 Bones of the shoulder illustrating the subacromial arch. (Courtesy of Mark W. Cornwall)

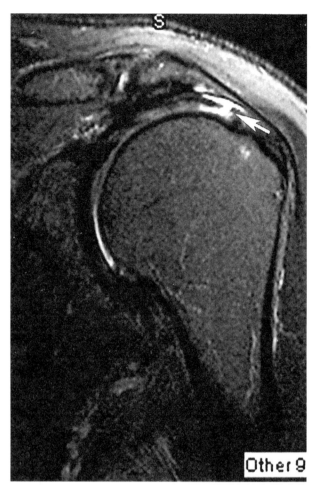

Figure 13.9 MRI showing signs of inflammation and a tear (arrow) in the supraspinatus tendon of the rotator cuff. Cornwall, MW, Nyre, E, Harris, JH: Imaging Handbook for Physical Therapists. Lippincott, Williams and Wilkins, 2013.

D. Sprains

The most common ligamentous sprain involving the shoulder complex is what is commonly referred to as a "shoulder separation." A shoulder separation involves a tear in one or more of the ligaments that support and reinforce the acromioclavicular joint. The condition is referred to as a separation because the lateral end of the clavicle separates from the acromion. If the ligamentous injury is sufficient, the clavicle is visibly elevated. Shoulder separations are most common in men between the age of 20 and 39 years and are generally the result of sport participation (Chillemi et al., 2013). Shoulder separations are frequently treated conservatively unless the ligamentous injury is total or rapid stabilization of the joint is desired.

E. Fractures and dislocations

The glenohumeral joint, because of its inherently unstable structure is prone to traumatic dislocation. Dislocation refers to the total loss of contact (luxation) between the surfaces of the glenohumeral joint. Such dislocations are generally from trauma and often involve the tearing of the joint capsule and supporting ligaments. When the displacement is incomplete or partial and the joint capsule remains intact, the injury is referred to as a partial dislocation or a subluxation. Dislocations or subluxations of the shoulder can be produced by both direct and indirect forces. They most often occur from forced external rotation of the humerus, pushing the head of the humerus forward and downward. Such anterior subluxations or dislocations may be combined with the rupture of the glenoid labrum and/or the joint capsule.

Structurally, the glenohumeral joint is most vulnerable when the humerus is extended or abducted overhead. A force directed along the humerus can drive the humeral head downward through the weakest part of the joint capsule. The inferior aspect of the joint is also the least protected by musculature. An important element of this mechanism of injury is that the higher the arm is raised, the more likely the humerus is to dislocate or sublux from the glenoid fossa (Rockwood, 2009).

Posterior dislocations form less than 5% of all glenohumeral dislocations. Such dislocations usually occur from falling forward onto an outstretched arm, which creates an axial force that drives the humeral head backwards. They may also occur from direct blows to the front of the shoulder (Iannotti & Williams, 2007; Rockwood, 2009). Posterior subluxations of the shoulder typically occur in conjunction with a bone lesion, such as in a separation

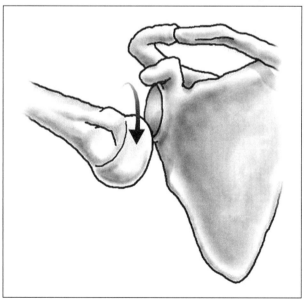

Figure 13.10 Anterior dislocation. (Courtesy of Robert Perry)

fracture of the greater tuberosity, or less frequently, with a fracture of the humeral head (Levine & Marra, 2016).

Dislocations of the shoulder joint are commonly divided into four groups based on the directional displacement of the humeral head: anterior, posterior, inferior, and superior. Anterior dislocations of the shoulder constitute approximately 95% of all shoulder dislocations. The most common type of anterior dislocation is the subcoracoid anterior dislocation in which the head of the humerus rests anteriorly to the coracoid process. A subglenoid anterior dislocation is the next most common type. In this situation, the head of the humerus lies anteriorly beneath the glenoid process. (Figure 13.10 and Figure 13.11) Subclavicular and intrathoracic are other types of anterior dislocations, but they are relatively rare. Inferior dislocations of the glenohumeral joint are also rare and occur when the top of the humeral head is displaced inferiorly as a result of a severe abduction force. Hyperabduction results in the displacement of the humeral head beneath the glenoid fossa. Motor vehicle accidents have been known to cause of this type of dislocation (Levine & Marra, 2016).

F. Fractures of the shoulder complex

1. Clavicular Fractures. Of the bones that form the joints of the shoulder girdle (scapula and clavicle), the clavicle is the most frequently fractured (Levine & Marra, 2016). The clavicle is easily injured because it lies in front and subcutaneously for its entire length. As such, it is exposed to direct trauma. Still the most common mechanism of clavicular fracture is the indirect application of force by

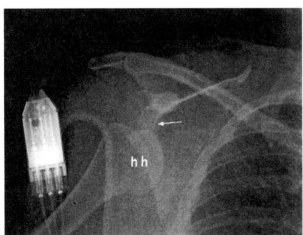

Figure 13.11 Radiograph of a posterior dislocation of the humerus. Notice the humerus (hh) is positioned below the glenoid fossa (arrow). Cornwall, MW, Nyre, E, Harris, JH: Imaging Handbook for Physical Therapists. Lippincott, Williams and Wilkins, 2013.

falling onto an outstretched hand or onto the point of the shoulder. Clavicular fractures are quite common in contact sports such as hockey, football, wrestling, and soccer. Clavicular fractures are commonly classified into three groups based on the segment of the clavicle where the fracture occurs. Zone I includes the middle of the clavicle and accounts for approximately 80% of all clavicular fractures. Zone II is the distal or lateral third of the clavicle and accounts for another 15% of clavicular fractures. Zone III is the proximal or medial third of the clavicle and accounts for the remaining 5% of all clavicular fractures. (Figure 13.12) This final group is mostly epiphyseal injuries in young athletes. In all of these types of clavicular fractures, the possibility of ligamentous injury to either the acromioclavicular or sternoclavicular joints is high.

2. Humeral fractures. Fractures of the proximal humerus account for a large percentage of upper extremity fractures. The type of injury sustained depends on the age of the individual, the thickness of the bone, the magnitude and direction of force, and/or the mechanics. The range of injury runs from overuse stress fractures to displaced and highly comminuted fractures (Ciullo, 1996). Fractures of the humeral head and neck are most often caused by a direct impact, but can also be caused indirectly by falling on the shoulder, the elbow, or the outstretched hand. In distal

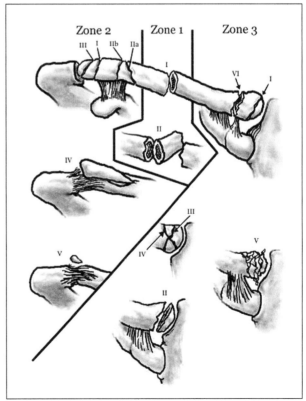

Figure 13.12 Fractures of the clavicle. (Courtesy of Robert Perry)

fractures of the humerus, direct trauma, especially falling on the elbow, is the most commonly seen in adults. In children, indirect trauma, such as falling on the hand with the elbow extended, is the most common (Levine & Marra, 2016). Direct trauma is the major cause of fractures of the proximal and mid-humerus, especially in young individuals. The thinning of bone associated with osteoporosis or osteopenia is correlated more highly with fractures in the elderly (Ciullo, 1996). In humeral shaft fractures, both rotational and linear force trauma to the upper arm occur. Fractures to the distal third of the humeral shaft are often associated with neurologic trauma to the radial nerve as the nerve travels around the back of the humeral shaft. (CD–Folder: Arm/Brachium, Movie: Nerves of the Arm).

13.4 Case Studies

A. Shoulder dislocation

Accident. A 25 year-old male injured his right shoulder when he fell into a holding tank while working on a commercial fishing vessel in Alaska. He was attempting to lower himself into the tank when the ship unexpectedly rolled. Although he was holding onto a rope at the time, he lost his footing on the ladder and fell approximately 2-3 feet before "catching" himself with the rope. He reported feeling a "popping" sound at the time of the injury.

Evaluation and anatomical structures involved. After climbing out of the holding tank, he was evaluated by a member of the crew that had some training in first-aid. Although very sore, he was able to move his arm and felt that he did not require additional medical attention. Even with extended rest, the shoulder continued to be painful and he eventually had to quit his job and return to his parent's home in Arizona. No medical imaging was performed on his shoulder while he was in Alaska, but he did obtain radiographs soon after returning to Arizona since he was still listed on his parent's insurance. The radiographs showed no signs of fracture or dislocation. Unfortunately, he continued to complain of pain and a feeling of "instability" in his shoulder and reported that if he moved his arm too far over his head or reached behind him, he would experience severe pain and a feeling that his shoulder was "coming out of place". Following a consult with an orthopedic surgeon, a magnetic resonance image (MRI) was performed which showed signs of an old injury to the anterior aspect of the shoulder joint capsule and a Hill-Sachs lesion to the right humeral head. A Hill–Sachs lesion, or Hill–Sachs fracture, is a depression in the posterolateral head of the humerus. He was told that he had previously dislocated his shoulder and was advised to have surgery to repair the

lesion to the humerus and to restore joint capsule integrity to prevent further dislocations.

Likely cause of injuries. The likely cause of this person's anterior shoulder dislocation and the Hill-Sach lesion to the right humeral head can both be directly attributed to the fall he experienced while working on the fishing boat. Although he was able to prevent falling completely into the holding tank by holding firmly onto the rope, the sudden halt to the downward force of his body weight by holding onto the rope caused the humerus to be jerked suddenly upward and forward, tearing the anterior joint capsule and resulting in its dislocation. The Hill-Sach lesion was caused when his humeral head impacted the anterior edge of the glenoid fossa when the humerus dislocated anteriorly. The fact that he was able to move his arm immediately after the injury is not unusual since spontaneous relocation following shoulder dislocation is fairly common.

B. Humerical fracture

Accident. An 83 year-old female fell while walking from her car toward her house. She had a caregiver walking with her at the time who was unable to keep her from falling.

Evaluation and anatomical structures involved. She complained of immediate pain in her right shoulder after the accident, but was able to stand and finish walking into her home with a significant amount of assistance. Medical personnel were called and after a brief examination, she was transported via ambulance to a local hospital. After further physical examination that included radiographs of her right shoulder, she was diagnosed with a non-displaced oblique fracture to her proximal humerus. She was referred to an orthopedic surgeon who elected to not perform surgery. Instead, her right shoulder was placed in a sling and referred to physical therapy for gentle range of motion exercises to prevent loss of motion in her shoulder.

Likely cause of injuries. The fracture of the proximal humerus sustained by this women was the direct result of the fall. Based on the type of fracture, the mechanism of injury was most likely from a forward fall on her outstretched arm with the humerus in slight internal rotation. In this position, her body weight was therefore directed at the shaft of the humerus, causing the oblique fracture (Sheehan, Gaviola, Sacks, & Gordon, 2013). Unfortunately, the women had osteoporosis as well as a history of falling several times in the last six months, which predisposed her to the injury. Non-surgical management of these types of fractures is fairly common since a majority of these injuries can be treated non-surgically with satisfactory outcomes, but a significant deterioration of their function (Yeap, Noor Zehan, Ezlan, Borhan Tan, & Harwant, 2001).

References

Chillemi, C., Franceschini, V., Dei Giudici, L., Alibardi, A., Salate Santone, F., Ramos Alday, L. J., & Osimani, M. (2013). Epidemiology of isolated acromioclavicular joint dislocation. *Emergency Medicine International*, 2013, 171609.

Ciullo, J."Shoulder Injuries in Sport: Evaluation, Treatment, and Rehabilitation." *Human Kinetics*. pp. 206–218. Human Kinetics P.O. Box 5076, Champaign, IL 61825-5076 USA. (1996)

Craig, R., Holt, T., & Rees, J. (2017). Acute rotator cuff tears. *BMJ,* 359, j5366.

Iannotti, J. P., & Williams, G. R. (2007). *Disorders of the Shoulder*. Lippincott Williams & Wilkins.

Inman, V. T., Saunders, J. B., & Abbott, L. C. (1996). Observations of the function of the shoulder joint. *Clinical Orthopaedics and Related Research*, 330, 3–12.

Lähdeoja, T., Karjalainen, T., Jokihaara, J., Salamh, P., Kavaja, L., Agarwal, A., ... Ardern, C. L. (2019). Subacromial decompression surgery for adults with shoulder pain: a systematic review with meta-analysis. *British Journal of Sports Medicine*, bjsports–2018–100486–10.

Levine, W. N., & Marra, G. (2016). *Fractures of the Shoulder Girdle*. CRC Press.

Rockwood, C. A. (2009). *The Shoulder*. Elsevier Health Sciences.

Sheehan, S., Gaviola, G., Sacks, A., & Gordon, R. (2013). Traumatic Shoulder Injuries: A Force Mechanism Analysis of Complex Injuries to the Shoulder Girdle and Proximal Humerus. *American Journal of Roentgenology,* 201, W409-W424. 10.2214/AJR.12.9987.

Yeap, J. S., Noor Zehan, A. R., Ezlan, S., Borhan Tan, A., & Harwant, S. (2001). Functional outcome of proximal humeral fractures. *The Medical Journal of Malaysia,* 56 Suppl C, 13–18.

Recommended Reading

Bartel, D. L., Davy, D. T., & Keaveny, T. M. (2006). *Orthopaedic Biomechanics*. Prentice Hall.

Bergmann, U., & Rinehart, M. A. (1987). *Musculoskeletal trauma*. Aspen Pub.

Garrick, J. G., & Webb, D. R. (1999). *Sports Injuries*. Saunders.

Levangie, P. K., & Norkin, C. C. (2011). *Joint Structure and Function*. F.A. Davis.

Moore, K. L., Dalley, A. F., & Agur, A. M. R. (2013). *Clinically Oriented Anatomy*. Lippincott Williams & Wilkins.

Neumann, D. A. (2017). *Kinesiology of the Musculoskeletal System*. (D. A. Neumann, Ed.). Elsevier.

Soderberg, G. L. (1997). *Kinesiology*. Lippincott Williams & Wilkins.

Symposium, A. A. O. O. S., Woo, S. L.-Y., Buckwalter, J. A., Surgeons, A. A. O. O., National Institute of Arthritis and Musculoskeletal and Skin Diseases (U.S.). (1988). Injury and repair of the musculoskeletal soft tissues. Amer Academy of Orthopaedic.

Whiting, W. C., & Zernicke, R. F. (2008). *Biomechanics of Musculoskeletal Injury*. Human Kinetics.

Chapter 14

The Elbow

Mark W. Cornwall

14.1 Introduction

The elbow is the joint around which flexion and extension of the forearm takes place. It is a critical articulation for secondary positioning of the hand and important to the forceful manipulation of objects. The elbow joint consists of three bones, two ligament capsules, seven major muscles, three major nerves, and two major arteries, all of which serve to facilitate the movements of the forearm. (CD-Rom Forearm/Hand) As with all joints, the elbow is subjected to a complex variety of stresses, both acute and chronic. This chapter will first discuss the anatomical and biomechanical features of the elbow and then some of the more common traumatic conditions that affect the elbow.

14.2 Anatomy of the Elbow

A. Bones and joints of the elbow

Three bones comprise the elbow complex. These include the humerus, ulna and radius. (Figure 14.1) Between the distal end of the humerus and the proximal ends of the ulna and radius there are three distinct articulations or joints; the "Humeroulnar" joint, the "Humeroradial" joint, and the proximal "Radioulnar" joint. For the humeroulnar joint, the ulna's olecranon and coronoid process form a hook-like structure that fits into the olecranon fossa of the humerus, thus providing much of that joint's stability, especially in the anterior-posterior direction. The humeroradial joint is made up of the radius, whose block shaped proximal end articulates with a spherical component on the lateral side of the distal humerus, called the "Capitulum." (Figure 14.1) The proximal radioulnar joint is formed where the radius and ulna bones meet, just distal to the previous two joints. These three joints are

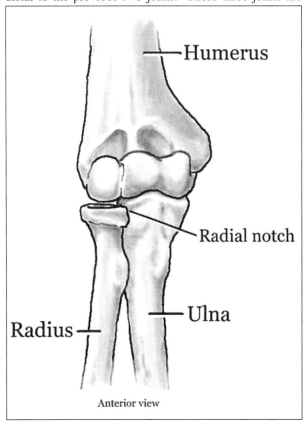

Figure 14.1 *Joints of the elbow. (Courtesy of Robert Perry)*

close enough to each other that they share the same joint capsule.

B. Major ligaments of the elbow

The elbow is considered to be a very stable joint, largely because of its bony architecture. Since the boney configuration of the joint provides stability primarily in the anterior-posterior direction, stability of the joint in the medial-lateral direction is afforded primarily by the joint capsule and the ligaments that reinforce it. On the medial side, the ulnar collateral ligament (UCL) complex protects the elbow from forces that try to "gap" the joint on the medial side. Such forces are referred to as valgus forces. This ligament is often described as being composed of

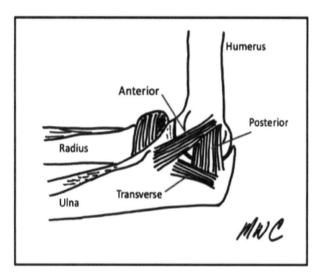

Figure 14.2 *Ligaments on the medial side of the elbow. (Courtesy of Mark W. Cornwall)*

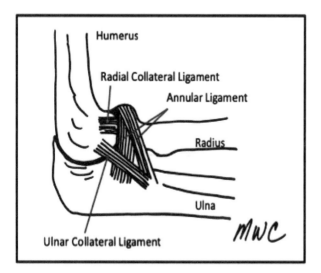

Figure 14.3 *Ligaments on the lateral side of the elbow. (Courtesy of Mark W. Cornwall)*

three different bundles of collagen fibers and are named for how the fibers are principally oriented; anterior, posterior and transverse or oblique. (Figure 14.2) The elbow joint is protected from varus forces, or those which try to "gap" the joint on the lateral side, by three distinct ligaments. These lateral ligaments include the radial collateral ligament (RCL) between the humerus and the radius, the lateral collateral ligament (LCL) between the humerus and ulna and the annular ligament between the radius and the ulna. (Figure 14.3) In addition to protecting the elbow from varus forces, the RCL also resists longitudinal distraction of the forearm relative to the humerus.

C. Muscles and available movements of the elbow

The three bony articulations of the elbow allow the forearm and hand to be positioned in space. The humeroulnar and the humeroradial joints behave essentially as a hinge to flex and extend the forearm. (Figure 14.4) Typical ROM values for the elbow are between -5° and 145° (Morrey, Askew, & Chao, 1981). Despite the large range of motion, for most functional tasks, a person needs just between 30° and 130° of flexion for most functional tasks (Sardelli, Tashjian, & MacWilliams, 2011). The humeroradial joint is also classified as a pivot joint and allows for rotation of the forearm and hand in the transverse plane. Such movement allows the palm of the hand to face superiorly (supination) or inferiorly (pronation). (Figure 14.5) The magnitude of this motion is roughly 75° for pronation and 85° for supination. For a majority of functional tasks, a person will need approximately 50° of both supination and pronation (Sardelli et al., 2011).

There are four major muscles that produce flexion of the elbow; the *brachialis*, the *biceps brachii*, the *brachioradialis* and the *pronator teres*. In addition to these four muscles, there are a number of other muscles that originate on the distal end of the humerus and end in the wrist or hand. These are also able to flex the elbow, but their contribution is much less compared to the first four. Of the four major muscles that flex the elbow, the *biceps brachii* and *brachialis* are the most important because of their overall size and orientation. The *biceps brachii* muscle not only is able to flex the elbow, but it is also able to supinate the forearm, especially during forceful contractions. There are two muscles which are able to extend the elbow, the *triceps brachii* and the *anconeus*. The *triceps brachii* is a large muscle with three heads or partitions which are able to extend the elbow as well as the shoulder. The *anconeus* is a fairly small triangular muscle that only extends the elbow. Supination of the forearm is

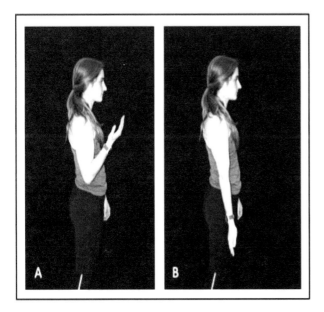

Figure 14.4 *Movement of elbow flexion (A) and extension (B). (Courtesy of Mark W. Cornwall)*

accomplished by two different muscles; the *biceps brachii*, which was mentioned previously and the supinator muscle. Pronation of the forearm is also accomplished by two different muscles; the *pronator teres* and the *pronator quadratus* muscle.

D. Nerves and arteries of the elbow

Three major nerves and one major artery cross the elbow on their way to the hand. The median, ulnar and radial nerves were each formed from the brachial plexus in the shoulder. The ulnar nerve crosses the elbow on the medial side, while the radial nerve crosses on the lateral side. The median nerve crosses the elbow in the front between the other two nerves. (Figure 14.6) The brachial artery is a continuation of the axillary artery of the shoulder and crosses the elbow in the front next to the median nerve. Soon after the brachial artery crosses the elbow joint, it divides into two separate arteries. The radial artery, which travels to the hand along the lateral side of the forearm and the ulnar artery which travels to the hand along the medial side of the forearm.

14.3 Elbow Injuries

Trauma to the elbow is not as prevalent compared to other parts of the body, but because it is involved in a wide variety of repetitive motions, it is prone to "overuse" injuries.

A. Overuse

Overuse or repetitive movement disorders may occur in either nerve, bone, connective tissue or muscle tendons. At the elbow, these injuries include the medial ligaments of the joint and the muscle tendons on the lateral aspect of the elbow which are responsible for extension or flexion of the fingers and wrist.

1. *Lateral epicondylitis.* This condition involves micro-trauma to the muscles over the lateral side of the elbow and is generally caused by their repeated or forceful contraction. This condition is sometimes referred to as "Tennis Elbow" because of the forceful muscle contraction observed during a "back hand" swing. Although it is not exclusively seen in those who play tennis, it is generally associated with repetitive movement of the wrist and/ or elbow (Descatha et al., 2016). Lateral epicondylitis has an occurrence rate of 2.4 per 1000. Although the majority of cases respond well to conservative care, as many as 1 in 10 individuals will have persistent symptoms after 6 months and require surgical intervention. A recurrence rate of approximately 8.5% has also been reported in the literature (Sanders ct al., 2015).

2. *Ulnar nerve entrapment.* This condition is when the ulnar nerve becomes impinged or irritated as it passes from the arm, around the medial side of the elbow through the "ulnar notch" or "cubital tunnel," on its way to the hand. Symptoms include paresthesia (numbness or tingling) over the medial elbow, distally along the ulnar (medial) aspect of the forearm or into the fourth and fifth digits in the hand. There are several proposed causes for "cubital tunnel syndrome," but the exact cause is not well known. The common feature of these proposed causes is some type of compression on the ulnar nerve. There are several things that can cause this increased pressure on the nerve at the elbow. Increased pressure may occur secondary to keeping the elbow bent for long periods or repeatedly bending the elbow. For example, many people sleep with their elbows bent, which can aggravate symptoms of ulnar nerve compression and cause the person to wake up at night with fingers asleep. Repetitive movement of the elbow is also seen in many sports such as pitching, racquetball, weight lifting and skiing that can lead to inflammation and subsequent pressure on the ulnar nerve (Chumbley, O'Connor, & Nirschl, 2000). Another possibility is that the nerve may slide out from behind the medial epicondyle when the elbow is bent. Over time, this sliding back and forth may irritate the nerve. Finally, a direct blow to the inside of the elbow can cause pain, electric shock sensation, and numbness in the little and ring fingers. This is commonly called "hitting your funny bone."

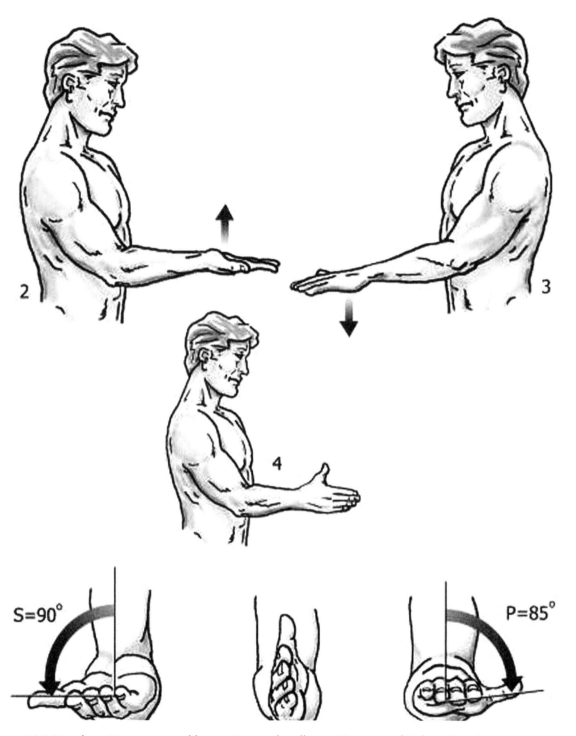

Figure 14.5 *Hand positions governed by rotation at the elbow. (Courtesy of Robert Perry)*

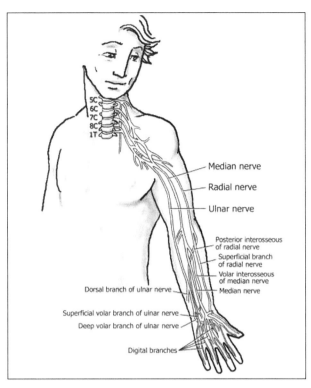

Figure 14.6 *Nerves of the upper extremity. (Courtesy of Robert Perry)*

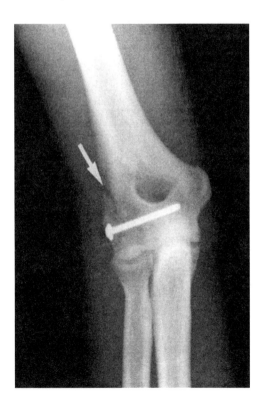

Figure 14.7 *Open Reduction Internal Fixation (ORIF) of a supracondylar fracture. The fracture is pointed to by the white arrow. Cornwall, MW, Nyre, E, Harris, JH: Imaging Handbook for Physical Therapists. Lippincott, Williams and Wilkins, 2014.*

Treatment of ulnar neuropathy at the elbow includes a variety of both surgical and non-surgical techniques.

B. Sprains

A sprain is a rupture of some or all of the fibers of a ligament. Sprains may be graded as I, II or III. A grade I is relatively minor and typically does not result in instability of the joint. A grade III, however, is where there is a complete tear of the ligament resulting in significant joint instability. Occasionally, the ligament itself does not rupture, but avulses (pulls) a fragment of bone to which it was attached. In such cases, it is generally treated as a fracture rather than a sprain.

1. *Medial collateral sprain.* An overuse injury to the medial collateral ligament of the elbow is fairly rare and almost exclusively found in overhead throwing athletes. The forces exerted on the elbow during throwing causes micro-tears, primarily in the anterior bundle of the ligament. Fortunately, surgical management of this type of injury results in between 80 and 90% return to the prior level of activity or competition (Lynch, Waitayawinyu, Hanel, & Trumble, 2008). Medial collateral ligament injury is characterized by vague medial elbow pain and valgus instability during late cocking and acceleration phases of a throw. The pain is generally relieved when the elbow is inactive (Chumbley et al., 2000). The medial collateral ligament of the elbow may also be injured by overt direct trauma rather than low grade repetitive stress as discussed above. In such cases, these are caused by a fall, typically on an outstretched arm.

C. Fractures and Dislocations

Bony trauma to the integrity and alignment of the bones and joints of the elbow can result in significant loss of function.

1. *Supracondylar fracture.* A fracture through the humerus, just proximal to the condyles. Such a fracture typically results from a fall on an outstretched hand, which commonly leads to a forced hyperextension of the elbow. In such situations, the olecranon acts as a fulcrum which focuses the stress on distal humerus (supracondylar area), predisposing the distal humerus to fracture. Epidemiologically, such falls occur most frequently in children three to ten years old with boys more often than girls. Supracondylar fractures characteristically displace the distal elbow posteriorly and proximally because of the upward force exerted on the forearm bones and the pull of the triceps muscle. Classification and direction of the displacement does not appear to influence functional outcome however (Ernat, Ho, Wimberly, Jo, & Riccio, 2017). Falling on an outstretched arm with the elbow hyperextended accounts for 60% of all elbow fractures.

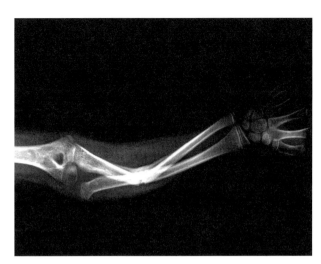

Figure 14.8 Radiograph showing a fracture of the ulna and concomitant dislocation of the radial head ("Monteggia" fracture). Shutterstock.com

A flexion-type of supracondylar humerus fracture is less common, but certainly is possible. These fractures are often the result of falling on the point of the elbow, or falling with the arm twisted behind the back. This causes an anterior dislocation of the proximal fragment of the humerus. Regardless of the mechanism of injury, these fractures are considered to be serious because important arteries and nerves (brachial artery, median nerve, radial nerve, and ulnar nerve) are located at the supracondylar area and can give rise to complications if these structures are injured. In order to restore stability to the elbow, open reduction, internal fixation (ORIF) is required. (Figure 14.7)

2. *Radial head dislocation/subluxation.* Isolated distal dislocation or subluxation of the radial head typically occurs in female children under the age of 5 years (mean age = 2.1 years) and is the most common musculoskeletal injury of the upper limb in children of this age. The mechanism of these injuries is either a fall (43.9%) or a sharp distractive pull on the toddler's arm (39.4%) (Welch, Chounthirath, & Smith, 2017). Because of the 'jerking' motion that takes place while lifting or swinging a child by their hand, this type of injury is sometimes referred to as "Nursemaid's elbow" (Vitello, Dvorkin, Sattler, Levy, & Ung, 2014) and may be a sign of child abuse.

3. *Monteggia fracture.* This is a group of injuries involving a fracture of the ulna and dislocation of the radial head. (Figure 14.8) A Monteggia fracture occurs from a fall on an outstretched hand with the forearm in excessive pronation. This results in anterior dislocation of the proximal radius by fracturing the proximal mid-ulna shaft. A direct blow to the posterior upper forearm is relatively uncommon, but is seen in defense against blunt trauma

situations. Such an isolated ulnar shaft fracture is technically not considered to be a Monteggia fracture because it rarely includes dislocation of the radial head. Instead, such injuries are sometimes referred to as a 'nightstick fracture.' Depending on the severity and complexity of the injury, these injuries can present a clinical management challenge. Fortunately, this type of injury is fairly rare. Management generally involves closed reduction and immobilization when they occur in children and ORIF when they occur in adults (Beutel, 2012).

4. *Terrible triad of the elbow.* This injury involves a fracture of the head of the radius and the coronoid process of the ulna as well as a dislocation of the humeroulnar joint. The mechanism of injury is generally a fall on the dominant arm, which results in a combination of valgus, axial and posterolateral rotary forces to dislocate the ulna in the posterolateral direction. Historically, the functional outcomes from this injury are poor secondary to persistent instability, stiffness and pain. As such, this type of injury can result in significant loss of function if not managed timely and effectively (Gomide et al., 2011).

5. *Dislocation.* After shoulder dislocation, the elbow is the second most commonly dislocated joint in adults. In children, it is the most commonly dislocated joint. In

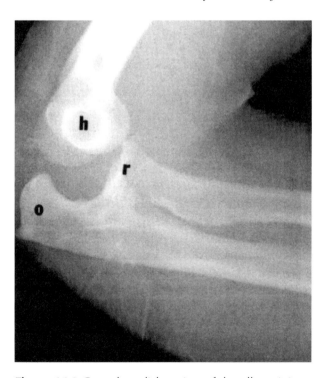

Figure 14.9 Complete dislocation of the elbow joint. "o" refers to the olecranon, "h" refers to humerus and "r" refers to radius. Cornwall, MW, Nyre, E, Harris, JH: Imaging Handbook for Physical Therapists. Lippincott, Williams and Wilkins, 2014.

addition, dislocations account for 10-25% of all injuries to the elbow. Elbow dislocations usually occur after a fall when the elbow and hand are fully extended. Elbow dislocations can be complete or partial. (Figure 14.9) A partial dislocation is referred to as a subluxation. The amount of force needed to cause an elbow dislocation is usually enough to cause a simultaneous bone fracture. These two injuries (dislocation and fracture) often occur together and produce a significant amount of elbow pain. Elbow dislocations are generally in the posterolateral direction following axial loading of the upper extremity while the forearm is supinated and externally rotated. This positioning creates a valgus and posterolateral force. A posteromedial dislocation has also been reported as a result of a varus and posteromedial force. It is not uncommon that injury to either the medial or lateral ligaments of the elbow occur simultaneously because of the mechanism of injury involved.

14.4 Case Study

A. Fracture and dislocation of the elbow

Accident. A 57-year-old female injured her right elbow following a fall. She slipped on some spilled water in a grocery store and fell backwards and to her right, landing on her right outstretched hand. She complained of pain immediately after the accident with rapid subsequent swelling of her right elbow. She told the paramedic who took her to the hospital that she heard a "crunching" sound when she landed.

Evaluation and anatomical structures involved. She was transported to a local emergency room where she was evaluated. Anterior-posterior and oblique radiographs of her right elbow views were taken. Based upon the radiograph, she was diagnosed with a fracture of her ulna, specifically that of the coronoid process. Since there was minimal displacement of the fracture, no surgical intervention was recommended. Instead, the elbow was immobilized and she was sent home. The immobilization device was removed six weeks later after sufficient callus formation was noted on a subsequent radiograph of the ulna. Because of significant loss of range of motion, she was referred to a physical therapist for stretching and strengthening. The physical therapist noted in her initial physical examination of the patient that she had tenderness over the medial joint line of the elbow with pronounced medial "gapping" of the joint from valgus stress testing. Although not specifically addressed in the emergency room immediately after the accident, the fall had also resulted in a sprain to the ulnar collateral ligament

Likely cause of injuries. The fracture of the coronoid process of the ulna and the rupture of the ulnar collateral ligament of the elbow are both consistent with a fall on an outstretched arm. The vertical force from the impact of the fall sheared off the coronoid process by the distal humerus. The angle at which she fell also resulted in a significant valgus force being applied to the elbow joint, thus tearing the ulnar collateral ligament.

References

Beutel, B. G. (2012). Monteggia fractures in pediatric and adult populations. *Orthopedics,* 35(2), 138–144.

Chumbley, E. M., O'Connor, F. G., & Nirschl, R. P. (2000). Evaluation of overuse elbow injuries. *American Family Physician*, 61(3), 691–700.

Descatha, A., Albo, F., Leclerc, A., Carton, M., Godeau, D., Roquelaure, Y., … Aublet-Cuvelier, A. (2016). Lateral Epicondylitis and Physical Exposure at Work? A Review of Prospective Studies and Meta-Analysis. *Arthritis Care & Research*, 68(11), 1681–1687.

Ernat, J., Ho, C., Wimberly, R. L., Jo, C., & Riccio, A. I. (2017). Fracture Classification Does Not Predict Functional Outcomes in Supracondylar Humerus Fractures: A Prospective Study. *Journal of Pediatric Orthopedics*, 37(4), e233–e237.

Gomide, L. C., Campos, D. de O., Ribeiro de Sá, J. M., Pamfílio de Sousa, M. R., do Carmo, T. C., & Brandão Andrada, F. (2011). Terrible triad of the elbow: evaluation of surgical treatment. *Revista Brasileira de Ortopedia (English Edition)*, 46(4), 374–379.

Lynch, J. R., Waitayawinyu, T., Hanel, D. P., & Trumble, T. E. (2008). Medial collateral ligament injury in the overhand-throwing athlete. *The Journal of Hand Surgery*, 33(3), 430–437.

Morrey, B. F., Askew, L. J., & Chao, E. Y. (1981). A biomechanical study of normal functional elbow motion. *Journal of Bone and Joint Surgery [Am]*, 63(6), 872–877.

Sanders, T. L., Maradit Kremers, H., Bryan, A. J., Ransom, J. E., Smith, J., & Morrey, B. F. (2015). The epidemiology and health care burden of tennis elbow: a population-based study. *American Journal of Sports Medicine*, 43(5), 1066–1071.

Sardelli, M., Tashjian, R. Z., & MacWilliams, B. A.

(2011). Functional elbow range of motion for contemporary tasks. *Journal of Bone and Joint Surgery [Am]*, 93(5), 471–477.

Vitello, S., Dvorkin, R., Sattler, S., Levy, D., & Ung, L. (2014). Epidemiology of nursemaid's elbow. *The Western Journal of Emergency Medicine*, 15(4), 554–557.

Welch, R., Chounthirath, T., & Smith, G. A. (2017). Radial Head Subluxation Among Young Children in the United States Associated With Consumer Products and Recreational Activities. *Clinical Pediatrics*, 56(8), 707–715.

Recommended Reading

Bartel, D. L., Davy, D. T., & Keaveny, T. M. (2006). *Orthopaedic Biomechanics*. Prentice Hall.

Bergmann, U., & Rinehart, M. A. (1987). *Musculoskeletal trauma*. Aspen Pub.

Garrick, J. G., & Webb, D. R. (1999). *Sports Injuries*. Saunders.

Levangie, P. K., & Norkin, C. C. (2011). *Joint Structure and Function*. F.A. Davis.

Moore, K. L., Dalley, A. F., & Agur, A. M. R. (2013). *Clinically Oriented Anatomy*. Lippincott Williams & Wilkins.

Neumann, D. A. (2017). *Kinesiology of the Musculoskeletal System*. (D. A. Neumann, Ed.). Elsevier.

Nordin, M., Frankel, V.H. (2001). *Basic Biomechanics of the Musculoskeletal System*. Lippincott Williams & Wilkins.

Soderberg, G. L. (1997). *Kinesiology*. Lippincott Williams & Wilkins.

Symposium, A. A. O. O. S., Woo, S. L.-Y., Buckwalter, J. A., Surgeons, A. A. O. O., National Institute of Arthritis and Musculoskeletal and Skin Diseases (U.S.). (1988). Injury and repair of the musculoskeletal soft tissues. Amer Academy of Orthopaedic.

Whiting, W. C., & Zernicke, R. F. (2008). *Biomechanics of Musculoskeletal Injury*. Human Kinetics.

Chapter 15

The Wrist and Hand

Mark W. Cornwall

15.1 Introduction

The wrist joint connects the forearm to the hand. The wrist is composed of the articulation between the distal end of the arm and the proximal end of the hand. The hand consists of nineteen bones and fourteen joints. The hand has remarkable mobility and functional adaptability, which allows individuals to grasp and manipulate a wide variety of objects. This chapter will discuss the anatomy of the wrist and hand, including its many joints and the motions that are available at each. Common injuries to the wrist and the hand will then be presented.

15.2 Anatomy of the Wrist and Hand
(CD–Forearm/Hand)

A. Bones and joints of the wrist and hand

The wrist complex is composed of the two bones of the forearm (radius and ulna) as well as three small bones called carpal bones located in the proximal hand. These carpal bones are arranged in a row and include the scaphoid, the lunate and the triquetrium. (Figure 15.1) The scaphoid bone is closest to the thumb and the triquetrium is closest to the little finger. The lunate bone is between the scaphoid and the triquetrium. The scaphoid and lunate each articulate with the radius to form the radiocarpal joint. This joint is responsible for transmitting approximately 85% of the compressive forces applied to the wrist to the forearm and then to the rest of the upper extremity (Palmer & Werner, 1984). This helps to explain why fractures of the radius are common with a fall on an outstretched arm. Because the ulna is slightly shorter than the radius, there

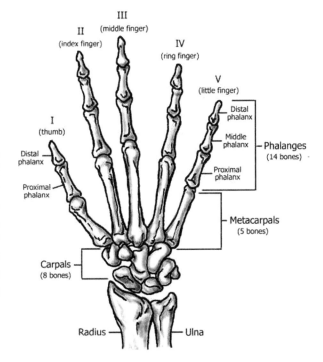

Figure 15.1 *Bones of the wrist and hand. (Courtesy of Robert Perry)*

281

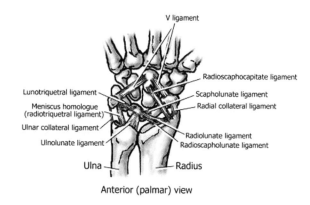

Anterior (palmar) view

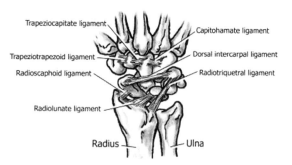

Figure 15.2 *Major ligaments of the wrist and hand.*
(Courtesy of Robert Perry)

is a fibrocartilaginous disc attached to the distal end of the ulna between it and the triquetrium bone in the hand. This disc is referred to as the Triangular Fibrocartilage Complex (TFCC) and fills in the gap between the ulna and the triquetrium. It also helps to stabilize the ulna against the radius during the movements of pronation and supination. The central portion of the TFCC is relatively avascular (poor blood supply) and therefore does not heal quickly or it may not heal completely after injury (Thiru, Ferlic, Clayton, & McClure, 1986).

The remainder of the wrist is composed of the proximal row of carpal bones mentioned above and a distal row of four carpal bones. The distal row contains the trapezium, trapezoid, capitate, and hamate bones. The two rows of carpal bones articulate with one another to form the midcarpal joint. (Figure 15.1) Although the carpal bones are arranged in rows, these rows are not straight. Rather they are curved with the palm side being concave, thus helping to form the carpal tunnel in which nerves, arteries and tendons are able to pass through into the hand.

The distal row of carpal bones further articulates with the relatively long metacarpal bones of the hand to form the carpometacarpal (CMC) joints. (Figure 15.1) There are five metacarpal bones radiating from the base of the hand to form the palm. These bones are numbered from one to five, starting at the thumb and moving to the little

finger. These joints are relatively immobile with only minimal motion available. The exception is the first CMC joint which forms the thumb and has a significantly amount of motion.

Finally, the distal ends of the metacarpal bones articulate with the proximal phalanges to form the metacarpophalangeal joints (MCP joints). Like the metacarpals, the digits are numbered from one to five, starting with the thumb and ending with the little finger. Each finger or digit is then composed of two or three phalanges. (Figure 15.1) Digits two through five each consist of three bones: the proximal, middle, and distal phalanx. Digit one, the thumb, has only two bones: the proximal and distal phalanx. Each phalanx articulates with one another, forming the proximal and distal interphalangeal (PIP and DIP) joints respectively.

B. Major ligaments of the wrist and hand

In addition to a relatively large and loose joint capsule that encompasses all of the joints in the wrist, there are multiple ligaments that contribute to the stability of the wrist complex. (Figure 15.2) These can be separated into two broad groups: extrinsic and intrinsic ligaments.

The extrinsic ligaments are those that originate outside of the wrist (i.e., forearm) and terminate on one or more bones in the wrist. On the palmar side of the wrist, the extrinsic system consists of several ligaments, including the radial collateral ligament, the palmar radiocarpal ligaments, and the palmer ulnocarpal ligament. It is further reinforced by the TFCC. On the dorsal aspect of the wrist, the extrinsic ligaments consist primarily of the ulnar collateral, dorsal radiocarpal and dorsal radiocarpal ligaments.

The intrinsic ligaments are those that typically originate in the wrist and also insert on one or more of the carpal bones of the wrist. They include the lunotriquetral, the scapholunate, and the scaphotrapezium ligaments.

In addition to the above individual ligaments, there is an extensor retinaculum that stretches from the anterior side of the radius to the triquetrium and distal ulna. This structure serves to secure the extensor tendons on the back of the wrist so that they do not "bow string" when they contract. On the palmar side, there is a flexor retinaculum which stretches from the scaphoid and triquetrium bones on the thumb side to the pisiform bone on the little finger side. This structure is very thick and holds the carpal bones in their "U" shape to form the carpal tunnel.

The articulations of the digits are stabilized by a collateral ligament on each side of the MCP and inter-

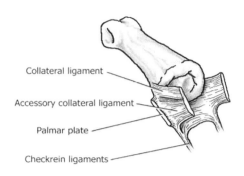

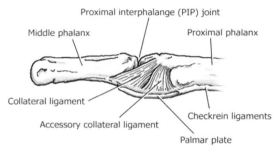

Figure 15.3 *Ligaments of the metacarpal-phalangeal joints of the hand. (Courtesy of Robert Perry)*

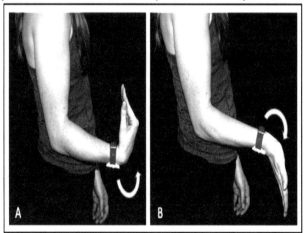

Figure 15.4 *Movement of wrist flexion (A) and extension (B).*

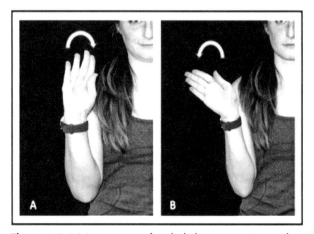

Figure 15.5 *Movement of radial deviation (A) and ulnar deviation (B).*

phalangeal joints. On the palmar side of each metacarpophalangeal joint is a fibrocartilaginous plate called the palmar or volar plate. (Figure 15.3) These palmar plates are firmly bound to the base of the proximal phalanx and are interconnected with its adjacent finger through transverse intermetacarpal ligaments. These palmar plates are also found at each interphalangeal joint, but without the transverse intercarpal ligament. The palmar plates play a significant role in preventing hyperextension (backward bending) of the fingers.

C. Muscles and available movements of the wrist and hand

Movement at the radiocarpal joint includes flexion and extension (Figure 15.4) as well as radial and ulnar deviation. (Figure 15.5) Radial and ulnar deviation is analogous to abduction (radial deviation) and adduction (ulnar deviation) of the hip or arm. Movement between the bones comprising the radiocarpal joint is a combination of rolling and sliding of the distal carpal bones on the radius. The inter-carpal articulations of the proximal and distal row of carpal bones are considered to be planar meaning they primarily slide between any two of them. Between the two rows of carpal bones, however, there is a combination of both rolling and sliding of one row on the other. The direction of this rolling and sliding is dictated by the particular movement being performed (i.e. flexion, extension, radial deviation or ulnar deviation) (Jenkins, Bamberger, Black, & Nowinski, 1998). The MCP joints of the hand are classified as being "condylar" with motion in two planes, flexion/extension and abduction/adduction. In contrast, the DIP and PIP joints of the fingers are only able to flex and extend. The thumb has many of the same features as the rest of the digits of the hand, but a key difference is the CMC joint. This joint is "saddle" shaped and therefore it is able to move in two different planes. It is able to flex or extend, abduct or adduct, and also "oppose." (Figure 15.6) This motion of thumb opposition is what distinguishes humans from apes.

There are two categories of muscles that function about the wrist and hand: extrinsic and intrinsic. The extrinsic muscles originate in the forearm and terminate in the hand, while the intrinsic muscles originate and terminate within the hand. The tendons of the hand are surrounded by a tendon sheath, which facilitates their gliding when the muscle contracts. (Figure 15.7). In the fingers, these tendon sheaths are held in place by a series of small ligamentous structures referred to as either "annular" or "cruciate" pulleys. (Figure 15.8) The annular pulleys are named because they go around the tendon sheath. The cruciate pulleys are named because they form an "X"

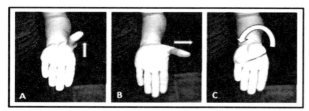

Figure 15.6 Movements of abduction (A), extension (b) and opposition (C) of the thumb.

on the palmar side of the tendon sheath. There are five muscles that are able to flex the wrist. These include the *flexor carpi ulnaris*, the *flexor carpi radialis longus*, the *palmaris longus*, the *flexor digitorum superficialis* and the *flexor digitorum profundus*. The latter two muscles also flex the fingers. (CD—Folder Forearm/Hand: *Flexor—Retinacula*) There are six muscles that are able to extend the wrist. These are the *extensor carpi radialis longus*, the *extensor carpi radialis brevis*, the *extensor carpi ulnaris brevis*, the *extensor indicis*, the *extensor digiti minimi* and the *extensor digitorum*. Again, the latter three muscles also extend the fingers. (CD–Folder: *Forearm/Hand: Structures of the Dorsal Wrist and Hand—Extensor Mechanism.*) If the flexor carpi ulnaris and the

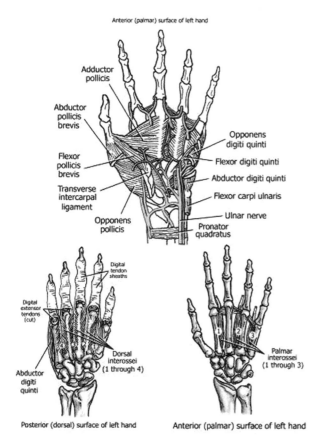

Figure 15.7 Intrinsic muscles of the hand. *(Courtesy of Robert Perry)*

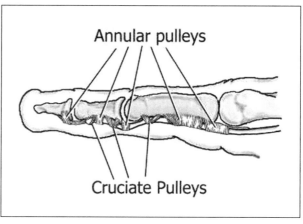

Figure 15.8 Tendons and tendon sheaths in the fingers. *(Courtesy of Robert Perry)*

extensor carpi ulnaris contract simultaneously, the wrist will move into ulnar deviation. For radial deviation, the *extensor carpi radialis* and the *flexor carpi radialis* muscles contract simultaneously. There are no muscles that specifically move an individual carpal bone. Rather their movement is dictated by the dorsal and palmar ligaments that bind them together.

Flexion of the fingers is primarily performed by the long flexors (*flexor digitorum superficialis* and *flexor digitorum profundus*). Extension of the fingers is produced by the long finger extensors (*extensor indicis, extensor digiti minimi* and *extensor digitorum*). In addition, the *flexor digiti minimi*, which is an intrinsic muscle is able to flex the fifth digit. Extension of the DIP is aided by what is called the "Extensor Mechanism." (Figure 15.9) This is a band of connective tissue that is draped over the MCP joint of each finger (not the thumb). The *extensor digitorum*, the dorsal and palmar *interossei* and the lumbrical muscle insert into the extensor mechanism. These muscles then work in concert to help extend the DIP joints. Without this mechanism or the proper functioning of the muscles that are attached to it, the DIP would be unable to fully extend. The thumb also has several muscles that the rest of the hand does not. These include two flexors (*flexor pollicis longus and brevis*), two extensors (*extensor pollicis longus, extensor pollicis brevis*), two abductors (*abductor pollicis brevis, abductor pollicis longus*), one adductor (*adductor pollicis*) and finally, one that opposes the thumb (*opponens pollicis*).

D. Nerves and arteries of the wrist and hand

Two large arteries provide blood to the hand. The radial and ulnar arteries were formed in the arm and continue into the hand to provide the needed nutrients to the muscles, connective tissue and joints of the wrist and hand.

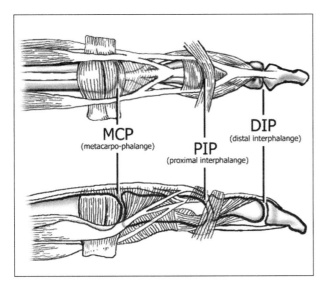

Figure 15.9 The joints of the fingers and the soft tissue structures that make up the "Extensor Mechanism". (Courtesy of Robert Perry)

There are three nerves in the hand, each of which were formed in the brachial plexus. The radial nerve innervates the muscles extending the wrist and fingers and provide sensation to the thumb and most of the back of the hand. The median nerve innervates most of the muscles that flex the wrist and hand and provides sensation to the palmar side of the thumb and the first two fingers. The ulnar nerve innervates the flexor carpi ulnaris muscle, the majority of the intrinsic muscles (interossei and lumbricals), and provides sensation to the fourth and fifth digits. (Figure 15.10) Knowledge of specific muscular dysfunction can be very helpful in diagnosing specific nerve injuries in the hand.

15.3 Wrist and Hand Injuries

A. Overuse

DeQuervain syndrome. DeQuervain's tenosynovitis is a painful wrist condition that was first described in 1895 by a Swiss physician, Fritz de Quervain. It is a stenosing or narrowing of the first dorsal tunnel of the wrist at the base of the back of the thumb through which the *abductor pollicis longus* and *extensor pollicis brevis* muscles pass on their way to the thumb. Pain is the principle complaint and gets worse with abduction of the thumb, grasping actions of the hand and ulnar deviation of the wrist. It is thought to be due to repetitive overuse of the wrist while in ulnar deviation and the thumb extended or abducted. Common activities that have been associated with the development of this condition include prolonged use of scissors and use of a computer mouse, particularly the "trackball" type that extensively utilizes the thumb. It is also associated with

pregnancy and rheumatoid arthritis (Ashraf & Devadoss, 2013).

B. Sprains

Because the wrist and hand are used in a wide variety of situations, injury to the its many ligaments are fairly common.

Finger sprain. This injury to the finger is sometimes referred to as a "jammed finger." This injury is often the result of a direct blow to the fingertip. When the distal phalanx is flexed suddenly and forcefully, it can result in damage to the insertion of the extensor digitorum tendon on the distal phalanx, causing a condition known as "mallet finger." Jamming the finger could also damage the central slip of the extensor digitorum muscle where it attaches to the middle phalanx. If this happens, a deformity referred to as a "boutoniere deformity" may occur. This deformity results in a gradual flexion contracture of the PIP joint and hyperextension of the DIP joint. A sprained finger may also be caused by hyperextension (backward bending) of the PIP or DIP joints. In these situations, there is injury of the collateral ligaments of the DIP or PIP joints or the palmar plate.

Wrist Sprain. This common injury is usually caused by a fall on an outstretch hand. The impact force is typically extension, which causes a tear in the palmar ligaments that stabilize the radiocarpal joint. Although not as

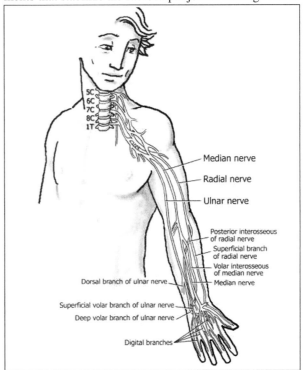

Figure 15.10 Nerves of the upper extremity. (Courtesy of Robert Perry)

frequent, the impact force can also be that of flexion, in which case the ligaments on the dorsal side of the radio-carpal joint are injured.

Carpal Instability. During hyperextension and rotational overload on the wrist, the relationship between the lunate and scaphoid bones can be disrupted through a tearing of the ligaments that bind these two carpal bones together. In such cases, the proximal carpal row rotates out of alignment, allowing proximal movement of the capitate and the distal row of carpal bones. This alteration leads to segmental instability, and the lunate bone rotates out of its normal position, either upward or downward. The resulting instability can significantly impair functioning of the hand as well as pain with almost all movements (Ramponi & McSwigan, 2016).

C. Degeneration

Osteoarthritis (OA) is typically thought of primarily occurring in large joints such as the knees, hips or shoulders. Although these are certainly more common, osteoarthritis may occur in just about any joint of the body. In the wrist and hand, the joint that is most commonly affected is that

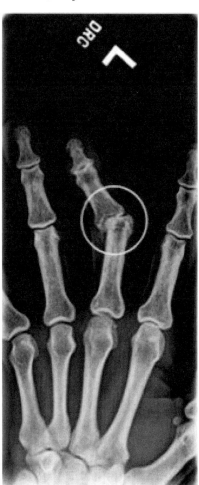

Figure 15.11 Radiograph showing significant osteoarthritis of the proximal interphalangeal joint. Courtesy of the Hand Center of Northern Arizona, Drs. Patrick Cole and Jack Quigley.

of the first CMC joint or the base of the thumb, especially in postmenopausal women (Ahern, Skyllas, Wajon, & Hush, 2018). Based on radiological examination, patients with OA of the first CMC joint are classified from Stage I to IV, with IV being the most severe. Patients presenting with Stage I or II thumb OA are most commonly managed with conservative treatment, while those with Stage III and IV are treated surgically. A recent review of the literature indicated that those in Stage I and II respond very favorably to conservative therapy (Ahern et al., 2018). Figure 15.11 shows significant osteoarthritis of the proximal interphalangeal joint. Note the loss of spacing in the joint from the degenerated cartilage as well as the presence of osteophytes (spurs) around the joint.

D. Nerve injuries

Median Nerve. The median nerve travels from the brachial plexus to the wrist and enters the hand by way of the carpal tunnel. This tunnel or space is relatively tight and as such, pressure from direct or repeated trauma can build from the resulting swelling, which compresses the nerve causing damage. When this happens, it is referred to as "carpal tunnel syndrome." Symptoms typically include a sensation of numbness or tingling in the thumb and first two fingers as well as pain in the wrist and hand. If it is severe or if it goes untreated, the individual nerve fibers start to die, leading to a more permanent loss of sensation as well as weakness in the muscles of the "thenar" eminence (thumb) of the hand.

Ulnar Nerve. The ulnar nerve travels from the brachial plexus to the medial (ulnar) side of the wrist and enters the hand at the base of the wrist. The ulnar nerve may be injured due to prolonged excess pressure on the ulnar side of the wrist and hand. Such a position and injury has been seen with competitive bicyclists during prolonged rides, especially if they use "ram-horned" handlebars, which place the wrist in radial deviation with subsequent pressure on the ulnar nerve against the handlebar. The nerve may also be injured as it travels around the medial side of the elbow through the "ulnar groove." Here the nerve is fairly close to the surface of the skin and therefore is vulnerable to injury. Regardless of where the nerve is injured, weakness of the muscles of the little finger are generally reported as well as the sensation of "tingling" or "numbness" over the 4th and 5th digits.

Radial Nerve. Injury to the radial nerve may also present with symptoms in the hand. Like the other two nerves, the radial nerve is formed in the brachial plexus. The nerve travels down the arm where it innervates the muscles primarily responsible for extension of the elbow,

Colles Fracture

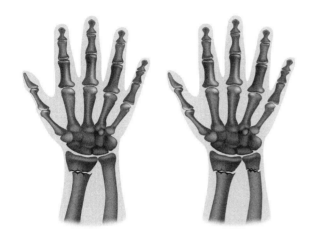

Figure 15.12 *Illustration of a Colles fracture involving either the radius or radius and ulna. Shutterstock.com*

Scaphoid Fracture

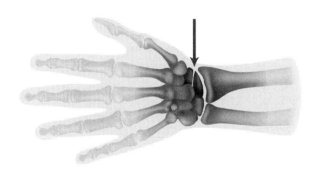

Figure 15.13 *Illustration of a fracture of the scaphoid bone in the hand. Shutterstock.com*

wrist and fingers. It also provides sensation to the back of the hand and thumb. Injury to the radial nerve will cause weakness in the muscles that perform these actions as well as altering sensation over the thumb and back of the hand. Because the radial nerve provides only sensation to the skin by the time it reaches the hand, injury to it is most likely to occur more proximally. The most common location for this proximal injury is in the upper arm as the nerve travels behind the humerus. If axillary crutches are used improperly by bearing weight through through the arm pit rather than the hands, the radial nerve can be injured in the arm. When this happens, it is frequently referred to as "crutch palsy."

E. Fractures and discolations

Colles fracture. A Colles fracture is produced by a fall on an outstretched hand and the wrist in extension. The fall causes radial deviation, resulting in a shortened and dorsally angulated radius. This causes the appearance of a "silver fork" deformity in which the distal segments of the radius and ulna are posteriorly displaced in relation to their proximal shafts (Pulos & Kakar, 2018). (Figure 15.12) Complications often occur with severely displaced fractures and may include arthritis and neuropathies of the median and/or ulnar nerves. In approximately 20 to 30% of Colles fractures there is enough comminution of the distal radius that posterior displacement with radial shortening and wrist radial deviation occurs after reduction of the boney failure. A loss in the radial length and radial deviation significantly impairs the functioning of the wrist and therefore the hand. Because of the severity of this type of fracture, the bone fragments are generally stabilized surgically with either pins or screws.

Smith's and Barton's fractures. In contrast to a Colles fracture, these two fractures are produced by a backward fall onto a hyperflexed wrist. These types of fractures are produced by the opposite mechanism to that of a Colles fracture. A Smith's fracture of the distal radius occurs 12 to 25 mm above the articulation. The carpal bones displace anteriorly along with the entire radial fragment and articular surface of the radius. In a Barton's fracture, a wedge-shaped fragment is sheared off the anterior portion of the radius. This causes the carpal bones to dislocate from their articulation with the radius. The result is a forward displacement of the carpus and the small fragment (Pulos & Kakar, 2018).

Scaphoid Fracture. The scaphoid bone spans both the proximal and distal carpal rows representing a linkage support for the carpal bones and making it vulnerable to injury. The scaphoid usually fractures in hyperextension, again from a fall on an outstretched hand. (Figure 15.13) Scaphoid fractures may occur at any of three different locations: the distal pole, the middle third, and the proximal pole. The middle third may be problematic because the blood supply to the bone is less here compared to either pole. As such, the healing of the fracture may take longer than usual (delayed union) or in some cases it may fail to heal at all (non-union) (Pulos & Kakar, 2018).

15.4 Case Studies

A. Finger fracture

Accident. A 34-year-old female was injured while riding in the back of a panel van. She was seated, but did not have a seatbelt on. When the van came to an abrupt stop, she was thrown forward into the back of the passenger seat. She put her hands up to try and stop herself, but was unsuccessful.

Evaluation and anatomical structures involved. The individual was transported to a local hospital where she was evaluated by the emergency medical staff. Radiographs of her left hand revealed multiple fractures and she was referred to a hand specialist for further evaluation and treatment. Upon further examination, it was revealed that she had sustained a non-displaced vertical fracture of the base of her 5th proximal phalanx as well as a posteriorly displaced horizontal fracture of the 4th proximal phalanx. (See Figure 15.14)

Likely cause of injuries. The most likely cause of the above injuries was the forceful impact of her left hand with the back of the passenger seat. This impact caused her 4th and 5th digits to be displaced posteriorly resulting in the observed fractures.

B. Thumb dislocation
Accident. A 20-year-old male was injured in a motor ve-

hicle accident when the car he was riding in as a passenger collided with a car in front that had slowed down unexpectedly. The individual raised his hands and placed them on the dashboard in an attempt to brace himself for the impending impact. The collision resulted in the passenger side airbag to inflate, impacting his raised hands.

Evaluation and anatomical structures involved. The individual complained of pain and obvious deformity of his right thumb following the accident and he was transported to a local hospital for evaluation. The emergency medical team evaluated him, which included radiographs of his right hand. Based upon the physical examination and the radiographs, his injury was diagnosed as a dislocation of his right 1st MCP joint. (Figure 15.15) The lateral joint capsule and the ulnar collateral ligament of the 1st MCP joint were completely torn resulting in the dislocation of the thumb. His thumb and hand were immobilized in a cast for approximately six weeks followed by physical therapy to address disuse atrophy and loss of range of motion in the thumb.

Likely Cause of Injuries. The impact of the passenger side airbag deployment with the thumb was the most

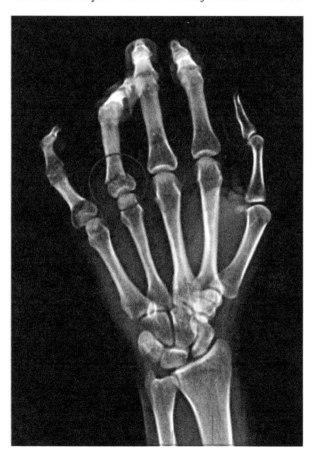

Figure 15.14 *Radiograph showing a fracture of the base of the proximal phalanx of the fourth digit.*

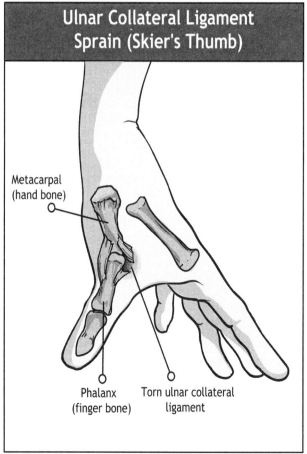

Figure 15.15 *Illustration of an ulnar collateral ligament sprain of the thumb. Shutterstock.com*

Figure 15.16
Lateral (sagittal) radiograph showing an obvious "swan neck" deformity of the 3rd digit. Courtesy of the Hand Center of Northern Arizona, Drs. Patrick Cole and Jack Quigley.

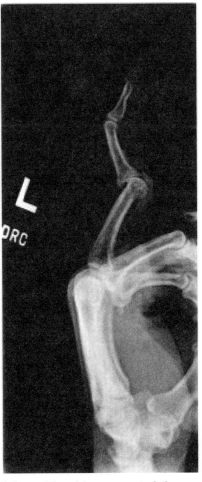

likely cause of the injury. The airbag contacted the extended thumb, forcing it posteriorly.

C. Swan neck deformity

Accident. A 72-year-old male suffered a traumatic injury to his left hand while wrestling at age 16.

Evaluation and anatomical structures involved. At the time of the injury, his hand was evaluated by the wrestling coach and his family physician. No radiographs or other imaging was obtained at that time. Both the coach and family physician felt that he had "sprained" his left middle finger. His pain decreased and he was able to use his hand for all functional and recreational activities. Approximately 10 years following the injury, ulnar deviation of the middle phalanx of his left middle finger began to develop. The magnitude of the deformity started to accelerate when he was 66 years-old. At the age of 71, a "Swan Neck" deformity began to develop in addition to the ulnar deviation (Figure 15.16). This deformity progressed rapidly, causing him to consult with an orthopedic hand surgeon. A "Swan Neck" deformity is characterized by hyperextension of the middle phalanx and flexion of the distal phalanx. In addition to the ulnar deviation and "Swan Neck" deformity seen in the accompanying radiographs, there are signs of osteoarthritis in the left proximal interphalangeal (PIP) joint. These signs include loss of joint space at the PIP joint, osteophyte development along the ulnar border of the PIP joint and likely subchondral cyst formation in the proximal phalanx.

Likely Cause of Injuries. The ulnar deviation of the middle phalanx was likely caused by the original injury, which most likely involved a tear of the lateral (radial) collateral ligament of the PIP joint. This resulted in instability that allowed the muscles of the finger (flexors, extensor, or both) to pull more toward the ulnar side of the hand, thus creating the deformity. Over time, the moment arm for this ulnar pull increased, accelerating the ulnar deviation deformity. A "Swan Neck" deformity is most commonly seen in individuals with rheumatoid arthritis, but in the present case, blood markers for this condition were negative. Rather, the swan neck deformity is most likely the result of the instability at the PIP joint caused by damage to the volar plate, which allowed the middle phalanx to be pulled into hyperextension by the extensor digitorum muscle. Without a functioning volar plate, the finger flexor muscles (flexor digitorum profundus and flexor digitorum superficialis) were unable to counteract the pull from the extensor digitorum. The osteoarthritis observed at the PIP joint is the consequence of abnormal muscle forces being exerted on the joint without the necessary stabilizing structures needed to prevent the deformities. These abnormal forces resulted in degeneration of the joint surface.

References

Agur, Ahern, M., Skyllas, J., Wajon, A., & Hush, J. (2018). The effectiveness of physical therapies for patients with base of thumb osteoarthritis_ Systematic review and meta-analysis. *Musculoskeletal Science and Practice,* 35, 46–54.

Ashraf, M. O., & Devadoss, V. G. (2013). Systematic review and meta-analysis on steroid injection therapy for de Quervain's tenosynovitis in adults. European *Journal of Orthopaedic Surgery & Traumatology,* 24(2), 149–157.

Jenkins, M., Bamberger, H. B., Black, L., & Nowinski, R. (1998). Thumb joint flexion. What is normal? *Journal of Hand Surgery* (Edinburgh, Scotland), 23(6), 796–797.

Palmer, A. K., & Werner, F. W. (1984). Biomechanics of

the distal radioulnar joint. *Clinical Orthopaedics & Related Research,* (187), 26–35.

Pulos, N., & Kakar, S. (2018). Hand and Wrist Injuries: Common Problems and Solutions. *Clinics in Sports Medicine*, 37(2), 217–243.

Ramponi, D., & McSwigan, T. (2016). Scapholunate Dissociation. *Advanced Emergency Nursing Journal,* 38(1), 10–14.

Thiru, R. G., Ferlic, D. C., Clayton, M. L., & McClure, D. C. (1986). Arterial anatomy of the triangular fibrocartilage of the wrist and its surgical significance. *The Journal of Hand Surgery*, 11(2), 258–263.

Recommended Reading

Bartel, D. L., Davy, D. T., & Keaveny, T. M. (2006). *Orthopaedic Biomechanics*. Prentice Hall.

Bergmann, U., & Rinehart, M. A. (1987). *Musculoskeletal trauma*. Aspen Pub.

Garrick, J. G., & Webb, D. R. (1999). *Sports Injuries*. Saunders.

Levangie, P. K., & Norkin, C. C. (2011). *Joint Structure and Function*. F.A. Davis.

Moore, K. L., Dalley, A. F., & Agur, A. M. R. (2013). *Clinically Oriented Anatomy*. Lippincott Williams & Wilkins.

Neumann, D. A. (2017). *Kinesiology of the Musculoskeletal System*. (D. A. Neumann, Ed.). Elsevier.

Nordin, M., Frankel, V.H. (2001). *Basic Biomechanics of the Musculoskeletal System*. Lippincott Williams & Wilkins.

Soderberg, G. L. (1997). *Kinesiology*. Lippincott Williams & Wilkins.

Symposium, A. A. O. O. S., Woo, S. L.-Y., Buckwalter, J. A., Surgeons, A. A. O. O., National Institute of Arthritis and Musculoskeletal and Skin Diseases (U.S.). (1988). Injury and repair of the musculoskeletal soft tissues. Amer Academy of Orthopaedic.

Whiting, W. C., & Zernicke, R. F. (2008). *Biomechanics of Musculoskeletal Injury*. Human Kinetics.

The Human Lower Extremity

Mark W. Cornwall

(CD–Rom Lower Extremity Anatomy)

The human lower extremity is designed for two major functions. The first is to provide a stable platform or base of support for the trunk and upper extremities and the second is to allow weightbearing through the legs and thus locomotion. Both of these functions are essential for humans to perform the many activities that they either need or want to do. Because the forces generated through these activities must travel through the lower extremity, its joints have a blend of both stability and mobility. In addition, the joints are uniquely designed to adapt to a wide range of terrains.

The next three chapters will examine the three major regions of the lower extremity; the hip, the knee and the ankle and foot. Common injuries or diseases seen in each of these regions will also be presented. In addition to the content in these chapters, the anatomical structures of the lower extremity are further illustrated on the accompanying CD.

Chapter 16

Anatomy of the Pelvis and Hip

Mark W. Cornwall

16.1 Introduction

The pelvis has a central location within the body and serves as the foundation for the lower extremities as well as for the superimposed spine and trunk. The hip joint has a number of anatomic features that allow the joint to be very stable during activities such as standing, walking and running. This chapter will first describe the basic anatomy of the pelvis and the actions of the surrounding musculature. We will then cover the anatomy of the hip, with its musculature and actions. This chapter will then discuss some of the more common injuries or disorders that are found in the pelvis and hip.

16.2 Anatomy of the Pelvis

A. Bones and joints of the pelvis

The pelvis is a general term for the irregular bony struc-

ture consisting of the two coxal bones (right and left), which articulate with each other anteriorly and with the sacrum posteriorly. The sacrum, coccyx, and pelvic girdle together form the "pelvic ring." The pelvis is bowl shaped. It serves to support the vertebral column by way of the sacrum and allows transmission of weight-bearing forces from the ground, through the lower extremities to the trunk as well as from the spine and trunk and vice versa. There are distinct differences between the pelvis of a male and that of a female. The female pelvis is larger and wider than that of a male and it has a more round pelvic inlet or superior aperture (bowl). Finally, the female iliac crests are lower than those of a male, which give them the appearance be being shorter. These unique differences are one of the most useful elements in forensics when trying to determine if the victim was a male or female. Each coxal bone actually develops from three parts: the ilium, the ishcium, and the pubis. Following birth, these three parts fuse and create a cup shaped region called the acetabulum (Figure 16.1). The acetabulum faces forward, outward, and downward. This orientation plays a significant role in determining how the lower extremity is oriented. In the back, the sacrum connects the ilium on each half of the body to form the sacroiliac joint. This joint is classified as a synovial plane joint. In the front, the two pubic bones are connected by way of the pubic symphysis, which is cartilaginous. There is no joint cavity or capsule.

B. Major ligaments of the pelvis

The pelvic ring is held in place with a number of very strong ligaments, primarily in the back where the sacrum is attached to each ilium. These ligaments include the sacrotuberous, the sacrospinus and the anterior and posterior sacroiliac. Each of these ligaments hold the sacrum firmly to the ischium. In the front, the two pubis bones from each half of the pelvis form a syndesmosis joint. This joint (pubic symphysis) does not have a joint cavity or capsule, but rather, it consists of a fibrocartilaginous connection.

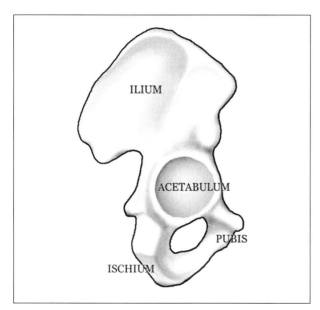

Figure 16.1 The coxal bone consisting of the ilium, ischium, and pubis fused together at the acetabulum. (Courtesy of Robert Perry)

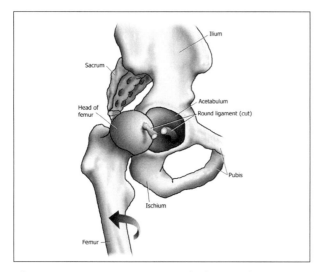

Figure 16.2 Bones comprising the human hip joint. (Courtesy of Robert Perry)

C. Muscles and available movements of the pelvis

Because the pelvis serves as a base for either the hip or spine, there is virtually no movement between any of its various components. With respect to the sacrioiliac joint, it is a synovial plane joint with irregular surfaces that create an interlocking of the sacrum and the ilium. This joint is typically very stable with less than one degree of motion (Kibsgard, Roise, Sturesson, Rohrl, & Stuge, 2014). The pubic symphysis, on the other hand has two to four times the motion compared to that of the sacroiliac joint, but is still less than two degrees. In women, this amount

increases during childbirth (Becker, I, Woodley, S.J., & Stringer, M.D., 2010).

There are a large number of muscles that originate on the pelvis, but all of them insert onto the femur and therefore only create motion at the hip joint. However, although there are no muscles that are specifically designed to move the sacroiliac joint, the gluteus maximus muscle is able to provide additional compressive stability to the joint.

D. Nerves and arteries of the pelvis

The majority of the nerves in the pelvis are formed in the lumbar plexus, which is a network of nerves coming from the lumbar portion of the spinal cord. They provide sensation to the skin around the pelvis and hips as well as motor or sensation to the muscles and organs within the pelvis.

The internal and external iliac arteries form deep in the pelvis and arise from the common iliac artery, which is a branch of the large abdominal artery in the trunk. These two arteries and their branches supply the needed blood to the muscles and organs of the pelvis. The internal iliac artery has several branches that will supply the muscles of the inner pelvis, the groin, the buttocks and medial thigh. The external iliac artery becomes the femoral artery at the groin.

16.3 Anatomy of the Hip

A. Bones and joints of the hip

The hip joint (iliofemoral joint) consists of the proximal head of the femur and the acetabulum of the pelvis. The proximal end of the femur has a large ball-shaped head which articulates with the deep cup-shaped acetabulum of the pelvis. The acetabulum is further deepened by a rim of fibrocartilage called the labrum. (Figure 16.2) This configuration, along with the ligamentous structures and several large and strong muscles makes the hip joint very stable.

B. Major ligaments of the hip

Although the deep cup of the acetabulum provides a great deal of anatomical stability, the hip joint is further strengthened by its capsule and reinforcing ligaments. These ligaments include the ishiofemoral, the iliofemoral and the pubofemoral. The iliofemoral ligament joins the ilium to the femur, while the ischiofemoral and pubofemoral ligaments connect the pubis and ischium to the femur. The iliofemoral ligament consists of a 'Y'-shaped band of very strong fibers that connect the anterior inferior iliac spine of the pelvis to the proximal femur. The iliofemoral ligament is the strongest single ligament in the body. Functionally, the iliofemoral ligament is responsible for preventing hyperextension of the hip. It also resists forces that produce tension in the hip when the hip is fully extended. By contrast, the pubofemoral ligament originates on the superior pubis, which is medial to the acetabulum. It then blends into the iliofemoral ligament. The pubofemoral ligament also resists hyperextension of the hip as well as hyper-abduction of the hip. The ischiofemoral ligament is a triangular shaped band of very strong fibers originating on the ischium, behind the acetabulum and then crosses over the head of the femur to attach to the proximal femur. The orientation of its fibers significantly reinforce the anterior aspect of the capsule. The ischiofemoral ligament resists hyper-extension and internal rotation of the hip. Together, these three ligaments are able to resist extreme movement in all directions, especially that of extension.

C. Muscles and available movements of the hip

(CD—Folder: Thigh Region, Movie: *External Rotators of the Thigh*).

Because the hip joint is classified as a "ball-and-socket" joint, or "enarthrodial," it is able to move in a wide variety of directions. Not only is the hip able to move in each of the four major planes of the body (flexion, extension, internal and external rotation), it is also able to move in two or more of these planes at the same time. This type of movement is referred to as "circumduction" or the ability to move in circles. This makes the hip joint not only a very versatile joint, but a very stable

one as well. The shoulder joint discussed in chapter 13, is also a "ball-and-socket" joint, but is much less stable compared to the hip. This increased stability of the hip is a direct result of its deeper socket and the thicker ligaments that reinforce the joint capsule. However, the hip sacrifices mobility for this increased stability.

There are approximately 20 different muscles situated about the hip. Many of these muscles are very large like the gluteus maximus, but others are quite small such as the gemellus superior and inferior. Not only are these muscles able to move the hip in each of the four different planes, when working in concert with each other, all conceivable movements of the hip may be produced.

There are seven muscles that are able to flex the hip, the biggest of these is the *Psoas Major* and *Iliacus*. (Figure 16.3) Other muscles that are able to flex the hip include the *tensor fascia latae*, the *sartorius* and the *rectus femoris*. There are four muscles that are able to extend the hip, the largest being the *gluteus maximus*, which originates at the iliac crest of the ilium, sacrum, coccyx, and lumbodorsal fascia. It produces external rotation of the thigh in addition to extension of the hip. The other large hip extensor muscles are the hamstrings, which include the *biceps femoris, semimembranosus,* and *semitendinosus.* The hamstring muscles not only extend the hip, but they also flex the knee. (Figures 16.4 and 16.5) Abduction of the hip is accomplished primarily by four muscles, the *gluteus medius, gluteus minimus, tensor fascia latae*, and *sartorius*. The largest is the *gluteus medius* muscle that originates at the anterior iliac crest and the lateral surface of the ilium. In addition to hip abduction, this muscle is able to internally or externally rotate the thigh, depending on which part of the muscle that is active. The *gluteus*

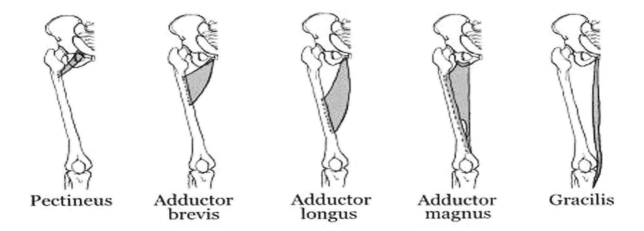

Pectineus   **Adductor brevis**   **Adductor longus**   **Adductor magnus**   **Gracilis**

Figure 16.3 Muscles of the medial hip and thigh (flexors). (Courtesy of Robert Perry)

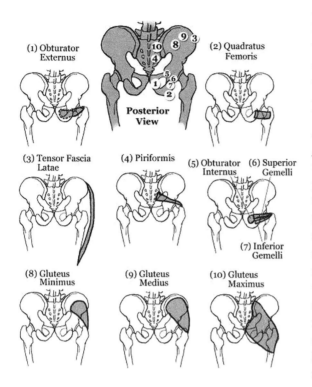

Figure 16.4 *Muscles of the posterior hip (extensors, abductors and external rotators). (Courtesy of Robert Perry)*

minimus originates on the lateral surface of the ilium, below the *gluteus medius*. Like the *gluteus medius*, it is able to internally rotate the thigh as well as abduct the hip. The *tensor fascia latae* and *sartorius* were mentioned previously because they are able to flex the hip in addition to abducting the hip. Adduction of the hip is accomplished by 5 different muscles. These include the *adductor magnus* (largest), the *adductor longus, adductor brevis*, the *pectineus* and the *gracilis* muscles. (Figure 16.6) Each of these muscles originate on either the superior or inferior pubic ramus of the pelvis and then insert into the shaft of the femur. These muscles are fairly large and make up the medial or inner aspect of the thigh. Internal rotation of the hip is accomplished by four different muscles, with the *gluteus medius* (posterior fibers) and *gluteus minimus* muscles being the largest. The *tensor fascia latae* muscle, which was mentioned previously as being a hip flexor and abductor is also able to internally rotate the thigh. The final muscle is the *adductor magnus,* which is primarily a hip adductor. It is, however, able to internally rotate the hip, but is generally not considered to be a major contributor because of its small moment arm for this action. (Figure 16.4) Finally, external rotation is performed by 10 different muscles, many of them being relatively small. The smaller ones include the *quadratus femoris, piriformis, obturator internus* and *externus* and *gemelli inferior* and *superior*. These muscles originate on the lateral side

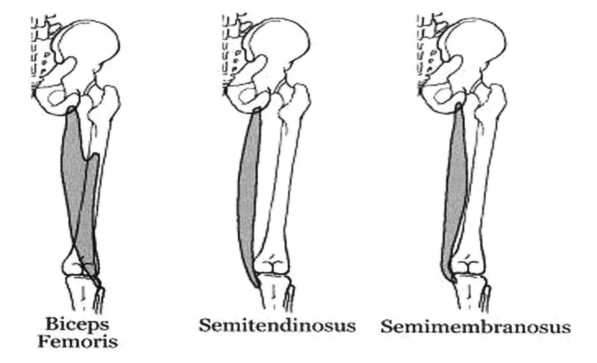

Figure 16.5 *Muscles of the posterior thigh (hamstrings: extensors). (Courtesy of Robert Perry)*

of the pelvis and then insert into the proximal femur. The remaining four muscles were mentioned previously because they also perform other actions at the hip. These include the *sartorius, pectineus, gluteus maximus* and the anterior fibers of the *gluteus medius*. (Figure 16.4)

D. Nerves and arteries of the hip

Although the lumbar plexus is responsible for many of the nerves in the pelvis, it also contains some important nerves to the muscles of the anterior and medial thigh. The femoral nerve is the largest of these nerves and innervates the large quadriceps muscle in the anterior thigh. The obturator nerve on the other hand, innervates the muscles in the medial thigh (adductors) as well as providing sensation to the medial aspect of the thigh.

The sacral plexus contains the nerves that supply the hip and the majority of the thigh. The most important of these nerves is the sciatic nerve. It arises from the sacral plexus inside the pelvis and then then exits into the posterior buttocks where it travels down the back of the thigh, giving off branches that will eventually innervate the muscles of the knee, ankle and foot. The sciatic nerve is susceptible to compressive forces in the posterior hip and pelvis, but injury is more common where it is formed in the spinal cord. As such, the damage occurs prior to the nerve forming. Regardless, the symptoms typically include radiating pain, numbness or tingling in the buttocks and down the leg and possibly into the foot. In addition, muscle weakness may result if the damage is severe enough or there is a prolonged compressive load on the nerve.

The femoral artery of the groin and thigh is a continuation of the external iliac artery that was mentioned above for the pelvis. The artery produces a large branch, called the deep femoral or profundus femoral artery. This artery provides the blood supply to the hip joint, proximal femur and the remainder of the thigh. Two of each branches early; the medial and lateral femoral circumflex arteries provide the majority of the blood to the proximal femur and lateral hip.

16.4 Injuries of the Pelvis and Hip

As we will see, many diseases of the pelvis and hip frequently occur among the very young and the elderly. Trauma, however, may occur at almost any age.

A. Congenital disorders

Hip dysplasia is one of the more common congenital disorders affecting the hip. It typically manifests itself at birth or within a few years. The disorder involves a wide range of conditions primarily associated with abnormal development and growth of the structures comprising the hip joint. These conditions include malformation of the femoral head or acetabulum. This malformation can lead to congenital dislocation or subluxation of the hip or general instability of the hip. The more severe cases can lead to permanent physical impairment if not treated properly. Because the child is still growing when these disorders are discovered, some of them may spontaneously resolve or respond well to non-surgical measures (Alsaleem, Set, & Saadeh, 2015).

B. Nerve injuries

Sciatica or irritation of the sciatic nerve is a fairly common complaint. As mentioned previously, this irritation may be the result of localized compression on the actual nerve, or compression of the individual nerve roots in the spinal cord that will comprise the nerve. The lifetime incidence of this condition has been estimated to be between 13% and 40%. Fortunately, most cases of sciatica resolve with simple conservative measures (e.g. analgesia and physical therapy). It is possible, however for the condition to become chronic, with major socio-economic implications. Such cases may require surgical intervention (Stafford, Peng, & Hill, 2007). The major symptoms of sciatica are altered sensation (numbness or tingling) and/or pain in the distribution of the sciatic nerve. This distribution includes the buttocks, posterior thigh and calf as well as the foot.

C. Labral injuries

Labral tears. The labrum of the hip consists of tough cartilage that rings the acetabulum and facilitates smooth hip motion, deepens the cup for the femoral head and helps to preserve proper alignment between the femoral head and the acetabulum. Tears in the labrum may result from any excessive forces directed to the hip joint. This may include falls, motor vehicle accidents including or at the time of a hip dislocation. This is especially true if the dislocation is in the posterior direction. (Groh & Herrera, 2009). In addition to direct trauma, the labrum may tear as a result of an accumulation of microtrauma secondary to some repeated activity. The most common injury pattern for a torn labrum is that of hyperextension with femoral external rotation. For example, individuals who participate in repetitive end-range movements of hyperflexion, hyperextension and abduction (track and field sports) are at greater risk of tearing their labrum. Such tears cause pain as well as a sensation of "clicking" or "popping" within the joint. It has been estimated that between 22%

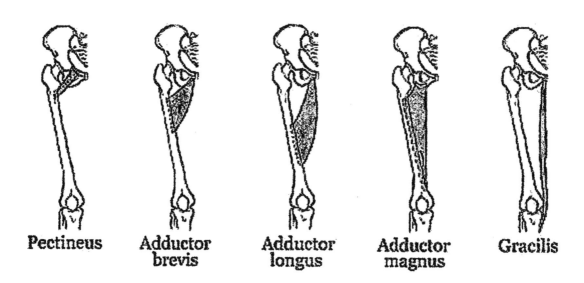

Pectineus   Adductor   Adductor   Adductor   Gracilis
              brevis   longus   magnus

Figure 16.6 Muscles of the medial thigh (adductors). (Courtesy of Robert Perry)

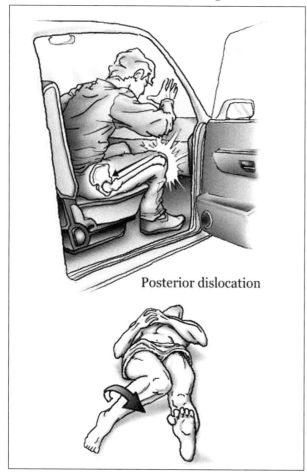

Posterior dislocation

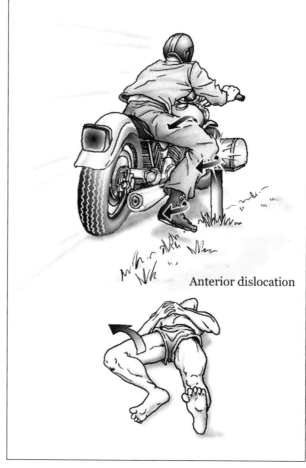

Anterior dislocation

Figure 16.7 Illustration of a mechanism of posterior hip dislocation and the common position of an individual following this type of injury. (Courtesy of Robert Perry)

Figure 16.8 Illustration of a mechanism of an anterior hip dislocation and the common position of an individual following this type of injury. (Courtesy of Robert Perry)

and 55% of patients who complain of hip or groin pain have a torn labrum. Women are more likely to experience this type of injury than to men (Leiboid, Huijbregts, & Jensen, 2008).

Labral impingement. Femoroacetabular impingement (Labral Impingement) is a relatively prevalent clinical syndrome and may be a primary contributor to idiopathic hip osteoarthritis (degeneration). It is characterized by an alteration in the shape of either the femoral head or the acetabulum. Individuals with hip (labral) impingement may have been born with this structural abnormality. This osseous pathomorphology alters normal biomechanics of the hip joint, causing accelerated joint degeneration. Over time, repetitive "bumping" or impingement of the femur on the rim of the acetabulum leads to cartilage and labral damage. Repetitive activity involving hip movement beyond the normal range of motion is typically associated with labral impingement. Such movements are commonly seen in individuals who participate in athletic activities such as football, baseball, soccer, tennis, hockey, lacrosse, dance, and golf. Symptoms of pain in the groin are most often reported by individuals during activities requiring repeated extreme flexion of the hip. Early intervention in well-selected patients can provide symptomatic relief and

delay progression to osteoarthritis (Ghaffari, Davis, Storey, & Moser, 2018). An injury to the hip may also cause symptoms of hip impingement.

D. Fractures and dislocations

Hip dislocation. Because the boney configuration of the hip makes it so stable, dislocation is relatively rare. When it does occur, it is from significant force as seen in a motor vehicle accident or a fall from a height (Sanders, Tejwani, & Egol, 2010). Hip dislocation secondary to direct or indirect trauma is typically seen in younger individuals. The direction of such dislocations may be anterior, posterior, or central. The most common direction of a hip dislocation, however, is posterior. This is usually caused by a blow to the knee with the hip flexed and internally rotated. Central dislocation can occur when the femoral head is driven medially through the acetabulum. This dislocation most often occurs from a direct impact to the greater trochanter from a lateral force or from a fall to the side onto the hip. Dislocations of the hip anteriorly are relatively uncommon but may occur with the hip flexed, abducted, and externally rotated. (Figures 16.7 and 16.8) Rapid identification and reduction of the dislocated hip is critical, since a long delay in reducing the dislocation increases the risk of developing avascular necrosis of the femoral head and posttraumatic osteoarthritis is a com-

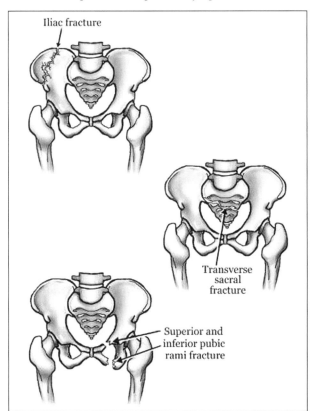

Figure 16.9 Illustration of three types of pelvic fractures. *(Courtesy of Robert Perry)*

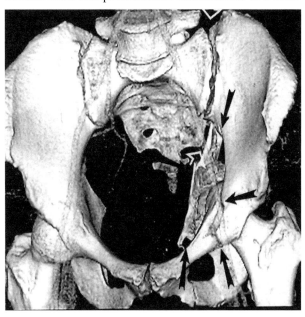

Figure 16.10 Reformatted computerized axial tomography (CT) of a pelvis showing multiple fractures involving the illium and pubis as well as dislocation of the sacroiliac joint. Cornwall, MW, Nyre, E, Harris, JH: Imaging Handbook for Physical Therapists. Lippincott, Williams and Wilkins, 2014.

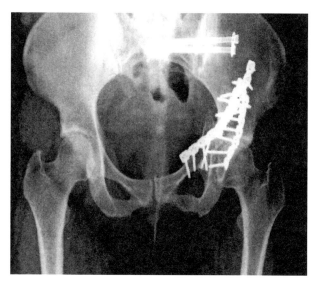

Figure 16.11 *Radiograph showing surgical fixation of the pelvic fracture illustrated in figure 16.10. Cornwall, MW, Nyre, E, Harris, JH: Imaging Handbook for Physical Therapists. Lippincott, Williams and Wilkins, 2014.*

mon complication, even in the absence of associated fractures (Mandell et al., 2017).

Pelvic fracture. Pelvic fractures are generally the result of high energy impacts such as a fall from a height or

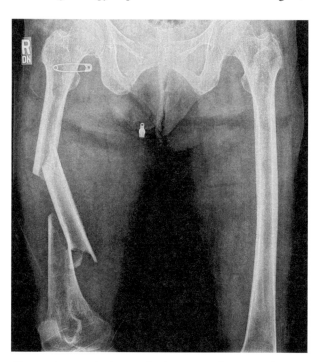

Figure 16.12 *Radiograph showing a fracture of the shaft of the femur. Cornwall, MW, Nyre, E, Harris, JH: Imaging Handbook for Physical Therapists. Lippincott, Williams and Wilkins, 2014.*

a motor vehicle accident. The pelvis typically fractures in one of three locations: the pubic ramis, which is also the most common site of stress fractures in the pelvis; the iliac wings; or the transverse sacrum. All three fractures are the result of a direct impact. (Figure 16.9) Pelvic fractures may be classified as being "stable" or "unstable". A "stable" pelvic fracture is one in which the pelvic ring is still able to withstand physiologic stresses without abnormal deformation (Khurana, Sheehan, Sodickson, & Weaver, 2014). Generally, this means that continuity of the pelvic ring remains intact, regardless of where the fracture is. For example, in Figure 16.9, the top two fractures would be considered "stable", but the bottom fracture would be considered "unstable" because the pelvic ring is no longer continuous. Stable pelvic fractures are often treated conservatively, but an unstable pelvic fracture will likely require surgical intervention. It is not unusual for pelvic fractures to be fairly complex, requiring computerized tomographs (CT) to clearly visualize the extent and location of the injuries. Figure 16.10 illustrates this point as it shows an unstable pelvic fracture involving multiple fractures to the ilium and pubis as well as a dislocation to the sacroiliac joint. Figure 16.11 shows the extent of surgical stabilization needed for such an injury.

Femoral Fractures. Fractures involving the femoral shaft are commonly seen with high energy trauma such as motor vehicle accidents, but may also occur with low energy trauma such as a fall. (Figure 16.12) The incidence of midshaft fractures of the femur is approximately 37 per 100,000 persons each year. Individuals younger than 40 are more likely to sustain a femoral shaft fracture from high energy trauma, while those over 40 years of age are more likely to sustain a fracture from low energy trauma such as a fall (Adnan, Zia, & Amin, 2012). Common complications from fractures to the shaft of the femur include disruption of blood supply to the lower extremity, malunion of the fracture and a leg length discrepancy.

A fracture of the neck of the femur, is common in the elderly, especially after a fall. In aging individuals, femoral neck fractures often occur as a result of the weakening of the bone due to osteoporosis or osteopenia. As such, the bone is unable to withstand the normal force of weight-bearing or that from a simple fall. Femoral neck fractures are therefore more common in women because their bones experience faster calcium loss with aging compared to males. There are two types of femoral neck fractures, transverse fractures that begin at the superior femoral neck and compression fractures that begin inferiorly. Compression fractures of the femoral neck are the more common of the two. Fractures of the femoral neck may interfere with blood supply to the femoral head and make recovery difficult or lead to necrosis of the femoral head. Because the head of the femur is the focal point for weight bearing, femoral neck fractures can have a devastating effect on functional mobility. Surgical stabilization (hip pinning or nailing) or replacement (total hip arthroplasty) is the treatment of choice followed by a significant period of physical rehabilitation (Raaymakers, 2006). Another option to surgical stabilization of the fracture is to perform a total joint replacement. (Figure 16.13) Such an option allows the person to bear weight on the injured limb immediately after surgery.

Acetabular fractures. Acetabular fractures are also the result of high energy forces to the hip joint such as high-speed motor vehicle accidents or a fall from a significant height. Acetabular injuries occur as a result of direct blows to the knees with the hips flexed or some other event producing linear loading through the femur. Acetabular fractures and hip dislocation may occur simultaneously.

E. Degeneration

In addition to the weakening of bones as people age, leading to possible fractures, gradual degeneration of the articular surfaces of the hip joint is also very common. As the degenerative process progresses, the cartilage covering the femoral head and inside the acetabulum is eroded followed by a hardening (sclerosis) of the bone just below where the cartilage was. In addition, osteophytes or boney lumps (bone spurs) develop around the joint. All of these changes cause the joints to become stiff and painful. (Figure 16.14) Osteoarthritis (OA), often referred to as "wear-and-tear" arthritis, "age-related" arthritis, or degenerative joint disease, is the most common form of joint disorder in the United States (Lespasio, 2018). OA is the most common form of arthritis and a leading cause of pain and disability worldwide. OA can affect any synovial joint, although the hips, knees, hands, feet and spine are the most commonly affected sites (O'Neill, McCabe, & McBeth, 2018). According to the Centers for Disease Control and Prevention, lifetime risk for symptomatic hip OA is 18.5% for men and 28.6% for women (Lespasio, 2018). It is estimated that more than 27 million Americans are affected (O'Neill et al., 2018). As the degeneration of the joint increases, the pain of weight-bearing increases and the person's functional abilities significantly decline. Surgical replacement of the affected boney components is generally the surgical solution, which not only removes the pain that the person is experiencing, it also significantly improves their function and quality of life. Conservative, non-surgical methods of treatment may be used in the early stages of the disease.

16.5 Case Studies

A. Acetabular fracture

Accident. A 37-year-old male was an unrestrained passenger in a "head-on" collision with another vehicle. The individual initially impacted his left knee into the dash of the van he was riding in and subsequently hit the windshield. He may have had a brief loss of consciousness at the time of the accident.

Evaluation and anatomical structures involved. The individual was alert and oriented at the time emergency personnel arrived at the scene of the accident. He complained of left hip pain and there was an obvious deformity of his left hip. He was unable to bear weight or

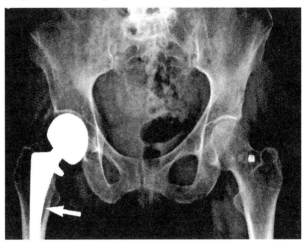

Figure 16.13 *Radiograph showing a total hip arthroplasty. Cornwall, MW, Nyre, E, Harris, JH: Imaging Handbook for Physical Therapists. Lippincott, Williams and Wilkins, 2014.*

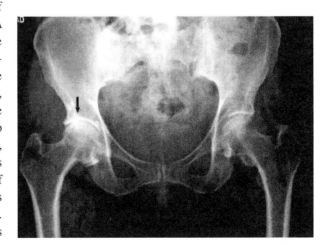

Figure 16.14 *Radiograph osteoarthritis of both hip joints. Cornwall, MW, Nyre, E, Harris, JH: Imaging Handbook for Physical Therapists. Lippincott, Williams and Wilkins, 2014.*

ambulate. As such, he was transported to the emergency department of a local hospital where a physical examination, including radiographs indicated a possible fracture of his left acetabulum. A computerized tomograph (CT) was ordered, which revealed a fracture dislocation of the posterior wall of his left acetabulum with concomitant fracture to the posterior column of the pelvis surrounding the acetabulum. He subsequently underwent an open reduction internal fixation (ORIF) of the posterior acetabulum and posterior wall fractures. Following surgery, the individual complained of left buttocks pain that radiated down his left leg. This pain was initially mild, but progressively increased as he recovered from the surgery and became more active. After additional evaluation as well as a magnetic resonance image (MRI), he was given the diagnosis of left sciatica.

Likely cause of injuries. The injury to this individual's acetabulum and pelvis was a direct result of the impact of his left knee with the dashboard of his vehicle, which pushed the head of his femur into the acetabulum, resulting in the fractures. (Figures 16.7) The sciatica was most likely the result of the trauma to the acetabulum and pelvis, since the large sciatic nerve passes close behind the hip joint and could easily have been injured at the same time as the other injuries. Alternatively, scar tissue from the acetabular and pelvic fractures could have compressed the nerve.

B. Femoral fracture

Accident. A 78-year-old female fell while shopping and immediately complained of severe pain in her right hip and the inability to bear any weight on the limb.

Evaluation and anatomical structures involved. She was transported to a local hospital by emergency medical personnel. Physical examination, including radiographs indicated that she had sustained a fracture of her right femoral neck inside the joint capsule. Because the fracture had occurred within the joint capsule, it was felt that total joint arthroplasty was preferred compared to ORIF with a compression screw.

Likely cause of injury. Although the women stated that she either slipped or tripped on something that was on the floor when she fell, no such evidence was found by those who came to her aide after she fell. Because the women had a long history of osteoporosis, a more likely cause of her injury was a spontaneous fracture secondary to significant weakening of the femur secondary to the osteoporosis. Such fractures are considered to be similar to what is seen with compression fractures of the lumbar spine (Horiuchi et al., 1988). As such, it is entirely likely that when her femur fractured, she fell to the ground rather than a fall causing the femur to break.

References

AAdnan, R., Zia, M., & Amin, J. (2012). Frequency of femoral fractures; comparison in patients less than and more than 40 years of age. *Professional Medical Journal*, 19, 11.

Alsaleem, M., Set, K. K., & Saadeh, L. (2015). Developmental Dysplasia of Hip: A Review. *Clinical Pediatrics*, 54(10), 921–928.

Becker, I, Woodley, S.J., & Stringer, M.D. (2010). The adult human pubic sympysis: a systematic reivew. *Journal of Anatomy*, 217(5), 475–487.

Ghaffari, A., Davis, I., Storey, T., & Moser, M. (2018). Current Concepts of Femoroacetabular Impingement. *Radiologic Clinics of North America*, 56(6), 965–982.

Groh, M. M., & Herrera, J. (2009). A comprehensive review of hip labral tears. *Current Reviews in Musculoskeletal Medicine*, 2(2), 105–117.

Horiuchi, T., Igarashi, M., Karube, S., Oda, H., Tokuyama, H., Huang, T., & Inoue, S. (1988). pontaneous fractures of the hip in the elderly. *Orthopedics*, 11(9), 1277–1280.

Khurana, B., Sheehan, S. E., Sodickson, A. D., & Weaver, M. J. (2014). Pelvic Ring Fractures: What the Orthopedic Surgeon Wants to Know. *RadioGraphics*, 34(5), 1317–1333.

Kibsgard, T. J., Roise, O., Sturesson, B., Rohrl, S. M., & Stuge, B. (2014). Radiosteriometric analysis of movement in the sacroiliac joint during a single-leg stance in patients with long-lasting pelvic girdle pain. *Clinical Biomechanics (Bristol, Avon)*, 29(4), 406–411.

Leiboid, M., Huijbregts, P., & Jensen, R. (2008). Concurrent Criterion-Related Validity of Physical Examination Tests for Hip Labral Lesions: A Systematic Review. *Journal of Manual Manipulative Therapy*, 16(2), E24-41.

Lespasio, M. (2018). Hip Osteoarthritis: A Primer. *The Permanente Journal*.

Mandell, J. C., Marshall, R. A., Weaver, M. J., Harris, M.

B., Sodickson, A. D., & Khurana, B. (2017). Traumatic Hip Dislocation: What the Orthopedic Surgeon Wants to Know. *RadioGraphics*, 37(7), 2181–2201.

O'Neill, T. W., McCabe, P. S., & McBeth, J. (2018). Update on the epidemiology, risk factors and disease outcomes of osteoarthritis. *Best Practice & Research. Clinical Rheumatology,* 32(2), 312–326.

Raaymakers, E. L. F. B. (2006). Fractures of the femoral neck: a review and personal statement. *Acta Chir Orthop Traumatol Cech,* 73(1), 45–59.

Sanders, S., Tejwani, N., & Egol, K. A. (2010). Traumatic hip dislocation–a review. *Bulletin of the NYU Hospital for Joint Diseases*, 68(2), 91–96.

Stafford, M. A., Peng, P., & Hill, D. A. (2007). Sciatica: a review of history, epidemiology, pathogenesis, and the role of epidural steroid injection in management. *British Journal of Anaesthesia*, 99(4), 461–473.

Recommended Reading

Bartel, D. L., Davy, D. T., & Keaveny, T. M. (2006). *Orthopaedic Biomechanics*. Prentice Hall.

Bergmann, U., & Rinehart, M. A. (1987). *Musculoskeletal trauma*. Aspen Pub.

Garrick, J. G., & Webb, D. R. (1999). *Sports Injuries*. Saunders.

Levangie, P. K., & Norkin, C. C. (2011). *Joint Structure and Function*. F.A. Davis.

Moore, K. L., Dalley, A. F., & Agur, A. M. R. (2013). *Clinically Oriented Anatomy*. Lippincott Williams & Wilkins.

Neumann, D. A. (2017). *Kinesiology of the Musculoskeletal System*. (D. A. Neumann, Ed.). Elsevier.

Soderberg, G. L. (1997). *Kinesiology*. Lippincott Williams & Wilkins.

Symposium, A. A. O. O. S., Woo, S. L.-Y., Buckwalter, J. A., Surgeons, A. A. O. O., National Institute of Arthritis and Musculoskeletal and Skin Diseases (U.S.). (1988). Injury and repair of the musculoskeletal soft tissues. Amer Academy of Orthopaedic.

Whiting, W. C., & Zernicke, R. F. (2008). *Biomechanics of Musculoskeletal Injury*. Human Kinetics.

Chapter 17

The Knee

Mark W. Cornwall

17.1 Introduction

The knee joint is situated between two relatively stable joints, the hip and the ankle. It is extremely important for overall physical function. It also plays a significant role in all weight bearing movements of the lower extremity such as walking, running and jumping, etc. The knee is the largest joint in the human body and is frequently the site of acute injury or degenerative changes, that can limit a person's overall function and mobility. This chapter will first discuss the anatomical and biomechanical features of the knee, followed by the more common injuries and degenerative conditions that affect the joint.

17.2 Anatomy
(CD—Folder: Knee Complex)

A. Bones and joints of the knee

The knee joint complex consists of three bones, the femur, tibia and patella. It is classified as a synovial bicondylar hinge joint ("ginglymus"). (Figure 17.1) The "true" knee joint is the tibiofemoral joint, which is composed of the distal tibia and the proximal femur. The patella, or "*knee cap,*" is considered to be a sesamoid bone because it is embedded within the tendon of the quadriceps muscle. Rather than directly assisting with the weight bearing forces on the knee, the patella plays a major role in optimizing the force produced by the quadriceps muscle by increasing the moment arm of the muscle. The bottom, or distal end of the femur consists of two round-shaped condyles, with the lateral one having a larger circumference

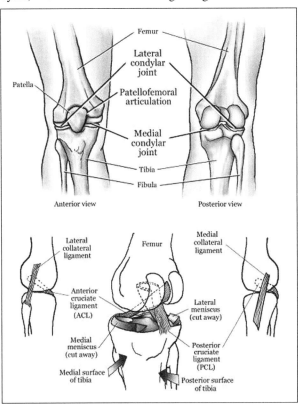

Figure 17.1 *Bones and ligaments of the knee joint. (Courtesy of Robert Perry)*

Table 17.1
Degrees of Freedom at the Knee

Axis	Rotational Movement	Translational Movement
Mediolateral	Flexion-Extension	Medial-Lateral
Anteroposterior	Abduction-Adduction	Anterior-Posterior (drawer)
Longitudinal	InterNal-external tibial	Compression-Distraction

Table 17.2
Ligamentous Restraints of the Knee

General Motion	Primary Restraint	Secondary Restraints
Anterior Drawer	Anterior Cruciate (ACL)	Medial Collateral, Lateral Collateral, Medial and Lateral Capsule
Posterior Drawer	Posterior Cruciate	Posterior Medial Capsule, Posterior Lateral Capsule, Medial Collateral, Lateral Collateral
Abduction	Medial Collateral	Anteriorcruciate, Posterior Cruciate, Medical Capsule, Postermedial Capsule
Adduction	Lateral Collateral	Anterior Cruciate, Posterior Cruciate, Lateral Capsule, Tendons of Iliofibial Tract and Popliteus

than that of the medial one. This fact plays an important role in how the two bones of the knee move relative to each other. The patella articulates with these two condyles as it slides up and down during extension and flexion. The two condyles of the femur are separated posteriorly by a large notch, called the intercondylar fossa. This notch provides the space necessary for the two large cruciate ligaments that is discussed below. The top, or proximal, end of the tibia is referred to as the tibial plateau and there is one for each condyle of the femur (medial and lateral). These plateaus are concave shaped, but are relatively shallow. Fibrocartilaginous discs, called menisci, are attached to each plateau and they help deepen the plateaus as well as act as shock absorbers between the femur and the tibia during weight bearing.

B. Major ligaments of the knee
In comparison to other joints like the hip, the knee does not enjoy significant boney stability. As previously noted,

the conflicting needs for stability and mobility are resolved mechanically through the complex interaction of the ligaments and the geometry of the two articulating surfaces. The connective tissue stability is provided by a large, fairly loose capsule surrounding both the femur and the tibia. Changes in joint position generally result in changes in the relative forces involved in the joint's passive stability (Andriacchi, T.P., Kramer, G.M., & Landon, G.C., 1985). It is most stable when it is fully extended because the ligaments and capsule are their tightest in this position.

The primary ligaments that reinforce the joint capsule are the lateral collateral (LCL) or fibular collateral ligament, the medial collateral (MCL) or tibial collateral ligament, and the oblique popliteal ligament (OPL). (Figure 17.1) The LCL and MCL are important side-to-side stabilizers of the knee. The OPL helps to limit posterior displacement of the femur on the tibia (hyperextension), sometimes referred to as "back knee." The knee joint is further stabilized by two large ligaments inside the knee joint. These ligaments are the anterior cruciate ligament (ACL) and the posterior cruciate ligament (PCL). The ACL originates on the front of the tibia between the two tibial plateaus and then courses superior and posterior to attach to the medial side of the lateral condyle, inside the joint. The ACL is primarily responsible for preventing the tibia from moving excessively forward (anterior) relative to the femur. The PCL, on the other hand begins on the posterior edge of the proximal tibia and then courses superior and anterior to attach to the lateral side of the medial condyle, again, inside the joint. This ligament is primarily responsible for preventing the tibia from moving excessively backward (posterior) relative to the femur. They are called "cruciate" ligaments because they cross each other inside the knee, thus forming an "X" configuration. Together, these two ligaments provide overall significant stability to the knee joint. In addition, they play an important role in guiding the movement between the two bones during motion.

C. Muscles and available movements of the knee
The knee has six degrees of freedom occurring around three axes (transverse, anteroposterior, longitudinal), with each axis allowing one rotation and one translation. (Table 17.1) Because the knee joint is a "modified" hinge joint, its movement is almost exclusively that of flexion and extension (transverse axis). The total amount of this motion is approximately 135°. About the longitudinal axis, the knee has approximately 40-50° of combined internal

and external rotation. The amount of external rotation is somewhat greater than that of internal rotation. This internal and external rotation plays an important role in how the femur or tibia moves relative to its adjacent bone, and without it, total range of motion would be significantly reduced. The least amount of motion occurs about the anteroposterior axis and is described as abduction and adduction.

Motions at the tibiofemoral joint are complex, being both voluntarily and involuntarily coupled, resulting in movement about axes oblique to the cardinal planes. It is the articulating surface between the femur and the tibia where this motion occurs. The round condyles of the femur are able to roll and slide as the knee flexes and extends. Additionally, the geometry of the articulating surfaces is irregular, creating axes of motion which are themselves transient with respect to any fixed reference point in the knee. The complex motions of the joint are controlled and restricted by joint geometry and the knee's ligamentous restraints. (Table 17.2) The cruciate ligaments significantly influence the movements of the knee joint. The passive action of the cruciate ligaments is partially responsible for the sliding action that occurs beyond 20° flexion, i.e., as the knee continues to roll back, a portion of the ACL becomes taut and prevents pure rolling from continuing, thus initiating sliding between the femur and tibia. During extension, the PCL serves the same function, causing posterior slide of the condyle (Kapandji, I.A., 1988). While the primary function of the collateral ligaments is medial-lateral stability, they also play a role in the above joint kinematics.

The major muscles about the knee include the *quadriceps*, which extends the knee and the *hamstrings*, which flex the knee. The hamstrings are actually three muscles, the *biceps femoris*, the *semimembranosis* and the *semitendinosis*. Together, they are able to flex the knee and also extend the hip. If the biceps femoris is acting alone, external rotation of the tibia occurs. On the other hand, if the *semimembranosis* and *semitendinosis* muscles act alone, internal rotation of the tibia occurs. In addition to these two large muscle groups, there are three other muscles (*popliteus, Sartorius, graciis*), which assist with knee flexion and internal rotation.

D. Nerves and arteries of the knee

There is one large nerve and one large artery that pass behind the knee on their way to the foot and ankle. Prior to reaching the knee, the large sciatic nerve divides into the common peroneal (fibular) and tibial nerve. After leaving the posterior aspect of the knee, the common peroneal

(fibular) nerve will divide into the superficial and deep peroneal (fibular) nerves. Together, these nerves will innervate the muscles on the lateral and anterior aspect of the lower leg. On the other hand, the tibial nerve continues distally down the back of the leg and will innervate the muscles of the calf. The tibial nerve will eventually end on the bottom of the foot. Behind the knee, the popliteal artery is the continuation of the femoral artery in the thigh. It produces several branches that provide blood supply to the knee joint. After leaving the knee, it divides into two arteries; the anterior tibial artery, which supplies the anterior shin and its muscles and the posterior tibial artery, which provides the blood supply to the calf of the leg.

17.3 Knee Injuries

A. Overuse

As with all other joints of the body, "wear-and-tear," irritation and inflammation of the knee can occur following repeated or excessive use. This is especially true with aging.

1. *Patellofemoral dysfunction.* This condition is characterized by pain centered on the front of the knee, especially around the patella, or knee cap. The pain is typically elicited with contraction of the quadriceps muscle during activities such as ascending or descending stairs or while stooping down to pick up an object. This condition is most frequently seen in young females. This gender bias is thought to be caused in part, by the fact that a female pelvis is wider than that of a male, which causes the pull from the quadriceps muscle to be more lateral, thus irritating the patella as it moves against the femur during flexion and extension (Rothermich, Glaviano, Li, & Hart, 2015). Conservative treatment such as muscle strengthening is favored for this condition and in most cases, the symptoms resolve within a relatively short period of time.

2. *"Jumper's" Knee.* This is an inflammation of the patellar or quadriceps tendon secondary to repeated contraction of the quadriceps muscle and its pull on the quadriceps tendon. Although it gets its name from the fact that jumpers often suffer from this condition as a result of repeated contraction of their quadriceps muscle when jumping, the resulting irritation can occur in anyone that is physically active (e.g. runners). Again, conservative care which frequently includes measures to decrease inflammation followed by muscle strengthening is the preferred treatment.

B. Sprains

Ligamentous injuries of the knee are relatively common, especially in those sports that involve "contact" such as football, soccer and basketball. Injury to the ligamentous structures of the knee result from abnormal forces being applied to one or more of the ligaments. The occurrence of these forces may damage the ligaments depending on numerous factors such as joint position, the force that is applied, the duration of force, the angular velocity of the limb segment, and the pretension stress on the tissue. Many ligamentous injuries of the knee involve multiple forces and directions. The complexity of knee joint motion and the large number of structures involved result in a highly variable and subjective classification. A common, but simplistic classification involves designating the injury as grade I: partial tear of the ligament, grade II: moderate tear of the ligament and grade III: complete tear of the ligament. Because ligamentous sprains of the knee often involve more than one structure as well as having a fairly complex mechanism of injury, other classification systems have been proposed. Noyes et al. (Noyes, F.R., Grood, W.J., Suntay, W.J., & Butler, D.L., 1982) attempted to improve accuracy and standardization of clas-

sification by focusing on the ligament's function with a specific motion and describing the relevant clinical tests to determine that function. Tables 17.3 and 17.4 illustrate a commonly used classification system (Mangine, R.E., 1988). Although there are non-invasive clinical tests available to make a clinical diagnose of a ligamentous injury, magnetic resonance image (MRI) is generally used, especially prior to any surgical intervention.

1. *Medial collateral ligament (MCL) tear.* This is an injury to the broad flat ligament that is situated on the medial side of the knee and acts to prevent excessive gapping of the knee joint on that side. It is generally caused when there is a force applied to the lateral side of the knee while the foot is planted on the ground. This laterally applied force gaps the medial side of the joint causing injury to the MCL. (Figure 17.2) Although surgical intervention may be necessary, a majority of cases of a sprain to the medial collateral ligament can be managed conservatively.

2. *Lateral collateral ligament (LCL) tear.* This is an injury to the ligament that is on the lateral side of the knee and is caused by a force opposite to that which caused an MCL tear. In this case, a force is applied on the lateral side of the knee while the foot is planted on the ground. This

Table 17.3
Classification of Ligament Injury

Sprain	1st Degree*	2nd Degree*	3rd Degree*
Symptoms	Mild	Moderate	Severe
Signs	Point tenderness No abnormal motion	Moderate loss of abnormal motion	Moderate loss of function Marked abnormal motion
Complications	Tendency to recurrence	Tendency to instability arthritis	Persistent instability Traumatic arthritis
Tears of fibers	Minor	Partial	Complete

*Degree of injury as defined by American Medication Association

Table 17.4
Functional Capacity Injured Ligament

Aspect Involved	1st Degree	2nd Degree	3rd Degree
Failure	Few Fibers	Partial to near complete	Complete failure
Strength	—	Decreased risk for complete failure	Complete failure
Length	—	Longer	Severely compromised
Functional Capacity	—	Requires healing	Lost

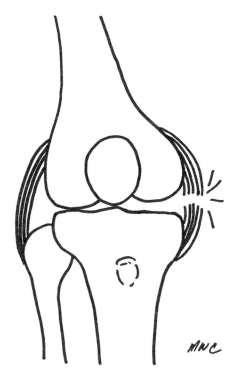

Figure 17.2 Illustration of the mechanism of injury to the medial collateral ligament of the knee. (Courtesy of Mark W. Cornwall)
Figure 17.3 Illustration of the mechanism of injury to the lateral collateral ligament of the knee. (Courtesy of Mark W. Cornwall)

medially applied force gaps the lateral side of the joint causing injury to the LCL. (Figure 17.3) The incidence of injury to this ligament is lower compared to the other injuries at the knee and is typically treated conservatively.

3. *Anterior cruciate ligament (ACL) tear.* Anterior cruciate ligament tears are common in young individuals who participate in jumping and pivoting sports. The mechanism for this injury may involve any of the following: a large medial force to the knee, a large rotational or twisting force to the knee, or a large hyperextension (backward bending) force to the knee. In all cases, the foot is firmly planted on the ground. This injury is most common in contact sports like football, but "non-contact" tears of the ACL may also occur. Compared to the previous two injuries, a tear of the ACL is much more serious and generally necessitates a repair or replacement of the ligament to allow the person to return to their previous level of activity. Studies have reported that approximately 81% of individuals return to sports following an ACL reconstruction, but only 65% of them return to their pre-injury activity level. Even with surgical repair, many do not return to play, suffer recurrent injury or develop osteoarthritis (Sepúlveda, Sánchez, Amy, & Micheo, 2017). Physical rehabilitation following surgical repair tends to be lengthy.

4. *Posterior cruciate ligament (PCL) tear.* The posterior cruciate ligament may be torn with very similar mechanisms as those seen with the anterior cruciate ligament. In fact, it is not uncommon for both ligaments to be torn at the same time. A mechanism of injury that is different from that of the anterior cruciate ligament is a powerful posterior force to the tibia. Although this mechanism certainly happens in contact sports, it is also seen with motor vehicle accidents where the person is thrown forward and their knee contacts the car's dashboard.

5. *Meniscal tears.* The fibrocartilaginous discs between the tibia and femur may become wedged between the two bones during twisting motions while the foot is planted on the ground, resulting in a tear. Symptoms of such an injury include pain, particularly on the lateral (outside) of the knee and symptoms of "locking." The sensation of "locking" occurs secondary to a fragment of the meniscus getting caught between the tibia and femur. Despite the shift toward preserving the menisci following injury, meniscectomy (removal) remains one of the most frequent orthopedic procedures (Beaufils & Pujol, 2017).

C. Dislocations

The vast majority of complete dislocations of the tibiofemoral joint are the result of high velocity traumas such as a motor vehicle accident or a significant fall. However, knee dislocations have also been reported from low velocity incidents. Such low velocity knee dislocations, and at times seemingly "spontaneous" dislocations, can be exacerbated by the subject's excess weight (Brautigan, B. & Johnson, D.L., 2000). Dislocation of the knee may occur in almost any direction; anterior, posterior, medial or lateral. The most common mechanism of injury for an anterior dislocation is forced hyperextension. The most common mechanism of injury for a posterior dislocation is a direct force applied to the tibia while the knee is flexed, thus forcing the tibia posteriorly relative to the femur. The mechanism of injury for a medial or lateral dislocation is the same as that for a tear in either the MCL or LCL, but with greater force being applied.

Dislocation of the knee, regardless of the direction is considered very serious because it is likely that many or most of the ligamentous structures designed to provide stability of the knee were injured. In addition, there is a high incidence of popliteal artery damage resulting from a knee dislocation (Henrichs, 2004). For this reason, routine assessment and monitoring for neurovascular integrity is performed for several days following injury to ensure that complication do not develop.

D. Fractures

Like ligamentous injuries, fractures to the bones comprising the knee joint can result in significant loss of function. In addition, as with any injury to bone, fractures can cause a number of other problems/complications to healing, resulting in non-union, delayed union, malunion, bone shortening, or avascular necrosis. Because there are very large arteries and nerves around the knee, such an injury may also result in damage to one or more of them. Fractures of either the tibia or the femur may result in nerve injury affecting either sensation, movement or both in the lower leg and foot. The loss of nerve function can lead to weakness or paralysis of muscle in the ankle and foot, thus complicating recovery and extending the time for rehabilitation. Depending on the complexity of the resulting fracture, surgical stabilization may be necessary in addition to immobilization to allow adequate healing and restoration of function.

Tibial plateau fractures. A fracture of the anterior tibial plateau is relatively common, comprising approximately 1% of all fractures in the body. (Figure 17.4) The incidence of tibial plateau fractures is 10.3 per 100,000 people annually. The average age of patients sustaining such a fracture is 52.6 years. The fracture can involve either the medial or lateral plateau or both with the most

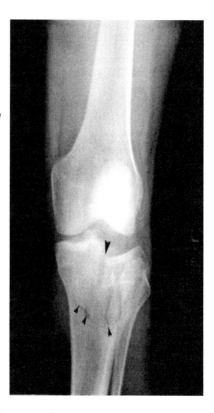

Figure 17.4 Radiograph showing a fracture to the proximal lateral tibial plateau (black arrows). Cornwall, MW, Nyre, E, Harris, JH: Imaging Handbook for Physical Therapists. Lippincott, Williams and Wilkins, 2014. See also Case Study 5.3, pp. 90-91.

common being a fracture of the lateral plateau. Overall, men are more likely to sustain a tibial plateau fracture compared to women. For men under the age of 50 years old, they are more likely to sustain this type of fracture secondary to a high energy mechanism such as a fall from a height or a motor vehicle accident. On the other hand, women over the age of 70 years old are more likely to sustain a fracture secondary to household or community fall. The mechanism of injury for these type of fractures typically involve a combination of compression and either a medially or laterally directed force. These are considered challenging fractures to treat, in part because they may involve multiple fragments and the possibility of injury to other structures is relatively high. Simultaneous injury to the popliteal artery, the tibial nerve, menisci as well as the major ligaments of the knee is possible (Wu, Huang, Lin, & Wang, 2017). In addition, since the tibial plateaus form the articulating surface for the femoral condyles, it is possible to disrupt the normal mechanics of the knee with subsequent development of osteoarthritis. The incidence of secondary osteoarthritis after a tibial plateau fracture has been reported to be approximately 44% (Honkonen, 1995).

Distal femoral fractures. Fracture of the distal femur is likely to occur in young people secondary high-energy trauma as well as in the elderly because of osteoporosis.

These fractures are always comminuted and unstable fractures, and often involve the articular surface and associated serious soft tissue injury (Chen & Lu, 2018). Treatment therefore of these injuries are challenging. Surgical stabilization is certainly indicated using internal fixation (pins, screws or nails).

E. Degeneration

As with many joints, the knee is susceptible to degeneration. The most common cause of joint degeneration is osteoarthritis, but similar destructive features may also be seen with various forms of arthritis, like rheumatoid arthritis. As with osteoarthritis of the hip joint that was discussed in chapter 16, the cartilage between tibia and the femur thins, the bone under the cartilage shows signs of sclerosis (hardening) and osteophytes develop. An osteophyte is a smooth boney growth or deposit that develops in response to stress or some disease process like osteoarthritis. It is sometimes also called a "bone spur." As the disease progresses, because the cartilage no longer provides sufficient cushioning between the bones, individuals complain of stiffness and pain, especially with weight bearing. Treatment for degenerative joint disease is primarily palliative, consisting of analgesic and anti-inflammatory drugs. When the pain begins to interfere with the person's daily functions or favorite activities, total joint replacement, or arthroplasty, is generally performed. (Figure 17.5) This option typically allows the person to

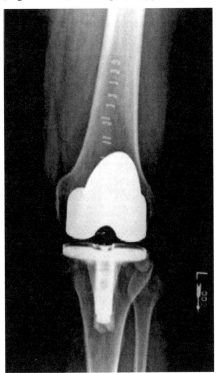

Figure 17.5
Radiograph following total knee arthroplasty. Cornwall, MW, Nyre, E, Harris, JH: Imaging Handbook for Physical Therapists. Lippincott, Williams and Wilkins, 2014.

function without pain or significantly lower pain and at the same time improve their function and quality of life.

17.4 Case Studies

A. ACL injury

Accident. A 34-year-old female injured her right knee while jogging. She reported that she was jogging along the right side of a country road when a passing car came very close to her and she jumped to her right to avoid being hit. She subsequently landed in a shallow ditch. The car did not stop. She complained of immediate pain and swelling in her right knee and had significant difficulty standing or walking.

Evaluation and anatomical structures involved. Her husband was also jogging that day and was able to stop and call for help. She was taken to a local hospital emergency department where her injury was evaluated. After a physical examination that included radiographs, she was diagnosed with a knee sprain, given a pair of axillary crutches to use and told to follow-up with her personal physician. Her personal physician saw her approximately one week later and the swelling was still significant as well as the pain. She was then referred to an orthopaedic surgeon with a suspected ligament injury. The orthopaedic surgeon performed a physical examination and suspected that she had torn her right ACL. An MRI was ordered to confirm this initial diagnosis. The result of the MRI showed a complete tear of the right ACL as well as a partial tear of the MCL of the right knee.

Likely Cause of Injuries. Based on the individual's personal statement as well as that of her husband who witnessed the accident, it was apparent that when she jumped to her right to avoid being hit by the car, that her right foot landed in a hole causing rapid and forceful hyperextension of her knee. The hyperextension of her knee resulted in the femur being displaced posteriorly relative to the tibia, thus tearing the ACL. At the time of the injury there was also a simultaneous medially-directed force to the knee, gapping the medial side of the joint and resulting in the partial tear of the MCL.

B. Tibial plateau fracture

Accident. An 84-year-old female fell in her kitchen while preparing her lunch and injured her left knee. She reported feeling immediate intense pain over her medial (inside) knee. She was unable to stand and required help from her daughter to get up from the floor.

Evaluation and anatomical structures involved. Paramedics were called and she was briefly evaluated before being taken to a local hospital emergency department where her injury was further evaluated. After a physical examination that included radiographs, she was diagnosed with a fracture of the medial plateau of her tibia. She was subsequently referred to an orthopedic surgeon. The orthopedic surgeon confirmed the initial diagnosis and recommended surgical decompression of the fracture, followed by immobilization, limited weight bearing and eventual physical therapy.

Likely Cause of Injuries. Because of mild impairment in her cognitive abilities, the exact mechanism of injury was difficulty to pinpoint. Based on what the patient could remember, plus information from her daughter, it appears that she was standing at a counter in her kitchen and turned quickly to reach something behind her. At this point, she reported getting entangled with her right slipper and falling. Based on the individual's radiograph and the most common mechanism of injury for these types of fractures, it is likely that when she began to fall, she attempted to 'catch' herself with the other foot. This caused her body weight to be shifted toward her left side and was directed primarily through the medial aspect of her knee. This sudden increased medially directly compressive force to the knee resulted in the observed fracture of the medial tibial plateau. The resulting injury from a relatively simple maneuver is explained by the fact that she had a long history of osteoporosis and had been taking calcium supplements for several years in a hope to prevent such an injury.

References

Andriacchi, T.P., Kramer, G.M., & Landon, G.C. (1985). The BioMechanics of Running and Knee Injuries. In Finerman, G. (Ed.), *Symposium on Sports Medicine: The Knee.* American Academy of Orthopaedic Surgeons, C.V. Mosby Co, St. Louis.

Beaufils, P., & Pujol, N. (2017). Management of traumatic meniscal tear and degenerative meniscal lesions. Save the meniscus. *Orthopaedics & Traumatology: Surgery & Research*, 103(8), S237–S244. https://doi.org/10.1016/j.otsr.2017.08.003

Brautigan, B., & Johnson, D.L. (2000). The epidemiology of knee dislocations. *Clinics in Sports Med, 19,* 387–396.

Chen, J., & Lu, H. (2018). [Current status and progress of clinical research on distal femoral fractures]. *Zhong-guo Xiu Fu Chong Jian Wai Ke Za Zhi = Zhongguo Xiufu Chongjian Waike Zazhi = Chinese Journal of Reparative and Reconstructive Surgery*, 32(2), 242–247.

Henrichs, A. (2004). A review of knee dislocations. *Journal of Athletic Training*, 39(4), 365–369.

Honkonen, S. E. (1995). Degenerative arthritis after tibial plateau fractures. *Journal of Orthopaedic Trauma*, 9(4), 273–277.

Kapandji, I.A. (1988). *The Physiology of the Joints* (Vol. 2). Churchill Livingston, Edinburgh.

Mangine, R.E. (1988). *Physical Therapy of the Knee.* Churchill Livingston, Edinburgh.

Noyes, F.R., Grood, W.J., Suntay, W.J., & Butler, D.L. (1982). The Three-Dimensional Laxity of the Anterior Cruciate Deficient Knee. *Iowa Orthopedic Journal*, 3(32).

Rothermich, M. A., Glaviano, N. R., Li, J., & Hart, J. M. (2015). Patellofemoral pain: epidemiology, pathophysiology, and treatment options. *Clinics in Sports Medicine,* 34(2), 313–327.

Sepúlveda, F., Sánchez, L., Amy, E., & Micheo, W. (2017). Anterior Cruciate Ligament Injury: Return to Play, Function and Long-Term Considerations. *Current Sports Medicine Reports*, 16(3), 172–178.

Wu, K., Huang, J., Lin, J., & Wang, Q. (2017). Diagnosis and Treatment of Anterior Tibial Plateau Fracture-Dislocation: A Case Series and Literature Review. *The Journal of Knee Surgery,* 30(2), 114–120.

Recommended Reading

Bartel, D. L., Davy, D. T., & Keaveny, T. M. (2006). *Orthopaedic Biomechanics*. Prentice Hall.

Bergmann, U., & Rinehart, M. A. (1987). *Musculoskeletal trauma.* Aspen Pub.

Garrick, J. G., & Webb, D. R. (1999). *Sports Injuries.* Saunders.

Levangie, P. K., & Norkin, C. C. (2011). *Joint Structure and Function.* F.A. Davis.

Moore, K. L., Dalley, A. F., & Agur, A. M. R. (2013). *Clinically Oriented Anatomy*. Lippincott Williams & Wilkins.

Neumann, D. A. (2017). *Kinesiology of the Musculoskeletal System*. (D. A. Neumann, Ed.). Elsevier.

Soderberg, G. L. (1997). *Kinesiology*. Lippincott Williams & Wilkins.

Symposium, A. A. O. O. S., Woo, S. L.-Y., Buckwalter, J. A., Surgeons, A. A. O. O., National Institute of Arthritis and Musculoskeletal and Skin Diseases (U.S.). (1988). Injury and repair of the musculoskeletal soft tissues. Amer Academy of Orthopaedic.

Whiting, W. C., & Zernicke, R. F. (2008). *Biomechanics of Musculoskeletal Injury*. Human Kinetics.

Chapter 18

The Foot and Ankle

Mark W. Cornwall

18.1 Introduction

The ankle and foot include 28 bones, 25 associated articulations (joints), and numerous ligamentous and soft tissue structures that provide a stable base of support when standing and locomoting. When powered by their 20 different muscles, the ankle and foot provide the ability to walk or run over a wide range of different terrains and under many different conditions.

In this chapter, we will first discuss the various anatomical and biomechanical features of the ankle and then the foot. When discussing the foot, we will focus on its three primary functional regions, the rearfoot, the midfoot, and the forefoot. Although discussed separately, it is important to appreciate that each of these regions interact in synchrony to produce the desired motion.

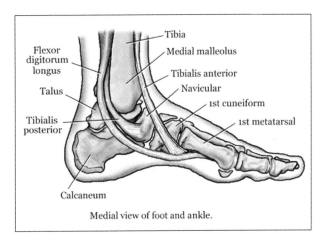

Medial view of foot and ankle.

Figure 18.1 Bones and medial muscle tendons of the ankle and foot. (Courtesy of Robert Perry)

18.2 Anatomy of the Ankle

A. Bones and joints of the ankle

The bones comprising the ankle or talocrural joint are the tibia, fibula and the talus. (Figure 18.1) The tibia and fibula together form what is called the "mortise" of the ankle, which articulates with the top of the talus. The tibia and fibula each articulate with the medial and lateral sides of the talus; the tibia on the medial or inside and the fibula on the lateral or outside. When viewed superiorly, the body of the talus is wider in the front than the back. As the foot dorsiflexes, the wider aspect of the talus wedges up into the mortise, thus restricting the amount of dorsiflexion range of motion available. As the foot is plantar flexed, the narrow aspect of the posterior talus results in slightly greater medial-lateral and rotatory movement within the mortis, thus allowing greater plantar flexion range, but less overall stability. Because the ankle is less stable in plantar flexion, this helps to explain why a majority of ankle sprains occur when the foot is plantar flexed.

B. Major ligaments of the ankle

The stability of the ankle joint is maintained using a num-

315

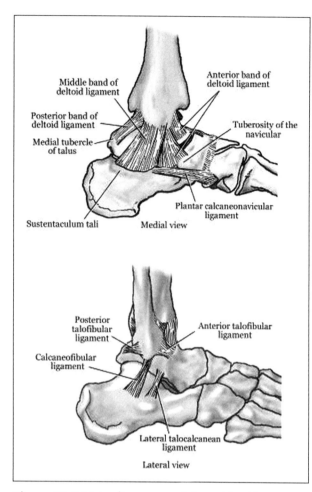

Figure 18.2 *Major ligaments of the ankle. (Courtesy of Robert Perry)*

ber of ligaments. The tibia and fibula are held together by posterior and anterior tibiofibular ligaments. The tibiofibular joint is referred to as a "syndesmosis" or fibrous joint and does not have a joint cavity or capsule surrounding it. Together with the interosseous membrane, which is a strong sheet of connective tissue positioned between the shafts of the tibia and fibula, they are responsible for maintaining a stable mortise for the talus to move within. Beyond the osseous architecture of the mortise, the stability of the talocrural joint is provided by a number of ligaments. On the medial side, the medial collateral or "deltoid" ligament has both superficial and deep fibers connecting the tibia with the navicular, talus, and calcaneus. (Figure 18.2) The deltoid ligament provides significant limitation to eversion of the ankle and pronation of the talus and calcaneus. The ligament, as a whole, is extremely strong and as such is not commonly injured. When it is injured, the mechanism is usually from an outward (eversion) rotation of the foot combined with inward rotation of the leg (tibia). It is not unusual for the tip of

the distal tibial bone to be avulsed (pulled off) before the ligament is actually torn.

The lateral side of the talocrural joint is reinforced with three distinct ligaments called the anterior talofibular, posterior talofibular, and calcaneofibular ligaments. (Figure 18.2) The first two ligaments run fairly horizontal to the foot, while the calcaneofibular ligament is nearly vertical when the foot is in its "neutral" position between plantar flexion and dorsiflexion. In contrast to the deltoid ligament, these three lateral ligaments help to control inversion of the ankle and supination of the talus and calcaneus. Injury to one or more of these ligaments is what is typically referred to as an "*ankle sprain*" and is often the result of an inward rotation of the foot combined with outward rotation of the tibia.

C. Muscles and available movements of the ankle

The ankle joint is typically thought of as having only a single degree of freedom (dorsiflexion/plantar flexion), in fact, there is movement in all three planes, but the other two movements (abduction/adduction and internal/external rotation) are very small in comparison to plantar flexion and dorsiflexion. Typical ROM for dorsiflexion is 20° while plantar flexion is 50°. It is generally accepted that a

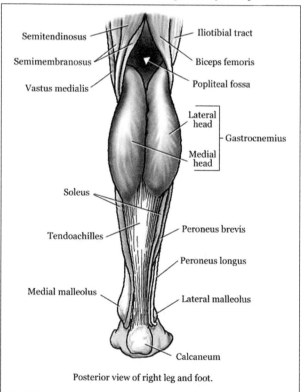

Figure 18.3 *Superficial posterior muscles (plantar flexors) of the ankle. (Courtesy of Robert Perry)*

person needs a minimum of 10° of dorsiflexion in order to ambulate normally (DiGiovanni et al., 2002).

Active control of the ankle is accomplished using extrinsic muscles, which originate outside of the foot, but terminate in the foot. An example of such a muscle would be those of the calf. They originate in the back of the leg and terminate on the calcaneus (heel). The largest and strongest muscles are those that comprise the posterior calf, in particular, the *gastrocnemius* and *soleus* muscles. (Figure 18.3) Other extrinsic muscles of the calf include the *posterior tibialis*, the *flexor hallucis longus*, and the *flexor digitorum longus*. (Figure 18.4) All of the muscles of the calf are considered to be plantar flexors and inverters. As an inverter, they are able to move the foot inward. Of particular importance is the *posterior tibialis* muscle, which is the only extrinsic muscle of the foot that is able to exert significant control over the arch of the foot. (Figure 18.5) The extrinsic muscles on the lateral side of the leg include the *fibularis (peroneus) longus* and *fibularis (peroneus) brevis* muscles. (Figure 18.6) Each of these are considered to be plantar flexors and everters of the foot. As an everter, they are able to move the foot outward. Finally, the extrinsic muscles of the anterior side of the leg include the *tibialis anterior, extensor hallucis longus, extensor digitorum longus*, and *peroneus tertius* muscles. (Figure 18.7) All of these muscles are considered to be

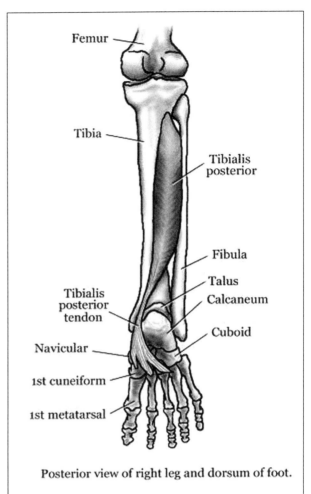

Posterior view of right leg and dorsum of foot.

Figure 18.5 Posterior tibialis muscle (inverter) of the ankle and foot. (Courtesy of Robert Perry)

dorsiflexors of the ankle with the *tibialis anterior* also being an inverter and the *extensor digitorum longus* and *peroneus tertius* being everters of the foot. Each of the above muscles play a role in either producing movement or preventing an excess of the opposite movement. For example, the *posterior tibialis* muscle is able to supinate the foot, but it also is able to control the rate and magnitude of pronation.

18.3 Anatomy of the Foot

A. Bones and joints of the foot

The foot is comprised of 26 bones. These bones are frequently grouped into 3 functional regions: (Figure 18.8)

1. The rearfoot or hindfoot, which is composed of the talus and the calcaneus.
2. The midfoot, consisting of the navicular, cuboid, and the three cuneiforms.

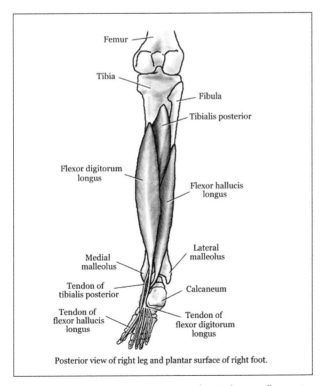

Posterior view of right leg and plantar surface of right foot.

Figure 18.4 Deep posterior muscles (plantar flexors) of the ankle. (Courtesy of Robert Perry)

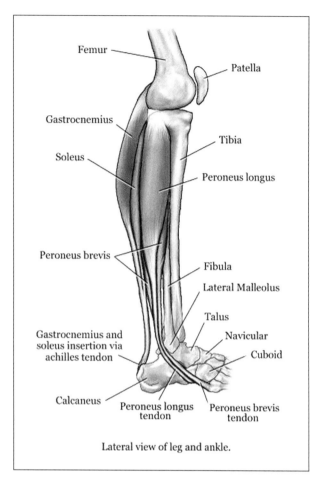

Lateral view of leg and ankle.

Figure 18.6 *Lateral muscles (everters) of the ankle and foot. (Courtesy of Robert Perry)*

3. The forefoot, which includes the 5 metatarsals and the 14 phalanges (toes).

These bones create a large number of joints, each with its own ROM and direction of movement. The movement at each of these joints, however, is not completely independent and the action of one or more joints can have a significant influence on adjacent joints. Because of the very large number of joints in the foot, we will focus on just five of them; the subtalar joint, the mid-tarsal joint, the tarsometatarsal joints, the metatarsophalangeal joints and the interphalangeal joints.

Subtalar joint. The talus and calcaneus below it, form the subtalar joint. Because of the shape of the two bones, there is a complex twisting or screw-like motion between them. It is estimated that 75% of a person's weightbearing force is transmitted through the subtalar joint (Keener & Sizensky, 2005). A prominent feature of the calcaneus is the sustentaculum tali, which is a bony outcropping on the medial side of the foot. This feature is used like a "pulley" by the flexor digitorum longus and flexor hallucis longus muscles as they pass from the back of the leg to the bottom of the foot to flex the toes.

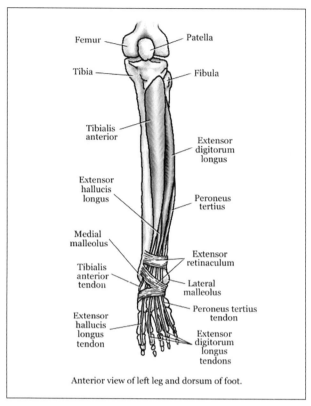

Anterior view of left leg and dorsum of foot.

Figure 18.7 *Anterior muscles (dorsiflexors) of the ankle and foot. (Courtesy of Robert Perry)*

Mid-Tarsal Joint. The transverse tarsal joint, sometimes called the "Transverse Tarsal" or "Chopart" joint is actually a composite of two joints; the talonavicular and the calcaneocuboid joints.

Tarsometatarsal Joints. The tarsometatarsal joints are formed from the distal row of tarsal bones (navicular, cuboid and cuneiform) and the bases of the metatarsals. (Figure 18.8) The first tarsometatarsal joint is comprised of the first metatarsal and the medial cuneiform bone. The second tarsometatarsal joint consists of the second metatarsal and the middle cuneiform bone. The tarsometatarsal joint is formed by the third metatarsal and the lateral cuneiform bone. The fourth and fifth metatarsals each articulate with the cuboid bone and share a common joint capsule.

Metatarsophalangeal Joints. The five metatarsal bones each articulate with the phalanges to form the five metatarsophalangeal joints. (Figure 18.8) The first metatarsophalangeal joint has two small bones called sesamoids located within the tendon of the *flexor hallucis longus* muscle on the bottom side of the joint of the big toe. These bones serve as anatomical pulleys for the muscle and protect the tendon from excessive weightbearing forces. These bones also help to absorb weight-bearing stresses.

Interphalangeal Joints. The interphalangeal joints

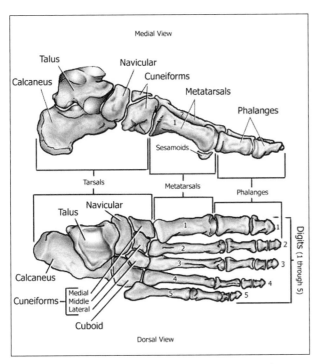

Figure 18.8 Bones of the foot. (Courtesy of Robert Perry)

of the toes are hinge joints with a single degree of freedom: flexion/extension. With the exception of the great toe, each of these is comprised of three phalanges, thus two interphalangeal joints (proximal and distal). (Figure 18.8) Their function is to help maintain postural stability through relatively light downward force with the ground during weight bearing and locomotion (Norkin & Levangie, 1992).

B. Major ligaments of the foot

The foot has a large number of ligaments that stabilize its many joints. We shall only cover a few in this chapter.

Stability of the subtalar joint comes from a combination of its bony architecture and several strong ligaments. These ligaments include the calcaneofibular ligament that was discussed with the ankle joint, the cervical ligament, the interosseous talocalcaneal ligament, and the calcaneonavicular ligament. The cervical ligament is considered to be the strongest of these structures and lies near the front and top of the calcaneus and attaches to the underside of the talus. The interosseous talocalcaneal ligament is situated directly under the talus and connects the two bones. The calcaneonavicular ligament, or "spring" ligament constitutes the bottom portion of the capsule for the talonavicular joint. The "spring" ligament plays an important role in supporting the medial longitudinal arch of the foot (Jennings & Christensen, 2008).

In addition to the above ligaments, the short and long

plantar ligaments on the bottom of the foot play a significant role in supporting both the rearfoot and midfoot regions as well as the helping to maintain the dome of the arch. In addition, the plantar aponeurosis or plantar fascia plays an important role in supporting the arch of the foot. The plantar fascia consists of dense connective tissue that extends almost the entire length of the foot, beginning at the heel and ending at the toes.

C. Muscles and available movements of the foot

There are 18 intrinsic muscles of the foot. These muscles are oriented on the bottom of the foot in four layers. Layer I contains the abductor hallucis, the *abductor digiti minimi*, and the *flexor digitorum brevis* muscles. The first two muscles abduct either the big or little toe, while the last one helps to flex the toes. Layer II contains the four *lumbrical* muscles and the *quadratus plantae* muscle. As in the hand, the *lumbrical* muscles assist extension of the IP joints of the toes. The *quadratus plantae* muscle assists the *flexor digitorum longus* muscle in flexing the toes. Layer III contains the *flexor hallucis brevis*, the *flexor digiti minimi*, and the *adductor hallucis muscle*. The first two muscles are able to flex either the big or little toes, while the last one adducts the big toe. Layer IV contains the four dorsal interossei muscles and the three plantar interossei muscles. As in the hand, these muscles are able to abduct or adduct the digits and also serve an important function in helping to fully extend the IP joints of the toes. In addition to their individual actions, all of the above muscles serve to stabilize the arch of the foot. This is particularly true for the *abductor hallucis brevis, flexor digitorum brevis*, and *quadratus plantae* muscles.

The individual motions described in this chapter work in concert during functional weightbearing tasks, such as walking. The motions of the foot during walking are typically described only for the stance phase since that is when both muscular and ground reaction forces are present. Most of the joints in the foot have what is referred to as "tri-plane" motion. What this means is that they have movement about a single axis, but that axis is not oriented perpendicular to any of the three cardinal planes. As such, the resulting motion is made up of a combination of dorsiflexion/plantar flexion, abduction/adduction and inversion/eversion rather than just one. These motions are coupled and cannot occur independent of each other. Rather than always listing the motion occurring in each plane, the terms "pronation" and "supination" have been devised to described the composite "tri-planar" motion that occurs.

Subtalar joint. With the foot in contact with the

ground, supination of the subtalar joint consist primarily of calcaneal inversion. Conversely, pronation of the subtalar joint is primarily calcaneal eversion. A similar description can be made for all of the other joints of the rearfoot and midfoot. Even with the use of the terms "pronation" and "supination," description of foot motion can still be confusing. A simplification of the two terms would be that with pronation, the heel and foot moving inward or medially (Figure 18.9A), while with supination, the opposite occurs, the foot move outward (laterally). (Figure 18.9B) During locomotion, the foot pronates during the first half of the stance phase, but then reverses direction and supinates. Alteration of this pattern of motion or alteration of its magnitude is frequently cited by clinicians as the cause of pain and dysfunction in the lower extremity.

Mid-Tarsal Joint. As a whole, the mid-tarsal joint is also able to pronate and supinate. The mid-tarsal joint allows the foot to move in two directions. The first is a longitudinal twisting of the foot relative to the heel. The second is a side-to-side movement of the foot relative to the heel. Although the magnitude of these movements varies from one individual to the next, they are essential for proper function of the foot and are interlinked with the motion occurring at the subtalar joint. As such, the mid-tarsal joint serves as the transitional link between the rearfoot and the forefoot. It is able to add to the available supination/pronation ROM of the subtalar joint and also ensures that the forefoot remains flat on the ground by rotating in the opposite direction as that of the subtalar joint (Inman & Mann, 1973). As such, when the subtalar joint is pronated, the transverse tarsal joint is supinated, thus helping to ensure that the forefoot remains flat on the ground.

Observation of the mid-tarsal joint sees the arch rise

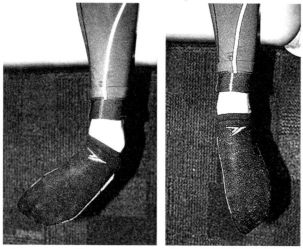

Figure 18.9 Illustration of the motions of inversion (A) and eversion (B) of the foot.

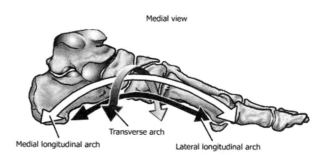

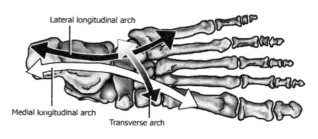

Plantar (bottom) view

Figure 18.10 Arches of the foot. (Courtesy of Robert Perry)

and depress during walking or running. With pronation of the mid-tarsal joint, the arch depresses and with supination, it rises. Therefore, during walking, as the subtalar joint is everting, the mid-tarsal joint is inverting (arch depression). This arch depression continues until about 75% of the stance phase when it reverses direction and begins to elevate for the rest of the stance phase (Leardini, O'Connor, & Giannini, 2014).

The principle function of the arch of the foot is to absorb or damp the impact of weight-bearing forces on the foot during walking, running, jumping, etc. The medial longitudinal arch of the foot may be described as either a curved beam constructed from interconnecting joints that rely upon ligaments for stability or as a truss which consists of two triangular struts connected at its base by a tie rod (plantar aponeurosis). (Figure 18.10) Both models have validity and can be demonstrated clinically (Sammarco & Hockenbury, 2001). The plantar aponeurosis and its role in supporting the arch are related to its attachment beyond the metatarsophalangeal joints. When the toes are extended (passively or actively), tension is applied to the plantar fascia, which draws the heel and toes closer together, thus raising the arch. This phenomenon has been referred to as the "windlass mechanism" and is considered to be important during the latter half of the stance phase of walking (Kappel-Bargas, Wolff, Cornwall, & McPoil, 1998).

Tarsometatarsal Joints. Because of the very small

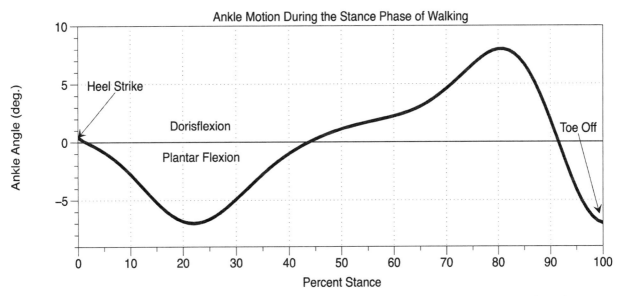

Figure 18.11 *Graph illustrating the typical movement of the ankle during walking. (Courtesy of Mark W. Cornwall)*

amount of movement between each metatarsal bone and the navicular, cuneiform or cuboid bones, they function as a single unit. Such rigidity helps the forefoot to remain stable during weightbearing activities.

Metatarsophalangeal Joints. The relatively small joints of the toes have two degrees of freedom; flexion/extension and abduction/adduction, with flexion/extension being the greatest of the two. The available extension at these joints has been reported in the literature to average between 56° and 100° depending on the age of the individual and the method used to make the measurement. It has been reported that between 36° and 65° of big toe extension is needed to demonstrate a normal walking pattern (Hopson, McPoil, & Cornwall, 1995).

Movement of the ankle and foot during walking. When the heel strikes the ground, initiating the stance phase, the ankle joint is typically in slight dorsiflexion and then goes through rapid plantar flexion, thus ensuring that the foot is quickly flat on the ground, providing a stable base of support. Soon after this first peak of plantar flexion, the joint reverses its motion and begins to dorsiflex. The dorsiflexion continues until late in the stance phase when it reverses direction once more and plantar flexes until the toe leaves the ground. (Figure 18.11) At the same time as the ankle is plantarflexing and dorsiflexing during the stance phase, the lower leg (tibia/fibula) is internally and externally rotating. The internal rotation seen during the initial portion of the stance phase (loading phase) of gait is a continuation of the internal rotation of the entire lower extremity that began during the latter half of the swing phase. At roughly the conclusion of the loading phase of

walking, the tibia/fibula reverses direction and begins to externally rotate. This external rotation continues for the duration of the stance phase, but will reverse its action back into internal rotation during the swing phase (Cornwall & McPoil, 1999, 2002).

While all of the previously described motions of the talocrural joint are happening, the subtalar and mid-tarsal joints are undergoing pronation and supination as well. At the instant of heel contact, the subtalar joint is typically supinated slightly, but pronates as the foot is loaded. This pronation continues well into the stance phase before it reverses its direction and begins to supinate at roughly 60% of the stance phase, which corresponds to when the heel begins to come off the ground in preparation for ending the stance phase and beginning the swing phase of walking. While the subtalar joint is pronating, the mid-tarsal joint in supinating and vise versa.

18.4 Nerves and Arteries of the Ankle and Foot

The popliteal artery in the back of the knee branches into two arteries that serve the lower leg and foot. The two branches are the anterior tibial and posterior tibial arteries. The anterior tibial artery provides blood to the front of the leg and top of the foot. The posterior tibial artery sends a branch called the peroneal or fibular artery to provide blood to the lateral leg before continuing down the back of the leg. The posterior tibial artery not only provides blood to the back of the leg, but also the bottom of the foot through two additional branches called the medial and lateral plantar arteries.

The large sciatic nerve splits into a common peroneal nerve and a tibial nerve behind the knee. The common peroneal nerve divides into the superficial and deep peroneal (fibular) nerves which innervate the muscles of the front and lateral side of the leg and top of the foot. It also provides sensation to the skin overlying these areas. The tibial nerve, on the other hand, innervates the muscles of the calf and bottom of the foot through two additional branches called the medial and lateral plantar nerves. The anterior tibial nerve and its branches also provide sensation to the skin overlying these areas.

18.5 Ankle and Foot Injuries

Trauma to the ankle and foot are relatively common and may be caused by either repetitive low-grade trauma, often referred to as "overuse" injuries, or from direct trauma.

A. Overuse

Overuse or repetitive movement disorders may occur in either bone, connective tissue or muscle tendons.

1. *Achilles tendinopathy.* Achilles tendinopathy, or pathology involving the Achilles tendon includes injuries caused by acute trauma as well as those from chronic, repetitive irritation. The chronic repetitive situations are sometimes referred to as "Achilles tendinosis." Approximately 4% of chronic situations of Achilles tendinopathy are thought to actually result in a rupture of the tendon (Cornwall & McPoil, 2002). Achilles tendinopathy is generally managed with conservative care unless there is no improvement in the person's condition within six months. Surgery is indicated for complete tears of the tendon. With partial tears of the tendon, either surgery or non-surgical care may be used with similar functional outcomes. Conservative treatment in these situations typically involves immobilization, "functional bracing" and early rehabilitation (Egger & Berkowitz, 2017).

2. *Posterior tibialis tendon dysfunction.* Because the posterior tibialis muscle plays an important role in controlling the magnitude and rate of pronation of the foot during walking and running, injury to the tendon impairs the foot's ability to maintain its arch, thus producing pain and impaired ambulation. Although sudden rupture of the posterior tibialis tendon is possible, it is more commonly the result of progressive degeneration secondary to repetitive trauma. Posterior tibialis tendon dysfunction is generally classified into one of four grades representing this progression. Grade I involves pain and inflammation of the tendon, but no resulting "flat foot" deformity. With Grade II, the tendon becomes dysfunctional and the person exhibits a characteristic "flat foot" deformity. Grade

III is characterized by advanced flat foot deformity and osteoarthritis of the subtalar joint. In Grade IV, the ankle joint becomes involved with concomitant joint degeneration (Bubra, Keighley, Rateesh, & Carmody, 2015). Conservative, non-operative management is recommended for Grades I and II. These measures include exercise and foot orthoses. With Grades III and IV, surgery and/or bracing is typically indicated (Bek, 2012).

3. *Peroneal tendon inflammation.* Injury or irritation of the lateral ankle tendons (*peroneus brevis* and *peroneus longus*) can be either from acute trauma or chronic inflammation secondary to overuse. These may involve overt tears to the tendon, degeneration of the tendon from repetitive trauma, or inflammation of the tendon's synovial sheaths. Because these tendons help to stabilize the lateral side of the ankle, it is not unusual for them to be injured during a lateral angle sprain. A large majority of these injuries may be resolved successfully without surgery (Roster, Michelier, & Giza, 2015).

B. Sprains

A sprain is the rupture of some or all of the fibers of a ligament. Sprains may be graded as I, II or III. A grade I is relatively minor and typically does not result in instability of the joint. A grade III, however, is where there is a complete tear of the ligament resulting in significant joint instability. Occasionally, the ligament itself does not rupture, but avulses or pulls off a fragment of bone to which it is attached. In such cases, it is generally treated as a fracture rather than a sprain. The following are the most common sprains in the ankle and foot.

1. *Lateral ankle sprains.* A lateral ankle sprain involves injuries to one or more of the three major ligaments on the lateral side of the ankle; the anterior talofibular, the calcaneofibular or the posterior talofibular. (Figure 18.2) The typical mechanism of injury for this type of sprain involves plantar flexion and simultaneous inversion of the foot. Such an injury is often described by the patient as "rolling" their foot toward the outside. With a relatively minor sprain, only the anterior talofibular ligament may be injured, but as the severity increases, involvement of the calcaneofibular and the posterior talofibular ligament occurs. The ultimate tensile strength of these ligaments in cadaver specimens ranges from 139N for the anterior talofibular ligament to 346N for the calcaneofibular ligament. The posterior talofibular ligament failed at 261N (Attarian, McCrackin, Devito, McElhaney, & Garrett, 1985). Depending upon the severity of the injury and the quality of post-injury management, most lateral ankle sprains respond well to non-operative treatment and result

in minimal long term dysfunction (Woitzik et al., 2015). Unfortunately, many individuals will sustain repeated ankle sprains leading to joint instability and long-term disability (van Rijn et al., 2008).

2. *"High ankle sprain."* A "high ankle sprain" is the term frequently used to describe a tear in the ligaments that bind the distal tibia and fibula together, namely the anterior and posterior talofibular ligaments. Such an injury results from a forceful outward rotation of the talus within the ankle mortis. It can occur in conjunction with or independent of a lateral ankle sprain. If severe, this injury results in significant ankle instability, requiring surgical stabilization of the injured joint.

3. *Lisfranc sprain.* Lisfranc, or mid-foot sprains involve the tarsometatarsal joints of the foot and may involve either just ligamentous structures or a combination of ligament and bone disruption. Lisfranc joint injuries occur 2 to 4 times more frequently in males compared to females and are most often the result of high-velocity trauma such as motor vehicle accidents, crushing loads to the mid-foot or falls from a height. The mean age of individuals who sustain an injury to their tarsometatarsal joint is between 30 and 36 years (Desmond & Chou, 2006). In sports, Lisfranc and other midfoot sprains are the second most common foot injury, second only to injury of the toes. Rather than being caused by high velocity trauma, they are the result of low-velocity trauma and their mechanism of injury may be either direct or indirect (Desmond & Chou, 2006). The direct method of injury is typically from a falling object, while indirect injuries involve an axial load applied to a plantar flexed and slightly rotated foot or if the foot is plantarflexed and the forefoot fixed to the ground. Such is the case when the foot is caught in a stirrup during an equestrian accident or during windsurfing. It is generally agreed that Lisfranc sprains that are stable can be successfully managed non-operatively with satisfactory results and the person is able to return to their prior level of activity. For unstable injuries, however, and all injuries with significant displacement, surgical management is advocated because of the poor outcomes from nonsurgical management with these cases (Eleftheriou & Rosenfeld, 2013).

C. Fractures

1. *Stress fractures (Reactions).* A stress fracture is the result of repeated low-level stress to a bone that eventually results in a disruption of the bone's cortex. Stress fractures of the lower extremity are common in those athletes and individuals participating in a wide range of activities. Although the term "fracture" is used, the injury does not typically result in a loss of the bone's continuity. Therefore, the term "stress reaction" is a more accurate term rather than "stress fracture." Many of the stress reactions seen in the ankle and foot are considered to be at low risk for developing complications such as delayed union or non-union. Common locations for stress reactions include the tibia, the calcaneus, the fibula and the metatarsals. A stress reaction involving a metatarsal is frequently referred to as a "march" fracture because they are relatively common in military recruits secondary to the large amount of running and marching that is involved during basic training. Young males and older females account for the majority of stress reactions in the fifth metatarsal (Kane et al., 2015). Regardless of the mechanism of injury, stress reactions are typically managed conservatively with rest and/or immobilization.

2. *Malleolar fractures.* A malleolar fracture is a fracture of the ankle that involves the lateral malleolus, the medial malleolus or any portion of the distal tibia. The distal posterior aspect of the tibia can be called the posterior malleolus. When this is fractured as well, the injury is referred to as a tri-malleolar fracture. The trauma may also be accompanied by ligamentous damage and/or dislocation. The three aforementioned parts of bone form the ankle mortis and articulate with the talus bone of the foot. Surgical repair using open reduction and internal fixation (ORIF) is generally required for these fractures with subsequent non-weightbearing until the bone is sufficiently healed. (Figure 18.12) Tri-malleolar fractures typically take six weeks in an otherwise healthy person to heal, but they may take much longer if there are complications such as a disruption of blood supply to the area, poor nutrition or diabetes. The impact to a person's functional activity from this type of injury is seen by the fact that individuals following this type of injury are typically less active and more sedentary compared to the general population (Beckenkamp et al., 2014).

3. *Tibial pilon fractures.* A tibial pilon fracture, sometimes referred to as a "plafond fracture," is one involving the distal end of the tibia and involves the weight-bearing surface of the ankle joint. The fibular bone is also frequently broken in this type of injury. The mechanism of injury involves high-energy rotational or axial forces, often as a result of a fall from a height or from a motor vehicle accident. *"Pilon"* is the French word for "pestle"—an instrument used for crushing or pounding. In many pilon fractures, the tibia may be crushed or split into several pieces due to the high-energy impact of the injury. In most cases, surgery is needed to restore the damaged bone to its normal position. Because of the seriousness of this

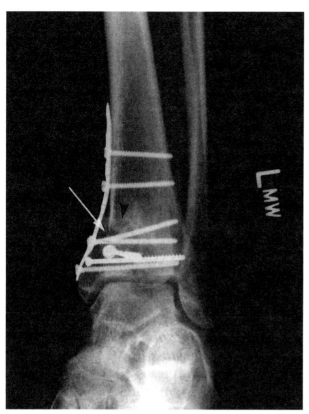

Figure 18.12 Radiograph showing surgical fixation of a distal tibial fracture with screws and plate. Cornwall, MW, Nyre, E, Harris, JH: Imaging Handbook for Physical Therapists. Lippincott, Williams and Wilkins, 2014.

injury, bone healing typically takes three to six months. Full recovery from the injury, however, may actually take 12 months or more. Further, tibial pilon fractures have a significant negative impact on the person's general health and quality of life, which further reflects its severity (Cutillas-Ybarra, Lizaur-Utrilla, & Lopez-Prats, 2015).

4. *Calcaneal fractures.* The calcaneus is the most frequently fractured tarsal bone of the foot. It is integral to normal daily function, especially since substantial forces between 300% and 400% of a person's body weight are endured by the calcaneus with every step (Griffin et al., 2014). In a civilian population, these fractures often occur at work due to falls from a height or from a motor vehicle accident. These are high energy axial load fractures and individuals frequently endure other simultaneous injuries such as fractures to the spine or lower extremity. Unlike other fractures, recovery after a calcaneal fracture is often two years, and even then, patients may have continued pain with walking, thus making a return to work as a laborer or other outdoor professions difficult or impossible (Fortin & Balazsy, 2001).

18.6 Case Studies

A. Lateral ankle injury

Accident. 68-year-old female sustained an injury to her right ankle. She reported being distracted by some teenagers in a passing car while stepping off of a curb. According to her testimony, she inadvertently stepped onto a section of the street that was uneven, twisting her right ankle. She reported falling to the ground and complained of severe pain in her right lateral ankle with rapid subsequent swelling.

Evaluation and anatomical structures involved. Emergency services were called and she was transported to a local medical clinic. Her past relevant medical history included a hip fracture secondary to a fall eight years previous with subsequent total hip arthroplasty and a history of frequent ankle sprains. In addition, she had a history of diabetes mellitus (Type II) and osteopenia. Radiographs were obtained as part of the physical examination, which revealed a possible fracture of her 5th metatarsal bone. (Figure 18.2) An MRI was then performed which showed that there was a non-displaced fracture of the styloid process of her 5th metatarsal bone. In addition, the MRI showed complete disruption of the right anterior talofibular ligament and a partial tear of the calcaneofibular ligament. (Figure 18.2) There was also signs of swelling and inflammation around the peroneus (fibularis) longus and peroneus (fibularis) brevis muscle tendons. (Figure 18.6) She was issued a "cast boot" for her right foot and ankle, given a walker and told to remain non-weightbearing.

Likely cause of injuries. The injuries seen in this individual were the result of an inversion force being applied to her right ankle. As she stepped off of the curb, her foot would have been in slight plantar flexion and inversion. As the foot contacted the uneven surface, the inversion force would have been increased because of her body weight. The lateral ligaments of the ankle are designed to resist such forces, but failed in her case. The fracture of the styloid process of the 5th metatarsal was also a result of the excessive inversion force. Because of her existing diagnosis of osteopenia, the metatarsal bone was most likely weakened, causing a fracture that may not have happened otherwise. The inflammation around the peroneus (fibularis) longus and peroneus (fibularis) brevis muscle tendons is most likely due to the body's attempt to prevent the excess inversion since these muscles are significant everters of the ankle and foot.

B. Calcaneal fracture

Accident. A 29-year-old male injured his right foot while

vacationing at a local lake. He stated that he jumped off of a rock 25 feet into the water and landed on a boulder just under the surface of the water with most of the weight through his right lower extremity.

Evaluation and anatomical structures involved. He initially went to the emergency department where radiographs showed a comminuted fracture of his right calcaneus. As such, he was then sent to an orthopedic surgeon for definitive management. Computerized Tomography (CT) and MRI images showed multiple fractures of the calcaneus as well as chondral bruising of the subtalar joint. After surgical stabilization, he was immobilized in a splint for three weeks and then given a walking boot, but continued to be non-weightbearing with a scooter for ambulation distances greater than 1,000 feet. As he became more active following surgery, he complained of increasing back pain. Radiographs at that point revealed compression fractures to the 10th and 11th thoracic vertebral bodies. He was then scheduled for surgical decompression of these injuries.

Likely cause of injuries. The injuries sustained by this individual were the result of his 25-foot jump onto a boulder. The significant compressive forces created from the jump and subsequent landing directly caused the fracture as well as the chondral bruising of the subtalar joint surfaces. In addition, the compressive forces from the jump were transmitted proximally, causing the compression fractures in his thoracic spine.

References

Attarian, D. E., McCrackin, H. J., Devito, D. P., McElhaney, J. H., & GAarrett, W. E. (1985). Biomechanical Characteristics of Human Ankle Ligaments. *Foot and Ankle*, 6(2), 54–58.

Beckenkamp, P. R., Lin, C.-W. C., Chagpar, S., Herbert, R. D., van der Ploeg, H. P., & Moseley, A. M. (2014). Prognosis of Physical Function Following Ankle Fracture: A Systematic Review With Meta-analysis. *Journal of Orthopaedic & Sports Physical Therapy*, 44(11), 841–851.

Bek, N. (2012). Home-based general versus center-based selective rehabilitation in patients with posterior tibial tendon dysfunction. *Acta Orthopaedica et Traumatologica Turcica*, 46(4), 286–292.

Bubra, P. S., Keighley, G., Rateesh, S., & Carmody, D. (2015). Posterior Tibial Tendon Dysfunction: An Overlooked Cause of Foot Deformity. *Journal of Family Medicine and Primary Care*, 4(1), 26–29.

Cornwall, M. W., & McPoil, T. G. (1999). Three-dimensional movement of Foot during the stance phase of walking. *Journal of the American Podiatric Medical Association*, 89(2), 56–66.

Cornwall, M. W., & McPoil, T. G. (2002). Motion of the calcaneus, navicular, and first metatarsal during the stance phase of walking. *Journal of the American Podiatric Medical Association*, 92(2), 67–76.

Cutillas-Ybarra, M. B., Lizaur-Utrilla, A., & Lopez-Prats, F. A. (2015). Prognostic factors of health-related quality of life in patients after tibial plafond fracture. A pilot study. *Injury*, 46(11), 2253–2257.

Desmond, E. A., & Chou, L. B. (2006). Current concepts review: Lisfranc injuries. *Foot and Ankle,* 27(8), 653–660.

DiGiovanni, C. W., Kuo, R., Tejwani, N., Price, R., Hansen, S. T., Cziernecki, J., & Sangeorzan, B. J. (2002). Isolated gastrocnemius tightness. *Journal of Bone and Joint Surgery [Am]*, 84-A(6), 962–970.

Egger, A. C., & Berkowitz, M. J. (2017). Achilles tendon injuries. *Current Reviews in Musculoskeletal Medicine*, 10(1), 1–9.

Eleftheriou, K. I., & Rosenfeld, P. F. (2013). Lisfranc injury in the athlete: evidence supporting management from sprain to fracture dislocation. *Foot Ankle Clin, 18(2)*, 219–236.

Fortin, P. T., & Balazsy, J. E. (2001). Talus fractures: evaluation and treatment. *J Am Acad Orthop Surg*, 9(2), 114–127.

Griffin, D., Parsons, N., Shaw, E., Kulikov, Y., Hutchinson, C., Thorogood, M., … UK Heel Fracture Trial Investigators. (2014). Operative versus non-operative treatment for closed, displaced, intra-articular fractures of the calcaneus: randomised controlled trial. *BMJ*, 349(jul24 5), g4483–g4483.

Hopson, M. M., McPoil, T. G., & Cornwall, M. W. (1995). Motion of the first metatarsophalangeal joint. Reliability and validity of four measurement techniques. *Journal of the American Podiatric Medical Association*, 85(4), 198–204.

Inman, V. T., & Mann, R. A. (1973). *Biomechanics of the foot and ankle.* Du'Vries surgery of the foot. 3rd ed. St. Louis: CV \ldots.

Jennings, M. M., & Christensen, J. C. (2008). The effects of sectioning the spring ligament on rearfoot stability and posterior tibial tendon efficiency. *Journal of Foot and Ankle Surgery*, 47(3), 219–224.

Kane, J. M., Sandrowski, K., Saffel, H., Albanese, A., Raikin, S. M., & Pedowitz, D. I. (2015). The Epidemiology of Fifth Metatarsal Fracture. *Foot and Ankle Specialist*, 8(5), 354–359.

Kappel-Bargas, A., Wolff, R. D., Cornwall, M. W., & McPoil, T. G. (1998). The Windlass Mechanism During Normal Walking and Passive First Metatarsalphalangeal Joint Extension. *Clinical Biomechanics*, 13(3), 190–194.

Keener, B. J., & Sizensky, J. A. (2005). The anatomy of the calcaneus and surrounding structures. *Foot Ankle Clin*, 10(3), 413–424.

Leardini, A., O'Connor, J. J., & Giannini, S. (2014). Biomechanics of the natural, arthritic, and replaced human ankle joint. *Journal of Foot and Ankle Research*, 7(1), 8.

Norkin, C. C., & Levangie, P. K. (1992). The Ankle-Foot Complex. In *Joint Structure and Function: A comprehensive analysis* (pp. 379–412). Philadelphia: F.A. Davis Co.

Roster, B., Michelier, P., & Giza, E. (2015). Peroneal Tendon Disorders. *Clinics in Sports Medicine*, 34(4), 625–641.

Sammarco, G. J., & Hockenbury, R. T. (2001). Biomechanics of the Foot and Ankle. In M. Nordin & V. H. Frankel (Eds.), *Basic biomechanics of the musculoskeletal system* (p. 235). Philadelphia.

van Rijn, R. M., van Os, A. G., Bernsen, R. M. D., Luijsterburg, P. A., Koes, B. W., & Bierma-Zeinstra, S. M. A. (2008). What is the clinical course of acute ankle sprains? A systematic literature review. *The American Journal of Medicine*, 121(4), 324-331.e6.

Woitzik, E., Jacobs, C., Wong, J. J., Côté, P., Shearer, H. M., Randhawa, K., … Carroll, L. J. (2015). The effectiveness of exercise on recovery and clinical outcomes of soft tissue injuries of the leg, ankle, and foot: A systematic review by the Ontario Protocol for Traffic Injury Management (OPTIMa) Collaboration. *Manual Therapy*, 20(5), 633–645.

Yasui, Y., Tonogai, I., Rosenbaum, A. J., Shimozono, Y.,

Kawano, H., & Kennedy, J. G. (2017). The Risk of Achilles Tendon Rupture in the Patients with Achilles Tendinopathy: Healthcare Database Analysis in the United States. *BioMed Research International*, 2017(4), 7021862–4.

Recommended Reading

Bartel, D. L., Davy, D. T., & Keaveny, T. M. (2006). *Orthopaedic Biomechanics*. Prentice Hall.

Bergmann, U., & Rinehart, M. A. (1987). *Musculoskeletal trauma*. Aspen Pub.

Garrick, J. G., & Webb, D. R. (1999). *Sports Injuries*. Saunders.

Levangie, P. K., & Norkin, C. C. (2011). *Joint Structure and Function*. F.A. Davis.

Moore, K. L., Dalley, A. F., & Agur, A. M. R. (2013). *Clinically Oriented Anatomy*. Lippincott Williams & Wilkins.

Neumann, D. A. (2017). *Kinesiology of the Musculoskeletal System*. (D. A. Neumann, Ed.). Elsevier.

Soderberg, G. L. (1997). *Kinesiology*. Lippincott Williams & Wilkins.

Symposium, A. A. O. O. S., Woo, S. L.-Y., Buckwalter, J. A., Surgeons, A. A. O. O., National Institute of Arthritis and Musculoskeletal and Skin Diseases (U.S.). (1988). Injury and repair of the musculoskeletal soft tissues. Amer Academy of Orthopaedic.

Whiting, W. C., & Zernicke, R. F. (2008). *Biomechanics of Musculoskeletal Injury*. Human Kinetics.

Chapter 19

A Brief Summary of Neurophysiology and Muscle Activity

Patrick Hannon

19.1 Introduction

Neurons are the conducting or information processing cells of the nervous system. The neuron consists of a cell body (soma), dendrites, and an axon. The dendrites receive information, and in a minority of cases in the mammalian nervous system may also transmit impulses. Axons are the most common transmitting appendage and may project microscopic distances or distances that may extend the length of the lower extremity to innervate distal intrinsic muscles of the foot. (Figure 19.1) Axons in a minority of cases may also receive impulses (axoaxonic synaptic junctions) within the central nervous system. Sensory neurons have specialized endings that are able to receive sensory stimuli and transduce these stimuli into digital electrical pulses which are then sent to the spinal cord or brain stem structures. Please note that some sensory modalities such as vision require several cell layers for this electrical transduction process to take place.

19.2 Neuron and Muscle Cell Physiology

Neurons communicate with other neurons, muscles, or glands in two different ways. One means is by way of the circulatory system whereby neurons will stimulate glands (e.g., pituitary gland) and a endocrine hormone is released into the circulating blood and transported to a target endocrine gland (e.g., adrenal glands). A second way is by means of synaptic junctions between neurons and neurons, neurons and glands, and neurons and muscle cells.

Synaptic junctions fall into two general categories. The first is electrotonic junctions (bridged junctions). These junctions move ionic current (typically sodium or calcium) directly through channels called connexons from one neuron to another. These junctions allow a very

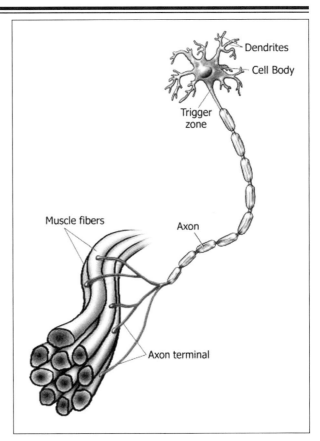

Figure 19.1 A multipolar neuron such as a motor neuron which sends impulses to muscle fibers. (Courtesy of Robert Perry)

quick influx of cations (positive ions) but are not easily modified by training or experience. They are a minority of nervous system synapses in mammalian species. (Figure 19.2a) The most common synapse in mammals is the unbridged or electrochemical junction in which a neurotransmitter chemical is released from small vesicles within the presynaptic bouton and diffuses across a space (*synaptic cleft*) and fuses with the receptor membrane of the receiving neuron (termed the *postsynaptic neuron*). This neurotransmitter will then directly or indirectly via a second messenger system selectively open or close ion

327

gates. If gates are opened by the transmitter, specific ions are able to flow through the neuron membrane due to a combined electrical and chemical (concentration) gradient termed the electrochemical gradient. (Figure 19.2b)

At rest most neurons fall into a range of -60 to -70 millivolts (mv) inside the cell membrane relative to outside the cell membrane. Skeletal muscle cells, which operate in similar fashion to neurons are usually around -90 mv inside the cell membrane at rest. When the neuron or muscle cell is at rest, it is not actively transmitting electrical signals. However, when a neuron is stimulated, ion gates typically open and cations are able to enter into the neuron along the electrochemical gradient leading to an action potential (firing) of the neuron or skeletal muscle cell. Cation influx (e.g., sodium {Na^+} or calcium {Ca^{++}}) is usually responsible for the action potential or firing of a neuron. The majority of neurons experience action potentials (termed *spiking*). When each action potential occurs, the neuron or the skeletal muscle cell moves from its threshold of approximately -55 mv past zero to an approximate +35 mv in many neurons or an approximate +50 mv in skeletal muscle cells. This is termed the depolarization phase and is followed by a repolarization period when the inside of the cell membrane returns to its resting membrane state of -60 mv to -70 mv for the neuron and -90 mv for the skeletal muscle cell. Figure 19.3 illustrates a typical neuron action potential (depolarization and repolarization). These action potentials occur over a very short time frame in the peripheral nervous system and may occur up to thirty-five to forty times each second for motor neurons which operate skeletal muscle fibers and up to six hundred times per second in some proprioceptor sensory neurons within muscle tissue. This rate of firing is termed the frequency of action potentials and is expressed in hertz (Hz) which equates to pulses per second. In the central nervous system, some neurons may fire up to one thousand times per second due to transmitter release.

In some neurons, the neurotransmitter utilizing a second messenger system may upon release have an effect that lasts for hours (although individual action potentials occur in milliseconds). Each action potential or pulse has the same intensity (amplitude), and therefore action potentials conform to the "all or none law" in these spiking neurons. These neurons either fire, or they do not fire.

Neurons, but not skeletal muscle cells, may also be inhibited by a neurotransmitter which makes a portion of the inside of the cell membrane more negative relative to the outside (perhaps to a -75 or -80 mv), and therefore the

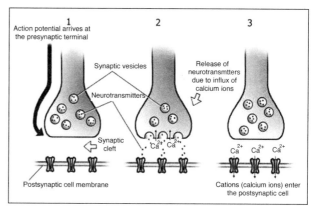

Figure 19.2a A chemical transmitter is released by the presynaptic neuron terminal ending (bouton) of one neuron and diffuses across the synaptic cleft in this case to directly open gates for cations (positive ions) or anions (negative ions). Note that calcium entry into the presynaptic terminal is necessary before transmitter release. (Courtesy of Robert Perry)

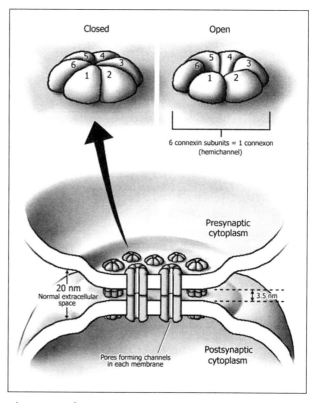

Figure 19.2b Connexons permit the movement of cations (positive ions) across a bridged space of two to three nanometers in the electrotonic synapse. (Courtesy of Robert Perry)

neuron becomes less likely to reach an action potential threshold of approximately a -55 mv to fire and communicate with other neurons or skeletal muscle cells. This is accomplished by the electrochemical gradient moving cations out of the neuron or by moving anions (negative ions) into the neuron when specific ion membrane gates open up on the target post-synaptic neuron. In many cases inhibitory effects will not completely arrest a neuron's activity but rather will simply slow its rate of firing (i.e., action potentials per second).

When skeletal muscle cells experience action potentials at 5 to approximately 40 Hz, they attempt to shorten. The two ends of the cell attempt to come together. Alpha motor neurons in the brain stem and spinal cord control skeletal muscle fibers. One motor neuron may control two or three muscle fibers as in the case of some extraocular muscles of the globe (eyeball) or more typically control 100–1,400 skeletal muscle fibers in larger muscles. The motor neuron and the innervated muscle fibers of that motor neuron are termed a "motor unit." When the motor neuron fires, the muscle fibers that are stimulated by that neuron's terminal endings also fire due to the release of the neurotransmitter acetylcholine (ACH) which is released at the neuromuscular junction, and this muscle cell's action potential in a series of rapid steps initiates muscle cell and whole muscle shortening. (Figure 19.4)

Therefore, gradations of muscle forces are controlled by two separate processes. When motor units (one motor neuron and all its innervated striated muscle fibers) fire at an increasing rate, force concomitantly increases. When the rate of firing decreases, that motor unit will produce less force. This change (up or down) is termed rate coding or frequency modulation and is responsible for how one motor unit can manipulate force levels. The second process is that of recruitment of motor units. An increase or decrease in the number of active motor units (recruitment) will also result in an increase or decrease respectively in the total muscle force.

19.3 Muscle Tension Forces

A. Voluntary skeletal muscle contraction

Coincident with this muscle cell contraction process is a series of steps resulting in protein strands being pulled in over other protein strands within microscopic functional muscle units known as sarcomeres. If the external load is not too high, these sarcomeres arranged in series throughout the muscle cell (within myofibrils) will continue to shorten until they reach their end range of motion. Muscles do not push but rather pull or attempt to pull. This process is responsible for both voluntary and reflexive

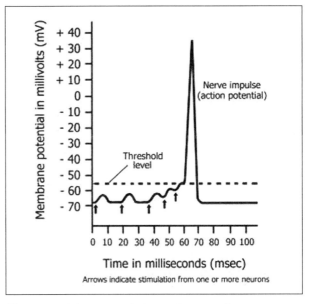

Figure 19.3 *A neuron in its resting membrane state and during an action potential is illustrated (oscilloscope tracing). (Courtesy of Robert Perry)*

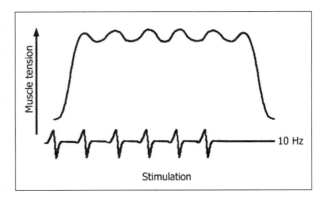

Figure 19.4 *Repeated action potentials of a single alpha motor unit and the corresponding muscle tension response above the action potentials as measured by a force transducer. Hundreds of alpha motor units may operate to produce muscle tension force within a single muscle. (Courtesy of Robert Perry)*

muscle contraction and is responsible for the high internal tension forces that can be achieved by muscle tissue.

Skeletal muscle tension obviously has functional value in terms of producing bone and joint movement, and in some cases muscle tension will actually protect other structures and tissues such as abdominal organs or bony structures. However, internal muscle elements may also produce tension so high that bony structures are brought to a failure point, as in the case of shock treatments for clinical depression or in the case of grand mal epileptic seizures producing failure of vertebral bodies. One such case follows.

Case Study 19.1

One afternoon following a 911 call, paramedics went to the home of a young man in his late twenties who was experiencing his first grand mal seizure. When they arrived, the man's wife related the story of the seizure episode. The patient was in the post-seizure period and subsequently became combative. In order to prevent self-inflicted injury, the patient was restrained by the two paramedics. On the way to hospital, the patient experienced a second grand mal seizure in the ambulance. At admission and complaining of back pain in the lower thoracic spine, radiographs were taken of the patient, and the radiographs indicated a partial compression fracture of two vertebral bodies at T9 and T10 without neurological sequela.

The patient brought suit against the city fire department with the rationale being that the physical restraint actions of the paramedics were directly responsible for the compression loading upon the lower thoracic spine and the resulting vertebral fractures. In trial testimony, it was explained that the external loads used in restraining the patient were in the wrong direction and of insufficient magnitude to produce these fractures. Instead, it was the patient's own active muscle elements (involuntary) within the spine which produced the large loads (approximately 1,400 lbs.) required to produce vertebral body compression failure at these levels during one or both of the grand mal episodes. A review of the biomechanical/medical literature documented several other case studies involving bone fractures resulting from tonic-clonic epileptic seizures.

Muscle tension may also produce other types of injury. Many times high tension loads will produce muscle strain as in the case of posterior neck muscle injury that occurs during a significant frontal impact with the occupant moving abruptly forward. This inertial forced neck flexion results in an eccentric muscle contraction (lengthening muscle from an external load while under tension), and muscle tissue and the associated connective tissue may be torn due to the tension stresses. In other cases, it is the muscle tendon that fails or even a portion of the bone may pull off as in the case of an avulsion bone fracture at the site of a muscle-tendon-bone attachment. Figure 19.5 illustrates a tension stress fracture of the calcaneus bone of the foot from a high tension load imposed by the Achilles tendon during posterior calf musculature contraction. More commonly, a rupture of the muscle belly or of the tendon itself occurs, especially when the loading to this region is applied rapidly.

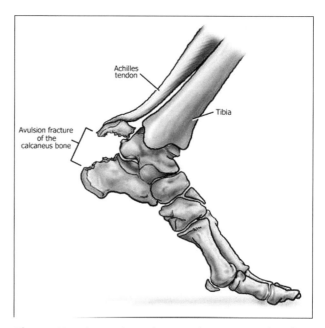

Figure 19.5 *An avulsion fracture has occurred at the Achilles tendon attachment at the calcaneus bone. Tension stresses have produced a complete rupture of a rather large tarsal bone. (Courtesy of Robert Perry)*

B. Reflexive skeletal muscle activity

Neuromuscular reflexes are designed to protect us or have some other functional value. Some reflexes that are present at birth disappear. A few others develop in early childhood, and others are overlaid by voluntary motor control as we mature. Finally, some reflexes remain and have real functional value throughout our lifetimes. A complete discussion of neuromuscular reflexes is beyond the scope of this text. However, four reflexes are discussed here because they have implications for injury and reflexive neural control that may be important in some matters of litigation.

1. Myotatic stretch reflex

The myotatic stretch reflex is a reflex that is mediated by an **Ia receptor** found inside the muscle spindle that lies parallel to skeletal muscle fibers. A medical practitioner who hammer taps the patellar tendon just below the knee cap will elicit the myotatic stretch reflex due to a slight lengthening of anterior thigh quadriceps musculature. When a muscle is stretched, the spindles within the Ia proprioceptors undergo a mechanical deformation which results in the Ia proprioceptors sending impulses (high rate coding) back to the anterior horns of the spinal cord which contain the motor neurons. (Figure 19.6) Excitatory impulses are transmitted directly (monosynaptically) to these "alpha motor neurons" from these spindle Ia afferents.

These motor neurons then send impulses out to the skeletal muscle fibers that now act to shorten and thereby reduce the stretch response in muscles. (Figure 19.7)

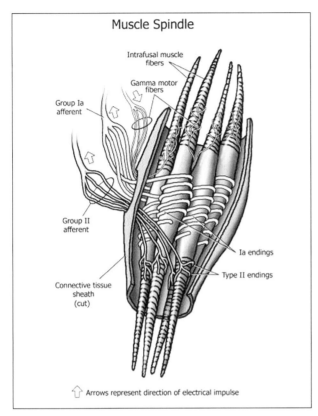

Figure 19.6 *When the muscle spindle is stretched, Ia and type II sensory endings within the spindle fire. The Ias are thought to mediate the myotatic stretch reflex and are most sensitive and respond most robustly to high rates of muscle stretch. (Courtesy of Robert Perry)*

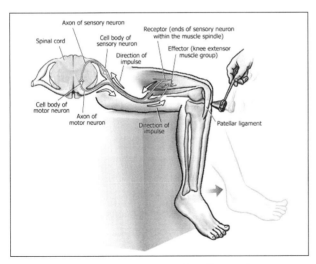

Figure 19.7 *The myotatic stretch reflex pathway is illustrated from receptor to spinal cord. (Courtesy of Robert Perry)*

Note that the alpha motor neurons stimulate muscle activity. In this way the myotatic stretch reflex is able to actively stop the stretch produced by external loading. In terms of lower limb support this reflex is able to increase tension in antigravity muscles and prevent a fall to the ground, and additionally it also provides a protective mechanism in terms of limiting the range of motion of both axial skeleton and limb joint movement. Finally, it permits the rapid adjustment of muscle force to compensate for an increased external load. One should keep in mind, however, that the myotatic stretch reflex results in an attempt at muscle shortening by muscle contraction. In some cases, this results in a forced eccentric muscle contraction with consequent damage to muscle fibers and associated connective tissue. Skeletal muscle can endure damage within the normal range of motion. This reflex can actually exacerbate muscle strain when muscle tissue fails and may also be responsible for delayed onset muscle soreness (DOMS) but more importantly may actually exacerbate muscle strain when muscle tissue fails.

2. Auditory startle reflex

This reflex is one that involves orienting the head and torso toward a possible threatening auditory stimulus. It obviously has protective value. This reflex may involve significant muscular contractions which move the spinal column during the orientation task. Once again under these circumstances, mild muscle strains are possible although not probable even though the head and torso components stay within their normal ROM. Injury beyond mild muscle strain has not been documented.

3. Pain reflexes

Two other reflexes that have protective value are normally paired together as they result from the same nociceptive (pain) stimulus. They are the flexor withdrawal reflex (FWR) and the crossed extensor reflex (CER) of the upper and lower extremities. These are reflexes that occur when one steps on a sharp object barefooted. The lower limb foot that steps on the sharp object will withdraw in flexion at the ankle, knee, and hip. In the opposite side lower limb, the knee and hip extensors are simulated to produce increased force to the antigravity muscles to maintain support of the body while the affected foot is lifted abruptly in the air. Therefore, flexion occurs on the nociceptive stimulus side (flexor withdrawal reflex) coincident with a reflex across the spinal cord that elicits the increase in muscle tension for the contralateral joint extensors (crossed extension reflex). Although both these reflexes involve a series of synapses (polysynaptic reflexes), they are relatively quick with significant force

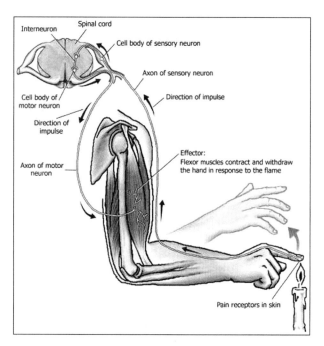

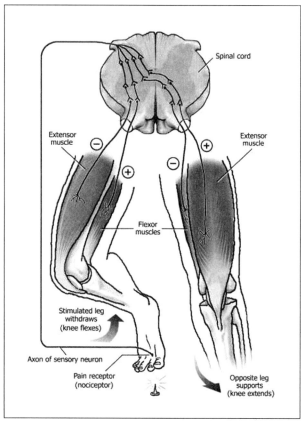

Figures 19.8a and *19.8b* The functional flexor with-
drawal reflex (FWR) and the crossed extensor reflex
(CER) are illustrated in response to a pain stimulus.
Please note the spinal cord effects in eliciting the CER
in this example of the lower extremities. (Courtesy of
Robert Perry)

production acquired at approximately 100 ms (one tenth
of one second). (Figures 19.8a and 19.8b)

Case Study 19.2

This case involved a health professional who
was trimming juniper bushes in his front yard.
His instrument of choice was a hatchet and in
the process of trimming he claimed to have cut
off parts of two fingers of the hand holding on to
the bushes. Parts of the two fingers were found in
the juniper bushes by fire department paramedics and promptly put on ice for possible re-at-
tachment. At the emergency room, the plaintiff
declined reattachment of the two finger parts.
The plaintiff made use of both his hands in his
healthcare practice and was disability insured.
This injury in his view left him disabled and unable to continue his practice.

We discovered early that even a brand new
hatchet is not an appropriate choice for trimming branches on a juniper bush. The branches
are very flexible and, when struck, simply move
without being cut. In some cases forty or fifty
strikes were required in our field experiment to
sever one medium sized branch (0.75-inch diameter). That issue aside, a second issue was
whether it was possible to strike the hand holding the branch seven or eight times during a forward fall to his knees without producing pain
and without eliciting the flexor withdrawal reflex (FWR). Individual lacerations on the dorsal
surface of the fingers indicated seven to eight
strikes based on a hand surgeon's drawing at the
hospital emergency room. These are also known
as anticipation cuts or marks that are many times
made in self-inflicted intentional injuries. Please
note that the weather was warm, and this individual was without any hand sensory loss. Yet, the
plaintiff indicated that he never experienced the
FWR. The literature is clear that the short loop
flexor withdrawal reflex (FWR) would have permitted only one hatchet strike to the hand, and
this would have elicited the FWR. It is possible
to intentionally override the FWR when the pain
stimulus is at a low level. Furthermore, there are
individuals who can override the reflex at much
higher pain levels through voluntary motor control of the limb experiencing the pain stimulus.
In all these cases, volitional control, with the expectation of a pain stimulus prior to the stimulus,

is required. Furthermore, this health professional would have had access to a local pain blocking injectible anesthetic in order to significantly reduce the nociceptive trauma stimulus.

Three biomechanical issues also played a part in this case. First, the dorsal surface cuts on the fingers were at inappropriate angles relative to the long axis of the fingers. The cuts were not consistent with plaintiff's testimony and simply could not have been produced given the human upper extremity positions required. The second biomechanical issue dealt with the amputations. Using exemplar bones, hatchet strikes were made with the bones lying on a hard wooden surface. All the strikes resulted in fracture-failure of the bones with transverse and oblique fracture patterns and small fractures at the edges of the fracture line made by the hatchet. In contrast, the hand surgeon indicated that the amputating cuts were clean, as if they has been sawed through with a some sort of serrated instrument. We were able to achieve cuts consistent with the treating hand surgeon's description with a sharp serrated knife and sawing action applied to our bone samples.

Finally, the plaintiff indicated that all the cuts were made during a short time period when he had slipped and fallen forward to the ground from a forward hip flexion position. A time analysis demonstrated that under this scenario there was time for only one strike to the branch-holding hand.

References and Recommended Reading

Enoka R. and Fuglevand, A. (2001) Motor Unit Physiology: some unresolved issues. Muscle Nerve v. 24, pp. 4-17.

Hannon, Patrick R., McMillan, James A., and Stevenson, Lisa, 1985. "Differential contributions of vastus medialis and rectus femoris to crossed extension reflex: affects of body position" Presented by Dr. Hannon at the Society for Neurosciences Convention, Oct., 1985.

Heckman, C. and Enoka, R. (2004) ch 6 Physiology of the motor neuron and the motor unit, Clinical Neurophysiology of Motor Neuron Diseases: Handbook of Clinical Neurophysiology, Vo. 4, A. Eisen (Ed.) Elsevier B.V.

Kandel, E., Schwartz, J., Jessell, T., Siegelbaum, S., Editors), and Hudspeth, A. (2013) Principles of Neural Science 5th Edition, McGraw Hill Medical, New York.

Kandel, E. (Editor), James H. Schwartz (Editor), Thomas M. Jessell (Editor) (1995) Essentials of Neural Science and Behavior, 1st Edition.

McMillan, James A., Hannon, Patrick R., and Stevenson, Lisa. 1985. "Differential contributions of the rectus femoris and vastus medialis to crossed extension reflex: prolonged central summation" Presented by Dr. McMillan at the Society for Neurosciences Convention Oct., 1985.

McMillan, James A., Hannon, Patrick, Stevenson, Leticea M., and Van Natta, Timothy L. (1991). "Effects of body position on crossed extension reflex in decerebrate cat: rectus femoris is more sensitive than is vastus medialis". Brain Research, 538, pp. 152-156.

Nigg, B. and Herzog, W. (eds) (1994) Biomechanics of the Musculo-skeletal System, Wiley Pub., Chichester.

Nolte, J. (2002) The Human Brain: An Introduction to Its Functional Anatomy 5th Edition

Shepherd, G. (1988) Neurobiology, Oxford University Press, New York.

Chapter 20

Anatomical Mechanics—A Concept and Quantitative Approach: Bones, Joints, and Muscles

Patrick Hannon

This chapter is a review of basic mechanics applied to bones, joints, and muscles. These soft and hard human tissues have been previously described within this text. This section addresses how these elements function together as mechanical machines, with bones providing major structural components. Where bones come together, joints are formed. Muscles provide the internal forces to produce movement at joints (articulations).

20.1 Types of Joints

Our focus in this text is on diarthrodial or freely moveable joints within the body, such as the knee, elbow, or shoulder. This mobility may also lead to increased vulnerability of these joints to injury when the range of motion is exceeded or when external forces directly or indirectly load these diarthrodial articulations. Joints such as the articulations between the vertebral bodies are classified as amphiarthrodial (slightly moveable) and may also be injured if components such as the ligament structures, vertebral bodies, end plates, or intervertebral disks fail as discussed within this text. Synarthrodial joints are the least moveable (little or no movement), and damage or failure is not as common and usually occurs in conjunction with bone failure.

20.2 Human Machines

The bones that make up diarthrodial and some amphiarthrodial joints move when muscle or external forces, moments, and torques are applied to these bony machines (levers, pulleys, and wheel and axle machines). Generally, muscle elements oppose the external loads. Skeletal muscles pull rather than push and do so by means of a sliding filament mechanism (see Lorenz, 2001, 148–171, for additional detail). These pulling forces act at a variable displacement away from a joint's axis and are therefore able to produce a torque or moment which serves to rotate a joint. In this text, we refer to moments as a force acting around a moment arm with an anterioposterior axis (front-to-back) or a mediolateral axis (side-to-side). The magnitude of a torque is calculated in the same way, but the angular motion occurs around a longitudinal axis. These moments and torques will produce movement on a lever, wheel and axle and simple pulley machine systems (Figures 20.1a, 20.1b, and 20.1c).

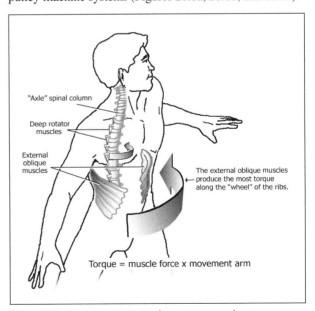

"Axle" spinal column

Deep rotator muscles

External oblique muscles

The external oblique muscles produce the most torque along the "wheel" of the ribs.

Torque = muscle force x movement arm

Figure 20.1a Moments and torques produce rotational movement in three human machine systems: the lever, wheel and axle, and simple pulley. (Courtesy of Robert Perry)

335

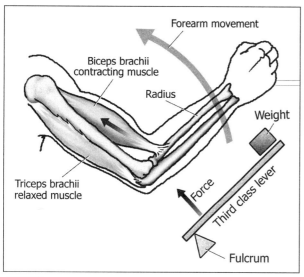

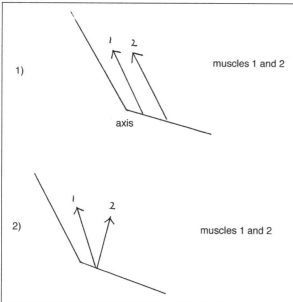

***Figure 20.1b** and **20.1c** Two factors will affect the
length of the force moment arm. First, the proximity
of the tendon attachment point or the point of force
application in relationship to the joint axis of rotation.
The relationship may be described as the greater the
distance the muscle force is applied away from the
axis of rotation, the greater the moment (1). Second,
as the angle of muscle pull (q) approximates 90° to
the bone, the force moment arm is maximized (2).*

*If the line of force is applied closer and closer
and finally coincident with the joint axis of rotation,
the moment disappears (muscle moment = F × 0 =
0). At this point any muscle force vector regardless
of its magnitude will only serve to compress and
stabilize the articular surfaces of the joint. (Courtesy
of Robert Perry and Patrick Hannon)*

20.3 Moments and Torques

Moments and torques are increased when there is an increase in a muscular force or an external weight (load)
and when we have an increase in the length of the moment (lever) arm. Imagine holding a bag of groceries as
far in front of your body as possible: a long resistance moment arm (rma). The groceries have not suddenly become
heavier, but rather the moment arm has increased dramatically to produce a large "gravity moment" (i.e., resistance
or weight × moment arm). (Figure 20.3)

Muscle moments also are determined by the distance
of the muscle tendon from the joint axis and when the
angle of muscle pull changes in relationship to the bone
(angle arms formed by the tendon and the bone). When the
angle between the tendon insertion and the bone (termed
angle theta (θ)) is a very acute angle, the actual moment
arm defined as the perpendicular distance from the line
of muscle force, will be smaller and therefore limit the
amount of muscle moment or muscle torque that can be
produced. At other points in the range of motion (ROM),
the moment arm, termed a force moment arm (fma), will
increase. If the muscle force stays the same, the moment
or torque will increase dramatically given a longer fma
(muscle moment or torque = force × fma). When θ increases beyond 90°, the fma will decrease, resulting in a
smaller moment or torque given the same muscle force. A
simple way to measure moment arms is with a graphic approach. (Figure 20.2b) The gravity or resistance moments
can easily be approximated by examining a photograph,
video recording, or a drawing that allows proper viewing perspective. Estimated muscle moment arms (fmas)
may also be graphically represented on a drawing. In both
cases, the rma and the fma are graphically calculated by
finding the perpendicular distance from the line of force
(or line of weight-resistance) to the axis of rotation.

A muscle moment may be calculated by the following statics equilibrium equation (F × fma = R × rma);
where F and R represent the muscle force and a resistance
(weight), respectively. If a resistance or weight is not
moving up or down as in the example of a man performing a dumbbell curl exercise, then the muscle moment and
the resistance moment around a mediolateral axis must be
equal and opposite (static equilibrium). The fma for any
given elbow position can be estimated from cadaver data
based on different degrees of elbow flexion. The tension
produced by the muscle is unknown but may be calculated
when the other three quantities are known. An algebraic
solution is presented in Calculation Box 20.1.

From this example, it can be seen that generated
muscle forces may (and usually do) far exceed an external
load due to the relatively short fma throughout the range

Calculation Box 20.1

Given:
Resistance = 40 lbs.
Resistance Moment Arm = 1.5 feet
Force Moment Arm = .08 feet

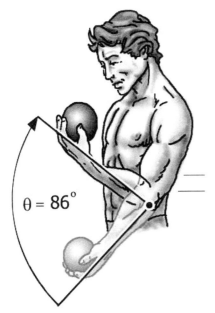

Figure 20.2 *Courtesy of Robert Perry*

F × fma = R × rma

F = R × rma ÷ fma

Force = 40 lbs. × 1.5 feet ÷ 08 feet
Force = 60 ft.-lbs. ÷ 08 feet
Muscle Force = 750 lbs.

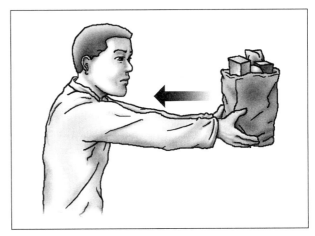

Figure 20.3 *Holding the grocery load far from the torso will increase the resistance moment arm with a coincident increase in the gravity moment. Holding the load close to the body minimizes this resistance moment arm and the resulting gravity moment. Therefore, less muscle moment is required to counterbalance the load (weight of groceries). (Courtesy of Robert Perry)*

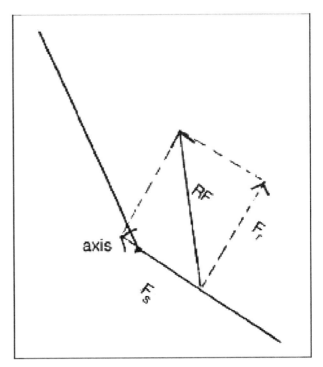

Figure 20.4 *An upper extremity example of force resolution using the graphic rectangle method to determine both rotating and stabilizing force components. It is the rotating force component that is multiplied by the simple force arm to calculate the muscle moment acting around the elbow joint mediolateral axis (Moment = F_r × sfa). (Courtesy of Patrick Hannon)*

of motion. To move an external load, the muscle moment must exceed this resistance moment of 60 ft.-lbs. with an increasing muscular moment producing greater acceleration of the load. Because the moment arm cannot be manipulated without changing body and elbow positions, flexor muscle force must increase in order to increase the muscle moment as in this elbow flexion example. As the elbow angle changes with a consequent change in the fma, the muscular force will increase or decrease depending upon the demands of the resistance moment produced by the external load and corresponding rma.

20.4 Muscle Force Resolution

An alternative, but equivalent, way to express moments is to multiply the component of force that actually produces rotation (F_r) times what is known as a simple moment arm (sfa), which is defined as the point of application of the force vector to the axis of rotation. The sfa does not change, but rather the calculated muscle moment changes in response to a changing rotating force component. This equivalent equation is sometimes expressed as moment or torque = F_r x sfa. It can be calculated graphically or by using a trigonometric method. This process of taking a single force (e.g., a muscle force) and breaking it up into components is termed *force resolution*. To resolve a force vector into two right angle components, one would use what is known as the rectangle method illustrated in Figure B.4. The total muscle or resultant force (RF) is resolved into its two components: one being perpendicular to the bony lever arm in many cases (i.e., F_r) and the other a stabilizing force component (F_s) that is parallel to the long bone with its arrow head approaching or passing through the joint. The rotary force component is in fact modified by the muscle's angle of pull (θ) from the bone. In the case of a force applied at 90° to the moment arm, 100% of the force serves to produce rotation. If the angle of pull is less than 90°, the force vector will produce both rotary and stabilizing force components. It is only the rotary component that makes a contribution to the muscle torque or moment. The stabilizing component (F_s) pulls the bones together to provide joint stabilization. When a muscular force acts at more than 90° to the bone relative to the joint axis, an F_r a destabilizing or a dislocating component (F_d) exists. Some joints during a portion of their range of motion (ROM) will create this F_d component which tends to pull the bones apart. Note that ligament structures or other muscles prevent this occurrence.

An alternative method of calculating force components is to make use of trigonometric functions. Angle theta (θ) is the angle of the hypotenuse and the side adjacent (between the point of force application and the joint axis). The F_r component is the side opposite. The relationship may be defined as follows: the F_r component equals the sine of angle theta θ times the total or resultant force (F_r = sin angle θ x RF). Similarly, the stabilization or dislocating component (side adjacent) is calculated by taking the cosine of angle θ times the resultant force (F_s or F_d = cos angle θ x RF). (Figure 20.5)

These graphic and mathematical techniques may also be used in determining acceleration, displacement, and velocity vectors that result from the imposed forces. If we want to know, for instance, how much acceleration occurs in a forward direction versus a sideways direction, we are able to apply this same method.

The discussion thus far has been limited to uniplanar

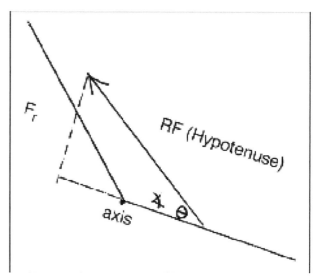

Figure 20.5 *A right triangle is created when a resultant muscle force (hypotenuse) pulls at angle q to the bone lever arm (muscle tendon's angle of pull). The side opposite corresponds to the F_r component, while the side adjacent in this right triangle in this example corresponds to the F_s component. (Courtesy of Patrick Hannon)*

forces, and it must be mentioned that a spatial analysis involving all three dimensions can be accomplished as well but the calculations are more complex and beyond the scope of this text (see Soderberg, 1996).

20.5 Muscle Force Composition

When forces and moments sum to zero, we are in a state of **static equilibrium**. When forces and moments do not sum to zero, we now have a **dynamics situation**. Again we will limit our discussion to single plane forces, moments, and torques. There are times in functional anatomy when we want to sum forces and sum moments and torques in order to predict or calculate a particular acceleration, velocity, and resultant joint motion (displacement). The forces (such as muscle forces) may be summed with vector addition. A simple graphic method that is sometimes used is the *tip-to-tail (polygon) method* that permits the adding of vectors in a sequential fashion and then finally determining the resultant force vector. Vectors are summed in succession by starting with any vector and then attaching the tail of a second force vector to the head of the first vector while maintaining a two-dimensional coordinate system. This process is repeated for the third vector and so on until all vectors are sequentially summed. Finally, a line is drawn from the point where all of the forces were applied to the head of the final vector added. This resultant vector then represents the total muscle force or resultant force.

(Figure 20.6) This method demands that all forces begin at the same point and that all force vectors act within a single plane and at a coincident time. Obviously there are limitations to this method in functional human anatomy. Nevertheless, this can be a useful method, and is one that juries can easily understand.

Uniplanar concurrent forces all imposed on the same point can also be calculated using the Pythagorean theorem if the two forces are perpendicular to one another (RF = $\sqrt{F_r^2 + F_s^2}$ or F_d^2). In anatomical examples this is useful but is rarely used in real-world-event situations because many anatomical force composition problems do not entail orthogonal (perpendicular) force vectors. However, an alternate method to sum any two muscle force vectors is to use the Law of Cosines which permits the calculation of the resultant force (magnitude and direction) of the side opposite (resultant) vector when the other two sides (force vectors) of the triangle and angle theta is known. A right triangle is not required. The law of cosines is: $c = \sqrt{a^2 + b^2 - 2ab \cos}$ angle C and applied to force vectors for example becomes RF = $\sqrt{Fr^2 + Fs^2}$ or Fd^2 - 2Fr Fs or Fd cos angle C. Note, only two force vectors at any one time can be calculated with the Law of Cosines. The process is simply repeated every time a co-planar, time coincident force is added The reader is referred to any text in basic trigonometry for examples and any functional anatomy text for useful human anatomy examples.

20.6 Moments in Static and Dynamic Problems

Moments can also be summed around a single axis operating in a single plane. The concurrent forces do not need to be imposed at the same point. Rather, moments simply need to be ascribed as being either clockwise (typically termed negative) or counterclockwise (typically termed positive). A net moment is then calculated and represents the tendency to rotate in a specific direction (clockwise or counterclockwise). (Figure 20.7) The reader should note that a free body diagram technique may be used to solve statics problems in which forces and moments sum to zero or in dynamics problems in which the sum of forces and moments does not equal zero as illustrated by movement of the knee joint in stair ascent or descent (unbalanced forces and moments). When ascending stairs, a muscle moment (quadriceps muscles) acts at the knee joint which exceeds the gravity moment, and therefore the knee extends in stair climbing. In descending stairs, during part of the step sequence, the moment produced by gravity is allowed to exceed the muscular moment produced by the knee extensors. During this time period the knee will bend in flexion,

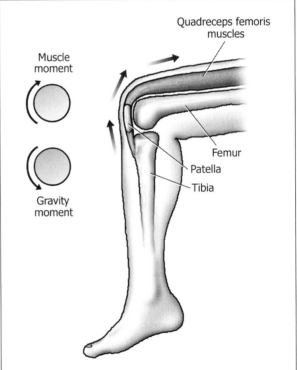

Figure 20.7 The quadriceps muscle moment and the body weight gravity moment present equal and opposite rotating moments. Both moments sum to zero when the body is not moving up or down (static equilibrium). (Courtesy of Robert Perry)

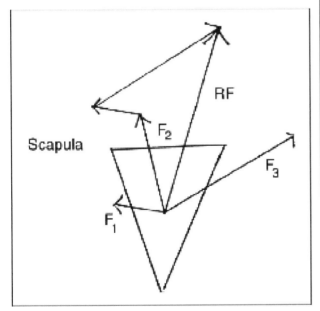

Figure 20.6 Force composition. The human scapula is acted upon by three concurrent uniplaner forces which are successively summed using the tip to tail vector composition method. (Courtesy of Patrick Hannon)

and the body will drop to a lower level (hopefully in a controlled fashion).

These types of analyses permit the biomechanist to quantify muscle and joint reaction forces during still and moving body mechanics. If video or film data of an accident event are available, then the kinematics data may be used to estimate forces, moments, and torques that are produced by internal human muscles or external loads (i.e., inverse dynamics). These forces and moments are then "distributed" or ascribed to various muscles or external loading by means of more sophisticated methods (reduction and optimization methods). The reader is referred to Mow and Hayes (1997) for a more complete discussion of these topics.

References

Lorenz, T., and M. Campello. Adapted from M. Pitman and L. Peterson. "Biomechanics of Skeletal Muscle." In M. Nordin and V. Frankel, eds. *Basic Biomechanics of the Musculoskeletal System*. Philadelphia: Lippincott Williams & Wilkins. (2001)

Mow,V.C., and W.C. Hayes. *Basic Orthopaedic Biomechanics*, Second edition. Philadelphia: Lippincott Williams & Wilkins. (1997)

Soderberg, Gary. *Kinesiology: Application to Pathological Motion*, Second edition. Philadelphia; Williams & Wilkins. (1996)

Chapter 21

The Biomechanics, Engineering Design and Failure Analysis of Implantable Medical Devices - An Overview

David Bosch, Scott Anderson and Patrick Hannon

21. Introduction

Medical implants are one of the greatest scientific breakthroughs and represent a huge and growing financial sector. According to McCloy (McCloy, 2016), the worldwide medical implant market exceeds $200 billion. He estimates that approximately 20% of adults in the U.S. have received an implant of one form or another. These number are substantiated by the U.S. Department of Commerce (2016, Top Markets Report) which states that the global market for medical devices in 2016 was $339.5 billion and predicted that it would grow to $435.8 billion by 2020. Inevitably, some of these devices will fail. The

failure of medical implants can be disastrous for the patient and the manufacturer of the implanted device often leading to litigation as an effort to both determine liability, drive improvements of medical technology and provide monetary compensation for the injured parities' incurred expenses and other compensatory damages.

The materials that comprise medical implants fail in many different ways for many different reasons. In the case of the failure of engineered materials, knowledge about biomaterials and many factors must be considered and investigated before any conclusions can been drawn regarding the underlying cause of the component failure. The primary factors that must be considered include, but are not limited to, manufacturability and manufacturing processing requirements, biocompatibility of the proposed material(s) and device geometry, the in vivo and in vitro environmental factors, the normal anticipated and traumatic (if any) loading conditions, and the health and condition of the patient.

This chapter provides the fundamental knowledge required by engineer and biomechanical professionals in order to analyze why an implanted orthopedic device has failed mechanically; generally, by fracture. The focus will be limited to the failure of metals that are used to fabricated orthopedic implanted devices. Information regarding the biocompatibility of various engineered materials and their interaction with tissues is also presented

After a failed implanted device is explanted (removed) from the patient, it must be subjected to appropriate examination and tests. Perhaps the most important testing in cases of mechanical failure is the macro and micro examination of the failed device fracture surfaces. By using a wide array of tools and techniques, the analyst can reveal important fracture surface features along with physical and mechanical properties of the failed device in order to determine if the device properties are consistent with those specified by the device manufacturer; and, ultimately determine the root cause of failure.

One of the more important analytical techniques regarding the failure of various devices is fractography. It is noted that the evaluation of fracture surface features often allows the analyst to determine what, if any, additional tests and/or investigations may be required to complete the failure analysis. For example, if fractography reveals that an explanted device has failed due to surface damage created during the surgical implantation procedure, then the termination of the investigation may be deemed appropriate. If not, then additional tools and techniques may be employed to further investigate the root cause of the failure.

In this chapter, discussions regarding the history and types of implants, along with the challenges of the development of biocompatible materials and related considerations are also presented. In addition, a review of the mechanics of materials is provided. These subjects are covered in order to give the reader context in which to view the application of the tools and techniques that are generally relied upon to determine the root cause of implant failures. Without this knowledge, it would be very difficult, if not impossible, to understand the changes that are necessary to avoid future failures and/or assist in the assignment of liability.

21.2 General Discussion and Types of Implants

The U.S. Food and Drug Administration (FDA) defines medical implants as "Devices or tissues that are placed inside or on the surface of the body." Implants are often prosthetics intended to replace missing or damaged human body parts. Other implants deliver medication, monitor body functions, and/or provide support to organs and tissues that have been damaged or are failing due to natural causes.

McIntyre (McIntyre, 2011) summarized research done by 24/7WallSt.com based on its examination of National Health Survey data, multiple professional physician services, peer-reviewed journals, and Securities and Exchange Commission (SEC) filings to complete a list of the most frequently implanted medical devices in the United States. The report contained data regarding the number of procedures for each of the top 11 implantable devices implanted each year and the total expenditure, average cost per procedure and the major manufactures of each device. The findings indicated that the most implanted medical device was the artificial eye lens (2.582 million lenses). In

descending order, based on the total number of implants, were ear tubes (715,000), coronary stents (560,000), artificial knee joints (543,000), metal screws, plates and rods (453,000), intra-uterine devices (425,000), spinal screws, rods and artificial spinal discs (413,000), breast implants (366,000), heart pacemakers (235,567), artificial hips (230,000) and implantable cardioverter defibrillators. The data and information for each device are summarized in Table 21.1.

In the U.S., implants are considered to be medical devices and are regulated by the FDA under three classification as defined in 21CFR 860.3. The three classes, Class I, Class II and Class III divide medical devices bases on increasing risk to the user. Examples of each of the aforementioned implant categories are discussed below. It is also noted that there are a large number of ASTM standards that are applicable to medical implants; several of which are referenced herein.

21.3 Engineering and Biomechanical Considerations in Orthopedic Implants

The ideal implant material could be described as having the following characteristics:1) chemically inert; 2) excellent wear resistance; 3) superior biocompatibility; 4) an appropriate modulus of elasticity; 5) high strength; 6) long fatigue life; 7) corrosion-proof; and, of course, 8) inexpensive.

Orthopedic implants are used to alleviate problems with joints (e.g. hip, knee, finger and toe, wrist and shoulder) and bones. They are used to repair bone fractures, scoliosis of the spine, osteoarthritis, spinal stenosis and to treat pain.

Any implant can fail for a number of reasons, including material defects, design defects and/or manufacturing defects. The following sections provide an overview of the engineering and biomechanical challenges associated with implantable devices.

A. Objectives and benefits of orthopedic implants

Orthopedic implants may be used in fracture fixation through a process termed "open reduction – internal fixation" (i.e., ORIF). Most typically at present, these materials are metal alloys. The purpose of this surgical procedure is to enable the orthopedic surgeon to adequately stabilize the two ends of the fractured long bone or to bring many bone fragments from a comminuted fracture together in a stable fashion. In some surgical procedures of the hand, for example, an arthrodesis may be achieved by removing a proximal interphalangeal (PIP) joint and approximating the saw cut ends of the two bones together proximal and middle phalanges and securing them with a bone screw or dorsal surface metal plate over the PIP joint at a desired arthrodesis PIP angle (see Case Study 21.1). In some spinal surgical procedures, metal plates are fixed to the anterior vertebral bodies in fusing functional spinal units in the cervical or lumbar spine; less frequently in the thoracic spine. Furthermore, in conjunction with hardware applied to anterior vertebral bodies, the posterior elements of vertebral structures may also be reinforced in a separate fusion procedure.

Other spinal pathology such as scoliosis (lateral curvature{s}) may also be treated by hardware such as Harrington or Luque rods that enable the physician to apply an apparatus which will apply tension on one side of the spine and compression on the other in an effort to correct the progressing scoliosis deformity. Currently, there are many different implants available for the treatment of scoliosis. Implant systems differ depending upon patient indications and an appreciation of spinal instrumentation is essential in the treatment of the patient with scoliosis (Mohaideen, et al., 2000).

Current joint replacements are not only being used for hips and knees but also for interphalangeal joints, ankles, shoulders (GH joint) and other joints. These joint replacements may be due to acute trauma but are more commonly implanted in cases of remote trauma or advancing osteoarthritis and/or chondromalacia with the advanced loss of joint articular cartilage. Whereas joint replacements many times would fail within 5 to 10 years, requiring revision, new knee and hip replacements may be expected to last 20 to 30 years as implant materials and joint designs continue to improve.

Case Study 21.1 - Swan Neck Deformity Repair

Sports Trauma. A 72-year-old male suffered a traumatic injury to his left hand while wrestling at age 16.

Evaluation and anatomical structures involved. At the time of the injury, his hand was evaluated by the wrestling coach and his family physician. Both the coach and family physician felt that he had "sprained" or torn his left-hand middle finger. His pain decreased and he was able to use his hand for all functional and sports activities. Approximately 10 years following the injury, ulnar deviation of the middle phalanx of his left index finger began to develop at the proximal interphalangeal joint (PIP) joint. The magnitude of the ulnar deviation deformity

started to accelerate when he was 66 years old. At the age of 71, a "Swan Neck" deformity developed in addition to the ulnar deviation (Figure 21.1). This deformity progressed rapidly, causing him to consult with an orthopedic hand surgeon. A "Swan Neck" deformity is characterized by hyperextension at the proximal interphalangeal joint (PIP) and flexion at the distal interphalangeal joint (DIP). In addition to the ulnar deviation and "Swan Neck" deformity seen in the accompanying radiographs, there were signs of osteoarthritis in the left-hand PIP joint. These signs include loss of joint space at the PIP joint and osteophyte development along the ulnar border of the PIP joint.

Likely Cause of Injuries. The ulnar devia-

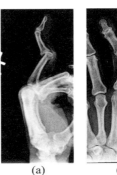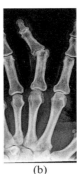

(a)   (b)

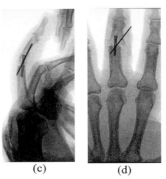

(c)   (d)

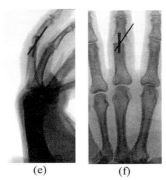

(e)   (f)

Figure 21.1 *"Swan Neck" Deformity of the third Ray-PIP and DIP joints- Pre-op (a) Sagittal View radiograph, (b) Anteroposterior View radiograph, (c) Sagittal View, (d) Anteroposterior View; Fluorocope Photo images of the same patient at 4 weeks post-op. Note woven bone has filled in the gap but remains to be fully mineralized which will require more time. The bone screw will remain in place, but the K wire will be pulled out when fusion of this proximal interphalangeal joint is more complete. Images (e) and (f) are of the same patient at 7 weeks post-op showing better but still incomplete fusion. The K wire was pulled out after this imaging. (Courtesy of the Hand Center of Northern Arizona, Drs. Patrick Cole and Jack Quigley).*

tion of the middle phalanx was likely caused by the original injury, which most likely involved a radial collateral ligament sprain of the PIP joint. This resulted in instability that allowed the extrinsic and intrinsic muscles of the middle finger (flexors, extensor, or both) to pull more toward the ulnar side of the hand, thus creating the ulnar deviation deformity. Over time, the moment arm for this ulnar pull increased, accelerating the ulnar deviation deformity. A "Swan Neck" deformity is most commonly seen in individuals with rheumatoid arthritis, but in the present case, blood markers for this condition were negative. Rather, the swan neck deformity is the result of the instability at the PIP joint caused by changes in the volar plate, which allowed the middle phalanx to be pulled into hyperextension at the PIP joint by the *extensor digitorum* tendon of the middle finger. Without a functioning volar plate, the extrinsic finger flexor muscles (*flexor digitorum profundus and flexor digitorum superficialis*) were unable to counteract the pull from the *extensor digitorum*. The osteoarthritis observed at the PIP joint is the consequence of abnormal intrinsic and extrinsic muscle forces being exerted on this joint without the necessary stabilizing structures needed to prevent the deformities which led to further degeneration of the PIP cartilage surfaces. (Courtesy of Patrick Hannon)

B. Biocompatibility of materials

1. Fretting, Metal Ion Transfer, and Biocompatibility

"The improvement of bone fixation and joint replacement hardware has been an evolutionary process involving a team approach with biomechanists, physicians, and mechanical/material engineers. Biomaterials in orthopedics or dentistry require that the implant material be very resistant to repeated stresses and metals, ceramics, and some composites meet this requirement" (Hannon, 2016). For example, improvements in joint replacement polyethylene components have also become more durable with reduced penetration by incorporating highly cross-linked polyethylene into the articulating surfaces leading to low friction durable components in moveable (i.e., diarthrodial) joints (Digas, 2005) and avoiding polyethylene debris (referred to as "poly" disease by some surgeons). The development of these hardware devices lies in complex factors and problems relating to: 1) biocompatibility 2) the use of modular components in joint replacements for an improved custom fit and 3) the failure of the bone fixation due to stress shielding of the underlying bone (Hannon, 2016).

Fretting is a process of wear, sometimes including corrosion damage at the surface asperities (roughness) of contact between two or more load bearing implant surfaces that move or slide relative to one another. The surface asperities of one surface act as an abrasive agent, wearing down the surface with which they are in contact. In joint replacements, the motion at the joint surfaces can be substantial. However, fracture fixation hardware can also result in fretting with relative micromotion between a metal plate or a long bone intramedulary rod and the bone tissue in contact with these pieces of hardware. Therefore, the quality of the surface layer can degrade with micropits and other forms of "roughness". This can lead to reduced fatigue strength with fracture of the components, as will be discussed in the next text section.

Biocompatibility is an increased concern in diarthrodial joint replacements where fretting due to sliding/rolling motion shear stresses may also potentially contribute to an increase in the migration of metal ions into human tissues as well as fatigue fracture of the implanted device over time. However, biocompatibility and the fretting process is still a concern in bone fracture/defect fixation due to the loosening of the fracture fixation implant and possible toxicity of metal fracture fixation implant components. Metal implants exhibiting a degree of biological tissue toxicity such as cobalt-chromium alloys are still used in joint replacement implants because of their resistance to these shear stresses and less fretting (Hannon, 2016). Yet, cobalt-chromium alloys have been found to be toxic to surrounding biological tissues at high levels in a small number of patients (i.e., cobalt mean of 6.0 ng/ml and chromium mean of 0.6 ng/ml) when used in a cobalt-chromium alloy femoral neck stem joined to the modular femoral head of the implant at the acetabulum (i.e., hip socket) (Cooper, et al. , 2013). Metal alloys containing nickel or aluminum, although corrosion resistant and low in mass relative to volume, have been found to be toxic and may result in inflammation of laminar bone and surrounding soft tissues. For example, an accumulation of aluminum but not titanium was found in soft tissues and newly formed bone lamella surrounding titanium plates affixed to human maxillae of the face with the use of Ti6Al4V titanium alloy bone screws (a titanium alloy with 6% aluminum and 4% vanadium) (Zaffe et al., 2004). Furthermore, the titanium alloy Ti6Al4V (a.k.a. Ti-64) is in widespread use in orthopedic joint and bone fixation plate/rod implants and is very corrosion resistant, exhibits a high tensile strength (860 MPa) in addition to exhibiting high stiffness with a Young's modulus of 114-120 GPa (Sidambe, 2014; Tanaka, et al. 2016). However, vanadium which is 4% of Ti-64 has also raised some concern in regard to its cytotoxicity and new alloys which substitute vanadium for a small percentage of iron (Ti-5Al-2.5FE) or niobium (Ti6Al-7Nb) address these concerns (Sidambe, 2014). New strong titanium alloys with metals including molybdenum and niobium have been found to be non-toxic at levels of 8.5 and 172.0 microg/L respectively, (Li, 2010). The standard that governs these assessments is ASTM F 918 (ASTM F 981).

2. Reducing stress shielding in bone

One concern of the physician is that stress shielding may take place with fracture fixation implants. Stress shielding results during fracture fixation when the inserted hardware absorbs the stresses that would normally be applied to the bone. In accord with Wolff's law, stress shielding can lead to bone atrophy (becomes thinner) through bone resorption and a concomitant significant loss in bone strength. When the hardware is removed, the bone under a plate may be significantly weaker. Coupled with the bone micro-damage involved in pulling out pins and bone screws, and leaving a "stress concentration", bone will be more susceptible to re-fracture after these surgical explant procedures. Within weeks, in most cases, the bone will remodel sufficiently to become much stronger, and re-fracture is much less likely.

Ti-64 alloy exhibits high stiffness which, due to stress shielding, can result in bone atrophy/degradation resulting in a failed implant-bone tissue interface with time. New titanium alloys which may include iron (Fe), niobium (Nb), molybdenum (Mo) or tin (Sn) act to reduce the stiffness of an orthopedic implant so as to more closely approximate the Young's Modulus of cortical bone (i.e., approximately 20 GPa). Titanium alloy implants incorporating such metals are less stiff with a Young's Modulus of 50-70 GPa and therefore more closely approximate the stiffness of the underlying cortical bone enabling the implant to better transfer the loads of daily human activity to the bone (Hannon, 2016). In accord with Wolff's law, this transfer of repeated significant loads to bone tissue results in maintaining the structural and functional integrity of both spongy and cortical (laminar) bone and therefore better maintains the implant-bone interface over the longer term extending or eliminating the need for a surgical implant revision. Other factors such as the length of the long bone inserted stem in knee and hip (TKA/THA) joint replacements (i.e., affect upon stress shielding) or using cemented v. non-cemented components in joint replacements may affect the long-term outcome in specific

patients. Biological individuality including factors such as gender, regional bone density/muscle density, age and general health can all affect the surgeon's choice of orthopedic hardware and method of fixation (Digas, 2005; Gargiulo, et al., 2013; Gargiulo, et al., 2014; Petursson, et al., 2015).

Joint replacements are increasingly being developed for new body regions and fracture fixation plating. Intramedullary rod fixation (long bones) has improved with changes in geometry and the implant material so as to reduce stress shielding. Plates and cages sometimes remain in the body over the human life span; some are removed at a later date and some implants are now biodegradable (over a predictable time period), eliminating the necessity of future removal (Park et al., 2007).

C. Resistance to fatigue and corrosion

The resistance to fatigue failure fractures and corrosion is one of many critical considerations in implant material selection. The more common orthopedic implant materials, such as commercially pure (CP) titanium, Ti-6Al-4V, and cobalt-chrome alloys have demonstrated relatively low resistances to fatigue; particularly when the surfaces are not prepared properly and/or the surface has been mechanically damaged and/or the metal's fatigue resistance has been reduced by excessive cold work (any metalworking process in which metal is shaped below its recrystallization temperature.).

Also, these materials have all shown deleterious effects to surrounding tissue due to corrosion; particularly in the case of wear particles caused by components rubbing against each other. Corrosion of these materials has also been shown to continuously change the form of the metals. Significant work has been done and is continuing in the area of corrosion and wear reduction primarily in the form of various coatings like anodization and changes of the polymetric material in modular components.

Even though significant advancements in fatigue, corrosion and wear reduction have been made, these challenges are likely to continue for the foreseeable future.

D. Fixation between the implant and bone: biomechanical considerations

Many times, fractures require only a cast to restrict movement and sometimes only a sling (e.g., common clavicle fracture). In other cases, such as fractures of spinous or transverse processes of vertebrae or some rib fractures, nothing is done and healing progresses without complication. Furthermore, research findings indicate that the small amounts of motion produced by small forces may actually aid in healing, and therefore restriction of movement is contraindicated. This is the rationale for treating fractures that do not heal with ultrasound stimulation treatment. The micro-motion produced by the ultrasound appears to induce small electrical currents in bone (bone is an example of a piezo-electric material) and therefore promote healing. Alternatively, the small motions of displaced rib fractures in adults may significantly prolong the healing of a rib or ribs (i.e., costae). Therefore, displaced rib fractures in some adult patients are treated with ORIF with inserted metal plates spanning the rib fracture site in order to minimize rib motion and promote more rapid healing and less pain.

Unstable fractures require external or internal fixation with multiple transcutaneous pins, screws, wires, plates, and rods. Good bone ends or bone fragment approximations are important for optimal healing (a satisfactory fracture reduction). A good blood supply is also very important, and this can be accomplished by preserving the soft tissue adjacent to the lesion site to ensure the continued blood supply to the outer layers of bone (two layers of periosteum). Bone screws alone may be sufficient to bring displaced bone fragments together and may be specifically designed for compact bone or for cancellous (spongy) bone. (Figures 21.2 and 21.3)

Sometimes metal plates are also attached by means of bone screws and are most critical on the side of the bone that is exposed to tension stresses as the result of bending loads but may be applied to both sides of the bone for better fixation. These plates or rods are also made from similar metal alloys. These plates can also protect the bone during torsion loads and the shear, tension, and compression stresses that result from these torsion loads, as discussed in Chapter 5. These same stresses are also applied to intramedullary devices (rods) inserted into the long bone intramedullary cavity. The hardware itself may also fail, and Kummer states that "sometimes there is a race between healing of the bone and fracture, usually by fatigue, of the device" (Kummer, 2001, p. 393). (Figure 21.4)

Hardware is also sometimes applied after an invasive surgical procedure which damages a bone. For example, the sternum may be bisected along its long axis by the cardiothoracic surgeon with a bone saw in order to expose the heart and pericardium as required for some procedures such as multi-artery bypass or some heart valve replacements. In closing reduction of the induced injury, sometimes metal plates (e.g., titanium) are fixated to the sternum body in addition to the placement of wrapped wire around the two halves of the sternum body. This procedure is said to provide increased stability of the sternum halves, less pain during recovery, and more rapid patient

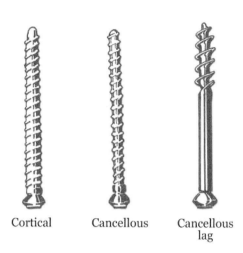

Cortical   Cancellous   Cancellous lag

Figure 21.2 Types of bone screws. Bone screws may be made from stainless steel, titanium alloy, or cobalt-chromium alloy. The thread pitch is greater in cancellous bone screws in similar fashion to "deck screws" used in carpentry. The holding capability of a bone screw is dependent upon the thread diameter times the thread length inside the bone (Kummer, 2001). Sometimes the screw holes are pre-tapped to minimize the micro-damage of screw insertion. The most important variable in screw fixation is the quality (density) of the compact (cortical) or cancellous bone. Those individuals with marked osteopena (lower bone density) are more likely to have screw loosening and inadequate fixation. Bone screwdrivers are also equipped with a force limiting mechanism (i.e., similar to a torque wrench) to prevent the stripping of bone caused by too much torque during screw insertion (Kummer, 2001). (Courtesy of Robert Perry)

healing of the sternum (a primary source of pain post-surgery in open thorax procedures).

In some cases, internal hardware is designed to stay in permanently, while in other cases the hardware may be removed later after satisfactory bone reduction, fixation, and healing has occurred. (Figure 21.4)

E. Orthopedic implant design and modularity

Engineers are confronted by many challenges when developing and testing implant devices. Some of these challenges include mechanical design, geometry of the human anatomy, material corrosion and fatigue, friction and wear, manufacturing and biocompatibility. It is not the intent of the authors to discuss in detail all of these challenges but only to suggest the complexities of bringing an implant-

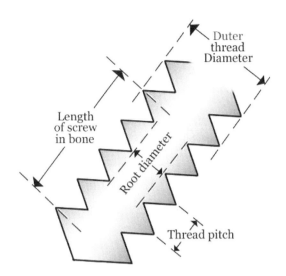

Figure 21.3 *Screw parameters. (Courtesy of Robert Perry)*

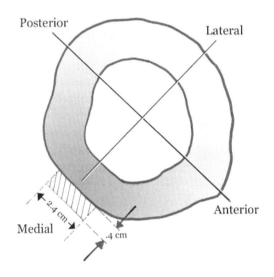

Figure 21.4 *The "area moment of inertia" or "polar moment of inertia" (closed cylinder) may be increased with fracture fixation hardware. This example illustrates how a metal plate is much more rigid (resistant to bending) in anterior-posterior bending because of the increased height (2.4 cm³) of the metal plate. (Courtesy of Robert Perry)*

able product to market.

For example, some surgeons prefer to use joint implant assembled components because they can better match the patient's anatomy and address several other factors. An example is a hip joint replacement where the surgeon would like to match the angle of the femoral neck to the femur long bone shaft of the contralateral non-surgical

side and/or correct for a discrepancy in left versus right lower extremity length. This custom fitting requires a wide range of modular components that can be assembled to provide correct alignment between the relevant bones. Additionally, a more acute angle at the implanted femoral neck-long shaft junction results in a longer moment arm for the hip abductor musculature and therefore increased ft-lbs of moment for post-operative abduction strength in the patient (Hannon, 2016).

Sometimes individual modular components will make use of different metal alloys because each alloy serves a different purpose in order to maximize bone fixation, resisting long bone re-fracture and reducing friction/adhesion characteristics of the moveable joint bearing in joint replacements. An example is when a surgeon during a total hip replacement uses a femoral shaft medullary canal stem of titanium alloy (Ti-64), a cobalt-chromium neck, and a ceramic or cobalt-chromium-molybdenum (CoCr-Mo) ball head (fitted into the hip socket) (Krishnan et al., 2013).

As stated above, one problem with joint replacements making use of metal component systems is that the junctions between components may result in significant fretting over time as discussed previously, due to the implant component micro movement with the consequent production of metal debris and metal soft tissues and/or bone. Also, galvanic corrosion is a challenge that has long been known to occur when dissimilar metals of screws, plates or rods come together in the presence of body tissue fluids (electrolytes) to form an electrical (galvanic) couple (Hannon, 2016). Many implants use dissimilar metals and the effects of mechanisms like galvanic corrosion have been well documented. It is noted that the presence of general corrosion and corrosion fatigue and their affects have also been well documented in the relevant literature (e.g., Azevedo (2002 Oct 8) Failure Analysis of Commercially…, Azevedo (2003) Environmental Effects…, Azevedo (2002 Jun 23) Failure Analysis of Surgical…)

21.4 Review of the Mechanics of Materials

A. Rigid body mechanics versus deformable solids

In rigid body mechanics objects are analyzed as if they are completely rigid. In other words, the materials do not deform or change shape when forces, moments, and torques are applied. The rigid body mechanics approach is useful in examining motion of objects. Also, additional assumptions may be made about the body or body segment, including a fixed center of mass and homogeneity of the material (Whiting and Zernicke, 1998). Reasonable approximations in the field of the mechanics of materials may make use of rigid body mechanics when addressing certain body and body segment motion. However, all materials subjected to a sufficient magnitude of force, moment, and torque are deformable. Therefore, in examining the application and failure of engineering and biological materials, we also need to explore the mechanics of deformable solids. Furthermore, the way in which materials deform under different stress magnitudes, directions, and rates of deformation will affect the consequent material strains, implant failure and injury trauma. Stresses and the strains they create are dependent upon the magnitude of the loading and upon the area over which the load is carried as well as the properties of the biological and non-biological materials involved.

B. Material properties of engineering biological materials

1. Effect of loads, stresses, and strains

When a tensile load is applied to a material (e.g., bone, metal, plastic, ceramic) the structure comprised by that material will elongate. Conversely, when a compression load is applied, the structure decreases in length. When a torsional load is applied, the material will twist. And finally, when a shear load is applied, the direction of the forces within the material will change angles with respect to the applied load within the structure. (Figure 21.5) Shear loads will produce a horizontal or vertical sliding of one layer over another as they act across a plane of an area (Whiting and Zernicke, 1998). (Figure 21.6) These changes in shape for the various loads are termed deformations and can be measured for tension and compression loads or in degrees (change in angle) for shear deformations.

When a load is imposed upon a material, it creates a stress. An axial load (compression or tension) will produce tensile or compressive stresses. Compression and tension stresses will result from a uniaxial load that is applied perpendicularly over a cross-section surface area. It is defined by σ = load/area, with stress being directly coupled to the magnitude of the load and inversely proportional to the cross-sectional area. In engineering, compressive stresses are treated as negative and tension stresses positive.

Pressure is related to compressive stress. The difference between pressure and a normal stress is that pressure describes the way in which stresses are applied in the x, y, and z directions, resulting in a change in volume (i.e., bulk

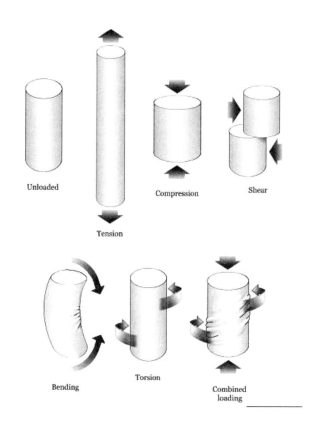

Figure 21.5 *Five basic types of loading exist: compression, tension, bending, shear, and torsion. (Courtesy of Robert Perry)*

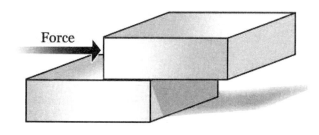

Figure 21.6 *One layer slides over an area plane. This shear load results in a shear stress (t) which is the parallel plane load over the cross section surface area. (Courtesy of Robert Perry)*

compressive stress). Furthermore, pressure has the potential to perform work (related to energy density) and is also a measure of potential energy per unit volume. Therefore, pressure differentiates from "compressive stress" in that it may be expressed in units such as joules per cubic meter (J/m^3).

Compressive stress is defined as the force per unit area and is expressed as pounds/inch^2 (psi) or Pascals

(Pa). Forces are tolerable when spread over a large area, but localized (stress raisers) force will cause compressive stress to rise dramatically and are more likely to cause material failure and/or injury. Compressive stress is increased when the load bearing area is decreased or the applied force is increased. The converse is also true. That is, by decreasing the load or increasing the area, we can reduce stress with a reduction of a tension or compression strain and a decreased probability of component failure and/or injury trauma.

A shear stress (tau: τ) is equal to the shear load $_{Tangential}$/cross-section surface area. Shear stress can also be reduced by decreasing the shear load or by increasing the cross-section surface area over which the shear load is applied. Shear stresses may also result from tension, compression, and torsion loads. Both engineered and biological structures may be subjected to shear stresses during axial loading depending on the orientation of structure relative to the applied force. When a shear stress occurs, it results in a shear strain which causes a change in angle or geometry within material structures represented by the symbol gamma (γ). The equations for normal stresses and shear stresses are presented in Figure 21.7.

Strains are deformations that occur as the result of stresses. Normal strains are the result of compression or tension stresses and may be measured in absolute terms (identical to deformations) or are more commonly presented as a percent deformation based on the original length or shape of the material and the new length or shape of the material (i.e., percent strain). The equations for normal strains and shear strains are presented in Figure 21.8.

The relationship of stresses and strains can best be appreciated by a stress/strain graph. It should be noted that the relationship between shear, tension, and compression stresses and strains is an example of a material property (Young's or elastic modulus). In the example presented below, a tension stress is applied to cortical bone. (Figure 21.9)

There are six specific points that are labeled as O, P, E, Y, U, and R. Point O is at the origin of the stress/strain diagram with both tension stress and tension strain at zero. No stress or deformation exists at this point. Point P represents the proportionality limit where tension stress and strain exhibit a linearly elastic relationship (point O to point P) (Ozkaya and Leger, 2001). A given amount of stress produces a proportional quantity of strain as evidenced by the straight line within this segment of the stress/strain curve (Hookes Law). Point E represents the elastic limit of a material, and point Y is the yield point. Point E indicates that point where the material moving

Compression and Tension Stresses (i.e., normal stresses):

Compressive or Tension Stress = Load or Force/Area

σ = F/A

These normal stresses are expressed as newtons per square meter (pascals) in Standard International or in pounds per square inch (psi) in the English System

Shear Stress:

Shear Stress = Force $_{tangential}$ /cross sectional area

τ = F_t /A

Figure 21.7 *The equations for tension/compression and shear stresses are presented.*

Positive Strain (ε) = Δ l/l
(a lengthening strain is equal to a change in length divided by the original length)

A compression stress producing a shortening. In the field of engineering, this is termed negative.

Negative Strain (ε) = Δ l/l
(a shortening strain is equal to a change in length divided by the original length)

A shear strain γ = d /h
(a shear strain results when the horizontal displacement is divided by the height as per the rectangle deforming into a parallelogram.)

Figure 21.8 *The equations for tension/compression and shear strains are presented.*

past point E and begins to enter into the plastic zone where permanent deformation takes place. Please note that reformation may still take place when the load is removed past point E, but the material will not return to its original shape (e.g., length). At point Y, the material deforms rapidly to small increases in stress, and therefore the curve flattens out with increasing amounts of strain or deformation along the horizontal axis. The yield stress (on the

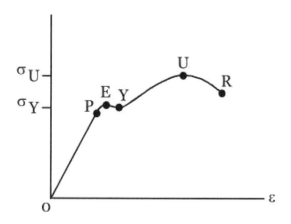

Figure 21.9 *The stress/strain graph for a cortical bone subjected to tension is represented above. In all cases the slope of the curve and the various points described are markers of tissue behavior and are important in terms of predicting tissue injury. (Courtesy of Robert Perry)*

vertical axis) and the yield strain (horizontal axis) of the graph are represented by this point. The yield point is also a representation of the yield strength of the material. Point U is the highest stress point on this stress-strain diagram and is known as the ultimate failure point, also termed the ultimate strength of the material. Ultimate stress is represented on the vertical axis and the ultimate strain is represented on the horizontal axis in our graph. The last point on the stress-strain graph is R, which represents the rupture or complete failure point. This is also termed the rupture strength of the material. For some materials such as bone, points U and R typically occur at the same point and at the same time. Other materials, such as peripheral nerve, represent a point U much before point R is reached on the strain axis. Points P, E, Y, U, and R are usually read off of the vertical (ordinate) scale.

2. Ductile versus rigid materials

Another value derived from stress/strain curves is an assessment of ductility versus rigidity. In terms of normal stresses and strains, this is known as the elastic or Young's modulus and may be specified as either the tension modulus or the compression modulus. The modulus is a ratio and typically E is used to represent the elastic modulus. That is, $E = \sigma / \varepsilon$, or stress divided by strain. This ratio describes the portion of the line on a stress/strain curve that is within the elastic region. When the elastic modulus is measured (up to point P on our stress/strain curve), it exhibits Hookian or linearly elastic behavior. Here, equal amounts of stress produce proportional amounts of strain. If the curve is steep, the engineering or biological material

(e.g., steel, dense bone) is described as having very low ductility. If the curve is shallow, an engineering or biological material (e.g., ductile iron, peripheral nerve) is referred as having high ductility. Engineering and biological materials fall along a continuum between stiff and ductile. Past point P, we enter into a stress/strain behavior and curve that is nonlinear in nature. When we reach point E, we establish the end of the elastic region. If the load is then removed at point E, the material will return to its original shape or length. However, as previously discussed, when the stress takes the engineering or biological material past point E, it will not return to its original length or shape. As a comparison, it is noted that a biological material at its yield point will experience a comparatively large deformation with a relatively small increase in stress. This is the opposite of the engineered materials that are typically used for implantation products. This difference in elasticity is one of the great engineering challenges in the development of advanced, implantable engineered materials for orthopedic implants.

The shear modulus or (G) is shear stress divided by shear strain ($G = \tau / \gamma$). It is also known as the modulus of rigidity. If a small shear stress produces a large shear strain within the elastic zone, the material would be categorized as very ductile (a low shear modulus; G). On the other hand, if a large shear stress is required to produce a relatively small shear strain, the material would be referred to as being rigid (a high shear modulus, G).

3. Viscoelastic material properties

Viscoelasticity is due to the fact that biological and some engineered materials have both fluid and solid material properties. Elastic solids will deform in response to a stress and then will re-form after the stress is removed if they remain within their elastic zones. Potential energy is stored during deformation and is released as kinetic energy during reformation. The rate at which the stress is applied will not affect the response of the solid elastic material. Spring steel or the metal alloys (memory metals) that make up some crush-resistant eyeglass frames exhibit this property.

A fluid will also deform and has the additional property of being able to flow. Viscosity is a fluid property which really examines the resistance to this flow. Viscoelastic materials have both fluid (viscous) and solid (elastic) mechanical properties. Animal biological materials as well as polymer plastics and metals at high temperatures exhibit viscoelastic (rate-dependent) behavior (Ozkaya and Leger, 2001). Within the elastic zone, when biological materials re-form, there is some variable loss in energy and the reformation curve does not match the original deformation curve. The area between the deformation and the reformation curves on the stress/strain graph is known as the "area of hysteresis" and represents the loss of energy of the viscoelastic material during the loading cycle. (Figure 21.10) Sometimes the material is taken past its elastic zone when loaded rapidly and may be taken to the point of rupture at which point the potential energy is released as kinetic energy. Because most biological materials will become stronger (variable in biological materials) and will store more potential energy when they are loaded quickly, the rupture point will release a larger amount of kinetic energy. (Figure 21.11) For example, in bones the fracture pattern may become very explosive, with fragments moving into soft tissues that surround bones. Gunshot projectile wounds to bones may produce extremely explosive, comminuted fractures due to a very high loading rate.

4. Creep and stress relaxation

Viscoelastic engineered and biological materials also

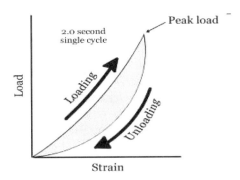

Figure 21.10 *The area of hysteresis is illustrated during loading and unloading of a material in tension over 2.0 seconds. (Courtesy of Robert Perry)*

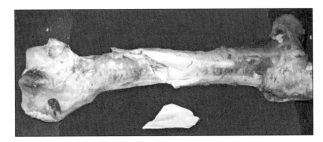

Figure 21.11 *The loading that occurs over a very short time will produce an explosive fracture, as indicated in this highly comminuted Elk femur subjected to very rapid loading. The femur is able to store more energy when loaded rapidly, and when brought to failure the energy release is enormous. (Courtesy of Patrick Hannon and Kerry Knapp)*

exhibit creep and stress relaxation. These two properties may affect biological tissue behavior. For examples, creep occurs when an orthodontist applies braces to a patient. Teeth will move due to creep deformation within bone and connective tissues within the maxilla and mandible that hold the teeth. This is followed by tissue remodeling of bone and connective tissue. An example of creep-based deformation in an engineered material is bending that occurs in a steel beam that is subjected to a load for a long time. The bending (deformation) of the beam depends on the time of loading, with additional deformation (creep) occurring with additional time. Biological materials subjected to a constant stress will usually exhibit the most amount of deformation and strain early on, with lesser deformation/strain occurring as time progresses. This is also true of most engineered materials (e.g. guitar strings, polymers). Note that as shown in Figure 21.12, if stress is increased, more creep (within rupture limits) will take place in biological and many engineered materials. Also note that an important characteristic of creep in metals is that creep can take place at stresses below the material yield strength.

5. Ductile versus brittle material properties

Brittleness is the material property related to the area of the plastic zone of the stress/strain curve. Materials that are relatively ductile have a large plastic zone and therefore may undergo a large amount of permanent deformation before they reach the point of rupture. Other materials, such as most ceramic materials, have a relatively small plastic zone and will break soon after reaching their yield point and are therefore termed brittle. The yield point (Y) and rupture point (R) are very close together in brittle materials. Note, however, that these properties are separate from material strength properties. Both ductile and brittle materials may be strong or weak under tension, compression, or shear stresses. Biological materials such as dense bone and many engineered materials (e.g., glass) are relatively brittle and are only able to endure relatively low levels of strain before rupture occurs. Other materials such as peripheral nerve and many engineered materials (e.g., many metals) are relatively ductile and in the laboratory setting can sustain significant deformation before complete rupture. Ductile materials such as peripheral nerve may exhibit some necking, albeit not to the extent of ductile metals. (Figure 21.13)

6. Toughness and resilience

Toughness is a measure of the total area within the elastic and plastic zones on a stress/strain test. If a ma-

Figure 21.12 *Creep deformation occurs within the thigh hamstring and spine musculature as the time of the stretching is increased over a thirty second period. This results in a greater joint range of motion at the iliofemoral (hip) joints and the thoraco-lumbar spine in this man. (Courtesy of Patrick Hannon)*

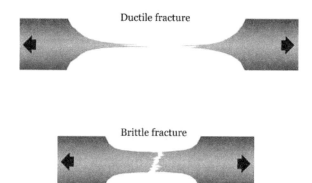

Figure 21.13 *A ductile metal rod experiences "necking" when subjected to a tension stress. This deformation point may lead to a steep drop in the engineering tension stress. Note that the physicist will point out that the "true stress" is actually still increasing as greater tension strain takes place. The necking is simply reducing the cross-sectional area of the metal rod, which results in a structural defect (Watts, 2003). (Courtesy of Robert Perry)*

terial (e.g., metal) is able to undergo a large amount of deformation and absorb a large amount of energy (equal to the area under the stress/strain curve), it has high toughness. This is obviously important in terms of materials used in motor vehicles that, when struck, will absorb large amounts of kinetic energy and therefore not transfer this energy to the occupants of the vehicle. Some degree of toughness is exhibited in biological tissues; however, the high loads and consequent permanent deformations of human tissues is not considered to be desirable. Significant elastic and/or plastic deformation in biological materials can result in significant tissue injury damage.

Material resilience is measured by the modulus of resilience and is related to the area under the elastic zone of the stress/strain graph. For example, a ligament structure or an engineered spring that is exposed to a rapidly applied tension load and still manages to stay within its elastic zone exhibits the property of resilience. This is generally a desirable result of loading. Biological and engineered materials fall along a continuum in this regard. However, many non-biological materials exhibit considerably more resilience than do biological tissues.

21.5 Failure Analysis and Prevention

Failure analysis can be defined as the process of collecting and analyzing data to resolve the root cause of failure and how to prevent it from recurring. Failure analysis is also a vital discipline that is used in the development of new products and improvement of products which have already entered the market. Failure analysis is especially important in manufacturing and field use of medical prod-

ucts and can be applied to both products and processes.

Failure analysis may be conducted at the design stage, prototype stage and at the field use stage of a product life cycle. Failure analysis and prevention involves the understanding of how structures (e.g., hip implant components) must be designed, the properties of materials, how materials and structures fail, and the forces and energies involved in the failure mechanisms. The fundamentals and principles of failure analysis relate to the chemistry, physics, engineering and design of the failed structure. In order to understand how and why a structure fails, it is necessary to understand the underlying design principles.

These concepts are not mutually exclusive. Potential failure modes must be understood in order to provide a sound design. Likewise, a proper predictive failure analysis must be understood and applied to the underlying design. Examinations, measurements and testing of the failed and new exemplar component are necessary in order to provide foundation for the understanding of the underlying principles related to the design and the failure modes.

An appropriate protocol should be followed during the analysis and testing of the failed component. The process should include a series of activities depending upon the context and conditions of the failure. Therefore, photographic and textural documentation of all failed components including mechanical damage, wear, fracture and related physical, chemical and structural conditions must be made, if possible, for the failed components. Also, similar technical information must be obtained from the manufacturer of the failed component. Scientific and engineering analyses of the failure mechanisms must be based upon accepted and verifiable testing methods.

In failure analysis, evaluation of the forces and energies involved in the failure mechanisms and their relationship to the physical evidence and reconstruction should be conducted. Comparisons to other improved structural designs and materials generally, but not always, should be made in order to determine alternative design or structures available which would have most probably avoided failure. Case Study 21.2 presents an analysis of the relevant factors that were present leading up to a knee implant failure.

The available technology (e.g., Scanning Electron Microscopes (SEM), Energy Dispersive X-ray Spectrograph (EDX), etc.) should be relied upon in addition to relevant technical reference and discovery documents, including testing and design materials available to evaluate the failed structure and for alternative comparisons. Often component and/or total system testing is used to ascertain the properties and performance of the components and alternative designs. Also, in the case where an alternative design has been proposed, a cost-benefit and risk-benefit analyses for the alternative structures is often desirable. Additionally, the expert should apply all applicable codes and standards.

Reliance on the relevant codes and standards must also stand the test of applicability and provide reliable procedures and scientifically valid results relative to the particular product behavior being evaluated. In some cases, the standards do not service the needs of the product and its reasonably foreseeable harmful conditions, and such standards should be challenged and criticized rather than blindly followed. This occurs often and is one of the challenges often encountered during technical investigations; primarily by plaintiffs' counsel and experts.

Case Study 21.2 - Knee Implant Failure

Accident: The plaintiff in this matter indicated that she was a front seat passenger in a pickup truck with her feet propped up on the dash. She was asleep and her seatback was slightly reclined at the time of a minor rear end collision and she did not hear the collision but the "jar" she felt woke her up. The Delta velocity determined by the accident reconstructionist was determined to be a maximum of 2.0 mph of forward vehicle movement. The drivers of both vehicles pulled

off to the side of the road and exchanged insurance information. As the plaintiff was stepping out of the passenger side of the pickup truck with her left hand still holding on to her door, she indicated that her knee "gave way". The plaintiff further indicated that when she put her right foot on the running board, her left foot stepped onto the ground and she started to collapse. A fall was avoided because she was holding onto the door handle with her left hand. She further indicated that she continued to stumble three times and then finally got her legs to where they would hold her up.

Evaluation and anatomical structures involved. The plaintiff's left knee had undergone a total knee replacement (TKR) nine years previous to this minor rear collision. In the ensuing years since her left TKR, the plaintiff had remained very active. However, examination of her left knee after the accident indicated collateral ligament laxity in valgus and varus. Follow-up standard X-ray imaging indicated wear mechanisms of the TKR components. The films revealed an "obvious varus malalignment" (a.k.a. misalignment) of the tibial component secondary to subsidence with a possible proximal medial tibia fracture. One orthopedic physician indicated "poly" disease within her left knee (fretting of her polyethylene tibial component). The plaintiff underwent a revision TKR some two years after the motor vehicle accident. The surgeon indicated that the major reason for the revision was the subsidence and malalignment of the tibial plateau component within the posteriomedial joint compartment which led to the general collateral and capsular ligament laxity of her left knee. Her active lifestyle combined with her body mass index (BMI) approaching 30.0 most probably strongly contributed to the "bone collapse-caving in" (subsidence) of the tibial component of her left total knee replacement (a.k.a. total knee arthroplasty).

Furthermore, the rearend collision to the pickup truck was in the wrong direction and of insignificant magnitude so as to produce any meaningful loading to either of the plaintiff's knees regardless of her report of her feet being propped up on the truck dashboard while she was sleeping. After the collision event, the step from the truck's running board to the ground below would have been similar to simply descending a staircase. Finally, some of her physical activities prior to the collision event that she discussed during her deposition testimony were calculated to have produced an estimated 7.6 times her body weight in joint reaction forces within the knee (tibiofemoral joint) much above taking one step down from the pickup truck. Therefore, a biomechanics injury causation analysis (ICA) indicated a mismatch between the rearend motor vehicle collision or stepping out of the vehicle and the plaintiff's left knee pathology. (Courtesy of Patrick Hannon)

21.6 Materials Failure Analysis and Testing Techniques and Tools

This chapter provides the reader with an overview of the tools and techniques generally used by failure analysts to determine the root cause(s) of product failures. The primary tools are the optical microscope (OM), scanning electron microscope (SEM), energy dispersive x-ray spectrograph (EDX), spark optical emission spectrograph (or spark OES), microhardness indentation tester and the various actions employed in and referred to as metallographic techniques. Each of these tools and techniques is discussed below. It should be noted that an investigator is not limited to the use of only these tools and techniques as many others are available to the material characterization analyst. For additional information on materials characterization tools and techniques, the reader is referred to the relevant references provided at the end of this paper (e.g., ASM Metals Handbook, Vol. 10).

A. Metallographic techniques - optical metallography

The primary advantage of optical microscopy is that images of the "as found" sample surface topography and other features can be very quickly and easily obtained using low cost equipment (optical microscopy with appropriate lighting and image capture capability). No pre-cleaning or other preparation is generally needed to obtain initial information.

Optical microscopy can also be used to evaluate the microstructure and determine grain and phase structure size in metallic samples that have been ground, polished and etched. Also, optical microscopy is used to evaluate heat treatments, the integrity of welds and to determine the effect(s) of processing on microstructure. Image analysis is greatly facilitated by the many references that provide micrographs/fractographs of sample surfaces that are identical to or very similar to (composition, process-

ing, etc.) the sample being analyzed. It is noted that automated image analysis devices or analyzers are available for image analysis in some applications (grain size, shape, boundary area, etc.). For most analyses, the samples must be sectioned, ground, polished and etched before the desired information can be obtained using these methods.

The primary limitation of optical microscopy is that the images are very limited in depth of field and relatively limited in magnification. Also, resolution is limited to approximately 1 μm (approximately 0.0000394 inch or ~1/50th of the diameter of a human hair). It is noted that it has been the authors' experience that the fatigue striations typically found on the fracture surfaces of failed orthopedic implants are generally identifiable using optical metallography but definitive discovery requires the examination by an scanning electron microscope (SEM), as discussed in the following section.

B. Scanning electron microscopy (SEM)

The SEM is a primary analytical tool for discovery in pure science, chemistry, material science, quality control and failure analysis. Modified SEMs have found wide application in the microelectronics industry for defect detection, surface imaging and quality control duties.

The primary strength of the scanning electron microscope (SEM) is the ability to create very high-resolution, high-magnification, high depth of field images of sample surfaces; images referred to as electron-micrographs, or simply micrographs. Magnifications of 1,000,000X are possible, although magnifications on the order of 10X to 5,000X are generally sufficient for sample surface and fracture surface analysis. Note that the maximum optical microscope magnification is approximately 1,000X under ideal conditions. Also, if magnification greater than approximately 100,000X are required, a transmission electron microscope (TEM) or scanning transmission electron microscope (STEM) can be used more effectively than an SEM.

The SEM can be used to image features as small as 3 to 100 nm (1 nanometer = 1x10[-9] meter =0.000000001 meter = 0.0000000394 inch). If the SEM is equipped with a backscattered electron detector, it can be used to image grain boundaries and second phases on unetched samples, and evaluation of crystallographic orientations. The SEM can be used to evaluate any solid or liquid sample material as long as the material vapor pressure is greater than approximately 10[-3] torr. In order to image low conductivity materials, it is often necessary to coat samples with a very thin layer of a conducting material such as gold or carbon. The thin layer of gold or carbon is sputtered (i.e., A technique for applying a molecular layer of atoms to a surface.) onto the relevant surface within a vacuum chamber. Also, the samples must be relatively clean and free from high vapor pressure liquids (e.g., oils, organics cleaning solutions, etc.).

One limitation of the typical SEM is that the samples must be placed in a relatively small vacuum chamber for analysis. The maximum sample size is on the order of two inches in the dimension that is perpendicular to the surface to be analyzed and four to six inches in any other dimension. Also, accommodating certain sample shapes can be challenging. SEMs with larger chambers are available, but the chamber sizes will not accept very large samples and the machines are not presently as readily available to the independent investigator. SEMs which operate at atmospheric (1 atmosphere or 14.70 psi) pressure have also been developed (i.e., environmental SEM). Note that the SEM's imaging capability of very flat, smooth samples (e.g., polished and etched metallographic sample surfaces) is often inferior to those obtainable using an optical microscopy. This is particularly true at magnifications lower than approximately 200X to 300X.

C. Energy dispersive x-ray spectrometry (EDS)

SEMs often include the capability to conduct qualitative (or semi-quantitative) compositional analysis or chemical composition of sample material. The EDS capability is created by adding the hardware necessary to analyze the x-rays emitted by samples when bombarded by an electron beam. Because different elements emit different x-ray energies, the hardware and software can determine which elements are present and semi-quantitatively determine the relative quantity of each element.

An advantage of SEM-EDS is that the required scan times are relatively short. However, the primary limitation of SEM-EDS is that the technique will not generally identify trace elements. Also, if the elements included in the sample have x-ray energies that overlap, the presence of one or more elements may not be apparent in the output spectra due to energy peak overlap(s). In short, the accuracy and repeatability of EDS is acceptable only for "first pass" elemental analysis in cases where more accuracy is not necessary. In these cases, the analyst is often only interested in determining if unexpected, relatively large quantities of elements (with significantly different x-ray energies) are present. For example, to determine if melted copper is present on the surface of steel that had been exposed to fire and electrical activity (i.e., arcing). EDS can also be used to identify relatively high levels of contaminates, if present. Note that EDS is also capable of accurately revealing an alloy composition where the output can be compared to the output from known alloy samples.

D. Electron probe x-ray microanalysis - wavelength dispersive x-ray spectrometry (WDS)

In the case where reliable quantitative (trace) elemental composition data is required, electron probe X-ray microanalysis (EPMA or microprobe) which includes multiple Wavelength dispersive X-ray spectrometry (WDS) detectors is used. The primary disadvantages of WDS relative to EDS is that the scan times are much longer and the equipment is significantly more expensive. The advantages of WDS include its ability to differentiate sulfur in the presence of lead or molybdenum, tungsten or tantalum in silicon or nickel in titanium due to its superior peak resolving capability. Also, WDS can detect much lower concentration species (10-100 ppm) such as phosphorus or sulfur in metals, contaminants in metal catalysts, trace heavy metal contamination and performance-degrading impurities in high temperature alloys. WDS is also capable of detecting low atomic number elements in such investigations as the search for unacceptable contaminates/impurities in biomedical materials. WDS also has much better performance in detecting lighter elements such as boron, nitrogen, beryllium, oxygen and fluorine. This is important because such impurities may result in degradation of material strength and/or fatigue resistance in the orthopedic implant materials.

E. Arc spark optical emission spectroscopy (spark OES)

Spark OES is generally used to identify the elements contained within a metal alloy sample, part of which has been vaporized using an electrical arc/spark. The advantage of spark OES is that the results are reliable, repeatable and quick to obtain.

F. Hardness testing

1. Rockwell hardness

Rockwell hardness is used to determine the hardness of metal parts by applying a load to materials through either a tungsten-carbide ball or a diamond spheroconical indenter. The material surface and the seating surface must be properly prepared before testing.

Following appropriate surface preparation, a relatively light load is applied to the indenter placed on the material to be tested (usually 3 kg [~29.4 N] or 5 kg [~49 N]) in order to "zero" the testing machine. A heavy load (from 15 kg [~147 Newtons (N)] to 150 kg [~1,471 N]) is then applied, depending on the material and its strength, and held for a time. The downward travel distance after the application of the light load until the release of the heavy load is then recorded and used to calculate hardness.

Various Rockwell hardness test procedures can be followed depending upon the material and strength of the specimen. The common Rockwell variants include:

a. HRC – "Rockwell C" A 150 kg [~1,471 N] load is applied through a diamond indenter. This technique is most commonly used on steels that are through hardened to increase strength. Components that are typically tested with this method include fasteners, tooling, springs, axles, and bearings.

b. HR15N – "Rockwell 15N" A 15 kg [~147 N] load is applied to case hardened components treated to achieve a minimum effective case depth of 0.007 inches or a total case thickness of 0.012 inches. Other Rockwell based techniques (e.g., HR30N and HR45N) apply higher loads for incrementally higher minimum effective or total case thicknesses.

c. HRBW – "Rockwell B" This technique uses a tungsten carbide ball. It is commonly used for relatively ductile materials like austenitic stainless steels and annealed materials.

Rockwell hardness testing is administered by ASTM E-18 Standard Test Methods for Rockwell Hardness and Rockwell Superficial Hardness of Metallic Materials (ASTM E-18).

2. Brinell hardness

Relatively high loads are applied to parts via a tungsten carbide ball. Brinell tests measure the diameter of the indentation made by the ball. A 10mm ball with an applied load of 3,000 kg [~29,420 N] is common for Brinell testing. Brinell tests are ideal for castings and forgings that may have rough surfaces or exhibit some chemical variation. The hardness values derived from Brinell hardness testing provide a more representative average hardness of a component.

Brinell hardness testing is administered by ASTM E 10 Standard Test Method for Brinell Hardness of Metallic Materials (ASTM E 10).

3. Microhardness testing

Microhardness tests apply considerably lighter loads compared to other methods. Precisely cut diamonds are used for these tests. The small diamond indenter is used to measure hardness in small, localized regions of components. The diamond indenter creates an diamond shaped indentation in the sample. A microscope with a calibrated

scale provides measurement of the indentation which is translated into hardness numbers. Microhardness tests are generally applied to determine the case thickness on case-hardened components. There are types of microhardness testing that use different shaped diamond indenters referred to as Vickers and Knoop.

The standard for microhardness testing is ASTM E 384 Standard Test Method for Microindentation Hardness of Materials (ASTM E 384).

21.7 Fractography

Fractography is the term used to describe the process of evaluating fracture surface topography. The macro and micro evaluation of fracture surface topography using optical and electron imaging techniques allows the analyst to determine the causes and/or basic mechanisms of fracture of the failed component(s).

Fractography is primarily aimed at determination of the prevailing fracture mode. There are three fracture modes that are typically focused on during the analysis fracture surfaces. They are: 1) dimple rupture, 2) fatigue and 3) cleavage.

A. Dimple rupture fracture

Dimple rupture describes the morphology that predominates a fracture surface that was created during the ductile overload of a material. The surface features associated with an overload failure are typically referred to as ductile dimples. The dimples are created by the process known as microvoid coalescence. When an excessive load is applied to the material, microvoids begin to develop within the material in areas of localized strain discontinuities such as second phase particles, grain boundaries, inclusions and dislocations. As the strain increases, the microvoids grow and begin to coalesce and eventually form a fracture surface. This process is represented graphically in Figure 21.14 (adapted from ASM Metals Handbook, Vol. 12). The surface features are often described as cuplike, as exhibited by the dimples shown in Figures 21.15a and 21.15b.

It is noteworthy that the shape of the dimples can provide the analyst with information regarding to loading conditions to which the material was subjected. The three typical conditions are uniaxial tensile loading, shear loading and tensile tearing. The elongated dimples that result from shear and tensile tearing are shown graphically in Figure 21.14. Figures 21.15a and 21.15b shows examples of ductile dimples with different topography and at different magnifications.

These examples represent dimple shapes that are consistent with the stated strain conditions. In reality, combinations of the listed strain conditions can result in dimple formations and shapes that can be difficult to properly interpret.

B. Fatigue fracture

Fatigue is a process of progressive cyclic damage as a part is loaded repetitively at stress levels below the yield strength of the material. The fatigue process can be divided into three distinct stages: crack initiation, stable progressive crack propagation, and fast final fracture (Das, 1996).

The first stage, crack initiation, typically begins at the

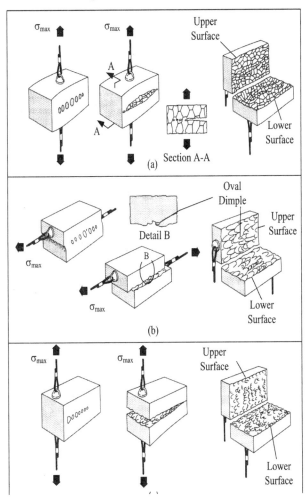

Figure 21.14 Process of Microvoid Development and Coalescence in Material Subjected to Maximum Stress (σmax). (a) Equiaxed dimples formed by material under uniaxial tensile strain. (b) Elongated dimples formed by material subjected to shear strain. (c) Elongated dimples formed by material subjected to tensile tearing. (Adapted from ASM Metals Handbook, Vol. 12)

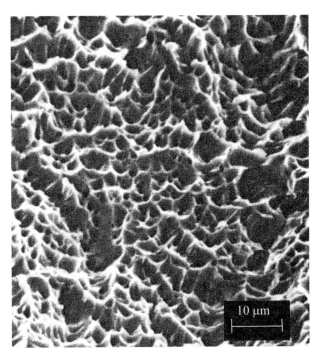

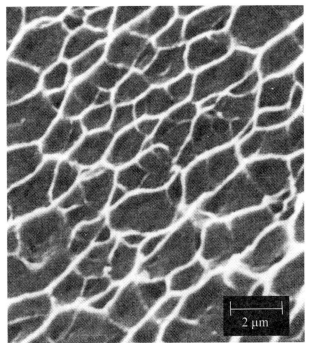

Figure 21.15 Examples of Ductile Dimple Patterned Fracture Surface (a) Deep dimples. (b) Shallow dimples.

location of a stress concentrator. Stress concentrators are inhomogeneities in the material or in its macroscopic geometry, such as second phase particles, voids, inclusions, notches, machining marks, surface damage or other surface flaws. It is important to note that fatigue crack initiation is often the life-limiting failure mechanism in the failure process. Discontinuities (e.g., machining marks, surface scratches, gouges or notches) created during the manufacture, installation or service can result in fatigue crack initiation under circumstances where an unflawed component would have had a satisfactory fatigue life (ASM Metals Handbook, Vol. 11).

In the second stage, stable progressive crack propagation, the crack advances a small distance every loading cycle, or several loading cycles, which enables the crack to advance. After one or more loading cycles, the crack advances a small distance and then arrests; this process leaves behind the characteristic markings on the fracture surface called fatigue striations (also referred to as crack arrest marks). After this process has been repeated many times, a fracture surface with numerous parallel lines is created.

In the final stage of the fatigue process, the cross-section of the component that remains intact (i.e., not yet cracked) has been reduced to such a small area that the final load applied to the part is sufficient for a complete fast overload or cleavage fracture. This final area of the fracture surface will exhibit the features seen in monotonic, overload failures, such as tears and dimples in ductile materials.

Information about the type of loading an orthopedic implant was subjected to can also be determined by inspecting the fracture surface. (Figure 21. 16) (ASM Metals Handbook, Vol. 11, Fractography…). It shows graphically that the lower the nominal stress that an implant component is subjected to, the smaller the fast fracture area will be and the larger the area covered with fatigue markings. If it can be established that the nominal stress upon the component was very low; the fast fracture area will be very small and the area that is covered with fatigue striations will comprise almost the entire fracture surface. Figure 21.17 shows an example of the surface features that are consistent with fatigue failure. The fatigue failure mode, its stages and its analysis are discussed in Case Study 21.3.

In addition to information about the loading conditions, counting striations may allow an estimate of the time to fracture failure. (DeVries, 2010).

C. Cleavage fracture

Cleavage is a low-energy fracture that propagates along cleavage planes that are comprised of low-index crystallographic planes. Cleavage fractures have generally smooth surfaces at very high magnification. Cleavage fracture surfaces exhibit distinct topography such as river patterns, tongues, cleavage steps, chevron (herringbone) patterns, feather marks, and other features at lower mag-

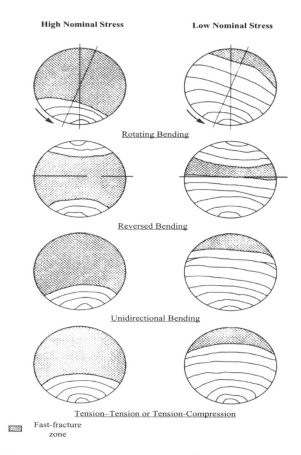

Figure 21.16 *Fatigue Fracture Surface Feature Patterns Under Different Loading Conditions (Adapted from ASM Handbook Vol. 11).*

nifications, as shown in Figure 21.18. Brittle cleavage would be expected to produce a fairly smooth and planar fracture surface at the bulk material level.

It has been the experience of the authors that investigations of hip, knee and spinal support metal implant failures are the result of surface damage created during manufacture, handling and/or implantation. The surface defects are the localized stress raisers and crack initiation locations. The crack(s) that develop eventually lead to fatigue crack propagation followed by fast fracture in the dimple rupture mode (or possibly cleavage) and final fracture of the implanted device.

Case Study 21.3 - Harrington Road Failure

Accident. The patient had had two titanium spinal support rods implanted in November 2005. In April of 2007, approximately 18 months after the initial surgery, the patient was involved in a vehicle accident in which the vehicle he was driving was broadsided on the right (passenger) side by another vehicle. The patient's vehicle

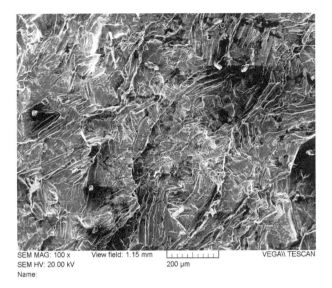

Figure 21.17 *Example of Fatigue Fracture Surface Patterns on CP Titanium at Mag. = 1,000X.*

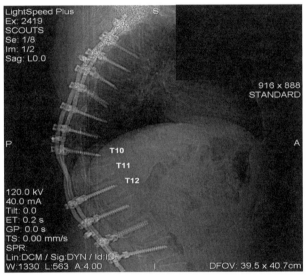

Figure 21.18 *Example of Cleavage Fracture Surface Patterns. (Adapted from ASM Metals Handbook, Vol. 12)*

also sideswiped a third vehicle before finally colliding with a telephone/light pole and reaching the point of rest.

Investigation: The patient's post-accident medical treatment was completed in April of 2007. The patient sought no further medical treatments with regard to his back until November of 2008, approximately 19 months after the accident. Radiographic imaging at that time revealed that the spinal support rods were fractured. The rods were explanted in February of 2009.

After the hardware including the spinal sup-

port rods were explanted, our investigation was conducted to determine when the rods failed and what failure mechanism was involved in order to investigate liability for the failure of the rods. Significant documentation was provided for review and analysis.

Figure 21.19 contains a radiograph of the rods after implantation (in November 2005) showing the positioning and condition of the supporting hardware. Examination of Figure 21.19 revealed that the spinal support rods and associated hardware were intact and that the attachment hardware was placed between the rods and all vertebrae adjacent to the rod except at the T11 vertebra. Therefore, the distance between the T10 and T12 hardware attachment points was more than double that of any other hardware separation distance along the length of the two rods. A rule of mechanics states that the greater the distance between fixed supports, the greater the magnitude of stress and strain (bending deflection) a spinal support rod will experience between the rod support attachments.

The location where the spinal support rods fractured in relation to the spine and attached hardware is shown in Figures 21.20 and 21.21, which are radiographs created in November of 2008. It can be seen that the rod fractures are located where the large gap existed between the fixation hardware as described.

Interestingly, during the investigation it was

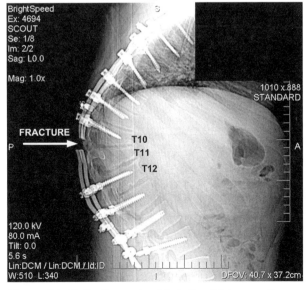

Figure 21.19 *Radiograph of Relative Distances Between the Rod Attachment Hardware. (November 2005)*

discovered that radiographs of the spinal support hardware created in October of 2006, six months before the vehicle accident, showed clearly that the right spinal support rod was fractured, as shown in Figures 21.22 and 21.23. The misalignment between the two fracture surfaces proved that one spinal support rod had fractured at some point before October 2006. Figures 21.24 and 21.25 show lateral views of the spinal support rods. The figures clearly show that one rod was fractured and the other rod had a surface notch which would have been the expected fracture initiation site, which would lead to the fracture of the second (left) rod. The fracture location and notch location were consistent with the fracture locations revealed by the November 2008 radiographs shown in Figures 21.20 and 21.21.

Failure Analysis. The explanted spinal support rods as they were received were labeled "A" and "B" and are shown in Figures 21.26 and. 21.27 respectively. Close views of the fracture areas for rods "A" and "B" are shown in Figures 21.28 and 21.29 respectively.

It was readily observed that the surface of each rod had been shot peened. Shot peening is generally performed to introduce compressive stresses into the surface of the rods which aids in the prevention of crack formation. This is typically done to parts where fatigue failure is a primary design concern, as was the case for these titanium rods (Dick, et al., 2001).

Multiple notches in the rod surfaces were observed along the length of each rod. The notches had been created by the attachment hardware fasteners and the tools used by the surgeon to bend the rods to the desired shape. Notches in the surface of the rods served as stress concentrators and crack initiation sites. Not surprisingly, notches were observed at the fracture locations. Figures 21.30 and 21.31 show some of the notches in the surface of rod "B".

The rods were initially straight. The surgeon had used special tools (e.g., French rod-bender) to bend the rods to the desired shape. The tools specified in rod manufacturer's documentation make notches on the rods consistent with those

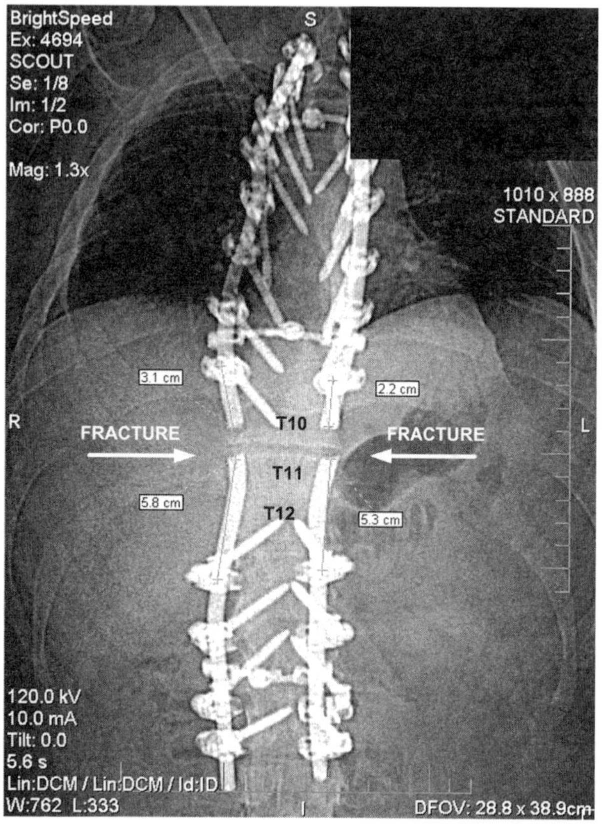

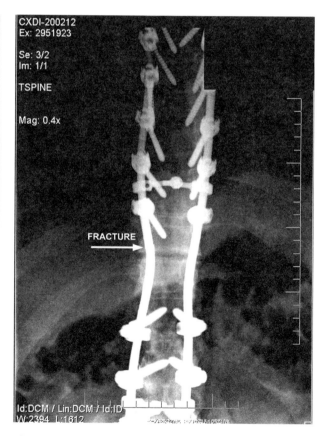

Figure 21.20 Radiograph of Fractured Rods, Rod Attachment Hardware and Spine. (November 2008)

Figure 21.21 Radiograph of Fractured Rods, Rod Attachment Hardware and Spine. (November 2008)

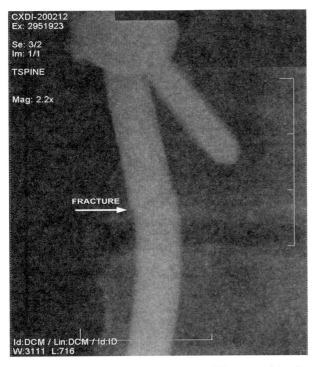

Figure 21.22 *Anteroposterior View of Fractured Rod. (October 2006)*

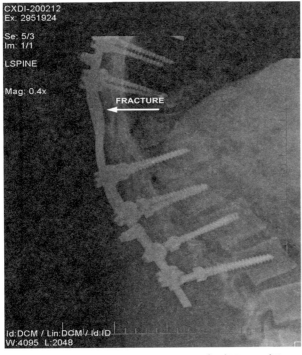

Figure 21.23 *Anteroposterior Magnified View of Fractured Rod. (October 2006)*

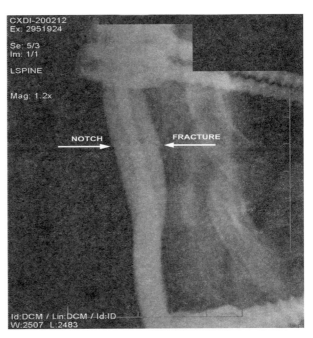

Figure 21.24 *Lateral View of Fractured Rod. (October 2006)*

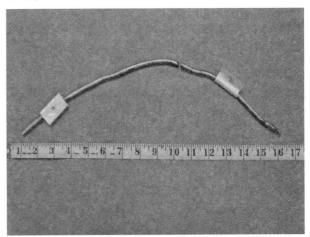

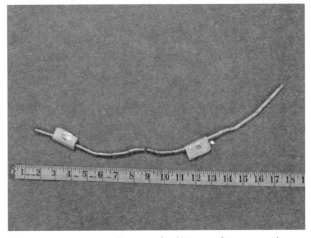

Figure 21.25 *Lateral Magnified View of Fractured Rod.(October 2006)*

Figure 21.26 *Explanted Rod "A."*

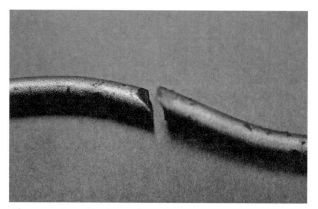

Figure 21.27 *Explanted Rod "B."*

Figure 21.28 *Close View of Fracture Area Rod "A."*

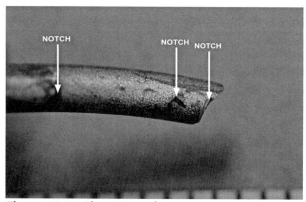

Figure 21.29 *Close View of Fracture Area Rod "B."*

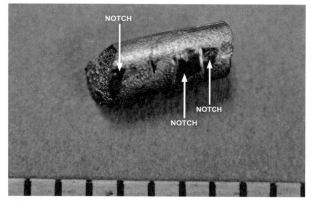

Figure 21.30 *Rod "B" Surface Notches.*

observed. Strain hardening of the rods occurred when they were bent. Strain hardening describes the increase in material strength induced, deliberately or accidentally, that occurs when a metal is subjected to plastic deformation. Strain hardening is detrimental in this case because it reduces ductility and increases brittleness. The amount of work hardening would increase with the degree of bending as well as the number of times a location was repeatedly bent/straightened during the procedure. In this case, the surgeon's description of the procedure revealed that the rods were bent multiple times and to the maximum amount (minimum radius) by the surgeon to achieve his desired orthopedic outcome.

The spinal support rods had multiple locations where surface damage was generated from contact with supporting hardware and the tools used to shape the rods. However, when the deep notches were cut into the surface by hardware and surgical tools, the protection that shot peening afforded was negated and sites that were susceptible to accelerated crack initiation were created.

The spinal support rod fracture surfaces were examined using scanning electron microscopy (SEM) and energy dispersive x-ray spectroscopy (EDX). Figure 21.32 shows an electron-micrograph of the fracture surface of rod "A" at 12 X magnification. The surface was examined using higher magnification at several locations. It was determined that the great majority of the surface was covered with fatigue striations as shown in Figures 21.33 to 21.36. Ductile dimples could also be seen in a small portion of the final fracture surface near the fracture surface edge, as shown in Figure 21.37.

Figure 21.38 provides a summary of the features found on the fracture surface of rod "A". The area annotated as "A" was a notch created by contact with a tool (likely a French rod-bender). The physical evidence indicates this was the origin of the fatigue crack. The area annotated as "B" is fatigue. Fatigue striations can be seen clearly when viewed at magnifications of 200 X or higher. As fatigue occurred, the crack slowly progressed across area "B" over time as it advanced from the origin, area "A", to the final fracture area, annotated as area "C". At the final fracture area, ductile dimples can be seen

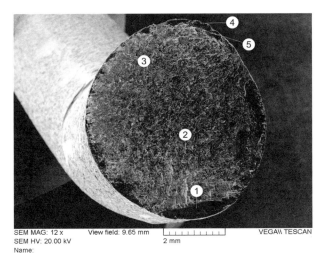

SEM MAG: 12 x   View field: 9.65 mm   VEGA\\ TESCAN
SEM HV: 20.00 kV   2 mm
Name:

Figure 21.31 Rod B Surface Notches.

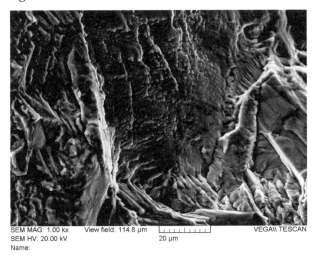

SEM MAG: 1.00 kx   View field: 114.8 μm   VEGA\\ TESCAN
SEM HV: 20.00 kV   20 μm
Name:

Figure 21.32 Image of Fracture Surface of Rod A – Numbers 1 through 5 Correspond to Location of Images Shown in Figures 21.15 through 21.19 respectively.

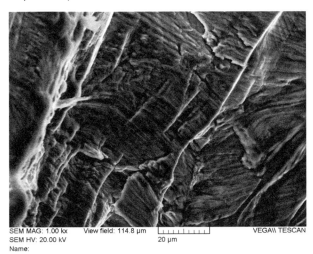

SEM MAG: 1.00 kx   View field: 114.8 μm   VEGA\\ TESCAN
SEM HV: 20.00 kV   20 μm
Name:

Figure 21.33 Fatigue Striations on the Fracture Surface of Rod A (1).

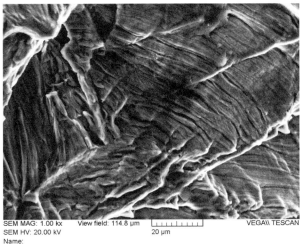

SEM MAG: 1.00 kx   View field: 114.8 μm   VEGA\\ TESCAN
SEM HV: 20.00 kV   20 μm
Name:

Figure 21.34 Fatigue Striations on the Fracture Surface of Rod A (2).

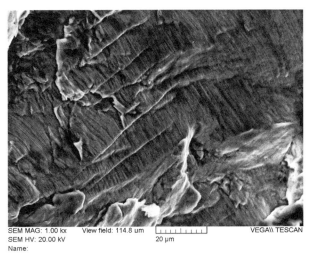

SEM MAG: 1.00 kx   View field: 114.8 μm   VEGA\\ TESCAN
SEM HV: 20.00 kV   20 μm
Name:

Figure 21.35 Fatigue Striations on the Fracture Surface of Rod A (3).

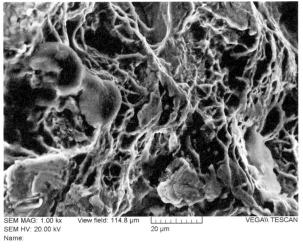

SEM MAG: 1.00 kx   View field: 114.8 μm   VEGA\\ TESCAN
SEM HV: 20.00 kV   20 μm
Name:

Figure 21.36 Fatigue Striations on the Fracture Surface of Rod A (4).

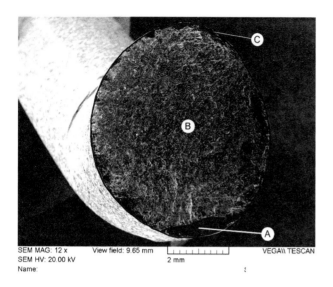

SEM MAG: 12 x   View field: 9.65 mm
SEM HV: 20.00 kV   2 mm   VEGA\\ TESCAN
Name:

Figure 21.37 *Ductile Dimples on the Outer Edge of the Fracture Surface of Rod A (5).*

at magnifications of 250 X or more. This was the last area of material connected when the final loading cycle took place and rod "A" fractured into two pieces.

Electron dispersive X-ray spectroscopy (EDS) revealed that the only absorbance bands detected in any appreciable quantity were those corresponding to titanium as shown in Figure 21.39. This finding confirmed that rod "A" and rod "B" were commercially pure (CP) titanium. Thousands of striations were present on the fracture surface of the rods, indicating that the fail-

ure occurred over at least thousands of cycles of loading and unloading. Note that the striations on the rod fracture surfaces shown in Figures 21.39 (adapted from ASM Metals Handbook, Vol. 12) and 21.23 (adapted from Narayan, 2009) for CP titanium match the striations shown in Figures 21.40 and 21.41.

Failure analysis and fractography revealed that the failure cause (surface damage) and mechanism (fatigue) for rod "B" was essentially identical to that of rod "A".

The rods were ductile, enabling them to be bent to fit the desired curvature of the spine. They were bent in vitro outside the body by a French rod-bending tool and then inserted and attached within the torso.

Examination of the relevant documents along with examination and testing of the physical evidence revealed that the subject rods failed over time by fatigue crack growth due to stress magnitudes consistent with those expected from the walking ambulation and the normal every day activity of the patient. Fatigue striations were seen to cover almost the entire fracture surface of both rods. Only a very small portion of the outer edge of the fracture surface contained the typical tensile ductile dimples that are consistent with the final fracture (i.e., rupture point) of the titanium rods. The fracture surface features were not consistent with a single impact overload failure. In other words, the motor vehicle accident in which

Label A: Sample 2 Fracture Surface 20kV

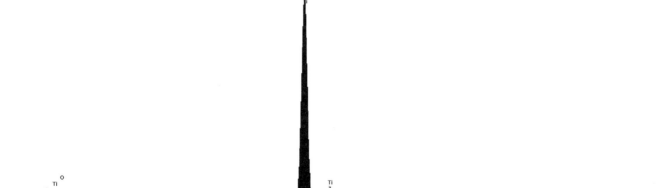

Figure 21.38 *Summary of Rod A Fracture Surface Features (Green – crack initiation, Blue – Crack propagation by fatigue, Red – final failure in overload).*

the patient was involved in 2005 was not the root cause of the back-support rods. There was no evidence of cleavage-related failure mechanisms. The fracture surfaces curve from a plane perpendicular to the rod at the origin to an angle at the fast fracture zone. This type of behavior is more typical of a fatigue fracture, where the direction of stress would change slightly as the cracks propagated.

The hardware used to fix the rods to the spine and the tools used to install and shape the rods created surface damage that led to the failure of both rods. The notches acted as stress concentrators (raisers) and fatigue crack initiation sites. The notches in the surfaces of both rods were found to be the origins of the fatigue cracks that ultimately led to the failure of the rods. This is not surprising given that the effect of subjecting both CP titanium and Ti-6Al-4V rods to contouring with a French rod-bender has been shown to significantly reduce the fatigue life of titanium spinal constructs (Lindsay, 2006). Also, given that the notch sensitivity of CP titanium and its alloys has been known (e.g., Dick, et al., 2001) and well documented, the fact that the cracks that led to the ultimate failure originated at notches is also not surprising. It is also noted that the effects of the in vivo environment also decrease the fatigue life of titanium and its reasonably biocompatible alloys (e.g., Rodrigues, et al., 2009), although the environmental effects were not investigated in this case.

During the period when the cracks were

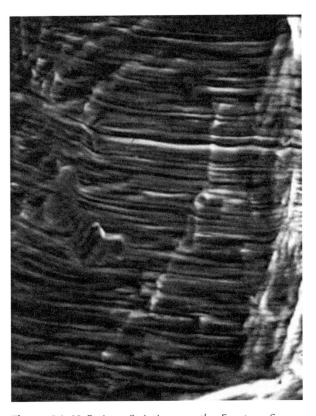

Figure 21.40 Fatigue Striations on the Fracture Surface of a Commercially Pure Titanium.
Specimen at Mag. = 1,000X (adapted from ASM Metals Handbook, Volume 12).

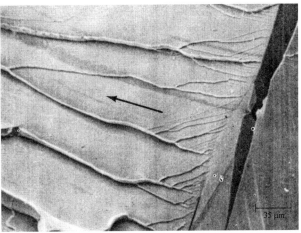

Figure 21.41 Fatigue Striations on the Fracture Surface of a Commercially Pure Titanium.
Specimen at Mag. = 5,000X (adapted from Biomedical Materials, Narayan, 2009).

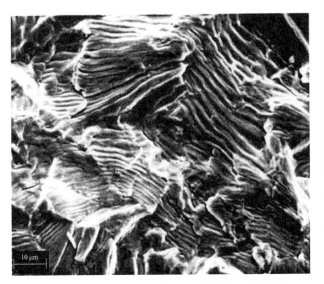

Figure 21.39 EDX Spectra for Rods "A" and "B."

propagating, the surfaces would tend to open and close from the bending. This likely caused the observed contact marks between the crack/fracture surfaces of rod "B". The contact marks suggested that rod "B" may have fractured first. Such markings were found mostly along the rod edges of the fracture surfaces. The low relative loading forces on the rods during crack growth did not lead to any significant fracture surface damage. After the rods both fractured, a significant separation distance was generated, thus ending any fracture surface contact. This is also evidence of the fact that the two sides of the cracking rods were tending to separate from one another, leading to little fracture surface-to-fracture surface damage.

One of the two rods most likely fractured first, due to differences in loading conditions and notch severity between rod "A" and rod "B". After the first rod fractured, the load on the second rod increased significantly as the portion of the load that was being carried by the first rod was then applied to and sustained by the remaining intact rod. This significantly shortened the fatigue life of the second rod.

It is noted that fatigue mode fractures are also often found to be the root cause of knee and hip replacement device failures. (Courtesy of David Bosch and Scott Anderson)

References

ASM International. (1987). Fractography. *ASM International Handbook, 9ᵗʰ Ed.*, Vol. 12, pp. 14, 20, 61, 177 & 441.

ASTM International. (1989). ASTM F 384-89: Standard Test Methods for Microhardness of Materials. American Society for Testing and Materials. 385-402. https://www.astm.org/Standard/standards-and-publications.html

ASTM International. (2000). ASTM E 18-00: Standard Test Methods for Rockwell Hardness and Rockwell Superficial Hardness of Metallic Materials. American Society for Testing and Materials. https://www.astm.org/Standard/standards-and-publications.html

ASTM International. (2001). ASTM E 10-01: Standard Test Method for Brinell Hardness of Metallic Materials. American Society for Testing and Materials.

https://www.astm.org/Standard/standards-and-publications.html

ASTM International. (1989). ASTM E 384-89: Standard Test Method for Microindentation Hardness of Materials. American Society for Testing and Materials. https://www.astm.org/Standard/standards-and-publications.html

ASTM International. (1992). ASTM F 981-92: Standard Practice for Assessment of Compatibility of Biomaterials for Surgical Implants with Respect to Effect of Materials on Muscle and Bone. American Society for Testing and Materials. 312-315. https://www.astm.org/Standard/standards-and-publications.html

Azevedo, C. R. F. (2002). Failure Analysis of a Commercially Pure Titanium Plate for Osteosynthesis. *Engineering Failure Analysis,* Vol. 10(2), 153-164. doi: 10.1016/S1350-6307(02)00067-5

Azevedo, C. R. F., dos Santos, A. P. (2003). Environmental Effects During Fatigue Testing: Fractographic Observation of Commercially Pure Titanium Plate for Cranio-Facial Fixation. *International Journal of Fatigue*, 10(4), 431-442. doi: 10.1016/S1350-6307(03)00013-X

Azevedo, C. R. F., Hippert, Jr., E. (2002). Failure Analyses of Surgical Implants in Brazil. *Engineering Failure Analysis*, 9(6), 621-631. doi: 10.1016/S1350-6307(02)00026-2

Cooper, H. J., Urban, R. M., Wixson, R. L., Meneghini, M., Jacobs, J. J. (2013). Adverse Local Tissue Reaction Arising From Corrosion at the Femoral Neck-Body Junction in Dual-Taper Stem with a Cobalt-Chromium Modular Neck. *The Journal of Bone and Joint Surgery*, 95(10), 865-72. doi: 10.2106/JBJS.L.01042

Das, A. K. (1996). Failure: Types and Characteristics. *Metallurgy of Failure Analysis*. 69-76.

DeVries, P. H., Ruth, K. T., Dennies, D. P. (2010). Counting on Fatigue: Striations and Their Measure. *Journal of Failure Analysis and Prevention*, 10, 120-137.

Dick, J. C., Bourgeault, C. A. (2001). Notch Sensitivity of Titanium Alloy, Commercially Pure Titanium, and Stainless Steel Spinal Implants. *SPINE*, 26(15), 1668-1672.

Digas, G. (2005). New Polymer Materials in Total Hip Arthroplasty: Evaluation with Radiostereometry, Bone Desitometry, Radiography and Clinical Parameters. *Acta Orthopaedica Supplementum*. 76(315), 4-82.

Gargiulo, P., Helgason T., Ramon, C., Jónsson, H. Jr., Carraro, U. (2014). CT and MRI Assessment and Characterization Using Segmentation and 3D Modeling Techniques: Applications to Muscle, Bone and Brain. *European Journal of Translational Myology*, 24(1), 3298. doi: 10.4081/ejtm.2014.3298.

Gargiulo, P., Pétursson, T., Magnússon, B., Bifulco, P., Cesarelli, M., Izzo, G. M., Magnúsdóttir, G., Halldórsson, G., Ludvigsdóttir, G. K., Tribel, J., Jónsson, H. Jr. (2013). Assessment of total hip arthroplasty by means of computed tomography 3D models and fracture risk evaluation. *Artificial Organs*, 37(6), 567-73. doi: 10.1111/aor.12033.

Hannon, P. (2016). A Brief Review of Current Orthopedic Implant Device Issues: Biomechanics and Biocompatibility. *Biology, Medicine and Engineering*, 1(1), 1-2.

Krishnan, H., Krishnan, S., Blunn, G., Skinner, J., Hart, A. (2013). Instructional Review: Hip Modular Neck Femoral Stems. *The Bone and Joint Journal*, 95B(8), 1011-1021.

Kummer, F. J. (2001). Introduction to the Biomechanics of Fracture Fixation. *Basic Biomechanics of the Musculoskeletal System*, 390-398.

Li, Y., Wong, C., Xiong, J., Hodgson, P., Wen, C. (2010). Cytotoxicity of Titanium and Titanium Alloying Elements. *J Dental Research*, 89(5), 493-497. doi. 10.1177/0022034510363675. E pub.

McIntyre, D. A. (2011). The Eleven Most Implanted Medical Devices in America. *Business Insider*. Retrieved by https://www.businessinsider.com/the-11-most-implanted-medical-devices-in-america-2011-7

McCloy, J. (2016). Medical Implants: The Cost of Failure. *Advanced Manufacturing*. Retrieved by https://advancedmanufacturing.org/medical-implants-cost-failuree/

Mohaideen, A., Nagarkatti, D., Banta, J., Foley, C. (2000). Not All Rods Are Harrington - An Overview of Spinal Instrumentation in Scoliosis Treatment. *Pediatric Radiology*, 30(2), 110-8.

Narayan, R., Ed., Pilliar, R. M. (2009). Metallic Biomaterials. *Biomedical Materials*. 52-53.

Ozkaya, N., Leger, D. (2001). Introduction to Biomechanics: Basic Terminology and Concepts. *Basic Biomechanics of the Musculoskeletal System*. Nordin, M. and Frankel, V. Lippencott, Williams and Wilkins, Baltimore, Md.

Park, H., Temenoff, J. S., Mikos, A. G. (2007). Biodegradable Orthopedic Implants. In.: Bronner, F., Farach-Carson, M. C., Mikos, A. G. (eds) *Engineering of Functional Skeletal Tissues*. Topics in Bone Biology, vol. 3, 55-68. Springer, London. doi: 10.1007/978-1-84628-366-6_4

Pétursson, Þ., Edmunds, K. J., Gíslason, M. K., Magnússon, B., Magnúsdóttir, G., Halldórsson, G., Jónsson, H. Jr., Gargiulo, P. (2015). Bone Mineral Density and Fracture Risk Assessment to Optimize Prosthesis Selection in Total Hip Replacement. *Computational Mathematical Methods in Medicine*, 2015(2015), 162481. doi: 10.1155/2015/162481.

Rodrigues, D. C., Urban, R. M., Jacobs, J. J., Gilbert, J. L. (2009). In Vivo Severe Corrosion and Hydrogen Embrittlement of Retrieved Modular Body Titanium Hip-Implants. *Journal of Biomedical Materials Research, Part B Applied Biomaterials*, 88(12), 206-219.

Sidambe, A. T. (2014). Biocompatibility of Advanced Manufactured Titanium Implants – A Review. *Materials (Basel)*, 7(12), 8168-8188. doi: 10.3390/ma7128168

Tanaka, H., Mori, Y., Noro, A., Kogure, A., Kamimura, M., Yamada, N., Hanada, S., Masahashi, N., Itoi, E. (2016). Apatite Formation and Biocompatibility of a Low Young's Modulus Ti-Nb-Sn Alloy Treated with Anodic Oxidation and Hot Water. *Public Library of Science (PLoS)* One, 11(2). Retrieved by https://journals.plos.org/plosone/article?id=10.1371/journal.pone.0150081

Whiting, W. C. and Zernicke, R. F. (1998). *Biomechanics of Musculoskeletal Injury* (Champaign, IL: Human Kinetics)

Zaffe, D., Bertoldi, C., Consolo, U. (2004). Accumulation of Aluminum in Lamellar Bone after Implantation of Titanium Plates, Ti-6AL-4V Screws, Hydroxyapatite Granules. *Biomaterials*, 25(17), 3837-3844. doi:

10.1016/j.biomaterials.2003.10.020

2016 Top Markets Report – Medical Devices. U. S. Department of Commerce, International Trade Administration, Retrieved by https://www.trade.gov/topmarkets/pdf/Medical_Devices_Executive_Summary.pdf

Recommended Reading

Acevedo, D., Loy, B. N., Lee, B., Omid, R., Itamura, J. (2013). Mixing Implants of Differing Metallic Composition in the Treatment of Upper-extremity Fractures. *Orthopedics*, 36(9), e1175-9. doi: 10.3928/01477447-20130821-21

ASTM International. (2013). ASTM F 1798-13: Standard Test Method for Evaluating the Static and Fatigue Properties of Interconnection Mechanisms and Subassemblies Used in Spinal Arthrodesis Implants. American Society for Testing and Materials. https://www.astm.org/Standard/standards-and-publications.html

ASTM International. (2012). ASTM F 1800-12: Standard Practice for Cyclic Fatigue Testing of Metal Tibial Tray Components of Total Knee Joint Replacements. American Society for Testing and Materials. https://www.astm.org/Standard/standards-and-publications.html

ASTM International. (2014). ASTM F 1801-97(2014). Standard Practice for Corrosion Fatigue Testing of Metallic Implant Materials. American Society for Testing and Materials. https://www.astm.org/Standard/standards-and-publications.html

Berven, S.H., Rawlins, B.A., Lenke, L.G. (2005). CD Horizon Engage 6.35 Spinal System Surgical Technique. *Medtronic*.

Burstein, A and Wright, T. (1994). Performance of Implant Systems. *Fundamentals of Orthopaedic Biomechanics*. Williams & Wilkins. Baltimore, 190-218.

Cadosch, D., Chan, E., Gautschi, O.P., Filgueira, L. (2009). Metal is Not Inert: Role of Metal Ions Released by Biocorrosion in Aseptic Loosening—Current Concepts. Journal of Biomedical Materials Research Part A. 91(4), 1252-62. doi: 10.1002/jbm.a.32625

Chakrabarty, G., Vashishtha, M., Leeder, D. (2015). Polyethylene in knee arthroplasty: A review. *Journal of Clinical Orthopaedics and Trauma*. 6(2) 108-112.

doi: 10.1016/j.jcot.2015.01.096

Dikici, B., Esen, Z., Duygulu, O., & Gungor, S. Corrosion of Metallic Biomaterials. In: Niinomi, M., Narushima, T., Nakai, M. (eds) Advances in Metallic Biomaterials. Springer Series in Biomaterials Science and Engineering, vol. 3. Springer, Berlin, Heidelberg. doi: 10.1007/978-3-662-46836-4_12

Gong, X, -Y., Chwirut, D. J., Mitchell, M. R., Choules, B. D. (2009). Fatigue to Fracture: An Informative, Fast, and Reliable Approach for Assessing Medical Implant Durability. *Journal of ASTM International*, 6(7), 1-10. doi: 10.1520/JAI102412

Hanke, L, (2012). Surface Characterization for Medical Devices. *ASM International Handbook*, Vol. 23, Materials for Medical Devices, 331-342.

James, B. A. (2012). Medical Device Failure Analysis. *ASM International Handbook*, Vol. 23, Materials for Medical Devices, 343-359.

Liddle, A. D., Pandit, H. G. Jenkins, C., Lobenhoffer, P., Jackson, W. F., Dodd, C. A., & Murray, D. W. (2014). Valgus subsidence of the tibial component in cementless Oxford unicompartmental knee replacement. *The Bone & Joint Journal*, 96B(3), 345-349. doi: 10.1302/0301-620X396B3.33182

Lindsey, C., Deviren, V., Xu, Z., Yeh, R-F., Puttlitz, C. M. (2006). The Effects of Rod Contorting of Spinal Contract Fatigue Strength. *SPINE*, 31(15), 1680-1687. doi: 10.1097/01.brs.0000224177.97846.00

McKellop, H. A., Rostland, T. V. (1990). The wear behavior of ion-implanted Ti-6Al-4V against UHMW polyethylene. *Journal of Biomedical Materials Research*, 24(11), 1413-1425. doi: 10.1002/jbm.820241102

Muratoglu, O. K., Bragdon, C. R., O'Connor, D. O., Perinchief, R. S., Jasty, M., Harris, W. H. (2002). Aggressive wear testing of a cross-linked polyethylene in total knee arthroplasty. *Clinical Orthopaedics and Related Research*, 404(404), 89-95. doi: 10.1097/00003086-200211000-00015

Muratoglu, O. K., Bragdon, C. R., O'Connor, D. O., Perinchief, R. S., Konrad, R., Harris, W. H. (2003). Metrology to quantify wear and creep of polyethylene tibial knee inserts. *Clinical Orthopaedics and Related Research*, (410), 155-164. doi: 101.1097/01.bio.0000063604.67412.04

Ozkaya, N., Nordin, M., Goldsheyder, D., Leger, D. (2012). Fundamentals of Biomechanics: Equilibrium, Motion, and Deformation. Springer, New York, NY. doi: 10.1007/978-1-4614-1150-5

Rifai, A., Tran, N., Lau, D. W., Elbourne, A., Zhan, H., Stacey, A. D., . . . Fox, K. (2018). Polycrystalline Diamond Coating of Additively Manufactured Titanium for Biomedical Applications. *ACS Applied Materials & Interfaces*, 10(10), 8474-8484. doi: 10.1021/acsami.7b18596

Russell, S. J., El-Khatib, F. H., Sinha, M., Magyar, K. L., McKeon, K., Goergen, L. G., . . . Damiano, E. R. (2014). Outpatient Glycemic Control with a Bionic Pancreas in Type 1 Diabetes. *The New England Journal of Medicine*, 371(4), 313-325. doi: 10.1056/NEJMoa1314474

Sarikaya, M., Aksay, I. A. (1992). Nacre of Abalone Shell: A Natural Multifunctional Nanolaminate Ceramic-Polymer Composite Material. In: Case, S.T. (eds) Structure, Cellular Synthesis and Assembly of Biopolymers. Results and Problems in Cell Differentiation (A Series of Topical Volumes in Developmental Biology), vol. 19. Springer, Berlin, Heidelberg. doi: 10.1007/978-3-540-47207-1_1

Shahgaldi, B. F., Heatley, F. W., Dewar, A., Corrin, B. (1995). In Vivo Corrosion of Cobalt-Chromium and Titanium Wear Particles. *The Journal of Bone and Joint Surgery,* Vol. 77, Issue 6, 962-966.

Teeter, M. G., Yuan, X., Naudie, D. D., & Holdsworth, D. W. (2010). Technique to quantify subsurface cracks in retrieved polyethylene components using micro-CT. *Journal of Long-Term Effects of Medical Implants.* 20(1): 27-34.

Teoh, S. H. (2000). Fatigue of Biomaterials: A Review. *International Journal of Fatigue*, 22(10), 825-837. doi: 10.1016/S0142-1123(00)00052-9

Tigani, D., Dallari, D., Coppola, C., Ayad, R., Sabbioni, G., & Fosco, M. (2011). Total knee arthroplasty for post-traumatic proximal tibial bone defect: three cases report. The *Open Orthopaedics Journal,* 5, 143-150. doi: 10.2174/1874325001105010143

Yamanaka, K., Mori, M., Yamazaki, K., Kumagai., Doita, M., Chiba, A. (2015). Analysis of the Fracture Mechanism of Ti-6Al-4V Alloy Rods That Failed Clinically After Spinal Instrumentation Surgery. *SPINE*, 40(13), E767-73. doi: 10.1097/BRS.0000000000000881

Appendix A

Anthropometric Measurements

Patrick Hannon

Anthropometric measurements and other data measurements to be taken by a qualified individual (e.g., qualified nurse, physical therapist, biomechanist, or physician):

- Age
- Weight
- Stature (height)
- Sitting height (from seat pan of vehicle to the top of the head)
- Acromial height from sitting position (from the seat pan to acromioclavicular joint)
- Knee height from sitting position (floor to superior-anterior patella)
- Popliteal height from sitting position (floor to back of knee)
- Buttock-knee length from sitting position (from posterior buttocks to anterior patella)
- Shoulder breath
- Seated hip breath
- Shoulder circumference
- Chest circumference
- Waist circumference
- Buttocks circumference
- Arm length (from glenohumeral joint to elbow)
- Forearm and hand length (from elbow to fingertips)

Additional measurements may be required.

Appendix B

Conversion Factors

Patrick Hannon

Acceleration

1 foot/second/second (ft/s^2)	=	1.097 kilometers/hour/second (km/hr/s)
1 foot/second/second (ft/s^2)	=	0.3048 meter/second/second (m/s^2)
1 kilometer/hour/second (km/hr/s)	=	27.78 centimeters/second/second (cm/s^2)
1 kilometer/hour/second (km/hr/s)	=	0.2778 meter/second/second (m/s^2)
1 G	=	32.2 feet/second/second (ft/s^2)
1 G	=	9.8 meters/second/second (m/s^2)
1 meter/second/second (m/s^2)	=	100 centimeters/second/second (cm/s^2)
1 mile/hour/second	=	0.447 meter/second/second (m/s^2)
1 revolution/minute/minute	=	0.001745 radian/second/second (rad/s^2)
1 revolution/second/second	=	6.283 radians/second/second (rad/s^2)

Area

1 square inch (in.^{2})	=	6.4516 square centimeters (cm^2)
1 square inch (in.^{2})	=	645.16 square millimeters (mm^2)
1 square foot (ft.^{2})	=	929 square centimeters (cm^2)
1 square foot (ft.^{2})	=	0.092903 square meter (m^2)
1 square foot (ft.^{2})	=	92,900 square millimeters (mm^2)

Density

1 pound/cubic foot (lb./ft^3)	=	16.01846 kilograms/cubic meter (kg/m^3)
1 slug/cubic foot (slug/ft^3)	=	515.3788 kilograms/cubic meter (kg/m^3)
1 pound/gallon (UK)	=	99.77633 kilograms/cubic meter (kg/m^3)
1 pound/gallon (USA)	=	119.8264 kilograms/cubic meter (kg/m^3)

Energy and Work

1 Btu (British thermal unit)	=	1,055 joules (J)
1 Btu	=	1.0548 kilojoules (kJ)
1 Btu	=	0.0002928 kilowatt-hour (kW-hr)
1 erg	=	0.0001 millijoule (mJ)
1 foot-poundal	=	0.04214 joule (J)
1 foot-pound force	=	1.355818 joules (J)
1 gram-centimeter	=	0.09807 millijoule (mJ)
1 horsepower-hour	=	2,684 kilojoules (kJ)
1 horsepower-hour	=	0.7457 kilowatt-hour (kW-hr)
1 kilocalorie (International)	=	4.1868 kilojoules (kJ)
1 kilocalorie	=	4,183 joules (J)
1 kilopond-meter (kp-m)	=	9.807 joules (J)
1 kilowatt-hour	=	3,600 kilojoules (kJ)

Force

1 dyne	=	0.01 millinewton (mN)
1 foot-pound (ft.-lb.)	=	1.356 joules (J)
1 foot-pound/second (ft.-lb./s)	=	0.001356 kilowatt (kW)
1 gram	=	9.807 millinewton (mN)
1 kilogram-force (kg-f)	=	9.807 newtons (N)
1 kilopond (kp)	=	9.807 newtons (N)
1 poundal	=	0.138255 newton (N)
1 pound-force (lb.-f)	=	4.448222 newtons (N)
1 stone (weight)	=	62.275 newtons (N)
1 ton (long)	=	9,964 newtons (N)
1 ton (metric)	=	9,807 newtons (N)

Length

1 angstrom (C)	=	0.0001 micrometer (mm)
1 centimeter (cm)	=	0.00001 kilometer (km)
1 centimeter (cm)	=	0.01 meter (m)
1 centimeter (cm)	=	10 millimeter (mm)
1 inch (in.)	=	2.54 centimeters (cm)
1 inch (in.)	=	0.0254 meter (m)
1 inch (in.)	=	25.4 millimeters (mm)
1 light-year	=	9,460,910,000,000 kilometers (9.46×10^{12} km)

Moment of Inertia

1 slug-foot squared (slug-ft^2)	=	1.35582 kilogram-square meters (kg m^2)
1 pound-foot squared (lb.-ft^2)	=	0.04214 kilogram-square meter (kg m^2)

Mass

1 ounce (oz)	=	28.3495 grams (g)
1 pound (lb.)	=	0.453592 kilogram (kg)
1 slug	=	14.59 kilograms (kg)
1 ton	=	1,016 kilograms (kg)

Power

1 Btu/hour	=	0.2931 watt (W)
1 Btu/minute	=	17.51 watts (W)
1 calorie/second	=	4.187 watts (W)
1 erg/second	=	10,000,000 megawatts (MW)
1 foot-pound/second	=	1.356 watts (W)
1 foot-poundal/second	=	0.04214 watt (W)
1 gram-calorie	=	0.001162 watt-hour
1 horsepower (UK)	=	745.7 watts (W)
1 horsepower (metric)	=	735.5 watts (W)
1 kilocalorie/minute (kcal/min)	=	69.767 watts (W)
1 kilogram-meter/second	=	9.807 watts (W)
1 kilopond-meter/minute (kpm/min)	=	0.1634 watt (W)

Pressure

1 atmosphere	=	760 millimeters of mercury (mmHg) at 0°C
1 atmosphere	=	101,340 pascals (Pa)
1 pound-force/square foot (lb./ft^2)	=	47.88026 pascals (Pa)
1 pound-force/square inch (lb./in.^{2})	=	6.8948 kilopascals (kPa)
1 poundal/square foot	=	1.488 pascals (Pa)

Temperature

1 degree centigrade (°C)	=	(°C × 9/5) + 32 degrees Fahrenheit (°F)
1 degree centigrade (°C)	=	°C + 273.18 Kelvin

Torques and Moments

1 foot-pound (ft.-lb.)	=	1.356 newton-meters (Nm)
1 kilopond-meter (kp-m)	=	9.807 newton-meters (Nm)

Velocity

1 foot/second (ft/s)	=	30.48 centimeters/second (cm/s)
1 foot/second (ft/s)	=	1.097 kilometers/hour (km/hr, or kph)
1 foot/second (ft/s)	=	18.29 meters/minute (m/min)
1 foot/second (ft/s)	=	0.3048 meter/second (m/s)
1 mile/hour (mph)	=	1.6093 kilometers/hour (km/hr, or kph)
1 mile/hour (mph)	=	0.447 meter/second (m/s)

Volume

1 cubic centimeter (cm^3)	=	0.000001 cubic meter (m^3)
1 cubic centimeter (cm^3)	=	0.001 liter (L)
1 cubic foot (ft^3)	=	0.02832 cubic meter (m^3)
1 cubic foot (ft^3)	=	28.32 liters (L)
1 gallon (USA)	=	3,785 cubic centimeters (cm^3)
1 gallon (USA)	=	0.003785 cubic meter (m^3)
1 gallon	=	3.785 liters (L)
1 ounce (fluid, USA)	=	0.02957 liter (L)
1 ounce (fluid, UK)	=	28.413 cubic centimeters (cm^3)
1 ounce (fluid, USA)	=	29.573 cubic centimeters (cm^3)

Appendix C

Instrumentation in Biomechanics

Patrick Hannon

C.1 Introduction

Instrumentation in biomechanics has become increasingly sophisticated over the past several years. Testing and analysis can now be done in the field as well as in the laboratory setting in many cases. Surveillance video and other event recording often provides important visual information that can be qualitatively and quantitatively analyzed.

In motor vehicle accidents, the new "black box" instrumentation in commercial and passenger vehicles provides a wealth of vehicle dynamics information related to the accident event. Event recorders are able to measure the vehicle speed prior to braking, time of braking, the deceleration profile during braking, the vehicle delta velocity, airbag deployments and the use of seat belts in addition to other measures.

C.2 Measurement of Kinematics

Kinematics is the branch of mechanics that describes motion. Motion is described in terms of displacement, velocity, and acceleration vectors.

A. Surveillance video

Old video is usually black and white acquired at a low frame rates and of variable quality. However, the utility can often be improved by computer enhancement to produce a clearer representation of the desired event or the identification of an individual. New digital color video is much improved over the last fifteen years. When required, a two-dimensional biomechanical analysis can be performed of the event kinematics. Human joint rotational measures and linear motion of the body and body segments can often be quantified. A single camera will permit the analysis of data in two dimensions within a single plane. Surveillance video is usually subject to some perspective error which makes a quantified analysis more difficult but not impossible. Furthermore, many times a qualitative analysis of the surveillance video is sufficient to answer the biomechanical question or to identify the individual.

A technique termed inverse dynamics may also allow an analysis of the relevant kinetics or causal factors of the motion which occurred during the event.

B. High speed laboratory grade video

In a laboratory situation, ultra high speed video can be employed at frequencies exceeding 50,000 thousand to 1,000,000 frames each second. Such systems are usually reserved for military applications involving high speed aircraft, explosions, or ballistics. These systems have replaced the rotating prism cameras of the past which were able to perform similar functions at lower speeds (approximately 10,000 Hz maximum). High speed video is a step down and may range from 60 frames each second on up to 100,000 frames each second. (Figure C.1) These video systems are less expensive and more appropriate for the biomechanist involved in human motion analysis or in most vehicle crash test protocols. Most human initiated motion can be quantified at frame speeds of 150 frames per second, and most impact events can be adequately recorded at 1,000 frames per second (the present standard in vehicle crash tests). The cost of this equipment is be-

Figure C.1 *High speed video camera Memrecam fx 6000. (Courtesy of NAC Corp)*

Figure C.2 *An elevated walkway is used to capture video data on patient's walking gait. Video cameras may be used to quantify human walking gait and provide a functional anatomy analysis of lower extremity joint motions. (Courtesy of the Gait Laboratory, Physical Therapy, Northern Arizona University, Mark Cornwall Ph.D. and Tom McPoil Ph.D.)*

coming increasing more affordable for consultants and universities.

In the laboratory, a technique termed photogrametric analysis can be employed. By attaching reflective markers or lights emitting diodes to the human subject on segments surrounding joints, precise body segment motion can be recorded. Manual operator digital analysis is required for some systems. However, many new systems perform automatic digitizing which is more precise and much less time consuming. These systems also allow for automatic analysis of recorded data once initial information of body segments has been defined. These systems may also allow for one, two, or three planes of angular motion depending upon the number of cameras used, camera placement and the sophistication of the system software. An example of this setting is seen in Figure C.2.

C. Optoelectric systems

Similar to the high speed video are the optoelectric systems which also permit the analysis of three-dimensional motion. Such systems may rely on light-emitting diodes which emit light in the infrared, near infrared, or the visible light spectrum. This light is picked up by the special cine cameras, and computer software is able to convert the raw data into x, y, and z coordinates. The x, y, and z data are then transformed by software to produce joint angular motion measures and linear motion measures of the human subject. (Figure C.3)

D. Magnetic field systems

Some kinematic motion systems make use of transmitters that generate near field, low frequency, magnetic field vectors, which allow for the production of real time graphics of human motion as well as quantified kinematic measures. (Figure C.4)

All of these laboratory kinematic systems require that an experiment be performed, usually using exemplar models of the individual(s) or biofidelic heads involved in an accident or criminal act. Once again, all these kinematic measures may be incorporated into an inverse dynamics set of calculations to yield estimated kinetics (forces, torques, and moments). The limits of such analyses are governed by (1) how closely the experiment approximates the actual circumstances of the event and (2) the fact that inverse dynamics analyses present less than a perfect measurement of generated forces, moments, and torques.

C.3 Measurement of Kinetics

Kinetics is the branch of mechanics that examines the

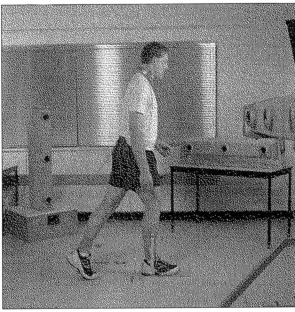

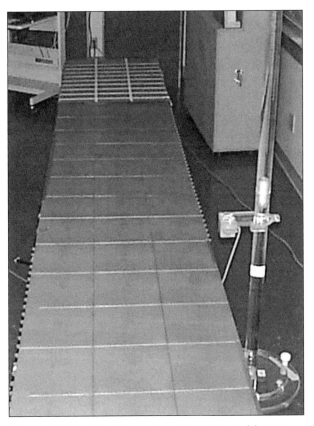

Figure C.3 The Optotrak System is featured by NDI, Waterloo, ON, Canada (www.ndigital.com). (Photo Courtesy of the University of Waterloo)

Figure C.4 The Six Dimension Magnetic Field System is illustrated at Northern Arizona University. Foot kinematics are illustrated. (Courtesy of the Gait Laboratory, Physical Therapy, Northern Arizona University, Mark Cornwall Ph.D. and Tom McPoil Ph.D.)

causal factors of motion. Forces, moments, and torques produce motion and may be measured by various means.

A. Force plates

The force plate records a history of loading (forces, moments and torques) applied to the ground. Force plates are able to measure forces downward just like a bathroom scale and furthermore are able to measure forces fore and aft and from side to side. This is sometimes important in an impact event where significant horizontal forces are important in addition to the vertical force recording. Moments and torques can also be computed by software manipulation of the raw force plate signals, and these data analyses of foot falls may be important in slips, trips, stumbles, and falls.

Force plates have real value in examining impact and coupled with a drop tower, head drops can be accomplished with a biofidelic head form (similar to a real human head). Figure C.5a illustrates a head drop to a 24-inch by 24-inch force plate in our laboratory. The effectiveness of a helmet may be assessed by this technique when the

head form is tested with and without a specific helmet. (Figure C.5b)

More complex force plate systems are also able to compute compressive stresses when forces are applied. Such instruments are most useful in foot compressive stress analysis rather than high magnitude impacts. In this instance, a foot fall occurs as an exemplar subject (or patient in a clinical setting) walks across the force plate and the vertical load and the compressive stresses (within the foot fall pattern) are recorded and displayed over the time history of the foot plant (compressive stress = load/foot-ground interface area). (Figures C.7a and C.7b) Additionally, cadaver foot specimens are useful in precise motion of joints within the human foot. (Figure C.7c)

B. Coefficient of friction testing

The coefficient of friction measurement is important in slip and fall cases. Measurement requires a known perpendicular force and the specific materials in question (e.g., flooring and shoe sole surface). Although this measure-

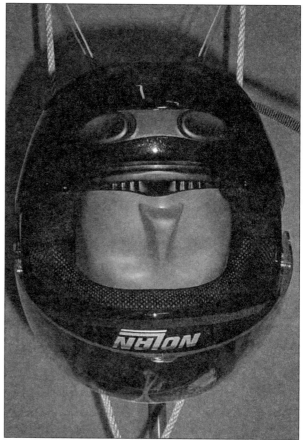

Figure C.6 *Head drop helmet. (Courtesy of Augs-purger Komm Engineering, Phoenix, Arizona, Hannon Biomechanics Analysis, and Northstar Biokinetics)*

Figure C.7a and **C.7b** *Compressive stresses are displayed within the foot fall pattern within seconds after the subject has stepped on the compressive stress sensitive plate. (Courtesy of the Gait Laboratory, Physical Therapy, Northern Arizona University, Mark Cornwall Ph.D. and Tom McPoil Ph.D.)*

Figure C.5 *Helmet testing may be accomplished by use of the drop tower, head form, and kinetic measures from a force plate or small accelerometer. (Courtesy of Augspurger Komm Engineering, Phoenix, Arizona, Hannon Biomechanics Analysis, and Northstar Biokinetics)*

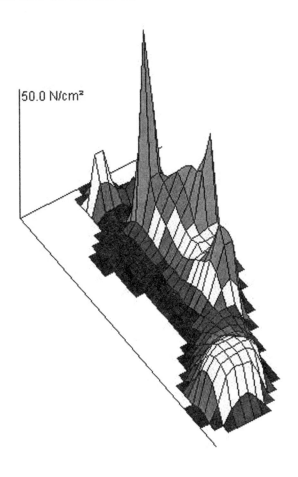

50.0 N/cm²

Figure C.8a *The "English" System is used by the expert in measuring the coefficient of friction in a field setting. (Courtesy of William Morrison, Las Vegas, Nevada)*

Figure C.7c *Cadaver foot specimen kinematics are measured. (Courtesy of the Gait Laboratory, Physical Therapy, Northern Arizona University, Mark Cornwall Ph.D. and Tom McPoil Ph.D.)*

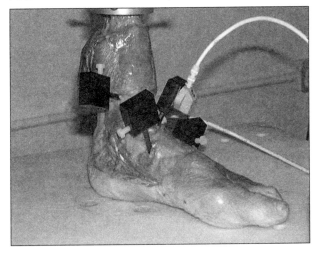

Figure C.8b *Brungraber Mark 1 Bathing Surface Slip Resistance Tester. (Courtesy of Dr. David Bosch)*

ment can be performed in the laboratory, field instrumentation is usually more useful in litigation. (Figure C.8a)

Sometimes very specialized equipment is used, such as the Brungraber Mark 1, in testing the surfaces of bathtubs and shower surfaces (Figure C.8b).

C. Accelerometry

Accelerometry makes use of instruments that are able to measure accelerations in one, two, or three directions. Triaxial (three directions) accelerometers are most common at present and come in a variety of sizes and acceleration ranges. Most common in the present are instruments that measure acceleration by means of a piezo-electric device

Figure C.9 The strain gauge force transducer which measures compression and tension loads from zero to 500 lbs. in 0.1 lb. increments. (Courtesy of Mr. Wes Grimes at Collision Engineering, Mesa, Arizona)

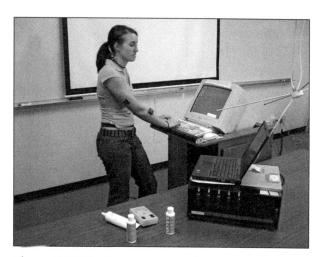

Figure C.10 Electromyographical measures of an experimental subject. (Courtesy of Northern Arizona University; Patrick Hannon Ed.D., Dept. of Biological Sciences)

within the accelerometer. Some are more suited to the standardized laboratory environment, and others may be used in the laboratory or utilized in a field setting (e.g., attached to a motor vehicle). Based on acceleration, loads and forces can be described for known masses. Recall the Force = mass × acceleration, and an acceleration or deceleration is:

(a) = force divided by mass. The head form in Figure C.5b is also equipped with a triaxial accelerometer.

D. Strain gauge cable tensiometers

This relatively simple technology is still very valuable in many injury biomechanics cases. The cable tensiometer measures a pulling force (tension) and may be used to measure the strength of a subject, for example, in performing a lifting task or may be used to isolate the force producing capabilities of a single muscle or muscle group for a human subject. In accident events, cable tensiometers may be used in a variety of situations. One common example may involve the force required to slide or tip over an object (which may have landed upon the plaintiff). These data coupled with plaintiff and witness testimony are many times useful in determining an accurate representation of the actual accident event. (Figure C.9)

E. Electromyography (measures of muscle activity)

Electromyography (EMG) is a measure of skeletal muscle electrical activity and is analogous to electrocardiography (ECG, a.k.a. EKG), which measures the electrical activity of the heart. Electromyography is able to provide data regarding the beginning and the end of muscle activity and has been used by several biomechanists in determining muscle activity (Szabo et al., 1996; Castro et al., 1997) during experimental impact events.

Electromyography involves placing surface electrodes on the skin over a muscle or less commonly by implanting fine wire electrodes directly into superficial musculature. The electrical signal of the muscle is amplified and recorded on a personal computer. Subjects perform a given task, and the muscle or muscle group activity is recorded by the biomechanist. Some crude estimates of muscle force from baseline measures may be accomplished by this EMG technique. However, electrode placement and skin condition (surface electrodes) limit determining forces from EMG. Determining the onset of muscle activity during a task or simulated accident event is a more common EMG measure in a biomechanics setting.

References

Castro, WHM. Schilgen, M. Meyer, S. Weber, M. Peu-
    ker, C. and Wortler, K. *Do whiplash injuries occur in
    low speed rear impacts?* (European Spine Journal.)
    The AcroMed Prize for Spinal Research, 6: 366–375.
    (1997)

Szabo, T. and Welcher, J. *Human subject kinematics and
    electromyographic activity during low speed rear im-
    pacts*, SAE paper 962432. (1996)

About the Authors

Patrick R. Hannon, Ed.D. taught at Northern Arizona University from 1980 to 2008 and presently holds Faculty Emeritus status within the Department of Biological Sciences (Physiology and Functional Morphology Section), College of The Environment, Forestry, and Natural Sciences. Dr. Hannon taught undergraduate/graduate level biomechanics, undergraduate level human functional anatomy and undergraduate/graduate neural control of movement. He has received grants in biomechanics and in the neurosciences from the National Science Foundation, the U.S. Air Force Office of Scientific Research, and the U.S. Department of Defense, and served as the principal investigator or as the project director for these research efforts. In addition to his teaching and academic research, he has served as an expert witness in injury biomechanics, human functional anatomy and the neurosciences (non-medical) since 1988 and presently owns and operates Hannon Biomechanics Analysis in the greater Phoenix, Arizona area, Flagstaff, Arizona, Las Vegas, Nevada, and in Dallas, Texas. Dr. Hannon has addressed hundreds of injury biomechanics, neurosciences and functional anatomy injury cases and has testified nationwide in over 450 civil and criminal cases in county, state and federal courts over the past thirty-two years. He has completed faculty fellowships at Wright-Patterson AFB (Ohio) in Biodynamics, Brooks AFB (Texas) in the neurosciences, and has accomplished a six month sabbatical at Thomas Jefferson Medical College (Dept. of Neurology) (Philadelphia). Additionally, Dr. Hannon serves on the Editorial Board of the international journal entitled the "Journal of Forensic Biomechanics" (sixteen Editorial Board members worldwide). Additionally, Dr. Hannon has been appointed to the Board of Editors for the new international journal entitled "Biology, Engineering and Medicine", (2016). Dr. Hannon is active in research paper reviews and is an active contributor of editorials and peer reviewed papers to these journals. Dr. Hannon can be contacted at www.hannonbiomechanics.com.

Mark W. Cornwall, PT, Ph.D, FAPTA received his bachelor's degree in Physical Therapy from the University of Maryland in 1977. He then went on to obtain a Master's degree in Biomechanics from the University of North Carolina in 1980 and a PhD in 1986 in Human Performance from Indiana University. His principle areas of research interest include the kinematics of the foot and how a person's foot posture can influence that movement during walking. He has published over 110 research articles in scientific and professional journals related to foot motion, foot posture, as well as examination and treatment of foot-related injuries. He has also authored or co-authored nine books or book chapters. Dr. Cornwall has presented at both scientific and professional meetings throughout the United States, Europe and Australia. Dr. Cornwall's background and training is extensive in the areas of anatomy, kinesiology and biomechanics. He has shared this knowledge and expertise with countless entry-level physical therapy students at Northern Arizona University where he taught human anatomy of the extremities for most of the thirty-two years that he was there.

Kerry L. Knapp Ph.D. has a broad educational and experience-based background in the physical sciences, engineering, computer modeling, and analytical techniques. Dr. Knapp's studies and research in human functional anatomy, physiology, human neuroscience, and human biomechanics form the basis for his current work in injury biomechanics.

Dr. Knapp holds two master's degrees (one in biomechanics) and a Ph.D. in Forensic Biomechanics. Professional affiliations include the Society of Automotive Engineers, the American College of Sports Medicine, and the American Academy of Forensic Sciences. Dr. Knapp has worked full time as a consultant and expert witness in the area of injury biomechanics since 1994. In addition, Dr. Knapp owns and manages Northstar Biokinetics, Inc., a firm specializing in human injury analysis and expert witness consulting in both civil and criminal courts.

Scott Anderson, M.S., holds a master's degree in mechanical engineering from Arizona State University. His studies at ASU were focused on material science with his final project correlated microscopically observed stain fields caused by in-situ loading to fatigue crack growth rates in ductile metals. Over the past 12 years he has provided materials science and engineering research and investigation services in over 100 product liability and personal injury cases. These investigations ranged from artificial heart implant polymer degradation to automotive composite bumper beam failure. Mr. Anderson has served as the expert witness in several cases and is a member of the American Society for Testing of Materials (ASTM).

David R. Bosch, Ph.D., completed his bachelor's degree in 1987 in Mechanical Engineering with honors and minors in Computer Science, Physics and Mathematics at South Dakota State University. He completed his master's degree in Mechanical Engineering in 1990 and his doctorate in Materials Science and Engineering in 1994, both at Arizona State University (ASU). While at ASU, he completed research under the U.S. Department of Defense, U.S. Airforce and U.S. Department of Energy contracts. His principle area of research involved the physical, thermodynamic and mechanical characterization of refractory metals and alloys for use in direct energy generation technology, including thermionic energy conversion. Dr. Bosch's university-based activities resulted in fifteen published research papers and several conference presentations. His background experience prior to college included fifteen years involved in the technology and engineering of automotive and truck failure analysis, diagnostics and repair, and building construction, including plumbing, electrical and structures.

Since completing his formal education, he worked more than ten years as a materials, process and equipment research and development scientist within the semiconductor industry. Since 2004, he has practiced as a forensic engineering consultant for both plaintiff and defendant, specializing in component failure analysis. Dr. Bosch has testified nationwide in more than 450 cases in state and federal courts. His forensic consulting work has resulted in hundreds of reports and technical presentations on at least ten occasions to various groups and organizations. Dr. Bosch can be contacted at Forensic Engineering, Inc. in Phoenix, Arizona. (www.ForensicEngineeringInc.com)

Michael Iliescu, M.D., has had seven years of teaching experience in the fields of Biochemistry, Histology and Pathology of Trauma, and Forensic Pathology. He has taught at several community colleges and universities, including Northern Arizona University; Scottsdale Community College; University of Arts, Sciences, and Technology, and PIHMA. Currently Dr. Iliescu is the Chairman of a doctoral program for the Basic Medical Sciences Department at PIHMA.

Dr. Iliescu has completed a Forensic fellowship at Broward County Medical Examiner's office in Fort Lauderdale, Florida. He worked as a medical examiner for the Maricopa Medical Examiner's office and for the Coconino County Medical Examiner's office. Dr. Iliescu also has an Autopsy and Forensic consultation business, where he specializes in performing private autopsies and giving forensic analysis consultations to attorneys.

About the Illustrator

Robert Perry, D.C., M.U.A.C. Originally from Oregon, Dr. Robert Perry, a board-certified chiropractic physician, has been in clinical practice in Northern Arizona for the past twelve years. Dr. Perry received his doctorate from Palmer College of Chiropractic West, and has also earned his Manipulation Under Anesthesia Certification (M.U.A.C.). Dr. Perry currently has staff privileges at two prominent surgical centers in Arizona. In addition, Dr. Perry teaches anatomy and physiology at a College in Flagstaff, Arizona.

Dr. Robert Perry is responsible for many of the illustrations in this text, except those in Chapters 2, 11, and 12.

Index

poisson's effect, 86
polyethylene, 344, 353, 368-369
polymetric material, 345
popliteal artery, 307, 310, 321
post-traumatic: headache, 168; impotence, 192
presynaptic bouton, 327
pretension stress, 308
proteoglycan, 105, 232
psoas major, 233, 235-236, 295
psychogenic disorders, 142
pubic: ramis, 300; symphysis, 293-294
pubofemoral, 294-295
pugilistic dementia, 151
pulmonary: contusion, 179; embolism, 189

Q

quadratus: femoris, 296; lumborum, 233, 235-236, 260
quadriceps muscle, 297, 305, 307, 339
quadriplegia, 123, 126, 203, 208, 213

R

radial: artery, 275; compression, 124-125, 129; deviation, 283-284, 286-287; nerves, 275; tears, 252
radicular symptoms, 248
radiocarpal joint, 281, 283, 285
radiographic, 208, 223, 255, 359
radiostereometry, 367
radioulnar, 273, 289
rear-end collision, 38, 152, 223, 227-228
receptor axons, 122-123
reconstructive surgery, 137, 166, 312
rectus: abdominis, 236-237, 260; femoris, 295, 333
reinnervation, 131
renal veins, 184
resuscitation procedure, 178
retro-peritoneal, 181, 184-185, 188
retrograde amnesia, 146
retrolisthesis, 3-4
retropatellar cartilage, 110
rheology, 118
rheopectic, 118
rheumatoid arthritis, 215, 285, 289, 311, 344
rheumatology, 226, 303
rhombencephalon, 134, 136
rib: cage, 82, 172, 177, 179, 181, 183-184, 243; fracture, 173, 175, 346; motion, 99, 346; puncture, 178; structures, 173
rockwell hardness, 355-356, 366
rolling friction, 50
rotational accelerations, 150
rouleaux method, 216

S

sacral: nerve, 233; plexus, 297; spine, 72, 121; vertebrae,
197
sacroiliac, 195, 293-294, 299-300, 302
sacrospinus, 293
sacrotuberous, 293
sacrum, 195, 202, 233, 235-236, 293-295, 300
sagittal plane, 25, 40-41, 152, 154, 195, 197, 199, 203, 206, 230, 232
sarcolemma membrane, 221, 256
sarcomeres, 329
sartorius, 295-297, 307
scalene muscles, 204
scalp: anatomy, 133; loading, 133, 135; trauma, 135, 140
scaphoid: bone, 281, 287; fracture, 281, 287
scapholunate, 282, 290
scaphotrapezium ligaments, 282
scapulae, 173, 205
scapulothoracic articulation, 264
scar tissue, 112, 114, 116, 138, 221, 256, 302
schmorl's nodes, 255
sciatic nerve, 248, 297, 302, 307, 322
sciatica, 228, 248, 259, 297, 302-303
scoliosis treatment, 367
semimembranosis, 307
semispinalis capitis, 204
semitendinosis, 307
sensory: axons, 124; nerve, 121, 254; neuron, 123; stimuli, 327
sepsis, 184
serotonin, 245
serratus, 222, 236, 265
sesamoid bone, 305
sharpey's fibers, 216, 245
slip failure, 95
soleus muscles, 317
somatoform disorder, 153, 157
somatostatin, 185
sphenoid bone, 96, 134, 137-138
spinalis: cervicis, 205; thoracis, 205, 235-236
spinous processes, 199, 202, 204, 208, 230, 233, 235-236, 243
spiral fracture, 92, 94
splenectomy, 183-184
splenius: capitis, 204; cervicis, 204
spondylolysis, 243-244, 248-249
sprains, 263, 267-268, 273, 275, 277, 281, 285, 305, 307-308, 315, 322-324, 326
spring ligament, 319, 326
stenosing, 285
sternal fractures, 172
sternoclavicular, 72, 263-265, 269
sternocleidomastoid, 121, 203, 217
sternum: body, 99, 172, 346; deflection, 178; fracture, 175
stomach organ, 185
stratum germinativum, 116